Keeping Students Safe and Helping Them Thrive

Keeping Students Safe and Helping Them Thrive

A Collaborative Handbook on School Safety, Mental Health, and Wellness

Volume 1

David Osher, Matthew J. Mayer, Robert J. Jagers, Kimberly Kendziora, and Lacy Wood, Editors

PRAEGER™

An Imprint of ABC-CLIO, LLC
Santa Barbara, California • Denver, Colorado

Library of Congress Cataloging-in-Publication Data

Names: Osher, David, editor. | Mayer, Matthew J., editor. | Jagers, Robert J., editor. | Kendziora, Kimberly, editor. | Wood, Lacy, editor.
Title: Keeping students safe and helping them thrive : a collaborative handbook on school safety, mental health, and wellness / David Osher, Matthew J. Mayer, Robert J. Jagers, Kimberly Kendziora, and Lacy Wood, editors.
Description: Santa Barbara, California : Praeger, an Imprint of ABC-CLIO, [2019] | Includes bibliographical references and index.
Identifiers: LCCN 2018043487 (print) | LCCN 2018044317 (ebook) | ISBN 9781440854149 (ebook) | ISBN 9781440854132 (set : alk. paper) | ISBN 9781440854156 (vol. 1 : alk. paper) | ISBN 9781440854163 (vol. 2 : alk. paper)
Subjects: | MESH: Child Health | Adolescent Health | School Health Services | Safety | Schools
Classification: LCC RJ101 (ebook) | LCC RJ101 (print) | NLM WS 440 | DDC 362.19892—dc23
LC record available at https://lccn.loc.gov/2018043487

ISBN: 978-1-4408-5413-2 (set)
978-1-4408-5415-6 (vol. 1)
978-1-4408-5416-3 (vol. 2)
978-1-4408-5414-9 (ebook)

23 22 21 20 19 1 2 3 4 5

This book is also available as an eBook.

Praeger
An Imprint of ABC-CLIO, LLC

ABC-CLIO, LLC
147 Castilian Drive
Santa Barbara, California 93117
www.abc-clio.com

This book is printed on acid-free paper ∞
Manufactured in the United States of America

Contents

Introduction

School Safety, Mental Health, and Thriving

David Osher, Matthew J. Mayer, Robert J. Jagers, Kimberly Kendziora, and Lacy Wood

Public concern about school safety, community violence, mental health, and related matters are regularly featured in media coverage—not only instances such as high-profile school shootings but also other safety and mental health related events that reflect our broader social ills. Policy, practice, and research often treat safety, mental health and wellness, learning, and thriving as separate domains. Although these domains should not be conflated, their relationship is not a simplistic one; they co-influence each other. They can be addressed in a comprehensive manner that attends to the:

- Dynamic nature of children's development within the child's ecology
- Dynamic nature of schools and their ecologies
- The important role and culture of families and communities.

This two-volume handbook addresses school safety, mental health and wellness, and student, educator, family, and community well-being and thriving. It aims at leveraging and aligning research, policy, and practice—disentangling the often simplistically conflated issues surrounding a multitude of events that captivate our attention. The chapters try to move beyond the deficit-based and fragmented perspectives we often see when dealing with these issues and address alternate ways to respond to complex, multidimensional human needs. The chapters provide thoughtful multifaceted approaches that balance health promotion and prevention, while addressing the multiple and nested individual, contextual, systemic, and historical factors that influence individual and collective outcomes, whether good or bad. As a whole, the chapters focus both on (1) prevention, remediation, and treatment and addressing needs and (2) promotion, asset development, resilience, well-being, and thriving.

This handbook contextualizes issues involving school safety, mental health, and well-being by examining how family, community, culture, gender, and developmental stage interact with each other and moderate outcomes for children. While grounded in research, the handbook focuses on practice and policy and the collaborations necessary to maximize wellness and safety and to help schools, families, and communities thrive. When possible, chapters were coauthored by researchers and practitioners. The target audience for the handbook includes: (1) college or university students and faculty; (2) educators, counselors, and psychologists; (3) family and community stakeholders; (4) human service agency administrators and staff at the local and state levels (including law enforcement and juvenile justice, social and human services, and mental health); (5) school and community teams; and (6) local and state level executive, legislative, and judicial branch officials. Both volumes are designed to enable diverse stakeholders to identify and understand areas of common interest and learn how to work together more collaboratively and effectively. This handbook is intended to inform students and scholars from related disciplines, but just as important to attract and interest college-educated lay readers.

The handbook conceptualizes safety broadly; it includes emotional safety and identity, as well as physical safety. Although there have been somewhat regular cycles of intense media attention and political debate surrounding high-profile school shootings over the years, a broader view of promoting school safety—not merely violence prevention—has eluded the fields of education and psychology and their extensions into policy and practice. A lack of school safety involves more than just physical safety, particularly school shootings; it includes micro-aggressions as well as ongoing forms of low-level aggression and anxiety-inducing behaviors such as harassment, intimidation, and bullying. Safety also includes positive conditions for learning and a healthy school environment that supports engagement, collaboration, and emotional, psychological, and identity safety.

The handbook is inclusive in its conceptualization of mental health and wellness. Mental health includes social and emotional competencies. The handbook also attempts to avoid and counter the harmful effects of stigma. Media stories of violence in schools and communities often zero in on mental health issues, contributing to harmful stereotypes that equate mental illness with violent behavior, when in fact violence is not intrinsically an outcome of mental illness. Mental health is a more diverse issue affecting a large proportion of individuals over their lifetime, where support systems and targeted treatment can sometimes be lacking, particularly for minority populations.

While prevalence estimates vary, close to 20% of students in schools may experience more serious mental health challenges requiring professional intervention. Yet relatively few receive appropriate systematic supports. From a public health perspective, schools offer the most efficient location for identification of need and provision of coordinated service delivery, as has been successfully implemented in hundreds of school communities nationwide and doing this well also contributes to the academic mission of schools. Several chapters in the handbook delve into these issues.

Wellness includes the experience of voice, agency, and the ability to adapt. As in the case of safety and mental health, the handbook takes a broad definition of wellness. Wellness is more than the absence of illness or the opposite end of a continuum with mental illness (Westerhof & Keyes, 2010). It can be conceived as a larger goal structure for students in schools, their families, and adults in local communities that enables them to thrive across all facets of their life, achieving long-term stability, autonomy, and self-direction addressing life goals, positive psychological adjustment, healthful social interactions, physical wellness, and general satisfaction in life. Schools can support wellness and be sites for the development of individual and collective resilience in the face of adversity. Schools can support resiliency and thriving when they (1) address the whole child; (2) provide meaningful opportunities to learn social, emotional, and academic skills, (3) offer learning environments that create a sense of belonging and are challenging and engaging, culturally responsive, and physically, emotionally, and identity safe; (4) provide developmental relationships and support; and (5) create opportunities for individual and collective student voice, leadership, and reflection (Osher, Kendziora, Spier, & Garibaldi, 2014; Osher & Termane, 2014). The intersection of safety, mental health, and a broader idea of wellness can all be considered with the school as a key "player," where it provides a setting for development of interpersonal and ecological assets toward such ends. These ideas are visited in multiple chapters throughout the handbook.

This handbook also stresses the interconnectedness of family, community, culture, gender, and developmental stages, with attention to intersectionality, cultural competence, and cultural responsiveness. Family-driven and youth-directed engagement with schools and the local community is key to most forms of success. Healthful family function can be facilitated and strengthened through opportunity structures, often based in schools. Things as basic as pre-literacy training for families where schools provide instruction and resource support for families to engage their children in early pre-literacy experiences can lay the groundwork not only for later school success but also for improved bonds between school, students, and their families. Likewise, student service programs that bring together families and community can foster longer-term generative outcomes. Multiple forms of culturally competent and responsive collaboration across schools, families, and the local community are examined across chapters in this handbook, bridging from the research base, to policy and practice, with examination of impact.

Multiple disciplines address the needs of youth and families regarding school safety, academic success, and social and emotional, behavioral, and related mental health issues. A confluence of historical streams across research, policy, and practice has laid the groundwork for our current knowledge base and the ways that systems address these issues. Yet allied disciplines such as general and special education; school, clinical, counseling, developmental, and community psychology; juvenile justice; community mental health; social welfare; and sociology pursue a wide variety of mid-range theories that align with broader theoretical frameworks.

Theoretical frameworks that address school safety, mental health, and related family and community issues include cognitive and social ecological, developmental, behavioral, public health, multicultural, and life-course, and developmental systems (Osher, Cantor, Berg, Strayer, & Rose, 2018). These are not tightly bound in compartments apart from one another, but rather, often overlap in multiple respects. For example, cognitive-behavioral interventions that address anger, aggression, anxiety, and related challenges span several of these theoretical frameworks.

Policy and practice can leverage particular areas such as public health and behavioral approaches, as found in early and later implementation of positive behavioral supports, beginning in the 1990s and embodied in the 1997 IDEA amendments. The Every Student Succeeds Act (ESSA) provides opportunities for school personnel to improve student academic progress by addressing the whole child and equity. The Title IV-A guidance states that education agencies may adopt strategies to support children's social and emotional development to achieve the grant priorities under "well-rounded education." ESSA's accountability guidance creates a "fifth indicator," which can include indicators of whole child development, student engagement, and school climate as part of state accountability systems. The legislation prioritizes equitable schools and opportunities for students to engage deeply in their academic experience and stakeholders, including families, to engage in improving implementation. ESSA emphasizes the use of data and stakeholder input to continually inform state and local improvements. Building on gradual progress over the decades in research on policy and practice requires more than just viewing situations through multiple theoretical and discipline-specific lenses.

A transdisciplinary approach is needed, distinct from what is sometimes referred to as cross-disciplinary and interdisciplinary perspectives. While all of these terms have sometimes been used loosely, cross-disciplinary often pertains to examining issues from the separate viewpoints of two or perhaps three disciplines, where interdisciplinary suggests a blending of these approaches. However, transdisciplinary implies a more sophisticated synthesis, transcending discipline-specific views (Cantor, Osher, Berg, Strayer, & Rose, 2018; Choi & Pak, 2006; Jensenius, 2012). Advances in policy and practice can benefit from a transdisciplinary approach that may not be available through more narrowly conceived approaches. Several parts of this handbook leverage a transdisciplinary knowledge base that promotes improved understanding of key research, policy, and practice across school safety, mental health, and family and community issues.

The handbook develops a series of interwoven themes including, but not limited to:

- Collaboration
- Understanding safety, mental health, and wellness from a relational, developmental, ecological systems prospective
- A multitiered approach to promotion, prevention, and intervention
- Understanding schools as dynamic systems
- Cultural competence and responsiveness
- Promoting Equity and Reducing Disparities
- Strengths-based approaches

The handbook is organized into eight sections that are presented across two volumes. Volume 1 includes sections that focus on foundational issues (e.g., frameworks); valuing and addressing diversity, and building student and teacher capacity; working with families and communities as assets; and collaboration. Volume 2 includes sections that focus on comprehensive approaches to promotion, prevention, intervention, and support as well as the particular application to students who experience trauma and school failure; creating emotionally and physically safe schools and communities; and planning, evaluation, and policy development. Although chapters fit neatly into these categories, they also could be read with reference to issues that are covered by other sections.

A fundamental goal of this handbook is to bridge chasms in our knowledge base and mend historical divides that have limited progress in the past. There are often gaps between research and practice and fragmentation between and among different professions and disciplines and disconnects between and among service providers and consumers. The entire book aims at enabling stakeholders to better understand the intersection of these systems, how their role and areas of interest can support outcomes for communities, families, and students and how they can work together more collaboratively and effectively to achieve common outcomes.

References

Cantor, P., Osher, D., Berg, J., Strayer, L., & Rose, T. (2018). Malleability, plasticity, and individuality: How children learn and develop in context. *Applied Developmental Science, 22*, 1–31.

Choi, B. C. K., & Pak, A. W. (2006). Multidisciplinary, interdisciplinarity and transdisciplinary in health research, services, education and policy: 1. Definitions, objectives, and evidence of effectiveness. *Clinical and Investigative Medicine, 29*, 351–364.

Jensenius, A. R. (2012). Disciplinarities: Intra, cross, multi, inter, trans. Retrieved from Alexander Refsum Jensenius website, http://www.arj.no/2012/03/12/disciplinarities-2/

Osher, D., Cantor, P., Berg, J., Strayer, L., & Rose, T. (2018). Drivers of human development: How relationships and context shape learning and development. *Applied Developmental Science, 22*, 1–31.

Osher, D., Kendziora, K., Spier, E., & Garibaldi, M. L. (2014). School influences on child and youth development. In Z. Sloboda & H. Petras (Eds.), *Advances in prevention science: Vol. 1. Defining prevention science* (pp. 151–170). New York: Springer.

Osher, D., & Thermane, M. (2014). Schools as enabling environments. *South African Journal of Education, 34*, 1–6.

Westerhof, G. J., & Keyes, C. L. M. (2010). Mental illness and mental health: The two continua model across the lifespan. *Journal of Adult Development, 17*(2), 110–119. doi:10.1007/s10804-009-9082-y

PART 1

Foundational Issues

CHAPTER ONE

Intersection of School Safety, Mental Health and Wellness, and Family and Community Issues

Howard S. Adelman, Linda Taylor, Kevin P. Dwyer, and Matthew J. Mayer

This text opens with an overview of the intersection of school safety, mental health and wellness, family and community factors, and related current issues. We use a multi-contextual lens, leveraging several conceptual approaches, including but not limited to public health, behaviorist, social-ecological, developmental, family systems, and life-course frameworks.

We begin by asking: How do public perceptions and media-driven accounts of school violence facilitate or impede our understanding of school safety? What are key matters to consider? What solution paths should be considered? We highlight multiple perspectives and approaches. We identify limitations and related problems with historically piecemeal and fragmented approaches to human services delivery and underscore how school- and community-based activities can be woven together in ways that minimize unnecessary duplication of efforts, lack of coordination, and counterproductive competition for scarce resources. In doing so, we stress the value of school transformation that embeds school safety concerns into a unified, comprehensive, and equitable system that addresses barriers to learning and teaching.

A Broad View of School Safety

High-profile school shootings have grabbed the public's attention as commercial media have broadcast disturbing video and related information depicting horrific events. Political leaders at the local and national levels have predictably responded with calls for greater security and many stakeholders have suggested rather simplistic solutions, including increased physical security, armed guards, armed teachers, and harsh zero tolerance policies. Yet research has shown that most of these approaches do little to increase school safety, and policies such as zero tolerance can do more harm than good (American Psychological Association Zero Tolerance Task Force, 2008).

School safety is about much more than just preventing school violence or focusing on school security. It reflects a confluence of concerns spanning school climate, academic instruction and achievement, interpersonal relations and processes, specific student and adult behaviors at school, positive engagement, collaboration, physical and psychological safety, and health of all school stakeholders. It requires continuous improvement in meeting shared goals for a positive and productive school environment.

Current conceptualizations of school safety are an outgrowth of research, policy, and practice across multiple fields, including but not limited to education; juvenile justice; mental health and social welfare; school, clinical, counseling, and community psychology; sociology; and related disciplines. Schools, of course, exist in the larger community, interfacing with families, mental health systems, and a variety of stakeholders and addressing the needs of broad segments of the population. Thus, well-conceived and integrated approaches must respond to the complex concerns faced by many schools and communities.

Theoretical Frameworks and Approaches

A range of frameworks can be used in discussing how to facilitate improved promotion of school safety and prevention of school violence, effective mental health services, and family- and community-based programming. For example, behaviorist approaches focus on individual, classroom, and school levels, leveraging principles of applied behavioral analysis (ABA), while also adopting ABA-conceived schoolwide approaches such as positive behavior interventions and supports (PBIS). A wide range of cognitive behavioral interventions for anger or aggression, anxiety, depression, and other needs areas have been successfully used for decades (Mayer, Van Acker, Lochman, & Gresham, 2008). For instance, self-regulated strategy development (SRSD), a writing intervention has been used with students with and without disabilities (Graham et al., 2012). Also, programs rooted in positive youth development and social-emotional learning (SEL) are widely used to promote positive school climate and cultural competence.

Attachment, developmental, and family systems theory focus on family-centered promotion and prevention efforts. Developmental cascades that span early aggression to later school failure and dropout help explicate child and adolescent trajectories (Masten et al., 2005), sometimes also in terms of life course theory. Public health theory is applied to many school- and community-based promotion and prevention programs. Social-ecological theory is widely used in bullying and related research, linked to prevention programming (Swearer, Espelage, Vaillancourt, & Hymel, 2010). Dynamic, relational, bioecological theories stress critical interrelationships. Qualitative research has explicated structures and processes that impact individual student, family, and community-related factors, many of which are culturally bound (Harry & Klingner, 2006). Other frameworks (e.g., social disorganization, social control, etc.) have also been used, with scores of so-called middle-range theories presented in the literature (Mayer & Furlong, 2010). Those who elect to take an "empirical integrationist" perspective leverage research across these varying perspectives to improve understanding of challenges with school safety. However, all of these frameworks are constrained and likely less effective when real world implementation is driven with a more silo-oriented, discipline-specific adherence to narrowly defined concepts, agendas, and planning approaches.

Prevailing Concerns

Multiple issues arise across research, policy, and practice with regard to school safety, mental health, and family and community challenges. School shootings, weapons in schools, violence against teachers and other adults, gang and drug activity, school climate and bullying, classroom disruptions interfering with learning, sexual harassment, exclusionary discipline, and theft are among the most common themes surfacing in school safety research. Related school-based challenges have included systems of academic accountability, early education (including zero to three issues), addressing needs of students with disabilities, English language learners (ELLs), LGBTQ youth, and students who are otherwise marginalized. Mental health in schools, school-family-community partnerships, and interagency collaboration remain areas of concern.

Broader concerns can include evolving family structure and employment patterns over recent decades along with large numbers of latchkey children and lack of safe and supervised places for children and adolescents after school. Extensive poverty and income inequality and economically and socially marginalized families, linked to food and housing insecurity, particularly among single female parents and families of color, can place children at heightened risk academically, and in terms of individual psychological and overall family wellness (Mayer & Leone, 2007). Community violence, gang and drug activity, and access to guns can be linked to several types of deleterious outcomes. Exposure to violence in entertainment media (e.g., television, movies, computer or mobile electronics games) may pose additional risk to youth (Nickerson et al., 2016).

Sometimes concerns across these domains can be considered in unhelpful ways. For example, there is a widespread public perception that school shootings and other acts of violence are closely linked to serious mental health issues, where mental illness and violence become conflated. Yet data demonstrate that only a very small percentage of individuals with serious mental health issues act out violently and that findings depend on the type of mental health problem, severity, and the presence or absence of adequate treatment support. Apart from substance abuse, which is linked to an increased risk of violence, individuals with serious mental health problems are only slightly more at risk for violent behavior than the general population, and those receiving appropriate treatment are at no higher risk (Van Dorn, Volavka, & Johnson, 2012; Varshney, Mahapatra, Krishnan, Gupta, & Deb, 2016). Families of students experiencing serious academic and disciplinary problems at school are often cast in a role of causing the problem in the minds of teachers and other school professionals (Skiba & Peterson, 2000), where there may be no such linkage. Schools situated within communities that experience intense violence are presumed in the minds of many to be beyond help, where the schools are preordained to fail. Yet several studies have shown the error of such presumptions (Mayer & Furlong, 2010).

Cutting Across Disciplines

The balance-communication-connectedness-support (BCCS) model is an approach to framing issues of school safety that connects to mental health and family and community challenges (the Interdisciplinary Group on Preventing School and Community Violence, 2013). The model originated as part of a position statement on the Fall 2006 school shootings, culminating in the Fall 2006 School Shootings Position Statement, which was disseminated nationally. A revised and expanded version of the statement was developed following the Sandy Hook school shooting in 2012 and disseminated nationally; it was endorsed by more than 100 major professional organizations representing well over 4 million professionals across education, psychology, social work, counseling, and allied fields.

The BCCS model cuts across findings from multiple disciplines and is likened to taking an MRI of issues, slicing images at various angles and positions, yielding views different from those of traditional systems that examine school safety. Our summary here reproduces segments from the first School Shooting Position Statement. The model stresses that a *balanced approach* includes a variety of efforts addressing physical safety, educational practices, and programs that support the social, emotional, and behavioral needs of students, not simply reacting with a singular focus on security. *Communication* includes maintaining close communication and trust with students, families, and others in the community, so that threats will be reported and can be investigated by responsible authorities, using evidence-based threat assessment protocols. Schools and communities must find effective means to overcome students' reluctance to break unwritten rules against "tattling" or "snitching" on their peers and channels of efficient, user-friendly communication need to be established and maintained. *Connectedness* refers to what binds people together as a social unit. Students need to feel that they belong at their school and that the school staff and the school community as a whole care for them. *Support* is critical for effective prevention. Both in schools and the local community, many people experience minor and major life stresses and difficulties. Every school should have the resources to maintain evidence-based programs designed to address students' needs, using a fully developed multitiered approach.

Current Research, Policy, and Practice Challenges

Research questions, data acquisition, and related analytic approaches that inform research, policy, and practice raise a series of challenges. The needs of researchers may sometimes be at odds with those of practitioners. For example, a clinical psychology researcher formally testing an anger management intervention would likely be concerned with having well-defined and controlled experimental conditions, but such procedures and conditions may not mesh well with the ability of students to participate in the intervention as well as work practically within the daily schedules and procedures of a school (Mayer & Van Acker, 2008). Likewise, researchers interested in learning disabilities may develop approaches that conflict with the day-to-day realities for teachers who must implement such interventions (MacMillan & Speece, 1999). Neither may fit well with the goals of advocates for policy change at the national level. Further, research questions are bound by theoretical constructs, available data, and related analytical approaches, which can constrain focus, utility, and broader application of findings.

Data are collected through multiple avenues, aligning with population, content focus, and purpose. For instance, school violence data can reflect measures of perpetration (e.g., law enforcement records, school disciplinary referrals) and victimization (e.g., self-report in surveys and other instruments). Information on overall school climate can be obtained through climate surveys and focus group sessions. Health status and related risk and protective attitudes, knowledge, beliefs, and behaviors can be measured through surveys and interviews. Mental health needs and services affecting a school population or other group can be measured through a combination of epidemiologically based surveys, rating scales, records analysis (e.g., clinical services log), and client service delivery reports. Family structure, status, practices, and perspectives can be assessed through surveys, interviews, ethnographic and other qualitative methods, focus groups, and census-type data. Related analysis is driven by research questions, units of analysis, data availability, and types of investigation (causal, correlational, descriptive, ethnographic, etc.). For example, understanding processes linked to student investment in school may require a structural modeling approach that leverages latent variables based on an empirically derived model, with each latent variable reflected in real-world measurable variables. Along with these challenges come definitional and measurement issues that are beyond the scope of this discussion (see Mayer & Furlong, 2010).

Transdisciplinary Approaches and Multiple Stakeholders

Transdisciplinary approaches are essential to understanding and addressing a wide array of factors and processes spanning school safety, mental health, and family and community needs. Mental health and allied disciplines work with school safety challenges but often in a fragmented and unnecessarily duplicative manner with limited collaboration (Kutash & Duchnowski, 2007; Pires, Lazear, & Conlan, 2008). Effectiveness can vary greatly depending on singular agency efforts versus coordinated approaches as a function of respective agency mission and goals, case analysis and deployment of resources, informational and accountability systems, and existing infrastructure geared to support interagency collaboration (Daly et al., 2006). Youth and their families who are at increased risk may demonstrate multiple areas of need that span the expertise of one human services discipline or agency and related prevention and intervention models may not pay sufficient attention to more complex needs when focused on more singular conditions (Weisz, Donenberg, Han, & Weiss, 1995). Increasingly comprehensive prevention and promotion models require multilevel efforts that can pose additional logistical and analytical challenges, and suspected moderators and mediators are often neglected in research and related prevention efforts, limiting benefits realized from such efforts (Clingempeel &

Henggeler, 2002; Lochman, 2000). These concerns also extend to the roles of various stakeholders in the school and community.

Multiple stakeholders play critical roles across school, family, and community systems, yet structures and supports to facilitate broader collaborative progress are limited. For example, school-family partnerships are the cornerstone of student progress, and schools nationally have engaged in multifaceted programming to improve these partnerships. Research on schoolwide change processes has repeatedly pointed to the necessity of stakeholder buy-in and collaboration, also identifying facilitators and barriers to such efforts. For example, Harry (1991) did breakthrough work explicating the nature of strained relations between the Puerto Rican families and the special education system in Syracuse, New York. Furthermore, mental health services often involve family-community agency partnerships as does related work by social workers in schools and communities. We further examine these issues in the following sections, beginning with consideration of health promotion and prevention, and approaches to address school safety and broader mental health concerns, including family and local community concerns.

Safe Schools, Health Promotion, and Prevention

Schools have a long history of promoting the behavioral and academic skills of the students they serve. For almost a century, schools also have addressed many of the safety and health needs of their students, regularly incorporating school nursing and counseling services into policy and practice. Originally, many of the prevention services these professionals provided were related to physical safety, contagious disease prevention, school attendance, and, for counselors, academic progress (Wiley & Cory, 2013). By the mid-20th century, states developed policies and practices mandating vaccinations, hygiene education as well as behavioral and attendance rules. Environmental factors that promoted health were also standardized (Institute of Medicine, 1997). Counselors focused on academic and vocational guidance and career preparation as well as providing child developmental information to teachers and families.

Today school health and its providers have a broad promotion and prevention focus, where wellness promotion and prevention are closely interwoven, jointly leading to improved mental health, positive social outcomes, and general well-being (Substance Abuse and Mental Health Services Administration [SAMHSA], Center for Mental Health Services [CMHS], 2007). The Institute of Medicine (IOM) has endorsed the following definition:

> A comprehensive school health program is an integrated set of planned, sequential, school-affiliated strategies, activities, and services designed to

> promote the optimal physical, emotional, social, and educational development of students. The program involves and is supportive of families and is determined by the local community, based on community needs, resources, standards, and requirements. It is coordinated by a multidisciplinary team and accountable to the community for program quality and effectiveness. (Institute of Medicine, 1997, p. 2)

Health and safety promotion and prevention science permeates school settings, from environmental requirements for air quality, toxin regulations, fire prevention, and safety drills. Schools have policies to prevent poisoning and respiratory illnesses and to promote safety. School safety and discipline have been moving from negative, punitive codes of conduct and reliance on suspension to PBIS and restorative justice (Sugai, Horner, & McIntosh, 2008). Many states now require health instruction about topics such as preventing sexually transmitted diseases; preventing the use of tobacco, drugs, and alcohol; and avoiding dangerous risky behaviors. All of these health promotion activities have seen reductions in suspensions, in teen pregnancy, smoking, fatal automobile accidents, and violence, including suicides during the last 25 years (Centers for Disease Control and Prevention [CDC], 2015). In the most recent decades, promoting social, emotional, and mental health functioning and preventing mental health problems have been incorporated into the vision, policies, and practices of effective safe community schools, and the results show promise (SAMHSA, 2015).

In 1998, after a rash of school shootings, the U.S. Departments of Education and Justice were directed by then President Clinton to produce and distribute guidance for schools and communities to address the promotion of school safety and the prevention of violence. The document *Early Warning Timely Response: A Guide to Safe Schools* (Dwyer, Osher, & Warger, 1998) was produced and distributed to all of the nation's public schools before the opening of the 1998–1999 school year. This document and related materials presented a comprehensive continuum of universal schoolwide promotion and prevention services, in combination with early and intensive interventions to make schools safer. Addressing safety was also connected to an examination of the school's climate, seeking a climate that enhances feeling safe, connected, respected, included, and academically challenged. It was clear that schools even in the most violent, poverty-ridden communities could be safe and more positively connected to their students and families.

Promoting emotional skills such as showing empathy, being self-aware, and using self-regulation and problem-solving are now more commonly in place in our schools (Collaborative for Academic, Social, and Emotional Learning [CASEL], 2015; Durlak, Weisberg, Dymnicki, Taylor, & Shellinger, 2011). Most schools now provide universal student safety programs such as proactively addressing bullying and having crisis prevention plans to address natural and man-made crises. Today some schools, although fewer in number, provide social skills instruction and positive discipline to promote safety. In their strategic plans, school systems have adopted policies and practices allowing time for teachers to closely connect with their students and families. Systems have provided training for building resilient classrooms (Doll, Brehm, & Zucker, 2014). Schools now support teaming of health and mental health staff to ensure coordination of services, thus avoiding silos of discrete services. Furthermore, most school districts now provide families with helpful developmental information, discipline guidelines, and other information that supports the schools' academic mission. Early childhood education is now the norm for promoting readiness to learn and for preventing primary grade failure. These are fundamental, universal promotion and prevention activities included in instruction, curriculum, and management procedures. They have their foundation in the application of safety and social and emotional best practices designed to enable mastery learning for all students (Osher, Dwyer, & Jackson, 2004). Many of these promotion and prevention activities extend developmental supports, including parent education to promote readiness for social and academic success. Many preschool programs also have folded universal social and emotional instruction into academic readiness (CASEL, 2016). Universal promotion and prevention policies and initiatives have been aligned and integrated into our nation's schools to lower risk and reduce failure.

In 2018, a U.S. Department of Education grant was awarded to WestEd to lead the *Center to Improve Social and Emotional Learning and School Safety*. The RAND Corporation, Council of Chief State School Officers, and Transforming Education serve as partners in the work (see announcement at https://www.wested.org/news-events/center-to-improve-social-and-emotional-learning-and-school-safety/).

Toward Improving Best Practices

To improve academic and social mastery for all students, schools can adopt the public health promotion, prevention, early and intensive intervention continuum (Dwyer & VanBuren, 2010; Osher & Dwyer, 2005). There is evidence that prevention and intervention can be implemented with fidelity to improve best practices in a variety of school communities (Campie, Tanyu, & Osher, 2017; Kendziora & Osher, 2016).

The Safe Schools/Healthy Students Grants' evaluation by SAMHSA (2013) highlights a representative array of school systems that have successfully reduced violence and other behavior problems that interfere with learning by implementing a comprehensive approach. These programs also have significantly increased access to mental health services to address student social and emotional problems (SAMHSA, 2015).

For many staff and families, improving current practices requires a change in thinking about intervention approaches and in how schools are structured. This includes recognizing the importance of social and emotional development and how the environment supports that development and fundamental conditions for learning.

Student, family, and staff perceptions of school climate are critical. When children feel safe and respected by staff, they show improved attention to instruction, connectedness, and academic achievement (Kendziora & Yoder, 2016). In a safe school climate, children, families, and staff feel cared for, connected, and respected. In particular, in a positive school climate, the students can readily identify an adult who cares about them. These are not "feel good" components of effective schools. They are grounded climate measures of success.

Periodic surveys of school climate are necessary to track improved climate with improvement in achievement and behavior. There are many examples of effective climate surveys that have merit. The U.S. Department of Education's National Center for Educational Statistics provides examples for use with students, teachers, staff, and families. Some student items like "Teachers are available when I need to talk with them" and "My teachers care about me" address caring connections with adults while other items such as, "Students at this school get along well with each other" may reflect safety and caring connections to peers. Climate surveys, when used by students, staff, and families can give us consistent continuing quality improvement measures of school climate initiatives (U.S. Department of Education, 2016). For example, Cleveland's Humanware school climate measures are reviewed annually and in some schools semiannually, to examine progress and help identify additional climate areas that need to be addressed. The finding that students' views of "caring" were very significantly lower than teachers' perceptions, warranted increased in-service training and more regular adherence to class meetings to help improve caring and connectedness. Examining and measuring school climate for safety, caring, and connectedness give staff progress measures that can enhance their support. Likewise, the School Climate Improvement Resource Package (SCIRP) from the National Center on Safe Supportive Learning Environments provides schools with tools for addressing climate needs.

Teachers and other staff and families regularly see the value of a safe school climate. They readily support fewer class disruptions and fewer incidences of fighting and bullying. They know that increased connecting and caring between and among students will result in a safer school climate. A safe and caring school climate where children can easily identify one or more trusted adults and where they feel respected and connected to staff and each other can have lasting positive outcomes for children. An unsafe, ineffective, uncaring school climate can cause anxiety and dysfunction in large numbers of students.

Inclusive Planning and Implementation

Implementation requires an inclusive planning process. Staff may not see health promotion activities as part of their instructional role so framing these activities as ways to increase engaged instructional time and decrease class disruptions can help secure that support. These are common outcomes of teaching functional social skills and knowledge (see http://www.casel.org/research/). Prevention activities might include reinforcing positive behavioral discipline standards (i.e., PBIS) and bullying prevention as well as class meetings. Promotion and prevention activities complement each other and there is an overlapping continuum of universal primary promotion and prevention activities that enhance the conditions for learning. When all are imbedded into the school's climate, more children thrive (Osher et al., 2004).

Universal mental health promotion and prevention is the necessary core for safe and effective schools but insufficient for addressing the needs of all students. Twenty percent or more students need more targeted and individualized academic and behavioral support to benefit from universal prevention and promotion initiatives and effective, challenging instruction.

Connectedness and caring require timely contact between school staff and students and families as well as connections among students and concurrently among staff, community partners, and other stakeholders. Connections with students and families can increase safety. When students connect with a trusted adult, they are more likely to share early warning signs of their own thoughts of violence, including suicidal thoughts or plans. Trusting connections are key, and schools can support this by providing students, staff, and families access to valid information and planned support when warning signs appear (National Association of School Psychologists [NASP], 2015). When teachers and families have easy access to effective mental health, behavioral, and academic interventions, their level of cooperation and involvement increases.

Teaching can be a lonely and sometimes frustrating profession unless schools provide teachers and other staff time and access to peers to collaborate and consult (Iowa Department of Education, 2009). Allotting time for grade-level teachers to consult with each other provides expanded problem-solving as well as shared support for implementation of universal school climate interventions. Administrative support for family-inclusive partnerships is essential (Mapp & Kuttner, 2013). Similarly, connecting and collaborating with families can be critical to supporting positive social-emotional development and academic progress. When strategies for effective school-family partnerships are properly resourced and designed, they are more likely to be sustained and incorporated into practice. Listening to the parent community, providing data-based information and building one-to-one relationships with families has improved attendance and behavior (Christenson & Reschly, 2010).

Classroom teachers and families need to be informed of the measured progress provided by early interventions. This support and its monitoring require more than the individual classroom teacher can provide. School student support teams (SST) that use data-based problem solving and resources to ensure the development and monitoring of early, targeted interventions (Dwyer & Osher, 2004). These teams work best when intervention monitoring is periodic and goals are both challenging and realistic. Successful implementation of Response to Intervention (RTI) within a multitiered system is also dependent upon the SST's periodic monitoring. Monitoring, at its minimum, should be as periodic as report cards. Interventions like cooperative learning and extended day or after school programs can be more effective when supported with instructional and behavioral materials whose content is connected to the classroom. In some schools where Promoting Alternative THinking Strategies (PATHS) is taught, other instructional support staff and clinicians are given training in that curriculum so that they can reinforce a child's use of those skills in remedial support (Greenberg, Kusché, Cook, & Quamma, 1995). And, families can be made aware of the social-emotional instructional goals that they can support at home. When clinicians partner with the SST and classroom teachers, there are more opportunities for coordination and consultation. Thus, making clinicians aware of SEL instruction reduces fragmentation. As one clinician stated, "I use the PATHS language as part of my behavioral treatment. I am reinforcing the instruction and the teacher is reinforcing the therapy."

School leadership can endorse a variety of targeted instructional supports including peer coaching, cooperative learning, diagnostic teaching, and grade-level teams for addressing behavioral or instructional issues. Principals can establish as part of their strategic plan addressing attendance as it relates to students being at-risk for academic failure and behavior problems. Principals can encourage student/learning supports that are provided within the classroom.

SSTs and RTI are effective when properly resourced and when interventions are documented and monitored for fidelity to the academic and behavioral plans. Teachers are encouraged to use strength-based interventions and to connect families to explore those strengths. Frequent family contact also can assist the SST to better understand and evaluate what is and what is not working (CASEL, 2008).

Intensive Interventions to Address Complex Student Needs

A multitiered system of supports (MTSS) model functions successfully when all levels are designed as a comprehensive and integrated set of subsystems and interventions are organized and implemented with integrity

(Center for MH in Schools & Student/Learning Supports, 2017). Promotion and prevention alone can leave many at-risk children frustrated and on a trajectory toward more serious academic and behavioral problems (Baker, Kamphaus, Horne, & Winsor, 2006). Their teachers, unable to remedy these problems, may feel isolated and even become disenchanted with the prevention strategies they have been trained and asked to implement. Peer consultation and easy access to SST support are critical to maintaining teacher support. When the teacher referral to the SST is seen as an active extension of the classroom support, the interventions are more likely to succeed. Their alignment enhances success. For example, when SEL instructional language is incorporated into remediation for those referred students, it supports transfer and teacher reinforcement in the classroom. Ways to make this happen will be discussed within this book.

An essential facet of a multitiered student support system is intensive, personalized intervention. Such interventions must be in place to address the complex needs of smaller numbers of students who have serious, complex barriers to learning and behavior. These interventions frequently require plans for even greater family involvement, multiple agency services, and the structured coordination of services (Weisz, Sandler, Durlak, & Anton, 2005). Coordination again requires inclusive interagency training and information sharing (under the framework of school and provider confidentiality regulations). The Wraparound service model is an example of an intensive intervention. Wraparound service includes multiple agents partnering with the child's school and teacher(s) and family. Measured goals of wraparound most usually include improved learning, behavior, grades, and attendance among other regular school measures as well as family and community measures of treatment effectiveness.

Untreated mental health problems are one of the most serious barriers to learning (Adelman & Taylor, 2010). Many mental health problems are compounded in schools where children and staff feel unsafe, where learning is disrupted and discipline is erratic, and where bullying and violence are too common. In communities stressed by poverty and safety issues, many more children suffer from trauma-based disabling mental health problems. These children tell us that their stress comes with them into the classroom and that this stress can be reduced through teacher-enhanced caring and connectedness combined with therapeutic treatment. Institutionalizing these resilience-building actions by staff is our collective goal and a goal of this book.

Making it a priority to better address mental health promotion and prevention as well as early and intensive interventions for existing mental health problems should be expected, particularly those schools serving our neediest students and families in communities suffering from poverty and violence.

Universal preventive and promotional mental health initiatives have increased during recent decades. For example, universal bullying prevention initiatives are commonly implemented in about three out of four of our schools (CDC, 2015).

Intensive, personalized services are provided, coordinated, or supported in 67% of U.S. schools according to the CDC's 2015 school health survey. These intensive services generally involve coordination and interagency services and include strong family involvement. Coordination among service providers, particularly for children and youth who have experienced physical, sexual, or psychological trauma is critical to intervention effectiveness. Without these supports, schools can fail, and school staffs show signs of burnout, classes are frequently disrupted, and suspensions are common. Families feel alienated and staff and students feel unsafe. Compounded by community violence, anxiety increases for students and staff (Baker et al., 2006; Oberle & Schonert-Reichl, 2016).

Community Outreach, Collaborative Engagement, and Systemic Development

Collaboration among agencies and schools is sound practice (Adelman & Taylor, 2007a). Collaboration at the policy level that supports macro-level decision-making based upon practitioner- and family-level feedback should be valued. Collaboration between clinicians and school staff brings policy to practice. Partnerships with community agencies enhance the desired coordinated and collaborative service delivery model that has the greatest impact for a complete array of services from preventive to intensive wrap-around models (Cleveland Municipal School District, 2015).

What has worked in practice are systems that have partnered with private and public agencies and community family advocates in the planning of integrated service models that enable services to blend so that, with consent, agency providers can meet with school teams and be active participants on those teams (Freeman et al., 2014). The Systems of Care literature has demonstrated that silos are detrimental to access and to effective interventions. Effective collaboration requires interagency agreement (i.e., memorandum of understanding) and interagency training. For example, in one school system the agency service providers work in the schools, provide regular consultation to the student's classroom teacher and parent, participate in the school's SST team and participate in an annual review of their measured effectiveness including input surveys from the teacher, family, and student. These surveys are analyzed by a local partnering university (Cleveland Municipal School District, 2015).

The last few decades have seen many initiatives to connect community services to schools in order to better meet the needs of children and their families. These initiatives have generated terms such as school-linked services, integrated services, one-stop shopping, wraparound services, seamless service delivery, coordinated school health, co-location of services, integrated student supports, full-service schools, community schools, systems of care, and more. All this has been bolstered by recent policy-oriented reports that have come from Child Trends using the term "Integrated Student Supports" and from the Association of Maternal & Child Health Programs (AMCHP) and the Lucile Packard Foundation for Children's Health focusing on "Systems of Care." And, the CDC has revamped their "Coordinated School Health Program."

For community agencies, connection with schools is seen as providing better access to families and their children, promoting greater engagement, and enhancing opportunities for having an impact on hard-to-reach clients. Moreover, the hope is that integrated interventions will increase the pool of resources for student and learning supports and address disparities. For school policy makers, connecting school-home-community is seen as an essential facet of promoting the well-being of children and youth and enhancing equity of opportunity for them to succeed at school and beyond (Hardiman, Curcio, & Fortune, 1998; Warren, 2005). While schools represent a key commodity in communities, too many currently are viewed as unconnected "islands." This works against addressing barriers to learning and teaching such as school and community safety—especially in poor neighborhoods.

Schools and the community in which they reside are dealing with multiple, interrelated concerns—poverty, child development, literacy, violence, crime, safety, substance abuse, housing, and employment. For schools to be seen as more effective and caring places, they must take steps to engage and collaborate with a wide range of community stakeholders, and they must play a key role in addressing barriers to learning and teaching as well as strengthening family and community life. A potent approach requires multifaceted and collaborative efforts. The goal is to maximize mutual benefits, including better student progress, positive socialization of the young, higher staff morale, improved use of resources, an enhanced sense of community, community development, and more. In the long run, the aims are to strengthen students, schools, families, and neighborhoods.

In too many schools, outreach to the community has a highly limited focus. Policy and related funding initiatives mostly support efforts to link community social services and physical and mental health services to schools. After-school programs also involve community providers. In addition, some schools recruit volunteers and solicit other forms of resource contributions, as well as encouraging positive votes for school-related ballot measures. The downside of such well-meaning outreach is that it narrows thinking about the role and functions of school-community collaboration and about transforming how schools provide student and learning supports (Adelman & Taylor, 2003, 2006, 2007b, 2017, 2018).

What Resources Are in the Community?

Researchers have mapped a wide range of community entities whose missions overlap that of the local schools. These include county and municipal agencies and bodies, mutual support and self- help groups, service clubs and philanthropic organizations, youth organizations, community-based organizations, faith institutions, legal assistance groups, ethnic associations, artists and cultural institutions, businesses, corporations, unions, media, family members, local residents, senior citizens groups, and more. Districts and schools need to consider outreach to the full range of resources that exist, especially in neighborhoods where poverty reigns.

Framing and Designing Interventions for Community Involvement and Collaborative Engagement

School and district efforts to enhance community connections can encompass four types of activities: (1) outreach to a broad range of community entities; (2) development of immediate links and connections with community resources that can help fill critical intervention gaps to address shared problems; (3) establishment of an effective operational infrastructure for a school-community collaborative; and (4) the blending, weaving, or redeploying of school and community resources where feasible to help with system development (see figure 1.1). In practice, all four activities often are not pursued, especially when the focus is mainly on connecting a few community services to a school. However, all are vital in developing a unified and comprehensive system of student and learning supports.

It should be noted that because community resources in many neighborhoods are sparse a school-by-school approach often leads to inequities (e.g., the first school to contact an agency might tie up all that a given agency can bring to a school). Therefore, district leadership needs to (1) help develop mechanisms that connect a "family" of schools (e.g., a high school feeder pattern, schools in the same neighborhood); and (2) play a role in outreaching and connecting community resources equitably to schools. A family of schools (e.g., an elementary to high school feeder pattern) also provides a good nucleus for creating a school-community collaborative.

Based on the available literature, here are examples of strategies related to pursuing the activities highlighted in figure 1.1 (Adelman & Taylor, 2006; Bodilly, Chun, Ikemoto, & Stockly, 2004; Epstein, Coates, Salinas, & Sanders, 2002).

Outreach to the Community

1. A social marketing campaign to inform and invite participation of all community stakeholders with respect to
   (a) district and school plans to work with the community to address barriers to student success and develop a cohesive and comprehensive system and
   (b) the variety of opportunities for involvement at schools
2. Interventions to (re)engage students and families who don't interact with the school on a regular basis (e.g., the disengaged, truants, dropouts)
3. Outreach to specific stakeholder groups to recruit a steady increase in the number of volunteers available to the schools

Developing Mechanisms to Link and Connect with Community Entities

1. Using school improvement planning to include a focus on analyzing and filling critical gaps in efforts to develop a unified and comprehensive system of learning supports
2. Establishing and training a multi-school workgroup to focus on recruiting and equitably integrating individuals and agencies who have resources that can help fill critical gaps

Establishing a Formal Collaborative and Building an Operational Infrastructure

1. Identifying community stakeholders who are interested in establishing a school-community collaborative
2. Formulating aims, short-term goals, and immediate objectives
3. Organizing participants into an effective operational infrastructure and establishing formal working agreements (e.g., Memorandum of Understanding) about roles and responsibilities
4. Forming and training work groups to accomplish immediate objectives
5. Monitoring and facilitating progress

Blending Resources to Improve System Development

1. Mapping school and community resources used to address barriers to student success
2. Analyzing resource use to determine redundancies and inefficiencies
3. Identifying ways resources can be redeployed and interwoven to meet current priorities

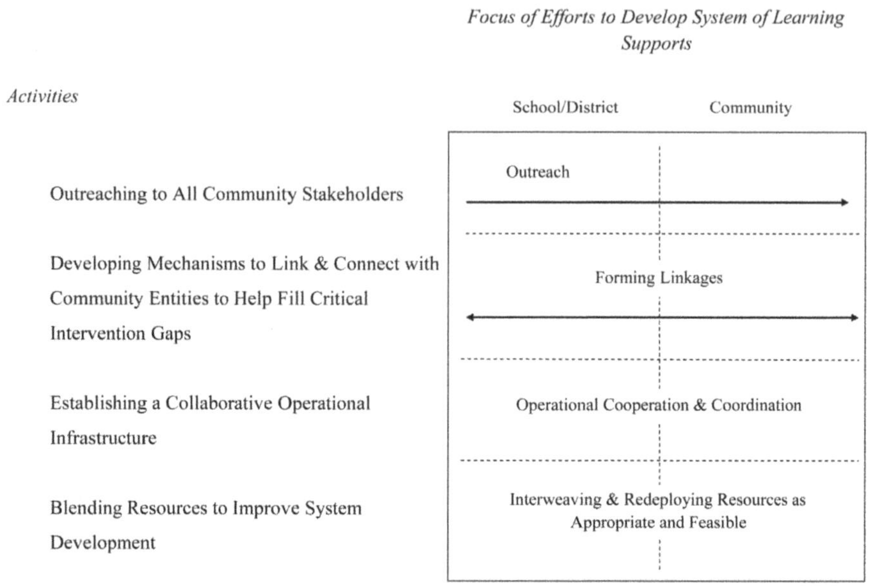

Figure 1.1 Framework for schools and community collaboration in developing a unified and comprehensive system of learning supports. Outreach is to all available community resources and decision makers (e.g., those associated with public and private agencies, colleges, and universities, artists and cultural institutions, businesses and professional organizations, and service, volunteer, faith-based organizations)

What Are Priorities in Enhancing Community Involvement and Collaborative Engagement?

Analyses related to school improvement can use the framework in figure 1.1 to identify next steps for enhancing school-community connections. A self-study survey also is available online at http://smhp.psych.ucla.edu/pdfdocs/toolsforpractice/communityoutreachsurvey.pdf). Immediate priorities usually involve establishing policy and operational mechanisms for (1) a broad-based social marketing outreach campaign aimed at connecting with a wide range of community entities and initiating work with those who indicate interest and (2) exploring the feasibility of building a school-community collaborative.

Toward Developing a School-Community Collaborative

With a view to establishing an effective school-community collaborative, the early priority is to create a work group charged with developing an operational infrastructure for the collaborative. The prototype illustrated in figure 1.2 indicates the type of mechanisms needed to provide oversight, leadership, capacity building, and ongoing support as a collaborative plans and implements strategic actions. Establishing such an infrastructure requires translating policy into authentic agreements about shared mission, vision, decision-making, priorities, goals, roles, functions, resource allocation, redeployment, enhancement, strategic implementation, evaluation, and accountability. A guidebook is available for establishing a productive collaborative (see "School-Community Partnerships: A Guide," available online at http://smhp.psych.ucla.edu/pdfdocs/guides/schoolcomm.pdf).

Finally, we note that interest in connecting school and community resources is growing at an exponential rate. A temporary connection often is established in the wake of a crisis or to address a particular problem. At some schools, efforts have been made to co-locate a few service agencies on a school campus. While limited and often informal linkages are relatively simple to make, establishing a comprehensive, long-term formal collaborative infrastructure is not easy. Development of an effective operational infrastructure requires formal and institutionalized systemic changes to enable sharing of a wide spectrum of responsibilities and resources and to ensure well-defined working relationships. In this last respect, as community agencies bring their staff to the table, care must be taken not to undervalue the role of existing student support personnel and other human and social capital found in homes and communities. To do so risks creating counterproductive competition for sparse resources and other problems.

In the long run, school-community connections must be driven by a comprehensive vision about the shared role schools, communities, and families can play in strengthening youngsters, families, schools, and neighborhoods. Such a vision encompasses safe schools and neighborhoods, whole child development and learning, personal, family, and economic well-being, and more. And this vision needs to be fully embedded into school improvement policy and practices.

Concluding Comments

In this chapter, we have stressed that it is essential to adopt a broad view of school safety and to adopt a comprehensive approach that weaves together the efforts of school and community. This sets the stage for the chapters that follow, which explore school safety, mental health, and related family and community concerns in greater depth.

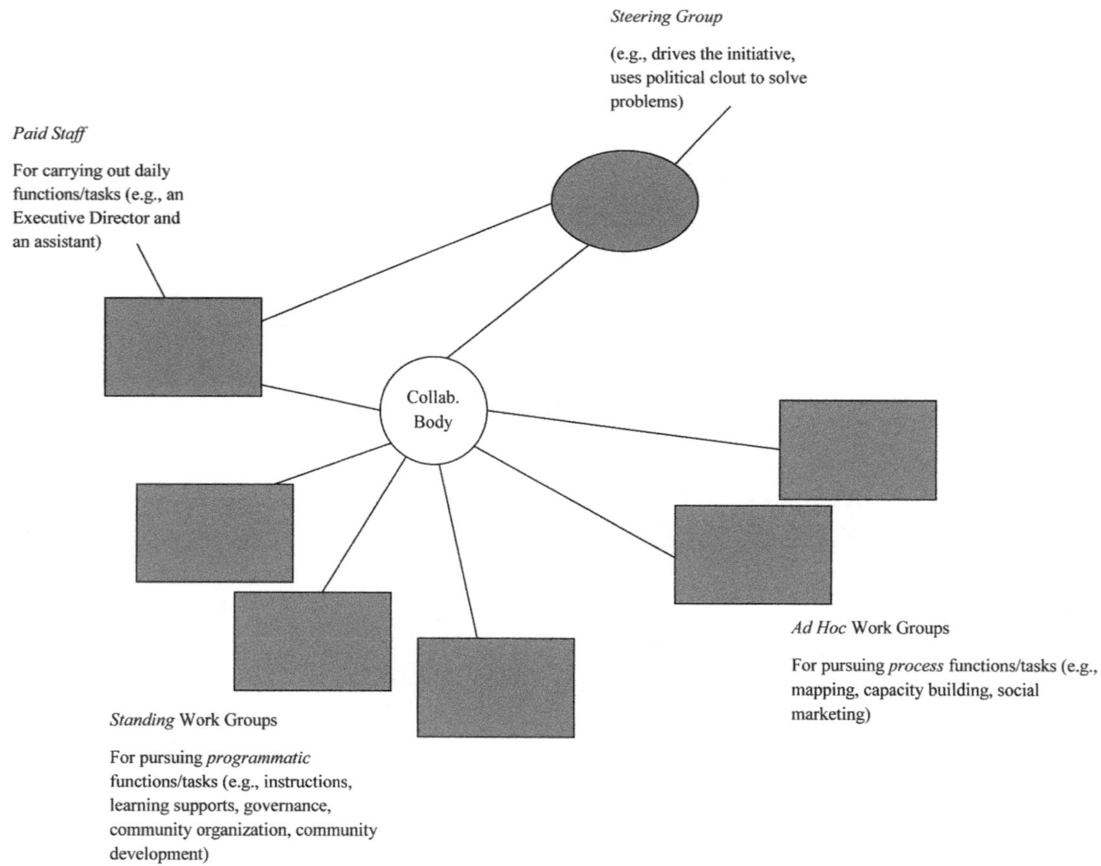

Figure 1.2 Prototype of a school-community collaborative operational infrastructure.

Note: Connecting the resources of schools, families, and a wide range of community entities through a formal collaborative facilitates developing a unified, comprehensive, and equitable system for addressing barriers to learning. Effectiveness, efficiencies, and economics of scale can be achieved by connecting a "family" (or complex) of schools (e.g., a high school and its feeder schools, schools in the same neighborhood). In a small community, the feeder pattern often is the school district.

Who should be at the table?

- Schools = formal institutions responsible for formal educations (e.g., pre-kindergarten, elementary, secondary, higher education entities). The intent is to interweave the resources of these institutions with community entities.
- Community entities = the many resources (public and private money, facilities, human and social capital) that can be brought to the table (e.g., health and social service agencies, businesses and unions, recreation, cultural, and youth development groups, libraries, juvenile justice and law enforcement, faith-based community institutions, service clubs, media). As the collaborative develops, additional steps must be taken to outreach to disenfranchised groups in the community.
- Families = representatives of all families in the community (not just representatives of organized family advocacy groups). The intent is to mobilize all the human and social capital represented by family members and other home caretakers of the young.

References

Adelman, H. S., & Taylor, L. (2003). Creating school and community partnerships for substance abuse prevention programs. *Journal of Primary Prevention, 23*, 331–369.

Adelman, H. S., & Taylor, L. (2006). *The school leader's guide to student learning supports: New directions for addressing barriers to learning*. Thousand Oaks, CA: Corwin Press.

Adelman, H. S., & Taylor, L. (2007a). *Fostering school, family, and community involvement*. Portland, OR: Northwest Regional Educational Laboratory & Hamilton fish Institute. Retrieved from http://smhp.psych.ucla.edu/dbsimple2.asp?primary=1202&number=9965

Adelman, H. S., & Taylor, L. (2007b). Systemic changes for school improvement. *Journal of Education and Psychological Consultation, 17*, 55–77.

Adelman, H. S. & Taylor, L. (2010). *Mental health in schools: Engaging learners, preventing problems, and improving schools*. Thousand Oaks, CA: Corwin Press.

Adelman, H. S. & Taylor, L. (2017). *Addressing barriers to learning: In the classroom and schoolwide*. Los Angeles: Center for MH in Schools & Student/Learning Supports at UCLA. Retrieved from http://smhp.psych.ucla.edu/improving_school_improvement.html

Adelman, H. S. & Taylor, L. (2018). *Improving school improvement*. Los Angeles: Center for MH in Schools & Student/Learning Supports at UCLA. Retrieved from http://smhp.psych.ucla.edu/improving_school_improvement.html

American Psychological Association Zero Tolerance Task Force. (2008). Are zero tolerance policies effective in schools? An evidentiary review and recommendations. *American Psychologist, 63*, 852–862.

Baker, J. A., Kamphaus, R. W., Horne, A. M., & Winsor, A. P. (2006). Evidence for population-based perspectives on children's behavioral adjustment and needs for service delivery in schools. *School Psychology Review, 35*, 31–46.

Bodilly, S., Chun, J., Ikemoto, G., & Stockly, S. (2004). *Challenges and potential of a collaborative approach to education reform*. Santa Monica, CA: RAND. Retrieved from http://www.rand.org/publications/MG/MG216/

Campie, P., Tanyu, M., & Osher, D. (2017). *California school safety toolkit*. Washington, DC: American Institutes for Research. Retrieved from http://www.air.org/resource/california-school-safety-toolkit

Centers for Disease Control and Prevention [CDC]. (2015). *School health policies and practices study 2000–2014*. Atlanta, GA: Author.

Centers for Disease Control and Prevention [CDC]. (2016). *Information for school districts and school administrators: Fostering school connectedness*. Division of Adolescent School Health, CDC, US Department of Health and Human Services. Retrieved from https://www.cdc.gov/healthyyouth/protective/pdf/connectedness_administrators.pdf

Center for MH in Schools & Student/Learning Supports (2017). *MTSS: Strengths and weaknesses*. Los Angeles: Author. Retrieved from http://smhp.psych.ucla.edu/pdfdocs/mtss.pdf

Christenson, S. & Reschly, A. (Eds.) (2010). *Handbook of school-family partnership*. New York: Routledge, Taylor and Francis.

Cleveland Municipal School District. (2015). *Humanware Annual Report 2015*. Cleveland, OH: Author.

Clingempeel, W. G., & Henggeler, S. W. (2002). Randomized clinical trials, developmental theory, and antisocial youth: Guidelines for research. *Development and Psychopathology, 14*, 695–711.

Collaborative for Academic, Social, and Emotional Learning [CASEL]. (2008). *Connecting social emotional learning with mental health*. Prepared for the National Center for Mental Health Promotion and Youth Violence Prevention by the University of Illinois. Chicago: Author.

Collaborative for Academic, Social, and Emotional Learning [CASEL]. (2015). *2015 CASEL guide: Effective social and emotional learning programs—Middle and high school edition*. Chicago: Author. Retrieved from http://www.casel.org/middle-and-high-school-edition-casel-guide

Daly, B. P., Burke, R., Hare, I., Mills, C., Owens, C., Moore, E., & Weist, M. D. (2006). Enhancing No Child Left Behind—school mental health connections. *Journal of School Health, 76*, 446–451.

Doll, B., Brehm, K., & Zucker, S. (2014). *Resilient classrooms: Creating healthy environments for learning* (2nd ed.). New York: Guilford Press.

Durlak, J. A., Weisberg, R. P., Dymnicki, A. B., Taylor, R. D., & Shellinger, K. B. (2011). The impact of enhancing students' social and emotional learning: A meta-analysis of school-based universal interventions. *Child Development, 82*, 405–432.

Dwyer, K., & Osher, D. (2000). *Safeguarding our children: An action guide*. Washington, DC: American Institutes for Research.

Dwyer, K., Osher, D., & Warger, C. (1998). *Early warning, timely response: a guide to safe schools*. Washington, DC: American Institutes for Research. Retrieved from https://files.eric.ed.gov/fulltext/ED418372.pdf

Dwyer, K., & VanBuren, E. (2010). School mental health: Prevention at all levels. In B. Doll, W. Pfohl, & J. Yoon (Eds.), *Handbook of youth prevention science* (pp. 45–69). New York: Routledge.

Epstein, J. L., Coates, L., Salinas, K. C., & Sanders, M. G. (2002). *School, family, and community partnerships: Your handbook for action* (2nd ed.). Thousand Oaks, CA: Corwin Press.

Freeman, E., Grabill, D., Rider, F., & Wells, K. (2014). *The role of system of care communities in developing and sustaining school mental health services*. Washington, DC: American Institutes for Research. Retrieved from https://www.air.org/sites/default/files/downloads/report/Systems%20of%20Care%20Communities%20in%20School%20Mental%20Health%20Systems.pdf

Graham, S., Bollinger, A., Booth Olson, C., D'Aoust, C., MacArthur, C., McCutchen, D., & Olinghouse, N. (2012). *Teaching elementary school students to be effective writers: A practice guide* (NCEE 2012-4058). Washington, DC: National Center for Education Evaluation and Regional Assistance, Institute of Education Sciences, U.S. Department of Education. Retrieved from https://ies.ed.gov/ncee/wwc/Docs/PracticeGuide/writing_pg_062612.pdf

Greenberg, M. T., Kusché, C. A., Cook, E. T., & Quamma, J. P. (1995). Promoting emotional competence in school-aged children: The effects of the PATHS Curriculum. *Development & Psychopathology, 7*, 117–136.

Hardiman, P. M., Curcio, J. L., & Fortune, J. C. (1998). School-linked services. *American School Board Journal, 185*, 37–40.

Harry, B. (1991). *Cultural diversity, families, and the special education system.* New York: Teachers College Press.

Harry, B., & Klingner, J. K. (2006). *Why are so many minority students in special education? Understanding race and disability in schools.* New York: Teachers College Press.

Institute of Medicine. (1997). Schools and health: Our nation's investment. Washington, DC: National Academies Press. Retrieved from https://www.nap.edu/catalog/5153/schools-and-health-our-nations-investment

Interdisciplinary Group on Preventing School and Community Violence. (2013). December 2012 Connecticut school shooting position statement. *Journal of School Violence, 12*, 119–133. doi:10.1080/15388220.2012.762488

Iowa Department of Education. (2009). *Iowa's co-teaching and collaborative consultation models.* Des Moines, IA: Author.

Kendziora, K., & Osher, D. (2016). Promoting children's and adolescents' social and emotional development: District adaptations of a theory of action. *Journal of Clinical Child and Adolescent Psychology, 45*, 797–811. Special Section: From Adoption to Adaptation.

Kendziora, K., & Yoder, N. (2016). *When districts support and integrate social and emotional learning (SEL): Findings from an ongoing evaluation of districtwide implementation of SEL.* Washington, DC: Education Policy Center, American Institutes for Research.

Kutash, K., & Duchnowski, A. J. (2007). *The role of mental health services in promoting safe and secure schools: Effective strategies for creating safer schools.* Washington, DC: Hamilton Fish Institute on School and Community Violence.

Lochman, J. E. (2000). Theory and empiricism in intervention research: A dialectic to be avoided. *Journal of School Psychology, 38*, 359–368.

MacMillan, D. L., & Speece, D. L. (1999). Utility of current diagnostic categories for research and practice. In R. Gallimore & L. P. Bernheimer (Eds.), *Developmental perspectives on children with high incidence disabilities* (pp. 111–133). Mahwah, NJ: Lawrence Erlbaum.

Mapp, K. L., & Kuttner, P. J. (2013). *Partners in education: A dual capacity-building framework for family-school partnerships.* Washington, DC: United States Department of Education.

Masten, A. S., Roisman, G. I., Long, J. D., Burt, K. B., Obradović, J., Riley, J. R., . . . Tellegen, A. (2005). Developmental cascades: Linking academic achievement, externalizing and internalizing symptoms over 20 years. *Developmental Psychology, 41*, 733–746.

Mayer, M. J., & Furlong, M. J. (2010). How safe are our schools? *Educational Researcher, 39*, 16–26.

Mayer, M. J., & Leone, P. E. (2007). School violence and disruption revisited: Establishing equity and safety in the school house. *Focus on Exceptional Children, 40*(1), 1–28.

Mayer, M. J., & Van Acker, R. (2008). Historical roots, theoretical and applied developments, and critical issues in cognitive-behavioral modification. In M. J. Mayer, R. Van Acker, J. E. Lochman, & F. M. Gresham (Eds.), *Cognitive-behavioral interventions for emotional and behavioral disorders: School-based practice* (pp. 3–28). New York: Guilford.

Mayer, M. J., Van Acker, R., Lochman, J. E., & Gresham, F. M. (Eds.). (2008). *Cognitive-behavioral interventions for emotional and behavioral disorders: School-based practice*. New York: Guilford Press.

National Association of School Psychologists. (2015). *Preventing youth suicide: Tips for parents and teachers*. Bethesda, MD: Author.

National Research Council and Institute of Medicine. (2000). *From neurons to neighborhoods: The science of early childhood development*. Washington, DC: Committee on Children & Youth National Science Foundation.

Nickerson, A. B., Mayer, M. J., Cornell, D. G., Jimerson, S. R., Osher, D., & Espelage, D. L. (2016). Violence prevention in schools and communities. In M. Casas, L. Suzuki, C. Alexander, & M. Jackson (Eds.), *Handbook of multicultural counseling* (4th ed., pp. 323–331). New York: Sage.

Oberle, E., & Schonert-Reichl, K. B. (2016). Stress contagion in the classroom? The link between classroom teacher burnout and morning cortisol in elementary school students. *Social Science and Medicine, 159*, 30–37.

Osher, D., & Dwyer, K. (2005). *Safeguarding our children: An action guide: revised and expanded*. Washington, DC: American Institutes for Research.

Osher, D., Dwyer, K., & Jackson, S. (2004). *Safe supportive and successful schools: Step by step*. Washington, DC: American Institutes for Research.

Pires, S. A., Lazear, K. J., & Conlan, L. (2008). *Building systems of care: A primer for child welfare*. Washington, DC: National Technical Assistance Center for Children's Mental Health Center for Child and Human Development, Georgetown University.

Skiba, R. J., & Peterson, R. L. (2000). School discipline at a crossroads: From zero tolerance to early response. *Exceptional Children, 66*(3), 335–346.

Sprague, J., & Walker, H. M. (2002). *Creating schoolwide prevention and intervention strategies. Safe and secure: Guides to creating safer schools*. Portland, OR: Northwest Regional Educational Laboratory. Retrieved from https://www.ncjrs.gov/pdffiles1/ojjdp/book1.pdf

Substance Abuse and Mental Health Services Administration. (2015). *Safe Schools/Healthy Students Initiative national evaluation: 2005–2008 Cohorts.* Rockville, MD: Author.

Substance Abuse and Mental Health Services Administration, Center for Mental Health Services. (2007). *Promotion and prevention in mental health: Strengthening parenting and enhancing child resilience* (DHHS Publication No.CMHS-SVP-0175). Rockville, MD: Author.

Sugai, G., Horner, R. H., & McIntosh, K. (2008). Best practices in developing a broad system of support for school-wide positive behavioral support. In A. Thomas & J. P. Grimes (Eds.), *Best practices in school psychology 3* (pp. 765–780). Bethesda, MD: National Association of School Psychologists.

Swearer, S. M., Espelage, D. L., Vaillancourt, T., & Hymel, S. (2010). What can be done about school bullying? Linking research to educational practice. *Educational Researcher, 39*(1), 38–47. doi:10.3102/0013189X09357622

U.S. Department of Education, National Center for Educational Statistics. (2016). *ED School Climate Surveys.* Washington, DC: Author.

U.S. Department of Education, Office of Special Education Services. (2010). *29th Annual report to Congress on the implementation of the Individuals with Disabilities Education Act* (Vol. 1). Washington, DC: Author.

U.S. Department of Health and Human Services. (1999). *Mental health: A report of the surgeon general.* Rockville, MD: Center for Mental Health Services.

Van Dorn, R., Volavka, J., & Johnson, N. (2012). Mental disorder and violence: Is there a relationship beyond substance use? *Social Psychiatry and Psychiatric Epidemiology, 47*(3), 487–503. doi:10.1007/s00127-011-0356-x

Varshney, M., Mahapatra, A., Krishnan, V., Gupta, R., & Deb, K. S. (2016). Violence and mental illness: What is the true story? *Journal of Epidemiological Community Health, 70*(3), 223–225. doi:10.1136/jech-2015-205546

Warren, M. R. (2005). Communities and schools: A new view of urban education reform. *Harvard Educational Review, 75*, 133–173.

Weisz, J., Donenberg, G., Han, S., & Weiss, B. (1995). Bridging the gap between lab and clinic in child and adolescent psychotherapy. *Journal of Consulting and Clinical Psychology, 63*, 688–701.

Weisz, J. R., Sandler, I. N., Durlak, J. A., & Anton, B. S. (2005). Preventing and protecting youth mental health through evidence-based prevention and treatment. *American Psychologist, 90*(6), 628–648.

Wiley, D. C., & Cory, A. C. (Eds.). (2013). *Encyclopedia of school health.* Washington, DC: Sage.

CHAPTER TWO

The Relational, Ecological, and Phenomenological Foundations of School Safety, Mental Health, Wellness, and Learning*

David Osher, Pamela Cantor, and Sarah Caverly

School safety, mental health, wellness, student support, and academic learning are interconnected and co-influential. School success and school safety have ecological roots and are correlates of academic achievement and academic success (Barton, 2003; Greenberg, Skidmore, Rhodes, & Nesbitt, 2002). Addressing such factors can help improve social and emotional function, reduce depressive symptoms, and enhance positive identity formation (Damon, Menon, & Bronk, 2003; Kellam, Rebok, Mayer, Ialongo, & Kalodner, 1994). Conversely, academic frustration and a lack of safety contribute to poorer mental health and wellness outcomes (Bandura, 1991; Blum, 2001; Harter, 1990).

---

* Portions have been adapted from Osher D., Cantor P., Berg J., Steyer, L., & Rose, T. (2018). Drivers of human development: How relationships and context shape learning and development. *Applied Developmental Science*, published online January 24, 2018. doi:10.1080/10888691.2017.1398650

The relationships between safety, mental health, wellness, and academics were captured in variable-centered impact studies where one of these factors was an independent variable and the other a dependent variable; other factors were sometimes included as mediating or moderating factors. This research was captured systematically in reviews of impact studies of positive youth development and social and emotional learning (e.g., Catalano, Berglund, Ryan, Lonczak, & Hawkins, 2004; Durlak, Weissberg, Dymnicki, Taylor, & Schellinger, 2011). These relationships were conceptualized by the Institute of Medicine Reports (1994, 2002, 2009) and the Surgeon General in a series of science-based reports (U.S. Public Health Service, 1999, 2000, 2001). This research, along with high-quality longitudinal research, contributed to a scientifically robust working model regarding school safety and mental health, and in some cases wellness and academic success (e.g., Benbenishty & Astor, 2005; Elliott, Williams, & Hamburg, 1996; Farrington, 2007; Goldstein & Conoley, 2004; Hunter et al., 2005; Mayer, 1995; Moffitt, 2007; Osher, Dwyer, & Jimerson, 2006; Osher, Dwyer, Jimerson, & Ward, 2012; Osher et al., 2004; Pepler & Slaby, 1994; Sprague & Walker, 2005; Tolan, 2007). Although the research came from a variety of disciplinary paradigms, the research converged on an ecological model built around transactional and ecological processes and the effects of risk and protective factors. The working model was operationalized in two scientific and practice-vetted Federal Guides that were prepared for the Departments of Education and Justice for Departmental and White House release: *Early warning, timely response: A guide to safe schools* (Dwyer, Osher, & Warger, 1998) and *Safeguarding our children: An action guide* (Dwyer & Osher, 2000). The working model has informed important responses to suicide, school shootings, and school mental health and discipline (e.g., Astor et al., 2013; Felix, Furlong, Sharkey, & Osher, 2007; Furlong, Paige, & Osher, 2003; Hinojosa, et al., 2015; Hunter et al., 2005; Institute of Medicine, 2002; Osher, Bear, Sprague, & Doyle, 2010).

As compelling as the working model has been, it has not always penetrated routine practice in schools and classrooms. School leaders often view and treat safety, student support, wellness, and academics as separate domains that compete for resources, and mental health is viewed through the lens of treatment and not prevention (Osher, Dwyer, & Jimerson, 2007; Weist et al., 2012). Student support and academic services often remain fragmented, underresourced, and poorly aligned to student and classroom needs. Schools and classrooms are often characterized by reactive and exclusionary discipline, unfriendly and unsupportive climates, and the marginalization of mental health (Gottfredson, Gottfredson, Payne, & Gottfredson, 2005; Gregory, Skiba, & Noguera, 2010; Osher & Kendziora, 2010; Weist et al., 2012). And although there have been many demonstration programs such as the Safe Schools, Healthy Students initiative, these advances were infrequently sustained with fidelity or scaled up after grants expired. This lack of penetration, scale-up, and sustainability is, in part, due to a lack of appreciation of the inextricable links between social, emotional, and cognitive development and to policy imperatives that singularly focused educators on improving test scores. However, the lack of penetration and scale-up also reflect individualistic, deficit-oriented mental models. Pianta and Walsh (1996, pp. 41–42) described this thinking as an "invidious triangle"—attributing school problems to cultural disadvantage, cultural difference, or individual student characteristics as well as to fixed mindsets, an unsophisticated understanding of risk and resilience, and an overreliance on aggregate data that fails to address the impacts of intersectionality and the individual (ideographic) nature of development.

Fortunately, we know more due to advances in epigenetics, neurobiology, resilience, sociology, and the science of dynamic systems. A recent synthesis of the science of learning and development identified convergences across multiple sciences and disciplines. These convergences include neural malleability and plasticity, the individuality of learning, and the roles of webs of support that can alter life trajectories. This synthesis illustrates how development is a multifaceted, continuous, bidirectional interaction between individuals, their individual relationships and experiences, and the demands and contingencies of the environments that they experience that can best be understood within a relational developmental systems framework (Cantor, Osher, Berg, Steyer, & Rose, 2018; Osher, Cantor, Berg, Steyer, & Rose, 2018; Osher, Cantor, Berg, Steyer, & Rose, 2017). These new findings align with the early childhood work of the Center on the Developing Child at Harvard University (Shonkoff, 2018). The findings are reinforced by consensus statements regarding social, emotional, and academic development (National Commission on Social, Emotional, and Academic Development, 2017) and the science of adolescence (Alliance for Excellence in Education, 2018), and the chapters in two major handbooks on psychology and developmental science (Cicchetti, 2016; Lerner, 2015).

This current chapter will (1) describe the development of the working model (2) summarize the new findings that can inform and extend the working model, and (3) elaborate upon the implications of the new findings, which suggest that a relational developmental systems approach can inform research and practice aimed at improving safety, mental health, wellness, and other positive developmental outcomes, including academic achievement.

The Working Model, 1994–2012

Osher, Dwyer, Jimerson, and Brown (2012) located the conceptual roots of a comprehensive approach to aligning safety, mental health support, and academic achievement in a variety of disciplines, frameworks, and fields related to children's learning and behavior. This comprehensive approach was based upon research that indicates that (1) there are risk and protective factors underlying problem behavior and (2) strategies that reduce risk and amplify protection enhance wellness and reduce future problem behaviors (Catalano, Berglund, Ryan, Lonczak, & Hawkins, 2004; Catalano, Hawkins, Berglund, Pollard, & Arthur, 2002). The key approaches, fields, and paradigms aligned with this framework include:

- *A public health approach* that focuses on population-based (as opposed to individual) approaches to problems and includes a focus on variation of effect and impact. This approach aligns promotion and prevention and includes universal, early (selective), and intensive interventions (Davis, 2002; Institute of Medicine, 2009; Mrazek & Haggerty, 1994; World Health Organization, 2002).
- *Prevention and developmental science*, which identify and address risk and protective factors and factors that mediate and moderate outcomes (e.g., Hawkins et al., 1998; Jessor, 1998; Kendziora & Osher, 2004).
- *Positive youth development and social and emotional learning*, which point to the importance of promotion, resilience, and developmental assets (Catalano et al., 2004; Cicchetti, Rappaport, Sandler, & Weissberg, 2000).
- *Life course and social field theory* that points to the key role of social fields, natural raters, and how the fields and raters change through people's life course (Kellam & Rebok, 1992).
- *Ecological theory* (Bronfenbrenner, 1977; Spencer, 2007) that indicate the importance of focusing on multi-person systems of interaction in immediate settings (e.g., home or a school); interrelations among major settings (e.g., home and school); other social structures that influence what goes on in the major settings (e.g., the presence of a system of care); and overarching institutional patterns (e.g., community resources and how they are allocated).
- *Transactional analyses*, which emphasize that developmental outcomes are the result of an ongoing dynamic interplay among child behavior, adults' responses, and environmental variables that influence both the child and youth and those who interact with him or her (Sameroff, 2000; Sutherland, 2000; Sutherland, Wehby, & Yoder, 2002).

The New Findings

Development is a cascade of changes over time that emerges through increasingly novel and complex transactions between an individual and his or her social and physical contexts (e.g., Lavigne, Gouze, Hopkins, & Bryant, 2016). Positive development emerges from the integration of several individual and contextual systems, from the biological and physiological to the cultural and historical (Spencer, 2007). In the words of Fischer and Bidell (2006), "there is no separation of nature and nurture, biology and environment, or brain and behavior, but only a collaborative coordination between them" (p. 383). The life cycle is not prefigured in a genetic program (Griffiths & Hochman, 2015; Moore, 2015). Rather, genes act as chemical followers, not prime movers, in developmental processes. As packages of biological instructions, genes require signals from the environmental context of children's lives influencing if, when, how, and which genes get expressed (Keating, 2016; Moore, 2015; Slavich & Cole, 2013).

Epigenetic adaptation is the biological process through which the ecology of relationships, experiences, perceptions, and physical and chemical toxins get "under the skin" and influence lifelong learning, behavior, neural integration and connectivity, and health (Bernstein, Meissner, & Lander, 2007; Siegel, 2012). Neural integration is the process through which the developing brain becomes increasingly interconnected and specialized, and capable of more and more complex skill development. The energy driving these neurodevelopmental processes is the bidirectional relational and experiential contexts in children's lives. An understanding of neural malleability and plasticity, the dynamics of resilience, and the interconnectedness of individuals with their social and physical contexts can help improve school safety, mental health, and wellness. Cantor, Osher, and colleagues (Cantor et al., 2018; Osher et al., 2017, 2018) identified 13 key findings, which are incorporated in table 2.1.

Individuals and contexts come together through relationships, and these relationships are affected by both positive and negative ecological factors (e.g., stress, attunement, and support). This relational and bioecological process can be understood through the lens of Developmental Systems Theories (DST; e.g., Ford & Lerner, 1992; Overton, 2015). DST enables us to view children's development as embodied, contextualized, and socially and culturally situated—understood in their ecologies and affected by the ecologies of those who interact with them (Bornstein, 2015; Bronfenbrenner & Morris, 2006; Cairns, 1979). When DST explicitly incorporates a phenomenological component (Spencer, 1995, 2007), it allows us to examine the role of context, culture, intra-subjective experiences, and social and emotional states, appraisal, meaning-making, and other factors in explaining human development. Children grow as individuals, in cultures and contexts, producing unique individual (idiographic) developmental pathways that reflect their own adaptation and meaning-making across the lifespan (Overton, 2015). Although everyone's developmental history is unique, individuals influence each other—they contribute to and are influenced by the idiographic pathways of others as well as to how others experience environments and make sense of their individual and collective experience. There is, as Georg Simmel conceptualized, a "web of group experience" (Simmel, 1955), but although a

Table 2.1 Key findings

- The ongoing, reciprocal relations between individuals' biology, their relationships, and the ecologies and contextual influences in which they are embedded determine the expression of their genetic endowment and ultimately their development as individuals.
- Genes are chemical "followers"; their expression is determined by contextual influences at the biological level; epigenetic adaptation determines the expression of our genetic makeup and is part of a system of ongoing two-way exchanges between human beings and the physical and social world that create qualitative changes over time.
- Malleability and neural plasticity are the core principles of human development.
- Each child's development is nonlinear, has its own unique pacing, and is highly responsive to context.
- The development of children's skills is progressive and does not occur in isolation; it requires the integration and layering of prerequisite skills.
- Social, emotional, and cognitive capabilities are fundamentally intertwined; they are interdependent in their development, experience, and use; neural integration and interconnectivity of children's cognitive, social, and emotional development is essential for well-being—both anatomically and functionally.
- Contextual influences and ecology cannot be ignored.
- Adversity can affect development, mental and physical health, and learning.
- Resilience and thriving in the face of adversity are possible and are a product of children's internal assets and supports from individuals within a child's social environment.
- Adults' buffering of stress plays a central role in healthy child development; therefore, building and supporting adult capacity are critically important tasks. Adults' experience of adversity and stress can affect their ability to provide this support.
- Schools and other child-serving systems are potentially powerful contexts through which stress can be buffered, neural integration and connectivity supported, and individual development nurtured.
- Culture, cultural responsiveness, and cultural competence are critical components of context and are profoundly important in shaping the experiences through which children grow.

group effect, the web is dynamic and is affected by the ideographic experiences of each group member.

Micro- and macro-contexts create risks as well as assets, which serve as protective factors and can prevent the actualization or impacts of risk. These assets can both reduce a child's *net vulnerability* (Spencer, 2007), foster resilience, and support well-being. Contexts such as schools can support healthy development (Fischer & Bidell, 2006; Spencer, Swanson, & Harpalani, 2015). The processes through which ecologies affect development can be observed in individuals at neurobiological, physiological, phenomenological, behavioral, and social levels. For example, relationships characterized by sensitivity, attunement, consistency, trustworthiness, cognitive stimulation, and scaffolding enable children to develop secure attachments and mature in progressively complex ways (Bornstein, 2015; Center on the Developing Child, 2016; Fischer & Bidell, 2006; Li & Julian, 2012; Thompson, 2015). Humans are responsive to relationships, experience, meaning-making, and context throughout their lives, and this plasticity offers opportunities to buffer and overcome the effects of risk factors throughout development.

Development within Contexts

Development, understood this way, takes place within interlinked bioecological and cultural contexts that encompass an array of environments and societal structures (Bornstein & Leventhal, 2015; Bronfenbrenner & Morris, 2006; Spencer, 2017). These contexts include the differential allocation of risk (e.g., exposure to violence) and hegemonic belief systems that legitimate or ignore the impacts of privilege (e.g., Gay & Kirkland, 2003; Spencer, 2017). Structural and social features of developmentally rich contexts support development and buffer the effects of adversity when they foster adults' capacities—say teachers—to attune with and support children and to teach, model, and co-regulate the development of social, emotional, and cognitive competencies. Developmentally rich contexts can provide a "constructive web" through which complex dynamic skills are developed and positive adaptation is fostered (Fischer & Bidell, 2006). Developmentally robust experiences lead to the integration of neural structures that establish representational templates through which future experiences are interpreted, reappraised, and processed (Siegel, 1999). The positive adaptations that young people make to one context can carry over to other contexts, therein enabling them to succeed in environments that pose new and differing challenges. Meanwhile, developmentally unsuitable, insufficiently supportive, and culturally incongruent contexts exacerbate stress and hinder the development of foundational competencies, which include bonds that children make with adults, skills to cope with and manage stressful conditions, and the regulation of emotion and attention to effectively engage and accomplish goals (e.g., Farmer, Dawes, Alexander, & Brooks, 2016; Stafford-Brizard, 2016).

Relationships between and among children and adults are primary processes through which biological and contextual factors influence and mutually reinforce each other. When they are reciprocal, attuned, culturally responsive, and trustful, relationships support positive developmental pathways, which are foundational for learning, adaptation, and the integration of social, affective, emotional, and cognitive processes. Developmental relationships can contribute both to changes in genetic expression (Bornstein & Leventhal, 2015; Bronfenbrenner & Morris, 2006) and to building social and emotional competence. These intraindividual changes can enhance positive and reduce negative environmental transactions with others, which include how natural raters and gatekeepers (Kellam & Rebok, 2002) respond to an individual. These improved transactions—and the risks they reduce and opportunities which they create—can alter predicted trajectories regarding school failure, mental disorder, and violence (e.g., Albert et al., 2015; Dodge et al., 2015; Osher, Kendziora, & Garibaldi, 2014; Salinger & Osher, 2018; Pasalich, Witkiewitz, McMahon, Pinderhughes, & The Conduct Problems Prevention Research Group, 2015).

Developmental relationships have been operationalized as having enduring emotional attachment, reciprocity, progressive complexity of joint activity, and a power balance that allows for transferability to new settings (Li & Julian, 2012). They are characterized by attunement (sensing and responding what others think and need), social synchrony, compassionate communication, co-regulation, support, modeling, consistency, trustworthiness, cognitive stimulation, and a caregiver's capacity to accurately perceive and respond to the child's mental state (Bergin & Bergin, 2009; Bornstein, 2015; Li & Julian, 2012; Siegel, 2012). Support should be developmentally constitutive; it should align with a child's social-historical life space; provide emotional security, information, and knowledge; and enable children to develop age-appropriate habits, skills, and mindsets (Thompson & Goodvin, 2016), emotion regulation, and cognitive processes (Center on the Developing Child, 2016; Siegel, 2012). These relationships have implications for mental health and wellness: perceived support is more strongly related to psychological well-being than other dimensions of support (Thompson & Goodvin, 2016), and this perception of support is affected by how developmental relationships are experienced, processed, and remembered (Cassidy & Shaver, 2008; Thompson, 2015).

Developmental relationships occur in nested ecological systems—communities and neighborhoods, families, child care, schools, and peers—whose composition, culture, and structure can constrain or foster these relationships. Relationships within these systems are affected by other ecological systems as well as by cultural factors, the attributes of individual children and adults, and the child's developmental stage (Bronfenbrenner & Morris, 2006; Spencer, 2007). Each microsystem provides opportunities for social learning and can influence social, emotional, and cognitive development through the quality of relationships and the extent to which children and youth experience safety, connectedness, engagement, challenge, and opportunities to develop competencies and access supports—both positively (e.g., social and emotional learning) and negatively (e.g., bullying).

Schools

Schools are multilevel, multilayered, dynamic systems where teachers, peers, classrooms, public spaces and structures, culture, composition, policies, and student attributes influence each other (Crosnoe & Benner, 2015; Pianta, 2016). These co-influential interactions produce differential effects that affect staff behavior and (in part though that effect) can alter student trajectories at both an individual and subgroup level over time (e.g., Beltz, Wright, Sprague, & Molenaar, 2016; Kremer, Flower, Huang, & Vaughn, 2016; Osher et al., 2014).

Developmentally rich schools that also support staff wellness provide students with safe, secure, enriching opportunities and developmental relationships with adults; support for building self-regulation, executive function, and social and behavioral skills; opportunities for practice and reinforcement of these skills; and opportunities to take on leadership roles and participate in collaborative and productive peer interactions (e.g., Darling-Hammond, Cook-Harvey, Flook, Barron, & Osher, 2018; Jones & Bouffard, 2012; Lerner, 2004). The structural and social features of schools can enhance (or hinder) developmental range, buffer (or amplify) the effects of stress and trauma, promote (or mitigate against) resilience, and accelerate (or attenuate) the development and integration of affective, cognitive, social, and emotional processes (Osher et al., 2014). Developmentally unsuitable, insufficiently supportive, and culturally incongruent schools (and other contexts) exacerbate stress; hinder the reinforcement of foundational competencies; and impel maladaptive behaviors by limiting healthy relationships with adults and enrichment and stimulating experiences; and by reducing the chances of interacting with prosocial peers (Farmer et al., 2015). These schools also normalize authoritarian, dulling, and aversive contexts as children who experience recurring and continuous negative contexts cease to recognize them as abnormal and become habituated to these contexts (Osher, 2016; Siegel, 1999).

Schools can support students by providing a web of support and fostering developmental relationships for students with their teachers and peers (Crosnoe & Benner, 2015; Osher & Kendziora, 2010). Schools support developmental relationships and the development of social and emotional skills when they foster the social and emotional conditions for learning: connectedness, support, challenge, engagement, respect, agency, and emotional, intellectual, identity, psychological, and physical safety (Berg, Osher, Moroney, & Yoder, 2017; Berkowitz, Moore, Astor, & Benbenishty, 2016; Osher et al., 2017). The classroom is a key location for developmental relationships. Positive classroom climates support students' social and emotional development and help them succeed as students (Hamre & Pianta, 2007). Schools that successfully integrate affective, cognitive, social, and emotional processes with curricular content accelerate the developmental range of students (Darling-Hammond et al., 2018; Hammond, 2016; Jones & Bouffard, 2012; Osher et al., 2016).

Schools that are culturally responsive and competent help build conditions for learning and support that minimize the tensions and the demands on psychic energy created by culturally challenging schools. Culturally challenging schools require additional attention for some students, who expend mental and emotional energy responding to hostile environments, thereby taking away cognitive and emotional energy for learning and socialization (e.g., Boykin, 1986; Spencer, 2017). Culturally competent schools support family engagement and cultural responsiveness by building staff cultural proficiency and cultural humility (Hook & Watkins, 2015; Hook et al., 2016), by regularly assessing how school policies and assessment procedures, as well as staff attitudes and practices, differentially affect culturally and linguistically diverse students and families, and by changing policies and practices that privilege some students and disadvantage others (King, Sims, & Osher, 2007; Osher, Cartledge, Oswald, Artiles, & Coutinho, 2004).

Culturally responsive approaches scaffold learning by helping connect learning (e.g., social and emotional learning) and instruction to students' individual experiences, cultural resources, and needs with an appreciation of individual variation and a non-judgmental understanding of the effects of macro-system factors on opportunities to learn (e.g., Gay, 2000; Spencer, 2017). Leveraging prior knowledge, experience, and interests can reduce cognitive load and mental effort, creating space for new learning. Culturally responsive approaches support opportunities to learn for all students by supporting communication between teachers and students (Gay, 2000; Hammond, 2016).

The social and emotional conditions for learning (CFL) are those aspects of the learning environment most proximal to learning and development, including safety, connectedness, support, challenge, and engagement. A subset of school and classroom climate, they are a product of interactions among members of a class or school community, the interpretation of such interactions, and a school's culture (e.g., Garibaldi, Ruddy, Osher, & Kendziora, 2015). CFL are inextricably linked to social and emotional learning (Berg et al., 2017).

CFL and interpersonal relationships affect learning and development both directly (e.g., through effects on engagement) and indirectly (e.g., through effects on teacher stress and or through effects of bullying) (Swearer, Espelage, Vaillancourt, & Hymel, 2010). Students' social behaviors and affect are affected by school staff members' perceptions of students as well as students' perceptions of teachers. Staff function as natural raters who reward or sanction students' behaviors (Kellam & Rebok, 1992). Teachers' behaviors toward and expression of explicit expectations of students' impact students' self-concept, engagement, motivation to succeed, and school-related behaviors (e.g., Osher, Kidron, DeCandia, Kendziora, & Weissberg, 2016). Interpersonal relationships between and among students and their teachers and, particularly, students' perceptions of teacher empathy and trust influence student engagement and capacity to persist through challenging academic tasks (e.g., Master, Butler, & Walton, 2017). The mutually reinforcing interactions between and among students and teachers are entwined with the way the brain responds to learning and the degree to which students tap their cognitive, emotional, social, and affective resources (National Research Council [NRC], 2012).

When the design and organization of schools do not foster conditions for learning, schools can harm students both immediately and over time. For example, classroom climates characterized by conflict are associated with poor peer relations, more aggression, and poorer academic. When students perceive CFL as unfavorable, they find it harder to engage and can become frustrated, have lower self-concepts and expectations, and lag academically (Hammond, 2016), contributing to off-task behavior that can trigger exclusionary discipline and its academic consequences, and to the experience of shame, student disengagement, grade retention, dropout, and arrests (e.g., Mallett, 2015). Over time, adverse experiences in school, including exclusionary discipline, can lead to a cascade of negative academic and behavioral transactions that can lead children to withdraw and become less motivated, fostering greater gaps in school performance and achievement (e.g., Masten et al., 2005; Ursache, Blair, & Raver, 2012). This disengagement can contribute to poor attendance and grades in core classes, repeating grades, and discipline problems (e.g., suspension), that can, in turn, lead to dropout and school failure (Kendziora, Osher, & Carey, 2014). Even one suspension increases the risk of repeating grades, school dropout, and incarceration and reduces the likelihood of postsecondary success (Arcia, 2006).

Contextual effects spill over or transfer to other contexts. One setting can positively affect another setting. Similarly, adaptations that children and youth make in one context carry over to other contexts. Children and youth cope with stress and adversity, including identity threat, in ways that may be adaptive or maladaptive. Adult support can promote positive adaptation when adults have the capacity to understand the origin of a problematic behavior in another context and provide the child with attuned, developmentally appropriate, and culturally competent mentoring and/or psychological support that helps the child meet the expectations of the new context (e.g., Pierce, Gould, & Camiré, 2017; Spencer, 2007). Adults can provide a web of support that helps children and youth develop cultural competence, a capacity to code switch, and the ability to employ socially effective scripts when encountering challenging and identity-assailing situations (Nasir, 2011; Oppedal & Toppelberg, 2016; Snyder, Shah, & Ross, 2012) all of which can help children and youth adapt to environments that have differing behavioral expectations and pose differing challenges (Goodnow & Lawrence, 2015; Jakonen, 2016; Spencer, 2017).

Relationships with Teachers and Other Adults

Teachers affect student motivation, engagement, learning, behavior, and psychological support (Pianta, 2016). Student-teacher relationships are particularly important for students who are placed at elevated levels of risk (Hamre & Pianta, 2005). Emotionally close, trustful relationships with nurturing teachers and high teacher responsiveness foster positive development and learning (Jones & Bouffard, 2012). Teachers' explicit expression of high expectations and belief in students' capabilities correlate with successful achievement (e.g., Steele, 2010). Positive teacher-student relationships promote both co-regulation and self-regulation, which support children's classroom behavior and, in turn, contribute to positive classroom climates. Positive climates are associated with school success-related skills and dispositions, such as greater social, emotional, cognitive and academic competence, self-esteem, school satisfaction and engagement, higher attendance, and less acting out (Berg et al., 2017; Hamre & Pianta, 2005).

Positive teacher-student relationships can help children modulate stress reactivity and provide working models for students about managing their behavior. Developmental constitutive relationships can contribute to relational trust (Bryk & Schneider, 2003) when students view teachers as reliable and trustworthy sources and teachers view students as effective learners (e.g., Mayer, 2014). Students who have close relationships with teachers are more likely to be confident and positive in their approaches to learning and are more comfortable asking for help (IOM & NRC, 2015). Positive student-teacher relationships can help students engage, regulate their emotions, and build social competence. High-quality teacher-student relationships may also (along with other teacher strategies) reduce stereotype threat (Steele, 2010), protect students who are at higher levels of risk for poor outcomes (e.g., Roorda, Koomen, Spilt, & Oort, 2011), and buffer the effects of victimization and other adversity (e.g., Norwalk, Hamm, Farmer, & Barnes, 2016).

The power of developmental relationships with teachers appears to be driven by the extent to which the relationships: (1) involve attuning to each other's feelings, needs by achieving social synchrony, so that the acts of the student and teacher support each other's goals (Farmer, Dawes, Alexander, & Brooks, 2015), and (2) to promote positive identity formation and increase student concepts of themselves as learners (e.g., Gregory & Korth, 2016; Li & Julian, 2012; Nasir, 2011).

Teacher capacity includes the technical, pedagogical, social, and emotional skills to teach content, manage classrooms, and develop supportive and culturally responsive relationships (e.g., Doyle, 2006; Osher, Bear, Sprague, & Doyle, 2010). Effective teaching depends on teacher qualities that include teacher social and emotional competence, the ability to accurately interpret student cues, and the ability to listen to students and to understand the meaning of student behavior (Evertson & Weinstein, 2006; Jennings & Greenberg, 2009).

Classroom management and instructional practices that employ communication and positive interactions as a way to increase engagement and maintain appropriate levels of arousal support the development of students' emotion regulation, executive functions, and academic skills (e.g., Zelazo, Blair, & Willoughby, 2016) and contribute to positive self-representations and more positive responses from others (e.g., Murray, Rosanbalm, Christopoulos, & Hamoudi, 2015). For example, reflective reprocessing of information and reappraising of prior knowledge and experience is thought to be necessary for the development of executive functions and to reduce cognitive load and can be encouraged through intentional instructional practices (Zelazo, 2015). Meditation, problem-solving tasks, and appropriate video-gaming tasks are instructional practices that can help develop executive function skills and the likelihood that they are activated in future activities (e.g., Galinsky, Bezos, McClelland, Carlson, & Zelazo, 2017).

Effective instructional practices, support for student behavior, and positive classroom climates can counter the effects of chronic stress on students and improve outcomes for students who are at placed at high levels of risk (e.g., Kellam et al., 2011) and through that improve mental health in the short and long term (Dodge et al., 2015; Kellam & Rebok, 1992). Conversely, negative interpersonal transactions that include teacher sarcasm and counteraggression, infrequent positive teacher support and attention during academic learning, lack of teacher praise, and limited opportunities to respond (e.g., Osher, Van Aker et al., 2004; Sutherland & Oswald, 2005), as well as teacher stereotype priming (Steele, 2010) can add or amplify stress. Heightened stress and anxiety can reduce available working memory and lead to trouble paying attention in class and completing work, especially for students struggling with regulating behavior in social situations in school and at home. These social and classroom behaviors lead to negative perceptions and expectations on the part of both the student and the teacher regarding the student being poorly regulated, not capable, and unable to learn. This can contribute to negative reinforcement, iatrogenic interventions, negative student self-identities, student learned helplessness, and a teachers' sense of inefficacy (e.g., Mayer, Davis, & Schoorman, 1995; Salinger & Osher, 2018). Psychological distress or appraisals of events as stressful or challenging are, in turn, associated with impaired self-regulation (e.g., Duckworth, Kim, & Tsukayama, 2013).

Teacher well-being is important (Jennings & Greenberg, 2009; Pianta, 2016). Many educators are challenged by excessive cognitive demands, lack of cultural and linguistic competence and humility, or an inability to attune to the development needs of children or to respond to the impacts of trauma on children and adults (Baird & Kracen, 2006), and this may be particularly problematic (at least at a group level) when students and teachers do not share the same demographic characteristics (Egalitie, Kisida, & Winters, 2015; Egalitie & Kisida, 2017; Yarnell & Bohrnstedt, 2018). Teacher stress matters and is affected by the teacher's own ecology, which includes the level of principal support, job-related pressures and demands, and the teacher's ability to manage student feelings and behaviors (e.g., Jennings & Greenberg, 2009; Johnson, Kraft, & Papay, 2012).

Findings from evaluations of school-based interventions, including ones that monitored student and teacher cortisol levels, suggest that teacher stress affects their interaction with students, student stress levels, teacher behavior, and student academic outcomes (e.g., Flook, Goldberg, Pinger, Bonus, & Davidson, 2013). Reducing teacher stress through interventions such as mindfulness interventions can reduce student stress biomarkers (e.g., Jennings & Greenberg, 2009; Oberle & Schonert-Reichl, 2016). Adults in schools and other agencies need effective preparation, training, and support, including positive conditions for teaching and supporting diverse children and youth. Staff benefit from respectful and supportive leadership and strategies that address stress and provide guidance on managing classroom and other setting dynamics (e.g., Farmer et al., 2016).

Macro-System Factors

Research often neglects the impact of macro-level factors at the microsystem and exosystem levels (Spencer, 2007). Children and adults experience macro-system factors regularly and directly. Macro-system factors are operationalized through rituals, policies, protocols, protocols, routinized practices, and opportunity structures. Children and adults experience macro-system factors directly through behaviors, and routines that affect how children experience and react to environments and indirectly through social stigma and exposure to contexts where opportunities for enrichment and choice are limited or absent (e.g., Oyserman & Lewis, 2017). Structural macro-system factors institutionalize practices, as in the case of public and private housing policy that promotes housing segregation, contribute to housing segregation and housing insecurity, which, in turn, affect educational and health outcomes as well as wealth accumulation. (Cutuli et al., 2013; Obradović et al., 2008; Reardon & Bischoff, 2011). Harmful structural macro-system factors can also be buffered by beneficial factors, such as connection to neighbors, neighborhood collective efficacy, and sense of belonging, and by positive micro-system contexts, including developmental relationships with family members, teachers, and peers (Luthar, Crossman, & Small, 2015). Cultural macro-system factors include hegemonic beliefs and mindsets such as victim-blaming approaches to understanding social problems that ignore or deemphasize the impacts of history, context, and privilege (Lee, 2010; Ryan, 1972).

Poverty and racism, both separately and together, make the experience of stress and adversity more likely for children and adults who must deal regularly with the consequences of economic hardship and prejudice in their daily lives in contexts that ignore the omnipresent effects of racism (Spencer, 2017). These effects may be visible in the moment (e.g., a racial slur), or they may be emergent and only visible upon analysis (e.g., racial disparities that are the product of multiple small and often subtle steps; Osher, 2015). They can also be indirect, such as the impacts of housing segregation on the differential resources available for schools under local funding formulas (Cutler & Glaeser, 1997; Owens, 2018).

Refining the Working Model

The "working model" still works—it incorporates an ecological and transactional public health approach that focuses on promotion, risk, and protection across a child's life space and development. Although statistically predictive, it is not sufficient to incorporate new knowledge, and to frame and drive change in schools that can dramatically improve safety, mental health, wellness, and equity with excellence. The working model does not sufficiently address what we know about bioecological processes, neural malleability and plasticity, the dynamics of resilience, and the interconnectedness of individuals with their social and physical contexts, the dynamics of complex systems, the contextualized individuality of learning and development, the importance of agency, the importance of cultural responsiveness and of conditions for learning and development, the power of developmental relationships, and the impact of culture and macro-system factors. We now know that "human development is not predetermined, fixed, or linear;

rather, it is unique to each and every individual, highly responsive to environments and relationships, and subject to change across the lifespan" (Osher et al., 2018, p. 26). Teasing out the implications of this knowledge can help us improve safety, mental health, wellness, and equity with excellence while addressing Pianta and Walsh's (1996) invidious triangle—as we now know three important things:

- Epigenetics are not destiny
- Cultural competence and responsiveness can address cultural disconnects and
- Individual behavior and performance cannot be understood without a phenomenological ecological perspective

Knowledge and frameworks are important, but only if they are realized in changes in practice which depend upon how change is supported and how schools and the relationship among schools and other service systems are designed, incentivized, and organized. These changes should address a minimum of eight principles in a coherent, cohesive, and fully integrated manner:

- *Address the relationship between social, emotional, and cognitive development and achievement.* Safety and mental health interventions should attend to academic engagement and success; academic interventions should leverage student social and emotional competence and address social and behavioral effects of academic intervention.
- *Address the individual nature of learning and development and the specificity of intervention effects.* Solutions aimed at the average student do not work whether they are academic, psychosocial, or focused on safety (Rose, Rouhani, & Fischer, 2013). Intervention selection should attend to findings that address the specificity and context of outcomes—what works for what children in what contextual conditions (Osher & Kane, 1993)—that specific experiences affect the development of specific characteristics in specific individuals at specific times in specific ways (Bornstein, 2015). Both research and practice should operationalize the individuality and specificity principles. Research, for example, could study developmental change with a focus on the individual as the unit of analysis, longitudinally examining the multiple factors that co-influence development employing such techniques as burst designs and dynamic factor analysis (Nesselroade, 2018). Artificial intelligence can provide tools for monitoring and address the multiple factors that affect an individual, groups, and schools as a whole in order to enhance the power of interventions (Butler et al., 2018).
- *Provide environmental conditions for learning and development that support student success along the developmental continuum.* These include supports for

developmentally positive, trusting relationships; attachment and emotional connections; individually and culturally responsive conditions for learning; physical, emotional, and identity safety; and a sense of belonging and purpose.

- *Support the intentional development of social, emotional, and cognitive skills, mindsets, and habits.* These include self-regulation, executive function, intrapersonal awareness, and interpersonal skills, as well as growth mindsets and a sense of agency that support resilience and productive action. Schools should provide regular opportunities to integrate social, emotional, and cognitive skills (e.g. cooperation, conflict resolution), the development of metacognitive skills, and motivation through their experiences and relationships in the school day.
- *Provide structures that reach beyond the classroom to provide systems of academic and social support, including personalized supports that respond to students' needs to address adversity.* Schools should create a collaborative multitiered system of supports, based a shared developmental framework uniting staff, families, and support providers as they address learning barriers and meet student needs both in and out of the classroom.
- *Develop the readiness and capacity of adults.* Teachers and other support staff need to have the motivation, organizational support, knowledge of cognitive processes and social and emotional skills and attitudes, and competencies that enable them to interact with children and youth in a culturally responsive, developmentally appropriate manner that addresses their individual needs, strengths, and trajectories (Yoder & Osher, 2018).
- *Implement culturally competent and culturally responsive practices.* School practices should be designed to strengthen relational trust and promote teacher and staff cultural responsiveness. These should include addressing implicit bias, concepts of cultural disadvantage (e.g., "culture of poverty"), and hegemonic belief systems that privilege some individuals and behaviors and mystify that privileging.
- *Eliminate iatrogenic interventions that undermine emotional and physical safety, foster unproductive mindsets, and undermine belief and identity formation.* We already know enough to act: We can cease doing things that hurt children, for example, putting students who have antisocial values and beliefs into an isolated intervention group, which can support problematic social learning (Dishion, McCord, & Poulin, 1999). These include exclusionary discipline, segregated groupings, and a focus on test preparation to the exclusion of engagement, learning, and emotional health.

While efforts at improving school safety, mental health, and wellness should address the key drivers of school safety, mental health, and wellness, they should also address the bidirectional and co-influential relationship between and among these factors, and learning. This includes the intentional development of integrated habits, skills, and mindsets; providing supportive and equitable conditions for learning and opportunities to learn; and the creation of culturally responsive classroom and school environments that support personalization of learning and the development of the whole child (Darling- Hammond et al., 2018; Osher, Moroney, & Williamson, 2018).

School safety and mental health and wellness for all children and youth requires public and political will, as well as sound policy, to ensure that all children experience safe and nurturing settings, 24/7, as supportive environments, experiences, and relationships harness brain malleability and social learning to promote social and emotional wellness. Policy and practices should avoid deficit-oriented victim-blaming approaches (Ryan, 1972) and be based on rigorous science, implemented with quality (Wandersman, Alia, Cook, Hsu, & Ramaswamy, 2016) and cultural competence, measured with an understanding of formative progression of individual development (Fischer & Kennedy, 1997; Rose, Rouhani, & Fischer, 2013), and adopted at scale (Dymnicki, Wandersman, Osher, & Pakstis, 2018)—with equitable outcomes for all children as an explicit goal.

References

Albert, D., Belsky, D. W., Crowley, D. M., Conduct Problems Prevention Research Group, Bates, J. E., Pettit, G. S., Lansford, J. E., Dick, D. M., & Dodge, K. R. (2015). Developmental mediation of genetic variation in response to the Fast Track Prevention Program. *Development and Psychopathology, 27*, 81–95.

Alliance for Excellent Education. (2018). *Science of adolescent learning consensus statement report series.* Washington, DC: Author.

Arcia, E. (2006). Achievement and enrollment status of suspended students: Outcomes in a large, multicultural school district. *Education and Urban Society, 38*(3), 359–369.

Astor, R., Cornell, D. G., Espelage, D. L., Furlong, M. J., Jimerson, S. J., Mayer, M. J., . . . Sugai, G. (2012). Connecticut school violence position statement. *Journal of School Violence, 12*(2), 119–133.

Baird, K., & Kracen, A. C. (2006). Vicarious traumatization and secondary traumatic stress: A research synthesis. *Counselling Psychology Quarterly, 19*(2), 181–188.

Bandura, A. (1991). Self-efficacy mechanism in physiological activation and health-promoting behavior. In J. Madden, IV (Ed.), *Neurobiology of learning, emotion and affect* (pp. 229–269). New York: Raven.

Barton, P. (2003). *Parsing the achievement gap: Baselines for tracking progress.* Princeton, NJ: Educational Testing Service.

Beltz, A. M., Wright, A. G. C., Sprague, B. N., & Molenaar, P. C. M. (2016). Bridging the nomothetic and idiographic approaches to the analysis of clinical data. *Assessment, 23*(4), 447–458.

Benbenishty, R., & Astor, R. A. (2005). *School violence in context: Culture, neighborhood, family, school, and gender.* New York: Oxford University Press.

Berg, J., Osher, D., Moroney, D., & Yoder, N. (2017). *The intersection of school climate and social and emotional development.* Washington, DC: American Institutes for Research.

Bergin, C., & Bergin, D. (2009). Attachment in the classroom. *Educational Psychology Review, 21*(2), 141–170. doi:10.1007/s10648-009-9104-0

Berkowitz, R., Moore, H., Astor, R. A., & Benbenishty, R. (2016). A research synthesis of the associations between socio-economic background, inequality, school climate, and academic achievement. *Review of Educational Research, 20*(10), 1–45.

Bernstein, B. E., Meissner, A., & Lander, E. S. (2007). The mammalian epigenome. *Cell, 128*(4), 669–681.

Blum, R. (2001). Early transitions: Risk and protective factors. *The Center,* 38–41.

Bornstein, M. H. (2015). Children's parents. In R. M. Lerner (Editor-in-Chief) & M. H. Bornstein & T. Leventhal (Vol. Eds.), *Handbook of child psychology and developmental science: Vol. 4. Ecological settings and processes in developmental systems* (7th ed., pp. 55–132). Hoboken, NJ: Wiley.

Bornstein, M. H., & Leventhal, T. (Eds.). (2015). *Handbook of child psychology and developmental science: Vol. 4. Ecological settings and processes* (7th ed.). Hoboken, NJ: Wiley.

Boykin, A. W. (1986). The triple quandary and the schooling of Afro-American children. In U. Neisser (Ed.), *The school achievement of minority children* (pp. 55–72). Hillsdale, NJ: Lawrence Erlbaum.

Bronfenbrenner, U. (1977). Toward an experimental ecology of human development. *American Psychologist, 32*(7), 513–531. doi:10.1037/0003-066X.32.7.513

Bronfenbrenner, U., & Morris, P. A. (2006). The bioecological model of human development. In W. Damon & R. M. Lerner (Eds.), *Handbook of child psychology: Vol. 1. Theoretical models of human development* (6th ed., pp. 793–828). New York: Wiley.

Bryk, A. S., & Schneider, B. (2003). Trust in schools: A core resource for school reform. *Educational Leadership, 60*(6), 40–45.

Butler, A., Katz, J., Johnson, J., Osher, D., Pentimonti, J., & Neiman, S. (2018). *Continuous improvement.* Washington, DC: American Institutes for Research.

Cairns, R. B. (Ed.). (1979). *The analysis of social interactions: Methods, issues, and illustrations.* Hillsdale, NJ: Lawrence Erlbaum.

Cantor, P., Osher, D., Berg, J., Steyer, L., & Rose, T. (2018). Malleability, plasticity, and individuality: How children learn and develop in context. *Applied Developmental Science.* doi:10.1080/10888691.2017.1398649

Cassidy, J., & Shaver, P. R. (Eds.). (2008). *Adult attachment: Theory, research, and clinical applications.* New York: Guilford Press.

Catalano, R. F., Berglund, M. L., Ryan, J. A. M., Lonczak, H. S., & Hawkins, J. D. (2004). Positive youth development in the United States: Research findings on evaluations of positive youth development programs. *Annals of the American Academy of Political and Social Science, 591*, 98–124.

Catalano, R. F., Hawkins, J. D., Berglund, M. L., Pollard, J. A., & Arthur, M. W. (2002). Prevention science and positive youth development: Competitive or cooperative frameworks? *Journal of Adolescent Health, 31*(6), 230–239.

Center on the Developing Child at Harvard University. (2016). *From best practices to breakthrough impacts: A science-based approach to building a more promising future for young children and families.* Retrieved from https://46y5eh11fhgw3ve3ytpwxt9r-wpengine.netdna-ssl.com/wp-content/uploads/2016/05/From_Best_Practices_to_Breakthrough_Impacts-4.pdf

Cicchetti, D. (2016). Socioemotional, personality, and biological development: Illustrations from a multilevel developmental psychopathology perspective on child maltreatment. *Annual Review of Psychology, 67*, 187–211. doi:10.1146/annurev-psych-122414-033259

Cicchetti, D., Rappaport, J., Sandler, I., & Weissberg, R. P. (Eds.). (2000). *The promotion of wellness in children and adolescents.* Washington, DC: Child Welfare League of America.

Crosnoe, R., & Benner, A. (2015). Children at school. In R. Lerner (Editor-in-Chief), & M. Bornstein & T. Levanthal (Vol. Eds.), *Handbook of child psychology and developmental science: Vol. 4. Ecological settings and processes* (7th ed., pp. 268–304). New York: Wiley.

Cutler, D. M., & Glaeser, E. L. (1997). Are ghettos good or bad? *Quarterly Journal of Economics, 112*(3), 827–872.

Damon, W., Menon, J., & Bronk, K. C. (2003). The development of purpose during adolescence. *Applied Developmental Science, 7*, 119–128.

Darling-Hammond, L., Cook-Harvey, C., Flook, L, Barron, B., & Osher, D. (in press). Science of learning and development: Implications for educational practice. *Applied Developmental Science.*

Davis, N. J. (2002). The promotion of mental health and the prevention of mental and behavioral disorders: Surely the time is right. *International Journal of Mental Health, 4*(1), 3–29.

Dishion, T. J., McCord, J., & Poulin, F. (1999). When interventions harm: Peer groups and problem behavior. *American Psychologist, 54*, 755–764.

Dodge, K., Bierman, K. L. Coie, J. D. Greenberg, M. T., Lochman J. E . . . Pinderhughes, E. E. (2015). Impact of early intervention on psychopathology, crime, and well-being at age twenty-five. *American Journal of Psychiatry, 172*, 59–270.

Doyle, W. (2006). Ecological approaches to classroom management. In C. Evertson & C. Weinstein (Eds.), *Handbook of classroom management: Research, practice, and contemporary issues* (pp. 97–125). New York: Lawrence Erlbaum.

Duckworth, A., Kim, B., & Tsukayama, E. (2013). Life stress impairs self-control in early adolescence. *Frontiers in Psychology, 3*, 608–638.

Durlak, J. A., Weissberg, R. P., Dymnicki, A. B., Taylor, R. D., & Schellinger, K. B. (2011). The impact of enhancing students' social and emotional learning: A meta-analysis of school-based universal interventions. *Child Development, 82*(1), 405–432.

Dwyer, K., & Osher, D. (2000). *Safeguarding our children: An action guide.* Washington, DC: U.S. Departments of Education and Justice, American Institutes for Research.

Dwyer, K., Osher, D., & Warger, C. (1998). *Early warning, timely response: A guide to safe schools.* Washington, DC: U.S. Department of Education.

Dymnicki, A., Wandersman, A., Osher, D., & Pakstis, A. (2018). Bringing interventions to scale. In C. Keyes & M. Bond (Eds.), *Handbook of community psychology* (pp. 59–81). Washington, DC: American Psychological Association.

Egalitie, A. J. & Kisida, B. (2017). The effects of teacher match on students' academic perceptions and attitudes. *Educational Evaluation and Policy Analysis, 40*(1), 59–81.

Egalitie, A. J., Kisida, B., & Winters, M. A. (2015). Representation in the classroom: The effect of own-race teachers on student achievement. *Economics of Education Review, 45*, 44–52.

Elliott, D. S., Williams, K. R., & Hamburg, B. A. (1996). An integrated approach to violence prevention. In D. S. Elliott, B. A. Hamburg, & R. Williams (Eds.), *Violence in American schools.* Cambridge, UK: Cambridge University Press.

Evertson, C., & Weinstein, C. (Eds.). (2006). *Handbook of classroom management: Research, practice, and contemporary issues.* New York: Lawrence Erlbaum.

Farmer, T. W., Dawes, M., Alexander, Q., & Brooks, D. S. (2015). Challenges associated with applications and interventions: Correlated constraints, shadows of synchrony, and teacher/institutional factors that impact social change. In K. Wentzel & G. Ramani (Eds.), *Handbook of social influences on social-emotional, motivation, and cognitive outcomes in school contexts* (pp. 423–435). New York: Routledge Taylor & Francis.

Farrington, D. P. (2007). Origins of violent behavior over the life span. In D. J. Flannery, A. T. Vazsonyi, & I. D. Waldman (Eds.), *The Cambridge handbook of violent behavior and aggression* (pp. 545–570). Cambridge, UK: Cambridge University Press.

Felix, E. D., Furlong, M. J., Sharkey, J. D., & Osher, D. (2007). Implication for evaluating multi-component, complex prevention initiatives: Taking guidance from the Safe School/Health Students Initiative. *Journal of School Violence, 6*(2), 3–22.

Fischer, K. W., & Bidell, T. R. (2006). Dynamic development of action, thought, and emotion. In R. M. Lerner (Ed.), *Handbook of child psychology: Vol. 1. Theoretical models of human development* (6th ed., pp. 313–399). New York: Wiley.

Fischer, K. W., & Kennedy, B. (1997). Tools for analyzing the many shapes of development: The case of self-in-relationships in Korea. In E. Amsel & K. A. Renninger (Eds.), *Change and development: Issues of theory, method, and application* (pp. 117–152). Mahwah, NJ: Erlbaum.

Flook, L., Goldberg, S. B., Pinger, L., Bonus, K., & Davidson, R. J. (2013). Mindfulness for teachers: A pilot study to assess effects on stress, burnout and teaching efficacy. *Mind, Brain and Education: The Official Journal of the International Mind, Brain, and Education Society, 7*(3), 182–195. doi:10.1111/mbe.12026

Ford, D. H., & Lerner, R. M. (1992). *Developmental systems theory: An integrative approach*. Thousand Oaks, CA: Sage.

Furlong, M., Paige, L. Z., & Osher, D. (2003). The Safe School, Healthy Students Initiative: Lessons learned from implementing healthy youth development programs. *Psychology in the Schools, 40*(5), 447–456.

Galinsky, E., Bezos, J., McClelland, M., Carlson, S. M., & Zelazo, P. D. (2017). Civic science for public use: Mind in the making and vroom. *Child Development, 88*, 1409–1418.

Garibaldi, M., Ruddy, S., Osher, D., & Kendziora, K. (2015). Assessment of climate and conditions for learning. In J. Durlak, T. Gulotta, & R. Weissberg (Eds.), *The handbook of social and emotional learning* (pp. 348–359). New York: Guilford.

Gay, G. (2000). *Culturally responsive teaching: Theory, research, and practice*. New York: Teachers College Press.

Gay, G., & Kirkland, K. N. (2003). Developing cultural critical consciousness and self-reflection in preservice teacher education. *Theory into practice, 42*(3), 181–187.

Goldstein, A. P., & Conoley, J. C. (2004). Student aggression: Current status. In J. C. Conoley & A. P. Goldstein (Eds.), *School violence intervention: A practical handbook* (2nd ed., pp. 131–163). New York: Guilford Press.

Goodnow, J. J., & Lawrence, J. A. (2015). Children and cultural contexts. In R. M. Lerner (Editor-in-Chief) & M. Bornstein & T. Leventhal (Vol. Eds.), *Handbook of child psychology and developmental science: Vol. 4. Ecological settings and processes in developmental systems* (7th ed., pp. 746–788). Hoboken, NJ: Wiley.

Gottfredson, G. D., Gottfredson, D. C., Payne, A. A., & Gottfredson, N. C. (2005). School climate predictors of school disorder: Results from a national study of delinquency prevention in schools. *Journal of Research in Crime and Delinquency, 42*, 412–444.

Greenberg, E., Skidmore, D., Rhodes, D., & Nesbitt, D. (2002). *Prepared to teach: Teacher preparation and student achievement in mathematics and science*. Washington, DC: American Institutes for Research.

Gregory, A., & Korth, J. (2016). Teacher-student relationships and behavioral engagement in the classroom. In K. Wentzel & G. Ramani (Eds.), *Handbook of social influences in school contexts: Social-emotional, motivation, and cognitive outcomes* (pp. 178–191). New York: Taylor & Francis.

Gregory, A., Skiba, R. J., & Noguera, P. (2010). The achievement gap and the discipline gap: Two sides of the same coin? *Educational Researcher, 39*, 59–68.

Griffiths, P. E., & Hochman, A. (2015). Developmental systems theory. Wiley Online Library. doi:10.1002/9780470015902.a0003452.pub2

Hammond, Z. (2016). *Culturally responsive teaching and the brain: Promoting authentic engagement and rigor among culturally and linguistically diverse students*. Thousand Oaks, CA: Corwin.

Hamre, B. K., & Pianta, R. C. (2005). Can instructional and emotional support in the first-grade classroom make a difference for children at risk of school failure? *Child Development, 76*(5), 949–967.

Hamre, B. K., & Pianta, R. C. (2007). Learning opportunities in preschool and early elementary classrooms. In R. Pianta, M. Cox, & K. Snow (Eds.), *School readiness & the transition to kindergarten in the era of accountability* (pp. 49–84). Baltimore: Brookes.

Harter, S. (1990). Processes underlying adolescent self-concept formation. In R. Montemayor, G. R. Adams, & T. P. Gulotta (Eds.), *From childhood to adolescence: A transition period?* Newbury, CA: Sage.

Hawkins, J. D., Herrenkohl, T., Farrington, D. P., Brewer, D., Catalano, R. F., & Harachi, T. W. (1998). A review of predictors of youth violence. In R. Loeber & D. P. Farrington (Eds.), *Serious and violent juvenile offenders: Risk factors and successful interventions* (pp. 106–146). Thousand Oaks, CA: Sage.

Hinojosa, T., Liu, F., O'Brien, B., Osher, D., Park, S., & Gorsky, D. (2015). *Whole child network evaluation: Year 3 report*. Washington, DC: American Institutes for Research.

Hook, J. N., & Watkins, C. E. Jr. (2015). Cultural humility: The cornerstone of positive contact with culturally different individuals and groups? *American Psychologist, 70*(7), 661–662.

Hook, J. N., Watkins, C. E. Jr., Davis, D. E., Owen, J., Van Tongeren, D. R., & Ramos, M. J. (2016). Cultural humility in psychotherapy supervision. *America Journal of Psychotherapy, 70*(2), 149–166.

Hunter, L., Hoagwood, K., Evans, S., Weist, M., Smith, C., Paternite, C., . . . The School Mental Health Alliance. (2005). *Working together to promote academic performance, social and emotional learning, and mental health for all children*. New York: Center for the Advancement of Children's Mental Health, Columbia University.

Institute of Medicine. (1994). Reducing risks for mental disorders: Frontiers for preventive intervention research. In P. J. Mrazek & R. J. Haggerty (Eds.), *Committee on Prevention of Mental Disorders, Division of Biobehavioral Sciences and Mental Disorders*. Washington, DC: National Academy Press.

Institute of Medicine. (2002). *Reducing suicide: A national imperative*. Washington, DC: National Academy Press.

Institute of Medicine & National Research Council. (2009). *Preventing Mental, Emotional, and Behavioral Disorders Among Young People: Progress and Possibilities*. Washington, DC: National Academies Press.

Institute of Medicine & National Research Council. (2015). *Transforming the workforce for children birth through age 8: A unifying foundation*. Washington, DC: National Academies Press.

Jakonen, T. (2016). The integration of content and language in students' task answer production in the bilingual classroom. *International Journal of*

Bilingual Education and Bilingualism, published online, 1–17. doi:10.1080/13670050.2016.1267694

Jennings, P. A., & Greenberg, M. T. (2009). The prosocial classroom: Teacher social and emotional competence in relation to student and classroom outcomes. *Review of Educational Research, 79*(1), 491–525. doi:10.3102/0034654308325693

Jessor, R. (1998). New perspectives on adolescent risk behavior. In R. Jessor (Ed.), *New perspectives on adolescent risk behavior.* New York: Cambridge University Press.

Johnson, S. M., Kraft, M. A., & Papay, J. P. (2012). How context matters in high-need schools: The effects of teachers' working conditions on their professional satisfaction and their students' achievement. *Teachers College Record, 114*, 1–39.

Jones, S. M., & Bouffard, S. M. (2012). Social and emotional learning in schools: From programs to strategies. *Social Policy Report, 26*(4), 1–33. Retrieved from http://eric.ed.gov/?id=ED540203

Kellam, S. G., & Rebok, G. W. (1992). Building developmental and etiological theory through epidemiologically based preventive intervention trials. In J. McCord & R. E. Tremblay (Eds.), *Preventing antisocial behavior: Interventions from birth through adolescence* (pp. 162–195). New York: Guilford.

Kellam, S. G., Rebok, G. W., Mayer, L. S., Ialongo, N., & Kalodner, C. R. (1994). Depressive symptoms over first grade and their response to a developmental epidemiologically based preventive trial aimed at improving achievement. *Development and Psychopathology, 6*, 463–481.

Kendziora, K., & Osher, D. (2004). Fostering resilience among youth in the juvenile justice system. In C. C. Clauss-Ehlers & M. Weist (Eds.), *Community planning to foster resiliency in children* (pp. 177–196). New York: Kluwer Academic.

Kendziora, K., Osher, D., & Carey, M. (2014). *Say yes to education student monitoring system: Updated literature review.* Washington, DC: American Institutes for Research.

King, M. A., Sims, A., & Osher, D. (2007). *How is cultural competence integrated into education?* Washington, DC: Center on Effective Collaboration and Practice, American Institutes for Research. Retrieved from http://cecp.air.org/cultural/Q_integrated.htm

Kremer, K. P., Flower, A., Huang, J., & Vaughn, M. G. (2016). Behavior problems and children's academic achievement: A test of growth-curve models with gender and racial differences. *Child Youth Services Review, 67*, 95–104.

Lavigne, J. V., Gouze, K. R., Hopkins, J., & Bryant, F. B. (2016). A multidomain cascade model of early childhood risk factors associated with oppositional defiant disorder symptoms in a community sample of 6-year-olds. *Development and Psychopathology, 28*(4, pt. 2), 1547–1562. doi:10.1017/S0954579415001194

Lee, C. D. (2010). Soaring above the clouds, delving the ocean's depths: Understanding the ecologies of human learning and the challenge for education science. *Educational Researcher, 39*(9), 643–655. doi:10.3102/0013189X10392139

Lerner, R. M. (2004). *Liberty: Thriving and civic engagement among American youth.* Thousand Oaks, CA: Sage.

Lerner, R. M. (2015). Preface. In R. M. Lerner (Editor-in-chief), *Handbook of child psychology and developmental science* (7th ed., pp. xv–xxi). Hoboken, NJ: Wiley.

Li, J., & Julian, M. (2012). Developing relationships as the active ingredient: A unifying working hypothesis of "what works" across intervention settings. *American Journal of Orthopsychiatry, 82*(2), 157–166.

Luthar, S. S., Crossman, E. J., & Small, P. J. (2015). Resilience and adversity. In R. M. Lerner (Editor-in-chief), *Handbook of child psychology and developmental science.* New York: Wiley. Retrieved from http://onlinelibrary.wiley.com/doi/10.1002/9781118963418.childpsy307/full

Mallett, C. A. (2015). The school-to-prison pipeline: A critical review of the punitive paradigm shift. *Child and Adolescent Social Work Journal, 33*(1), 15–24. doi:10.1007/s10560-015-0397-1

Masten, A. S., Roisman, G. I., Long, J. D., Burt, K. B., Obradovic, J., Riley, J. R., . . . Tellegen, A. (2005). Developmental cascades: Linking academic achievement and externalizing and internalizing symptoms over 20 years. *Developmental Psychology, 41*(5), 733–746. doi:10.1037/0012-1649.41.5.733

Master, A., Butler, L. P., & Walton, G. M. (2017). How the subjective relationship between the self, others, and a task drives interest. In P. A. O'Keefe & J. M. Harackiewicz (Eds.), *The science of interest.* New York: Springer.

Mayer, G. R. (1995). Preventing antisocial behavior in the schools. *Journal of Applied Behavior Analysis, 28*, 467–478.

Mayer, R. C., Davis, J. H., & Schoorman, F. D. (1995). An integrative model of organizational trust. *Academy of Management Review, 20*(3), 709–734. doi:10.2307/258792

Mayer, R. E. (2014). Research-based principles for designing multimedia instruction. In V. A. Benassi, C. E. Overson, & C. M. Hakala (Eds.), *Applying science of learning in education: Infusing psychological science into the curriculum* (pp. 7–19). Retrieved from http://teachpsych.org/ebooks/asle2014/index.php

Moffitt, T. E. (2007). A review of research on the taxonomy of life-course persistent and adolescence-limited offending. In D. Flannery, A. Vazonsyi, & I. Waldman (Eds.), *The Cambridge handbook of violent behavior* (pp. 49–76). New York: Cambridge University Press.

Moore, D. (2015). *The developing genome: An introduction to behavioral epigenetics.* Oxford: Oxford University Press.

Mrazek, P. J., & Haggerty, R. J. (Eds.). (1994). *Committee on Prevention of Mental Disorders, Division of Biobehavioral Sciences and Mental Disorders*. Washington, DC: National Academy Press.

Murray, D. W., Rosanbalm, K., Christopoulos, C., & Hamoudi, A. (2015). *Self-regulation and toxic stress: Foundations for understanding self-regulation from an applied developmental perspective* (OPRE Report #2015-21). Washington, DC: Office of Planning, Research and Evaluation, Administration for Children and Families, U.S. Department of Health and Human Services.

Nasir, N. S. (2011). Racialized identities: Race and achievement among African American youth. Palo Alto: Stanford University Press.

National Commission on Social, Emotional, and Academic Development, Council of Distinguished Scientists. (2017). *The evidence base for how we learn: Supporting students' social, emotional, and academic development*. Washington, DC: Author.

National Research Council. (2012). Education for life and work: Developing transferable knowledge and skills in the 21st century. Committee on Defining Deeper Learning and 21st Century Skills, J. W. Pellegrino, & M. L. Hilton (Eds.), *Board on Testing and Assessment and Board on Science Education, Division of Behavioral and Social Sciences and Education*. Washington, DC: National Academies Press.

Nesselroade, J. R. (2018). Developments in developmental research and theory. *Applied Developmental Science*. doi:10.1080/10888691.2017.1403529

Norwalk, K., Hamm, J., Farmer, T., & Barnes, K. (2016). Improving the school context of early adolescence through teacher attunement to victimization. *Journal of Early Adolescence, 36*(7), 989–1009.

Oberle, E., & Schonert-Reichl, K. A. (2016). Stress contagion in the classroom? The link between classroom teacher burnout and morning cortisol in elementary school students. *Social Science & Medicine, 159*, 30–37. doi:10.1016/j.socscimed.2016.04.031

Oppedal, B., & Toppelberg, C. (2016). Culture competence: A developmental task of acculturation. In J. W. Berry & D. L. Sam (Eds.), *The Cambridge handbook of acculturation psychology revised* (pp. 71–92). Cambridge, UK: Cambridge University Press.

Osher, D. (2015). The pedagogy of real talk and the promotion of student well-being and success. In P. Hernandez (Ed.), *The pedagogy of real talk: Engaging, teaching, and connecting with students at risk* (pp. viii–ix). New York: Corwin.

Osher, D. (2016). Forward: Pro-social discipline for American democracy. In P. M. Brown (Ed.) *Student discipline: a pro-social perspective* (pp. ix–xv). Lanham, MD: Rowman & Littlefield.

Osher, D., Bear, G., Sprague, J., & Doyle, W. (2010). How we can improve school discipline? *Educational Researcher, 39*(1), 48–58.

Osher, D., Cantor, P., Berg, J., Steyer, J., & Rose, T. (2017). *Science of learning and development: A synthesis*. Washington, DC: American Institutes for Research.

Osher, D., Cantor, P., Berg, J., Steyer, J., & Rose, T. (2018). Drivers of human development: How relationships and context shape learning and development. *Applied Developmental Science.* doi:10.1080/10888691.2017.1398650

Osher, D., Cartledge, G., Oswald, D., Artiles, A. J., & Coutinho, M. (2004). Issues of cultural and linguistic competency and disproportionate representation. In R. Rutherford, M. Quinn, & S. Mather (Eds.), *Handbook of research in behavioral disorders* (pp. 54–77). New York: Guilford.

Osher, D., Dwyer, K. P., & Jimerson, S. R. (2006). Safe, supportive, and effective schools: Promoting school success to reduce school violence. In S. R. Jimerson & M. J. Furlong (Eds.), *Handbooks of school violence and school safety: International research and practice.* New York: Routledge.

Osher, D., Dwyer, K. P., Jimerson, S. R., & Brown, J. A. (2012). Developing safe, supportive, and effective schools: Facilitating student success to reduce school violence. In S. R. Jimerson, A. B. Nickerson, M. J. Mayer, & M. J. Furlong (Eds.), *Handbook of school violence and school safety: International research and practice* (2nd ed., pp. 27–44). New York: Routledge.

Osher, D., & Kane, M. (1993). *Describing and studying innovations in the education of children with attention deficit disorder. A series of papers on the federal role in improving practice in special education.* Washington, DC: Directed Research Branch, Division of Innovation and Development, Office of Special Education Programs, U.S. Department of Education.

Osher, D., & Kendziora, K. (2010). Building conditions for learning and healthy adolescent development: Strategic approaches. In B. Doll, W. Pfohl, & J. Yoon (Eds.), *Handbook of youth prevention science* (pp. 121–140). New York: Routledge.

Osher, D., Kendziora, K., Spier, E., & Garibaldi, M. L. (2014). School influences on child and youth development. In Z. Sloboda & H. Petras (Eds.), *Advances in prevention science Vol. 1: Defining prevention science* (pp. 151–170). New York, NY: Springer.

Osher, D., Kidron, Y., Brackett, M., Dymnicki, A., Jones, S., & Weissberg, R. P. (2016). Advancing the science and practice of social and emotional learning: Looking back and moving forward. *Review of Research in Education, 40*, 644–681.

Osher, D., Kidron, Y., DeCandia, C. J., Kendziora, K., & Weissberg, R. P. (2016). Interventions to promote safe and supportive school climate. In K. R. Wentzel & G. B. Ramani (Eds.), *Handbook of social influences in school contexts* (pp. 384–404). New York: Routledge.

Osher, D., Van Aker, R., Morrison, G., Gable, R., Dwyer, K., & Quinn, M. (2004). Warning signs of problems in schools: Ecological perspectives and effective practices for combating school aggression and violence. In M. J. Furlong, G. M. Morrison, D. Cornell, & R. Skiba (Eds.), *Issues in school violence research* (pp. 13–38). Binghamton, NY: Haworth Press.

Overton, W. F. (2015). Processes, relations and relational-developmental-systems. In W. F. Overton & P. C. M. Molenaar (Eds.), *Handbook of child psychology and developmental science: Vol. 1. Theory and method* (7th ed., pp. 9–62). Hoboken, NJ: Wiley.

Owens, A. (2018). Income segregation between school districts and inequality in students' achievement. *Sociology of Education*, *91*(1), 1–27. https://doi.org/10.1177/0038040717741180

Oyserman, D., & Lewis, N. (2017). Seeing the destination and the path: Using identity-based motivation to understand and reduce racial disparities in academic achievement. *Social Issues and Policy Review, 11*(1), 159–194.

Pasalich, D. S., Witkiewitz, K., McMahon, R. J., Pinderhughes, E. E., & The Conduct Problems Prevention Research Group (2015). Indirect effects of the Fast Track intervention on conduct disorder symptoms and callous-unemotional traits: distinct pathways involving discipline and warmth. *Journal of Abnormal Child Psychology*. PMID: 26242993.

Pepler, D. J., & Slaby, R. G. (1994). Theoretic and developmental perspectives on youth and violence. In L. D. Eron, J. H. Gentry, & P. Schlegel (Eds.), *Reason to hope: A psychological perspective on violence & youth*. Washington, DC: American Psychological Association.

Pianta, R. C. (2016). Teacher-student interactions: Measurement, impacts, improvement, and policy. *Policy Insights from the Behavioral and Brain Sciences*, *3*(1), 98–105. doi:10.1177/2372732215622457

Pianta, R. C., & Walsh, D. J. (1996). *High-risk children in schools: Constructing sustaining relationships*. Palo Alto, CA: Psychology Press.

Pierce, S., Gould, D., & Camiré, M. (2017). Definition and model of life skills transfer. *International Review of Sport and Exercise Psychology*, *10*(1), 186–211.

Reardon, S. F., & Bischoff, K. (2011). Income inequality and income segregation. *American Journal of Sociology*, *116*(4), 1092–1153.

Roorda, D. L., Koomen, H. M., Spilt, J. L., & Oort, F. J. (2011). The influence of affective teacher-student relationships on students' school engagement and achievement: A meta-analytic approach. *Review of Educational Research*, *81*(4), 493–529.

Rose, L. T., Rouhani, P., & Fischer, K. W. (2013). The science of the individual. *Mind, Brain, and Education,* *7*(3), 152–158.

Ryan, W. (1972). *Blaming the victim*. New York: Vintage Books.

Salinger, T. & Osher, D. (2018). Academic interventions—Use with care. In Osher, D., Moroney, D., & Williamson, S. (Eds.), *Creating Safe, Equitable, Engaging Schools: A Comprehensive, Evidence-Based Approach to Supporting Students*. Cambridge, MA: Harvard Education Press.

Sameroff, A. J. (2000). Developmental systems and psychopathology. *Development and Psychopathology, 12*, 297–312.

Shonkoff, J. (2018). Making developmental science accessible, usable, and a catalyst for innovation. *Applied Developmental Science*. doi:10.1080/10888691.2017.1421430

Siegel, D. J. (1999). *The developing mind: Toward a neurobiology of interpersonal experience*. New York: Guilford.

Siegel, D. J. (2012). *The developing mind: How relationships and the brain interact to shape who we are* (2nd ed.). New York: Guilford.

Simmel, G. (1955). Conflict and the web of group-affiliations. New York, NY: Free Press.

Slavich, G. M., & Cole, S. W. (2013). The emerging field of human social genomics. *Clinical Psychological Science*, *1*(3), 331–348.

Snyder, C. R., Shah, N., & Ross, K. M. (2012). Racial storylines and implications for learning. *Human Development*, *55*(5–6), 285–301.

Spencer, M. B. (1995). Old issues and new theorizing about African-American youth: A phenomenological variate of ecological systems theory. In R. L. Taylor (Ed.), *African-American Youth: Their Social and Economic Status in the United States* (pp. 37–69). Westport, CT: Praeger.

Spencer, M. B. (2007). Phenomenology and ecological systems theory: Development of diverse groups. In R. M. Lerner (Editor-in-Chief), *Handbook of child psychology*. New York: Wiley. Retrieved from http://onlinelibrary.wiley.com/doi/10.1002/9780470147658.chpsy0115/abstract

Spencer, M. B. (2017). Privilege and critical race perspectives' intersectional contributions to a systems theory of human development. In N. Budwig, E. Turiel, & P. Zelazo (Eds.), *New perspectives on human development* (pp. 287–312). Cambridge, UK: Cambridge University Press.

Spencer, M. B., Swanson, D. P., & Harpalani, V. (2015). Conceptualizing the self: Contributions of normative human processes, diverse contexts and social opportunity. In M. Lamb, C. G. Coll, & R. Lerner (Eds.), *Handbook of child psychology and developmental science* (pp. 750–793). New York: John Wiley.

Sprague, J. R., & Walker, H. M. (2005). *Safe & healthy schools: Practical prevention strategies*. New York: Guilford.

Stafford-Brizard, K. (2015). *Building blocks for learning: A framework for comprehensive student development*. New York: Turnaround for Children.

Steele, C. (2010). *Whistling Vivaldi: And other clues to how stereotypes affect us*. New York: Norton.

Sutherland, K. S. (2000). Promoting positive interactions between teachers and students with emotional/behavioral disorders. *Preventing School Failure, 44*, 110–115.

Sutherland, K. S., & Oswald, D. (2005). The relationship between teacher and student behavior in classrooms for students with emotional and behavioral disorders: Transactional processes. *Journal of Child and Family Studies, 14*, 1–14.

Sutherland, K. S., Wehby, J. H., & Yoder, P. J. (2002). Examination of the relationship between teacher praise and opportunities for students with ED to respond to academic requests. *Journal of Emotional and Behavioral Disorders, 10*(1), 5–13.

Swearer, S. M., Espelage, D. L., Vaillancourt, T., & Hymel, S. (2010). What can be done about school bullying? Linking research to educational practice. *Educational Researcher, 39*(1), 38–47.

Thompson, R. A. (2015). Early attachment and later development: Familiar questions, new answers. In J. Cassidy & P. R. Shaver (Eds.), *Handbook of attachments* (2nd ed., pp. 348–365). New York: Guilford Press.

Thompson, R. A., & Goodvin, R. (2016). Social support and developmental psychopathology. In D. Cicchetti (Ed.), *Developmental psychopathology* (pp. 1–50). New York: Wiley.

Tolan, P. H. (2007). Understanding violence. In D. Flannery, A. T. Vazsonyi, & I. D. Waldman (Eds.), *Cambridge handbook of violent behavior and aggression* (pp. 5–18). Cambridge, UK: Cambridge University Press.

Ursache, A., Blair, C., & Raver, C. C. (2012). The promotion of self-regulation as a means of enhancing school readiness and early achievement in children at risk for school failure: Promotion of self-regulation in school. *Child Development Perspectives*, 6(2), 122–128. doi:10.1111/j.1750-8606.2011.00209.x

U.S. Public Health Service. (1999). *Mental Health: A report of the surgeon general mental*. Washington, DC: Author.

U.S. Public Health Service. (2000). *Youth violence: A report of the surgeon general*. Washington, DC: Author.

U.S. Public Health Service. (2001). *Mental health: culture, race, ethnicity: A supplement to the surgeon general's report on mental health*. Washington, DC: Author.

Wandersman, A., Alia, K., Cook, B. S., Hsu, L. L., & Ramaswamy, R. (2016). Evidence-based interventions are necessary but not sufficient for achieving outcomes in each setting in a complex world: Empowerment evaluation, getting to outcomes, and demonstrating accountability. *American Journal of Evaluation*, *37*(4), 544–561. doi:10.1177/1098214016660613

Weist, M., Mellin, E., Chambers, K. L., Haber, D., & Blaber, C. (2012). Challenges to collaboration in school mental health and strategies for overcoming them. *Journal of School Health*, *82*, 97–105.

World Health Organization. (2002). *The mental health report 202—Reducing risks, promoting healthy life*. Geneva: Author.

Yarnell, L. M. & Bohrnstedt, G. (2018). Student-Teacher Racial Match and Its Association with Black Student Achievement: An Exploration Using Multilevel Structural Equation Modeling. *American Educational Research Journal*, *55*(2), 287–324.

Yoder & Osher. (2018). Educators matter. In D. Osher, D. Moroney, & S. Williamson (Eds.), *Creating safe, equitable, engaging schools: A comprehensive, evidence-based approach to supporting students*. Cambridge, MA: Harvard Education Press.

Zelazo, P. D. (2015). Executive function: Reflection, iterative reprocessing, complexity, and the developing brain. *Developmental Review*, *38*, 55–68. doi:10.1016/j.dr.2015.07.001

Zelazo, P. D., Blair, C. B., & Willoughby, M. T. (2016). *Executive function: Implications for education* (NCER 2017-2000). Washington, DC: National Center for Education Research, Institute of Education Sciences, U.S. Department of Education.

CHAPTER THREE

Mental Health Services for Youth

History, Key Data, and Major Challenges

Erum Nadeem, Sharon Hoover, and Marleen Wong

It is estimated that about 20% to 30% of adolescents in the United States will have suffered from some kind of mental illness over their lifetime (Merikangas et al., 2010), which can have debilitating and long-ranging effects on individuals, families, and society. Children's mental disorders are among the top five most costly medical conditions, constituting $8.9 billion annually, or 9% of total medical spending on children from birth through age 17 (Agency for Healthcare Research & Quality, 2009). Children and adolescents with mental health challenges are less likely to succeed in school and are at risk for poor mental health and worse outcomes as adults (Masten & Curtis, 2000). Moreover, data show that the majority of children with a mental illness do not access mental health care, with ethnic minority children being most chronically underserved (Kataoka, Zhang, & Wells, 2002; Saloner, 2017). These data underscore the continued need to improve the quality and access to mental health care for children and adolescents. In this chapter, we will briefly review the history of the children's mental health system, with a particular focus on the public mental health systems and schools. We highlight continued needs in the system related to access, quality of care, and engagement of families; and key opportunities for the field as it moves forward.

History of Mental Health Care for Children and Adolescents

In the United States, there has never been one single system through which children, adolescents, and their families receive support for mental health issues. Rather, service systems have largely emerged from within the many systems that serve youth, including specialty mental health settings, schools, juvenile justice services, or child welfare agencies. This history can be divided into three phases of policy and practice that have shaped modern mental health care services for youth (Lourie & Hernandez, 2003).

During the field's infancy, in the early 20th century, some of the first mental health services in the country were provided by the juvenile justice system via "court clinics" (Jones, 1999). These clinics were formed to provide "corrective" rather than "punitive" services to children, and although they were never formalized, they were foundational for bringing mental health promotion into child-serving systems (Lourie & Hernandez, 2003). Despite limited federal policies in these early years, a Children's Bureau was formed in the 1930s to advocate for children's needs through mental health supports and education (Lourie & Hernandez, 2003). In addition, the "child guidance" movement, which began in Europe and took root in the United States during the 1940s, aimed to provide mental health services to children to help prevent adult mental health problems. Child guidance clinic services were offered for free or on a sliding scale; these charitable organizations represented the earliest child mental health clinics in the United States (Jones, 1999; Lourie & Hernandez, 2003).

A second wave of systems change took place in the 1960s and 1970s as a result of the community mental health movement and other federal efforts in health and education. The Community Mental Health Act of 1963 (also known as the Mental Retardation and Community Mental Health Centers Construction Act of 1963) provided federal funding to establish community mental health centers in the United States. This legislation did not include any provisions for children's mental health services, but rather was focused on issues related to the deinstitutionalization of adult patients with mental illness. During this same time period, however, Medicaid was instituted to fund health care for the poor and did include a mandate for children's mental health (Lourie & Hernandez, 2003). In addition, the Joint Commission on the Mental Health of Children, formed in the 1960s, laid out proposed principles for children's mental health supports across multiple service systems, including schools, child welfare, and juvenile justice. As a result of these efforts, there were a number of federally funded community mental health demonstration projects that included children's services. The success of these programs led to a federal mandate for children's services as part of community mental health center programs. However, due to a lack of sufficient state and federal funding, the mandates were not widely realized

(Lourie & Hernandez, 2003; Lourie, Katz-Leavy, DeCarolis, & Quinlan, 1996).

As the community mental health system developed, federal policy related to education also began to address mental health. Specifically, the Education for all Handicapped Children Act was passed in 1975. This bill, now known as the Individuals with Disabilities Education Act (IDEA), required states to provide special education and related services to children with disabilities, including serious emotional disturbance (SED), a mandate that remains in place today. Similarly, section 504 of the Rehabilitation Act of 1973 protects children with disabilities from being denied a free and appropriate education (U.S. Department of Health, Education, and Welfare, 1978). Children with a documented "physical or mental impairment that substantially limits one or more major life activities" must receive supports (U.S. Department of Health, Education, and Welfare, "Students Protected under Section 504," para. 1). These policies have been important facilitators in moving mental health professionals from outside consultants to integral members of the school staff who perform evaluations and provide supports and necessary educational accommodations; these roles have expanded over time (Flaherty & Osher, 2003; Weist, Flaherty, Lever, Stephan, Van Eck, & Albright, 2017).

The modern era of children's mental health services began in the 1980s and was significantly shaped by documented problems in the children's mental health services such as dearth of services, insufficient quality and access, overuse and inappropriate use of residential treatment, and a failure of policy makers to respond adequately (Knitzer & Olson, 1982). One critical response to these issues came in the form of the Child and Adolescent Service System Program (CASSP). This effort, which was initiated by the National Institute of Mental Health and is now managed by the Substance Abuse and Mental Health Services Administration, has focused on helping states and local communities implement *systems of care* through specialized funding and training efforts (Lourie & Hernandez, 2003).

The systems-of-care movement has several core principles that continue to be important in shaping children's mental health care. First, a core component of the systems-of-care framework is the development of integrated child-centered service systems that are focused on providing children with the most appropriate and least restrictive services. This involves collaboration across agencies, families, and youth to improve access and expand the array of coordinated community-based, culturally and linguistically competent services (Pires, 2002; Stroul & Friedman, 1986). This contrasts with the complex, fragmented systems and silos that had come to characterize the child mental health system. Second, systems of care have been important in developing child-centered and family-focused care that empowers families to help shape their care and provide peer-to-peer family support. Family organizations such as the Federation of Families for Children's Mental Health and the National Alliance on Mental Illness (NAMI) have been critical in these efforts (Hoagwood et al., 2010; Osher, Penn, & Spencer, 2008; Robbins et al., 2008). Third, the framework emphasizes the critical importance of participation of families from diverse communities and backgrounds in shaping services and ensuring that services are culturally competent and culturally informed (Cross, 1989). The principles set forth through CASSP and the systems-of-care movement were largely echoed in 2003's President's New Freedom Commission on Mental Health (U.S. Department of Health and Human Services, 2003). In addition, the New Freedom Commission called the nation to take action (1) to address disparities in access to quality of care for underserved communities (including rural communities); (2) use evidence-based practices (EBPs); (3) increase the use of screening and referral in schools and primary care; and (4) expand early intervention and mental health services in schools (Eaton et al., 2008; U.S. Department of Health and Human Services, 2003). These efforts also helped prompt state and local governments' allocation of funding for children's services (Lourie & Hernandez, 2003).

Today, the public mental health system is composed of a diverse array of community-based treatment, rehabilitation, and support services across different service sectors (e.g., specialty mental health, child welfare, juvenile justice, and education) that are managed at the state and sometimes the county levels. Financing is largely dependent upon Medicaid and state general funds (Hoagwood et al., 2014). Medicaid is commonly administered through managed care systems, which are a significant force in shaping service delivery and were put in place in large part to reduce costs of care, particularly for inpatient services (Hutchinson & Foster, 2003; Raghavan et al., 2006).

Current Challenges and Key Data

Efforts to improve integration of mental health services for children in specialty and non-specialty mental health settings continue today. To understand how the youth mental health system currently functions, we review key data in three major areas: child outcomes, access to care, and family and youth engagement.

Child Outcomes and Quality of Care

As children's mental health services have grown and developed over time, attention has shifted to ensuring positive outcomes for children and families. The need for quality improvement within health care was identified in the 1980s with a call to improve quality by adopting the principles of continuous quality improvement used in industry (Berwick, 1989; Laffel & Blumenthal, 1989). Since then, the Institute of Medicine's (IOM) seminal report, "Crossing the Quality Chasm" (Committee on Quality of Health Care in America, Institute of Medicine, 2001) documented significant deficiencies in the quality of U.S. health care, which have been echoed specifically for mental health by the President's New Freedom Commission (U.S. Department of Health and Human Services, 2003), in further work on mental health and substance abuse from the IOM (Committee on Quality of Health Care in America, Institute of Medicine, 2006), and most recently in the Affordable Care Act (ACA). The core messages of these initiatives can be distilled to three key points: (1) there is both a great need and a great demand for mental health and substance abuse services in this country; (2) effective treatments for mental health issues exist but are not being widely implemented; and (3) problems with the quality of care hinder effective treatment and recovery (Ganju, 2006).

Over the past three decades, child outcomes have benefited by tremendous growth in the development of EBTs. These treatments have increasingly demonstrated impacts on both symptoms and functional outcomes (Hoagwood et al., 2012), and include cognitive behavioral therapies for depression, anxiety, and post-traumatic stress; parent management strategies for disruptive behavior disorders; medication therapies; and combined interventions. There are also a host of effective practices that can support and enhance service delivery, such as mental health screening tools, diagnostic assessments, measurement feedback systems and outcome monitoring tools, data-based decision-making methods, and family engagement strategies (Bickman, 2008; Burns & Hoagwood, 2004; Chorpita, Bernstein, & Daleiden, 2008, Kazdin & Weisz, 2003; McCellan & Werry, 2003; Silverman & Hinshaw, 2008; Stoiber & Kratochwill, 2000; Weisz, Weiss, Han, Granger, & Morton, 1995). Historically, many of the empirically supported treatments and practices were not developed with ethnic minority families and underserved communities in mind. However, over time, the use of community-partnered research methods to both develop and test interventions in close partnership with key stakeholders has facilitated better inclusivity and recognition of the strengths of diverse cultures (Stein et al., 2002; Wells et al., 2006). Empirical research supports the use of cognitive-behavioral and similar evidence-based approaches in many ethnic minority communities (Miranda et al., 2005), with selective and directed cultural adaptations made as needed (Lau, 2006; Ngo et al., 2008). It is the lack of consistent and effective provision of such services to underserved children and their families that has become one of the major issues in the field.

Access to Care

By adolescence, 20% to 30% of youth have experienced mental illness, but the majority do not access care (Merikangas et al., 2010). Even among those who get care, many youth drop out after a few visits (Burns et al., 1995;

McKay & Bannon, 2004), and the average numbers of mental health visits by children have been reported to be as low as four visits in a six-month period (Harpaz-Rotem, Leslie, & Rosenheck, 2004). The patterns of usage are particularly poor for ethnic minority families. Children and youth from diverse racial and ethnic groups and from families who may face language and culture-related barriers are often less likely to receive services for their mental health problems than white children and youth. In numerous studies across different public health service sectors, utilization of mental health services for ethnic minority youth, particularly Latino and African American youth, falls behind their white counterparts (Barksdale, Azur, & Leaf, 2010; Garland, Landsverk, & Lau, 2003; Garland et al., 2005; Kataoka et al., 2002; Kataoka, Stein, Nadeem, & Wong, 2007; Saloner, 2017). Ethnic minority children and adolescents have high levels of unmet need for mental health care with about 80% of those who need care not receiving it (Kataoka et al., 2002). These ethnic and racial disparities hold in both urban and rural settings (Howell & McFeeters, 2008), even though overall rates of accessibility of mental health services are documented to be lower in rural than in urban settings (Howell & McFeeters, 2008; Wang et al., 2005).

Among youth who do access care, it has been repeatedly reported that non-specialty settings are critical for children and families to receive care. Because schools allow for the provision of services to children who may not go to traditional mental health clinics (Garrison, Roy, & Azar, 1999), there has been a great interest in supporting schools as a setting for mental health service delivery. In fact, 70% to 80 % of children who receive mental health services get these services in schools (Burns et al., 1995). A study conducted after Hurricane Katrina that randomized children with post-traumatic stress symptoms to two empirically supported trauma treatments (one provided at school, one at the clinic) found that despite providing substantial logistical support (transportation assistance, childcare) to the clinic-assigned families, 91% of youth completed the school-based treatment compared to only 9% of youth served in the clinic (Jaycox et al., 2010). As a result of these findings, many suggest that schools have, in essence, become the de facto mental health system for children (Burns et al., 1995; Jacob & Coutasse, 2008).

Another service sector often accessed by children and families is pediatric primary care. One-third of children receiving Medicaid outpatient care for mental health conditions sought this care from their primary care physician only, with nearly an additional quarter of children seeing multiple providers, and only 15% going to specialty mental health providers that were not psychiatrists (Anderson, Chen, Perrin, & Van Cleave, 2015). The group of children who sought care from pediatricians only was disproportionately comprised of children with attention-deficit/hyperactivity disorder (ADHD) versus children with anxiety/mood disorders (41.8% vs. 17.2%) (Anderson et al., 2015). Approximately 6% of medical visits for children under 12 and approximately 12% of adolescent visits were associated with mental health care (Centers for Disease Control and Prevention, 2014). In response to these trends, the American Academy of Pediatrics has issued practice guidelines to encourage use of the chronic care model for managing mental illness, integration of mental health screening and behavioral health practitioners, and strengthening and expanding referral systems and networks (Foy, Kelleher, & Laraque, 2010). States have also responded by offering specialized training and consultation programs for physicians to support their treatment of mental health issues, particularly those serving underserved and rural areas (Kerker et al., 2015).

Family and Youth Engagement

Given the continued complexities inherent in the child mental health care system, it is no surprise that family and youth engagement in the child mental health care system is less than optimal. In short, the system remains unfriendly to families with many obstacles that families often have to confront to access services (Olin et al., 2016). Wait times for initial appointments are often cited as an important barrier to treatment (Westin, Barksdale, & Stephan, 2014), and the length of time between intake and the first scheduled appointment has been linked to higher rates of no shows for psychiatric appointments (Ho et al., 2015).

Consequently, parents report high levels of stress and strain in managing their children's mental health needs (Angold et al., 1998; Wu et al., 1999). Low parental socioeconomic status, being from a traditionally underserved racial or ethnic group, being a single parent, and parental mental health challenges are all associated with reduced likelihood of initiating or completing mental health treatment (Haine-Schlagel & Walsh, 2015). Additional common barriers to mental health service utilization include structural constraints and logistical barriers (e.g., competing demands, transportation, and time constraints), parental perceptions and attributions about mental health issues, perceived need for care, and perceptions of services (Bussing, Zima, Gary, & Garvan, 2003; Owens et al., 2002).

Other possible reasons for reduced access to care may be a reluctance to engage with the system, with over two-thirds of parents of minority youth indicating that seeking help from mental health professionals and service agencies was not a first choice (McMiller & Weisz, 1996). Fear of stigmatization and judgment, uncertainty about the treatment process, concerns about medication, prior negative experiences in the system, and parents' own beliefs and ambivalence have also been identified as issues pertinent to family engagement (Breland-Noble, Bell, & Nicolas, 2006; Gordon, Antshel, Lewandowski, & Seigers, 2010; Larson, Stewart, Kushner, Frosch, & Solomon, 2013; Lindsey, Chambers, Pohle, Beall, & Lucksted, 2013; Thompson et al., 2013). Yet, there is also evidence that families do indeed want and seek care. In a study of families referred to a community mental health agency, despite 33% to 62% of families not attending their initial appointments (Harrison, McKay, & Bannon, 2004; McKay, Nudelman, McCadam, & Gonzales, 1996), they indicated that they still wanted services (Harrison, McKay, & Bannon, 2004). Many caregivers cited miscommunication between caregiver and providers as the most common reason for non-attendance (Harrison, McKay, & Bannon, 2004).

Current Trends and Opportunities

Although the past two decades have been marked with some important strides in the child mental health care system, there are a clear set of needs around improving outcomes, quality, service integration, family engagement, and access to care. In this section, we highlight some of the current trends in research and practice and point out areas for growth and opportunity.

Implementation Science to Enhance Quality of Care

Despite the considerable investment in EBP development, it has been noted that it takes 17 years for original research to change practice (Green, 2001). And although there has been progress in the treatment of some childhood disorders (Hoagwood et al., 2016), the research to practice gap persists in the child mental health services across service sectors (e.g., Hoagwood, Burns, Kiser, Ringeisen, & Schoenwald, 2001; Kratochwill & Hoagwood, 2005; Schoenwald et al., 2008). In response, more than 20 states are actively supporting implementation of evidence-based psychotherapy (Bruns, Hoagwood, & Hamilton, 2008) or medication practices (Essock et al., 2009). Some states have established contracts with treatment developers and purveyor organizations to assist their agencies in implementation of specific EBPs (Fixsen, Naoom, Blase, Friedman, & Wallace, 2005). At the same time, states have been challenged by budget shortfalls that have led to significant reduction in funding for services (Miller, 2011), and policy makers need research evidence to inform them on the most effective and efficient methods to improve care. For example, investigation of the relative success of pooling, blending, or braiding funding from multiple distinct sources (e.g., health and human services, education, child welfare, and juvenile services) could prove useful in decisions about how to appropriately maximize funding within each mechanism to achieve a fiscally viable and impactful model service delivery (Cammack, Brandt, Slade, Lever, & Stephan, 2014; Evans et al., 2003).

Because one-time workshop training of providers has been ineffective in improving care (Davis, Thomson, Oxman, & Haynes, 1995; Ferlie & Shortell, 2001; Raghavan, Bright, & Shadoin, 2008), training is now routinely augmented by ongoing consultation and coaching from experts (Nadeem, Gleacher, & Beidas, 2013). However, because of the complexity of mental health systems, in addition to clinically focused consultation, there is a need for targeted implementation strategies that focus on theoretically and empirically guided processes aligned with both the inner (intraorganizational) and outer context (systems). Key factors include characteristics of the innovation; innovation fit with patient, clinician, organizational needs, and context; leadership; organization cultural and climate; and alignment with the larger policy and fiscal context. Each of these domains affects implementation of innovations at different phases of the process: exploration of whether to deploy a new practice, adoption of a new practice, initial implementation, active implementation, and sustainment (e.g., Aarons, Hurlburt, & Horwitz, 2011; Damschroder et al., 2009; Powell et al., 2011).

In the field of implementation science, studies have focused on observations of implementation processes and interventions to improve implementation outcomes. For example, observational studies show that better organizational cultural and climate is linked to better child mental health outcomes (Glisson & Green, 2011) and higher quality family support services (Olin et al., 2014). Research also demonstrated that having colleagues who are implementing a given practice is associated with clinicians' increased likelihood of using an EBP (Langley, Nadeem, Kataoka, Stein, & Jaycox, 2010). At the agency level, strong social networks and collaboration across agencies can predict program implementation (Palinkas et al., 2011). Research examining specific implementation processes and activities has shown that agencies' timely and thorough completion of implementation activities within key stages of the implementation process (i.e., engagement of staff and stakeholders, feasibility consideration, and readiness planning) predicts successful program start-up (Saldana, Chamberlain, Wang, & Brown, 2012).

With respect to implementation interventions, there is still a great need for research that distills the core components of effective implementation strategies and provides guidance on which implementation-focused interventions are effective, for whom, and at what stage of the process. However, some advances have been made in examining implementation strategies such as ongoing implementation-focused coaching and consultation, audit and feedback methods, quality improvement collaboratives, and organizational improvement interventions (e.g., Brown et al., 2014; Glisson et al., 2012; Glisson et al., 2010; Gustafson et al., 2013; Ivers et al., 2012; Nadeem, Olin, Hill, Hoagwood, & Horwitz, 2014). Importantly, implementation research requires partnered research models that involve stakeholders from multiple levels of a system (e.g., youth, families, front-line staff, leadership, partnering agencies, and policy makers) taking part in both the research and implementation process (e.g., Fixsen, Blase, Metz, & Van Dyke, 2013; Hoagwood, Jensen, McKay, & Olin, 2009; Wells et al., 2006). This also allows for faster uptake of research knowledge and the ability of stakeholders to ensure that empirical research addresses the questions that are most pertinent to their needs.

Public Health Frameworks, Tiered Supports, and Integrated Care

An important movement in current mental health practice for children involves the use of public health frameworks for organizing care. This is nicely exemplified in school mental health. In a public health framework, services and supports are provided at three tiers: universal supports (Tier 1), targeted supports (Tier 2), and intensive supports (Tier 3). *Universal supports* address all individuals in the setting or context (e.g., classrooms or schoolwide intervention), with the main aim of preventing mental health problems and promoting overall wellness. *Targeted supports* are deployed for those groups or individuals identified as being at risk for a mental health problem or those who have developing early symptoms. They focus on building resilience and preventing more serious consequences. *Intensive supports* are reserved for those who require more intensive, individualized intervention and support (e.g., individual treatments and intensive supports) (Fix et al., 2017; Nastasi, 2004).

This approach to services is well aligned with current educational practice. For example, the current iteration of IDEA ("IDEA Regulations," 2006, section 1) allows for a response to intervention (RTI) approach to determine the presence of a disability and whether more intense interventions are needed. RTI is designed to reduce the base rates of problems in the general population through the use of universal interventions that are followed by increasingly more intense services (secondary and tertiary interventions) for students presenting with educational problems who are not responding to the less intensive interventions (Kratochwill, Clements, & Kalymon, 2007; Reschly & Bergstrom, 2009). In an increasing number of districts, this model has been expanded to encompass social-emotional and behavioral interventions as well. A similar multitiered framework is used to organize positive behavioral interventions and supports (PBIS) (Sugai & Horner, 2006). Together, these frameworks can be thought of as models for providing multitiered systems of supports (MTSS) that address social-emotional well-being and mental health. MTSS frameworks are being increasingly used to organize social-emotional learning, behavioral supports, and mental health interventions, and to address timely clinical and practice issues in the field, such has how to build trauma-informed schools (e.g., Cappella et al., 2012; Cicchetti & Dunlap, 2015; Nadeem, Jaycox, Kataoka, Langley, & Stein, 2011).

Integration of mental health within the larger public health framework has also been important in the public mental health sector. Recent legislation such as the 2007 Mental Health Equity and Addictions Parity Act and the 2009 Patient Protection and Affordable Care Act (ACA) has been integral to placing mental health within the broader public health system and framework (Hoagwood et al., 2014). In fact, specialty mental health services are being replaced with regionalized networks of health care providers (Kelleher, 2010), and mental health clinics are unlikely to continue to operate in isolation from the rest of the health care system (Hoagwood et al., 2014; Kelleher, 2010). In the near term, this has led to significant growth in behavioral health integration into health care systems. Several models of integration have been developed, including co-location of mental health providers in medical settings (e.g., primary care, hospitals, and health centers), direct psychosocial treatment delivered by medical providers (American Academy of Child and Adolescent Psychiatry, 2010), and behavioral health care provided within school-based health centers (Weist, Goldstein, Morris, & Bryant, 2003). There is tremendous need for further research in these areas. One promising signal comes in a recent meta-analysis of randomized clinical trials that evaluated integrated behavioral health in primary care for children and adolescents compared with usual care in primary care. The study concluded that integrated care interventions outperform usual care on behavioral health outcomes (Asarnow, Rozenman, Wiblin, & Zeltzer, 2015).

Family Engagement, Support, and Family-Centered Care

In addressing family engagement issues discussed in the last section, advocacy efforts led by youth and families have been critical to current thinking around family-centered care and strength-based approaches (Hoagwood et al., 2008; Osher et al., 2008). Family advocacy has also continued to shine light on the needs for better engagement and culturally and contextually informed clinical practice, and a focus on outcomes that are identified by consumers to be of relevance to them. In fact, a recent review of the empirical literature on intervention for child and adolescent mental health issues identified tremendous growth in the inclusion of consumer-oriented outcomes in research studies. This expansion of outcomes to include functional domains as well as domains such as quality of life, satisfaction with care, family strain or burden, perceptions and beliefs about treatment, sense of competence and empowerment, and knowledge marks a major shift toward the inclusion of family-centered outcomes in child mental health (Hoagwood et al., 2012).

Two burgeoning research areas relevant to family engagement have included the development of family support services and the identification of the core components of effective family engagement interventions. First, although the research base is not yet robust, there has been notable growth in the development of family support interventions in child mental health prevention and intervention delivered either by family peer advocates (also known as family partners or peer family members), clinicians, or teams (Cavaleri, Olin, Kim, Hoagwood, & Burns, 2011; Hoagwood et al., 2010). The five salient components of family support include: (1) informational, (2) instructional, (3) emotional, (4) instrumental, and (5) advocacy support (Hoagwood et al., 2010).

Second, a recent review examined the common elements in family engagement strategies and identified assessment, accessibility promotion, psychoeducation about services, homework assignment, and appointment reminders as core engagement practices across engagement interventions. Assessment and accessibility promotion were particularly salient in effective interventions (Lindsey et al., 2014).

Importantly, some states are moving toward models that allow for both delivery and billing of services provided by nontraditional mental health staff. Peer specialists are increasingly employed at organizations across the country (Walker & Crocker, 2008), and national surveys suggest that there is growth in the number of family support specialists in children's mental health as a number of states are developing certification standards (Hoagwood et al., 2008; Hoagwood et al., 2014; Walker & Crocker, 2008). In addition, family engagement and support interventions are being delivered across a range of contexts, with an increasing number of investigations focused on the unique challenges of engaging families in school-based mental health services (Lindsey et al., 2013; Nadeem, Santiago, Kataoka, Chang, & Stein, 2016), and methods to engage families across multitiered systems of services and supports in schools (Fix et al., 2017).

School Mental Health

We close the chapter with two brief case examples of school-based mental health models that illustrate the historical evolution of such services and how they align with current innovations in child mental health services research and practice. Although all of the systems mentioned thus far are important, from the perspective of providing access to services and reaching the greatest amount of children, schools are arguably the most critical (Burns et al., 1995; Eaton et al., 2008; Garrison, Roy, & Azar, 1999; U.S. Department of Health and Human Services, 2003).

School-based service provision has been driven by federal and local educational mandates. IDEA and section 504 ensure that students who have emotional disturbances or other identified mental health issues that directly affect their school performance receive services. IDEA now allows and encourages districts to address prevention and early intervention for special education through the use of RTI approaches ("IDEA Regulations," 2006, section 1), which is nicely aligned with the tiered systems of universal prevention, early/targeted intervention, and intensive intervention in public health frameworks (Nastasi, 2004). In practice, the school mental health service models used have varied tremendously, but often represent programs that are housed within districts using district-employed staff, programs that leverage school-community partnerships, and programs that combine resources. Below, we briefly describe the history of two school mental health service models and how they have evolved to align with public health service models and integrated behavioral health care (Flaherty & Osher, 2003; Weist et al., 2017; Weist et al., 2003).

Sample Model: Los Angeles Unified School District

One of the earliest examples of an in-district school mental health program is the School Mental Health Services Department in the Los Angeles Unified School District (LAUSD). This unit was established in 1933 and has been in continuous operation since that date. Initial staffing consisted of two nurses and a physician, in recognition of the fact that special education students with physical disabilities also suffered from emotional distress and difficulties with poor self-esteem and peer relationships in school. In 1945, following the child guidance movement in Europe, services were expanded and organized into child guidance clinics (supported in part by the Parent Teacher Association), located in five locations across LAUSD. In the mid-1980s, in response to a tragic shooting outside an elementary school in 1984, the first crisis intervention team was created by the superintendent and board of education of LAUSD. The School Mental Health Service was tasked with its development.

Further expansion of the program led to a model in which schools each had their own crisis team (this model that ultimately planted the seed for a trauma-informed lens in school mental health). In 1992, one of the authors (Wong) was appointed director of School Mental Health. Due to a history of partnership between LAUSD's Crisis Counseling Programs, the Los Angeles County Department of Mental Health (LAC/DMH), and the Department of Justice Office of Community Services, in 1992 LAUSD and the leadership at LAC/DMH developed some of the earliest "blended funding" contracts to establish full scope, district-based Medicaid reimbursed mental health and health services. This included psychiatric care. Disaster response and recovery services also expanded during this time.

The LAUSD Crisis Intervention Teams have grown to over 350 members within each of the subdistrict bureaucratic units and became integrated with school police, nursing, pupil services, attendance counselors, and others. In addition, the School Mental Health Services Department now includes over 300 school mental health professionals who support resilience, positive student connections with peers, family, school, and self-reflection and problem-solving skills to optimize school success. They also provide supports to help students manage traumatic experiences, crises, and other mental health issues. The program consists of tiered mental health supports aligned with RTI and PBIS, and includes partnerships with community mental health agencies. The district has been a national leader in trauma-informed practice and crisis response, and has a long-standing partnership with clinician-researchers at RAND and UCLA. This team developed the Cognitive Behavioral Intervention for Trauma in Schools (CBITS) (Stein et al., 2002; Stein et al., 2003), and has been funded for many years as part SAMHSA's National Child Traumatic Stress Network. Most recently, LAUSD's mental health service model has expanded further into LAUSD Wellness Centers that focus on integration of physical and mental health, which is directly aligned with current trends toward integrated behavioral health care.

Sample Model: Expanded School Mental Health in Baltimore City

The national Center for School Mental Health (CSMH) at the University of Maryland (co-directed by author, Hoover) was established in 1995, with funding from the Maternal and Child Health Bureau (MCHB) of the Health Resources and Services Administration, to support the advancement of school mental health programs and services in the United States (see http://csmh.umaryland.edu). The center has continued to receive federal funding from the MCHB and has received funding from a number of other federal, state, and local agencies to advance SMH training, practice, research, and policy. The foundation of the CSMH is the school mental health experience in Baltimore, long recognized as a national leader for providing "expanded" school mental health (ESMH) services to students and their families in public schools (Flaherty & Weist, 1999). ESMH services involve family-school-community partnerships to support a full continuum of mental health supports that reflect a public health approach to care, including universal, targeted, and intensive services (Weist, 1997). ESMH in Baltimore began in the late 1980s in the context of school-based health centers (SBHCs) that provided comprehensive health care to students in schools. It was quickly established that mental health was the primary reason for referral to the SBHCs (Flaherty & Weist, 1999), and a formal partnership between the city mental health and education systems was established to support a network of community-partnered school behavioral health providers. Initially, partnership involved staff from local community mental health centers meeting weekly with school personnel to discuss children being seen in the clinics. These relationships later served as the foundation for the establishment of the ESMH Network in Baltimore City. ESMH has grown progressively—to 32 Baltimore schools by 1993, 79 schools in 1999, 84 schools in 2003, and to over half of the approximately 191 schools in the 2016–2017 academic year

(Weist et al., 2009). Pooled education and behavioral health funding now supports four community behavioral health provider agencies to partner with city school support staff to provide a comprehensive range of services (promotion, screening and assessment, prevention, case management, and treatment) that are available to youth in special and regular education.

Since its inception, and in partnership with the national Center for School Mental Health, the ESMH Network in Baltimore has emphasized strong partnerships between school, families, and community partners, to support a full continuum of mental health supports to students. In contrast to many community-partnered school mental health models that rely primarily on fee-for-service funding that requires their time to be almost exclusively focused on tertiary care, the ESMH Network has consistently funded mental health promotion and prevention activities. This funding, and related professional development and accountability mechanisms, ensure that community partners are supporting a multitiered system of supports that focuses on promoting wellness and practicing early identification and intervention. Community partners are required, for example, to conduct several universal mental health promotion activities, such as supporting social-emotional classroom learning or substance abuse prevention programming, while at the same time providing some intensive mental health treatment for students with identified needs.

The Baltimore ESMH Network has also consistently employed a continuous quality assessment and improvement framework, infusing best practices from the research field into practice. Most recently, the ESMH Network and City Schools partnered in a rigorous quality improvement collaborative with several other school districts in the United States. As part of the School Health Services National Quality Initiative, a team of school mental health stakeholders from Baltimore engaged in a 15-month, continuous assessment of quality and sustainability performance (using national performance standards on the School Health Assessment and Performance Evaluation system, https://www.theSHAPEsystem.com) (Connors et al., 2016) to guide ongoing school mental health improvement efforts. Quality improvement focused on a variety of domains, including mental health screening and assessment, teaming, resource mapping, and evidence-based services and implementation, with notable and documented growth in the areas of school-community teaming and evidence-based assessment.

Conclusion

There has been tremendous growth in the field of children's mental health services. In the earliest years, the system focus was largely on the establishment of services for children, in both specialty and non-specialty settings. Since that time, children's mental health supports have grown tremendously across service sectors, with non-specialty sectors being particularly important in providing access and opportunity to serve both those with high levels of needs and those who may be at risk for future problems. However, despite efforts to the contrary, many of the problems that have plagued the system for decades continue. The system remains unwieldy and difficult for families to navigate. Many families, particularly ethnic minorities, have poor access to care, and the quality of care is inconsistent. What is striking though is the important role that research has played in both documenting successes and areas of challenge for the field. It continues to be critical is shaping the future with respect to the development and implementation of effective treatments and well as effective strategies to make these practices available to the public. It is also immensely heartening to see that community stakeholders and families have gone from being marginalized, to now being active partners in shaping the research and practice agenda. While the field has many more gains to make in these areas, continuing down this path is critical.

References

Aarons, G. A., Hurlburt, M., & Horwitz, S. M. C. (2011). Advancing a conceptual model of evidence-based practice implementation in public service sectors. *Administration and Policy in Mental Health and Mental Health Services Research, 38*(1), 4–23.

Agency for Healthcare Research & Quality. (2009). Mental disorders among most costly conditions in children. *AHRQ News and Numbers*. Retrieved from https://meps.ahrq.gov/data_files/publications/st248/stat248.pdf

American Academy of Child and Adolescent Psychiatry. (2010). A guide to building collaborative mental health care partnerships in pediatric primary care. Retrieved from http://www.aacap.org/App_Themes/AACAP/docs/clinical_practice_center/guide_to_building_collaborative_mental_health_care_partnerships.pdf

Anderson, L. E., Chen, M. L., Perrin, J. M., & Van Cleave, J. (2015). Outpatient visits and medication prescribing for US children with mental health conditions. *Pediatrics, 136*(5), e1178–e1185.

Angold, A., Messer, S. C., Stangl, D., Farmer, E. M., Costello, E. J., & Burns, B. J. (1998). Perceived parental burden and service use for child and adolescent psychiatric disorders. *American Journal of Public Health, 88*(1), 75–80.

Asarnow, J. R., Rozenman, M., Wiblin, J., & Zeltzer, L. (2015). Integrated medical-behavioral care compared with usual primary care for child and adolescent behavioral health: A meta-analysis. *JAMA Pediatrics, 169*(10), 929–937.

Barksdale, C. L., Azur, M., & Leaf, P. J. (2010). Differences in mental health service sector utilization among African American and Caucasian youth entering systems of care programs. *Journal of Behavioral Health Services & Research, 37*(3), 363–373.

Berwick, D. (1989). Continuous improvement as an ideal in health care. *New England Journal of Medicine, 320*(1), 53–56.
Bickman, L. (2008). A measurement feedback system (MFS) is necessary to improve mental health outcomes. *Journal of the American Academy of Child and Adolescent Psychiatry, 47*(10), 1114–1119.
Breland-Noble, A. M., Bell, C., & Nicolas, G. (2006). Family First: The development of an evidence-based family intervention for increasing participation in psychiatric clinical care and research in depressed African American adolescents. *Family Process, 45*(2), 153–169.
Brown, C. H., Chamberlain, P., Saldana, L., Padgett, C., Wang, W., & Cruden, G. (2014). Evaluation of two implementation strategies in 51 child county public service systems in two states: Results of a cluster randomized head-to-head implementation trial. *Implementation Science, 9*(1), 1–15.
Bruns, E. J., Hoagwood, K. E., & Hamilton, J. D. (2008). State implementation of evidence-based practice for youths, part I: Responses to the state of the evidence. *Journal of the American Academy of Child & Adolescent Psychiatry, 47*(4), 369–373.
Burns, B. J., Costello, E. J., Angold, A., Tweed, D., Stangl, D., Farmer, E. M., & Erkanli, A. (1995). Children's mental health service use across service sectors. *Health Affairs, 14*(3), 147–159.
Burns, B. J., & Hoagwood, K. E. (2004). Preface. Evidence-based practice, part I: Research update. *Child and Adolescent Psychiatric Clinics of North America, 13*(4), xi–xiii.
Bussing, R., Zima, B. T., Gary, F. A., & Garvan, C. W. (2003). Barriers to detection, help-seeking, and service use for children with ADHD symptoms *Journal of Behavioral Health Services & Research, 30*(2), 176–189.
Cammack, N. L., Brandt, N. E., Slade, E., Lever, N. A., & Stephan, S. (2014). Funding expanded school mental health programs. In M. D. Weist, N. A. Lever, C. P. Bradshaw, & J. S. Owens (Eds.), *Handbook of school mental health* (pp. 17–30). New York: Springer.
Cappella, E., Hamre, B. K., Kim, H. Y., Henry, D. B., Frazier, S. L., Atkins, M. S., & Schoenwald, S. K. (2012). Teacher consultation and coaching within mental health practice: Classroom and child effects in urban elementary schools. *Journal of Consulting and Clinical Psychology, 80*(4), 597–610.
Cavaleri, M. A., Olin, S. S., Kim, A., Hoagwood, K. E., & Burns, B. J. (2011). Family support in prevention programs for children at risk for emotional/behav ioral problems. *Clinical Child & Family Psychology Review, 14*(4), 399–412.
Centers for Disease Control and Prevention. (2014). QuickStats: Percentage of mental health–related primary care office visits, by age group—National Ambulatory Medical Care Survey, United States, 2010. *Morbidity and Mortality Weekly Report (MMWR), 63*(47), 1118.
Chorpita, B. F., Bernstein, A., & Daleiden, E. L. (2008). Driving with roadmaps and dashboards: Using information resources to structure the decision models in service organizations. *Administration and Policy in Mental Health and Mental Health Services Research, 35*(1–2), 114–123.

Cicchetti, C., & Dunlap, S. (2015). *Building a trauma informed school: A three tiered approach*. Paper presented at the Illinois Association of School Social Workers.

Committee on Quality of Health Care in America, Institute of Medicine. (2001). *Crossing the quality chasm: A new health system for the 21st century* (0309072808). Retrieved from http://www.nationalacademies.org/hmd/Reports/2001/Crossing-the-Quality-Chasm-A-New-Health-System-for-the-21st-Century.aspx

Committee on Quality of Health Care in America, Institute of Medicine. (2006). *Improving the quality of health care for mental and substance-use conditions: Quality chasm series*. Washington, DC: National Academies Press (US).

Connors, E. H., Stephan, S. H., Lever, N., Ereshefsky, S., Mosby, A., & Bohnenkamp, J. (2016). A national initiative to advance school mental health performance measurement in the US. *Advances in School Mental Health Promotion, 9*(1), 50–69.

Cross, T. L. (1989). *Towards a culturally competent system of care: A monograph on effective services for minority children who are severely emotionally disturbed*. Retrieved from Washington, DC: Georgetown University Child Development Center, CASSP Technical Assistance Center.

Damschroder, L. J., Aron, D. C., Keith, R. E., Kirsh, S. R., Alexander, J. A., & Lowery, J. C. (2009). Fostering implementation of health services research findings into practice: A consolidated framework for advancing implementation science. *Implementation Science, 4*(1), 50–64.

Davis, D., Thomson, M., Oxman, A., & Haynes, B. (1995). Changing physician performance: A systematic review of the effect of continuing medical education strategies. *JAMA, 274*, 700–705.

Eaton, D. K., Kann, L., Kinchen, S., Shanklin, S., Ross, J., Hawkins, J., . . . Wechsler, H. (2008). Youth risk behavior surveillance—United States, 2007. *MMWR Surveillance Summaries, 57*, 1–131.

Essock, S., Covell, N., Leckman-Westin, E., Lieberman, J., Sederer, L., Kealey, E., & Finnerty, M. (2009). Identifying clinically questionable psychotropic prescribing practices for Medicaid recipients in New York State. *Psychiatric Services, 60*(12), 1595–1602.

Evans, S. W., Glass-Siegel, M., Frank, A., Van Treuren, R., Lever, N. A., & Weist, M. D. (2003). Overcoming the challenges of funding school mental health programs. In M. D. Weist, N. A. Lever, C. P. Bradshaw, & J. S. Owens (Eds.), *Handbook of school mental health: Advancing practice and research* (pp. 73–86). New York: Springer.

Ferlie, E., & Shortell, S. (2001). Improving the quality of health care in the United Kingdom and the United States: A framework for change. *Milbank Quarterly, 79*(2), 281–315.

Fix, R. L., Mayworm, A., Lawson, G. M., Becker, K. D., Lever, N. A., & Stephan, S. H. (2017). Strategies for effective family engagement in elementary and middle schools. In M. D. Weist, S. A. Garbacz, K. L. Lane, & D. Kincaid (Eds.), *Aligning and integrating family engagement in Positive Behavioral Interventions and Supports (PBIS): Concepts and strategies for families and schools in key contexts* (pp. 98–119). Eugene, Oregon: University of Oregon Press.

Fixsen, D., Blase, K., Metz, A., & Van Dyke, M. (2013). Statewide implementation of evidence-based programs. *Exceptional Children, 79*(2), 213–230.

Fixsen, D., Naoom, S., Blase, K., Friedman, R., & Wallace, F. (2005). *Implementation research: A synthesis of the literature* (Louis de la Parte Florida Mental Health Institute Publication# 231). Tampa, FL: University of South Florida, Louis de la Parte Florida Mental Health Institute, The National Implementation Research Network.

Flaherty, L. T., & Osher, D. (2003). History of school-based mental health services in the United States. In S. E. M. D. Weist & N. Lever (Eds.), *Handbook of school mental health: Advancing practice and research* (pp. 11–22). New York: Springer.

Flaherty, L. T., & Weist, M. D. (1999). School-based mental health services: The Baltimore models. *Psychology in the Schools, 36*(5), 379–389.

Foy, J. M., Kelleher, K. J., & Laraque, D. (2010). Enhancing pediatric mental health care: Strategies for preparing a primary care practice. *Pediatrics, 125*(Supplement 3), S87–S108.

Ganju, V. (2006). Mental health quality and accountability: The role of evidence-based practices and performance measurement. *Administration and Policy in Mental Health and Mental Health Services Research, 33*(6), 659–665.

Garland, A. F., Landsverk, J. A., & Lau, A. S. (2003). Racial/ethnic disparities in mental health service use among children in foster care. *Children and Youth Services Review, 25*(5), 491–507.

Garland, A. F., Lau, A. S., Yeh, M., McCabe, K. M., Hough, R. L., & Landsverk, J. A. (2005). Racial and ethnic differences in utilization of mental health services among high-risk youths. *American Journal of Psychiatry, 162*(7), 1336–1343.

Garrison, E. G., Roy, I. S., & Azar, V. (1999). Responding to the mental health needs of Latino children and families through school-based services. *Clinical Psychology Review, 19*(2), 199–219.

Glisson, C., & Green, P. (2011). Organizational climate, services, and outcomes in child welfare systems. *Child Abuse & Neglect, 35*(8), 582–591.

Glisson, C., Hemmelgarn, A., Green, P., Dukes, D., Atkinson, S., & Williams, N. J. (2012). Randomized trial of the Availability, Responsiveness, and Continuity (ARC) organizational intervention with community-based mental health programs and clinicians serving youth. *Journal of the American Academy of Child & Adolescent Psychiatry, 51*(8), 780–787.

Glisson, C., Schoenwald, S. K., Hemmelgarn, A., Green, P., Dukes, D., Armstrong, K. S., & Chapman, J. E. (2010). Randomized trial of MST and ARC in a two-level evidence-based treatment implementation strategy. *Journal of Consulting and Clinical Psychology, 78*(4), 537–550.

Gordon, M., Antshel, K. M., Lewandowski, L., & Seigers, D. (2010). Predictors of missed appointments over the course of child mental health treatment. *Psychiatric Services, 61*(7), 657–659.

Green, L. W. (2001). From research to "best practices" in other settings and populations. *American Journal of Health Behavior, 25*(3), 165–178.

Gustafson, D. H., Quanbeck, A. R., Robinson, J. M., Ford, J. H., Pulvermacher, A., French, M. T., . . . McCarty, D. (2013). Which elements of improvement collaboratives are most effective? A cluster-randomized trial. *Addiction, 108*(6), 1145–1157.

Haine-Schlagel, R., & Walsh, N. E. (2015). A review of parent participation engagement in child and family mental health treatment. *Clinical Child & Family Psychology Review, 18*(2), 133–150.

Harpaz-Rotem, I., Leslie, D., & Rosenheck, R. A. (2004). Treatment retention among children entering a new episode of mental health care. *Psychiatric Services, 55*(9), 1022–1028.

Harrison, M. E., McKay, M. M., & Bannon, W. M., Jr. (2004). Inner-city child mental health service use: The real question is why youth and families do not use services. *Community Mental Health Journal, 40*(2), 119–131.

Ho, C. P., Zinski, A., Fogger, S. A., Peters, J. D., Westfall, A. O., Mugavero, M. J., . . . Willig, J. H. (2015). Factors associated with missed psychiatry visits in an urban HIV clinic. *AIDS and Behavior, 19*(8), 1423–1429.

Hoagwood, K., Burns, B. J., Kiser, L., Ringeisen, H., & Schoenwald, S. K. (2001). Evidence-based practice in child and adolescent mental health services. *Psychiatric Services, 52*(9), 1179–1189.

Hoagwood, K. E., Cavaleri, M. A., Olin, S. S., Burns, B. J., Slaton, E., Gruttadaro, D., & Hughes, R. (2010). Family support in children's mental health: A review and synthesis. *Clinical child & Family Psychology Review, 13*(1), 1–45.

Hoagwood, K. E., Green, E., Kelleher, K., Schoenwald, S., Rolls-Reutz, J., Landsverk, J., . . . Research Network on Youth Mental Health. (2008). Family advocacy, support and education in children's mental health: Results of a national survey. *Administration and Policy in Mental Health and Mental Health Services Research, 35*(1–2), 73–83.

Hoagwood, K. E., Jensen, P. S., Acri, M. C., Olin, S. S., Lewandowski, R. E., & Herman, R. J. (2012). Outcome domains in child mental health research since 1996: Have they changed and why does it matter? *Journal of the American Academy of Child & Adolescent Psychiatry, 51*(12), 1241–1260.

Hoagwood, K., Jensen, P. S., McKay, M. M., & Olin, S. S. (Eds.). (2009). *Redefining the boundaries: Creating family and research partnerships to improve children's mental health.* New York: Oxford University Press.

Hoagwood, K. E., Kelleher, K., Zima, B. T., Perrin, J. M., Bilder, S., & Crystal, S. (2016). Ten-year trends in treatment services for children with attention deficit hyperactivity disorder enrolled in Medicaid. *Health Affairs, 35*(7), 1266–1270.

Hoagwood, K. E., Olin, S. S., Horwitz, S. M., McKay, M., Cleek, A., Gleacher, A., . . . Kuppinger, A. (2014). Scaling up evidence-based practices for children and families in New York State: Toward evidence-based policies on implementation for state mental health systems. *Journal of Clinical Child & Adolescent Psychology, 43*(2), 145–157.

Howell, E., & McFeeters, J. (2008). Children's mental health care: Differences by race/ethnicity in urban/rural areas. *Journal of Health Care for the Poor and Underserved, 19*(1), 237–247.

Hutchinson, A. B., & Foster, E. M. (2003). The effect of Medicaid managed care on mental health care for children: A review of the literature. *Mental Health Services Research, 5*(1), 39–54.

Ivers, N., Jamtvedt, G., Flottorp, S., Young, J. M., Odgaard-Jensen, J., French, S. D., . . . Oxman, A. D. (2012). Audit and feedback: Effects on professional practice and healthcare outcomes. *The Cochrane Library*, 7.

Jacob, S., & Coustasse, A. (2008). School-based mental health: A de facto mental health system for children. *Journal of Hospital Marketing & Public Relations, 18*(2), 197–211.

Jaycox, L. H., Cohen, J. A., Mannarino, A. P., Walker, D. W., Langley, A. K., Gegenheimer, K. L., . . . Schonlau, M. (2010). Children's mental health care following Hurricane Katrina: A field trial of trauma-focused psychotherapies. *Journal of Traumatic Stress, 23*(2), 223–231.

Jones, K. W. (1999). *Taming the troublesome child: American families, child guidance, and the limits of psychiatric authority.* Cambridge, MA: Harvard University Press.

Kataoka, S., Stein, B. D., Nadeem, E., & Wong, M. (2007). Who gets care? Mental health service use following a school-based suicide prevention program. *Journal of the American Academy of Child and Adolescent Psychiatry, 46*(10), 1341–1348.

Kataoka, S. H., Zhang, L., & Wells, K. B. (2002). Unmet need for mental health care among U.S. children: Variation by ethnicity and insurance status. *American Journal of Psychiatry, 159*(9), 1548–1555.

Kazdin, A. E., & Weisz, J. R. (2003). *Evidenced-based psychotherapy for children and adolescents.* New York: Guilford Press.

Kelleher, K. (2010). Organizational capacity to deliver effective treatments for children and adolescents. *Administration and Policy in Mental Health and Mental Health Services Research, 37*(1–2), 89–94.

Kerker, B. D., Chor, K. H. B., Hoagwood, K. E., Radigan, M., Perkins, M. B., Setias, J., . . . Horwitz, S. M. (2015). Detection and treatment of mental health issues by pediatric PCPs in New York State: An evaluation of Project TEACH. *Psychiatric Services, 66*(4), 430–433.

Knitzer, J., & Olson, L. (1982). *Unclaimed children: The failure of public responsibility to children and adolescents in need of mental health services.*

Kratochwill, T. R., Clements, M. A., & Kalymon, K. M. (2007). Response to intervention: Conceptual and methodological issues in implementation. In S. R. Jimmerson, M. K. Burns, & A. M. VanDerHeyeden (Eds.), *Handbook of response to intervention: The science and practice of assessment and intervention* (pp. 25–52). New York: Springer.

Kratochwill, T. R., & Hoagwood, K. E. (2005). Evidence-based parent and family interventions in school psychology: Conceptual and methodological considerations in advancing best practices. *School Psychology Quarterly, 20*(4), 504–511.

Laffel, G., & Blumenthal, D. (1989). The case for using industrial quality management science in health care organizations. *JAMA, 262*(20), 2869–2873.

Langley, A. K., Nadeem, E., Kataoka, S. H., Stein, B. D., & Jaycox, L. H. (2010). Evidence-based mental health programs in schools: Barriers and facilitators of successful implementation. *School Mental Health, 2*(3), 105–113.

Larson, J., Stewart, M., Kushner, R., Frosch, E., & Solomon, B. (2013). Barriers to mental health care for urban, lower income families referred from pediatric primary care. *Administration and Policy in Mental Health and Mental Health Services Research, 40*(3), 159–167.

Lau, A. S. (2006). Making the case for selective and directed cultural adaptations of evidence-based treatments: Examples from parent training. *Clinical Psychology: Science and Practice, 13*(4), 295–310.

Lindsey, M. A., Brandt, N. E., Becker, K. D., Lee, B. R., Barth, R. P., Daleiden, E. L., & Chorpita, B. F. (2014). Identifying the common elements of treatment engagement interventions in children's mental health services. *Clinical Child and Family Psychology Review, 17*(3), 283–298.

Lindsey, M. A., Chambers, K., Pohle, C., Beall, P., & Lucksted, A. (2013). Understanding the behavioral determinants of mental health service use by urban, under-resourced black youth: Adolescent and caregiver perspectives. *Journal of Child and Family Studies, 22*(1), 107–121.

Lourie, I. S., & Hernandez, M. (2003). A historical perspective on national child mental health policy. *Journal of Emotional and Behavioral Disorders, 11*(1), 5–9.

Lourie, I. S., Katz-Leavy, J., DeCarolis, G., & Quinlan, W. (1996). The role of the federal government. In B. A. Stroul (Ed.), *Children's mental health: Creating systems of care in a changing society* (pp. 99–114). Baltimore: Brookes.

Masten, A. S., & Curtis, W. J. (2000). Integrating competence and psychopathology: pathways toward a comprehensive science of adaptation in development. *Development & Psychopathology, 12*(3), 529–550.

McCellan, J., & Werry, J. (2003). Evidence-based treatments in child and adolescent psychiatry: an inventory. *Journal of the American Academy of Child & Adolescent Psychiatry, 42*(12), 1388–1400.

McKay, M. M., & Bannon, W. M., Jr. (2004). Engaging families in child mental health services. *Child & Adolescent Psychiatric Clinics of North America, 13*(4), 905–921.

McKay, M. M., Nudelman, R., McCadam, K., & Gonzales, J. (1996). Evaluating a social work engagement approach to involving inner-city children and their families in mental health care. *Research on Social Work Practice, 6*(4), 462–472.

McMiller, W. P., & Weisz, J. R. (1996). Help-seeking preceding mental health clinic intake among African-American, Latino, and Caucasian youths. *Journal of the American Academy of Child & Adolescent Psychiatry, 35*(8), 1086–1094.

Merikangas, K. R., He, J. P., Burstein, M., Swanson, S. A., Avenevoli, S., Cui, L., . . . Swendsen, J. (2010). Lifetime prevalence of mental disorders in US adolescents: results from the National Comorbidity Survey Replication–Adolescent Supplement (NCS-A). *Journal of the American Academy of Child & Adolescent Psychiatry, 49*(10), 980–989.

Miller, J. E. (2011). *The changing landscape of behavioral health and going into the future.* Paper presented at the NASMHPD 2011 Annual Commissioners Meeting.

Miranda, J., Bernal, G., Lau, A., Kohn, L., Hwang, W. C., & LaFromboise, T. (2005). State of the science on psychosocial interventions for ethnic minorities. *Annual Review of Clinical Psychology, 1*, 113–142.

Nadeem, E., Gleacher, A., & Beidas, R. S. (2013). Consultation as an implementation strategy for evidence-based practices across multiple contexts: Unpacking the black box. *Administration and Policy in Mental Health and Mental Health Services Research, 40*(6), 439–450.

Nadeem, E., Jaycox, L., Kataoka, S. H., Langley, A. K., & Stein, B. D. (2011). Going to scale: Experiences implementing a school-based trauma intervention. *School Psychology Review, 40*(4), 549–568.

Nadeem, E., Olin, S. S., Hill, L. C., Hoagwood, K. E., & Horwitz, S. M. (2014). Learning Collaboratives in mental health: Used but untested. *Psychiatric Services, 65*(9), 1088–1099.

Nadeem, E., Santiago, C. D., Kataoka, S. K., Chang, V. Y., & Stein, B. D. (2016). School personnel experiences in notifying parents about their child's risk for suicide: Lessons learned. *Journal of School Health, 86*(1), 3–10.

Nastasi, B. K. (2004). Meeting the challenges of the future: Integrating public health and public education for mental health promotion. *Journal of Educational and Psychological Consultation, 15*(3–4), 295–312.

Ngo, V., Langley, A., Kataoka, S. H., Nadeem, E., Escudero, P., & Stein, B. D. (2008). Providing evidence-based practice to ethnically diverse youths: examples from the Cognitive Behavioral Intervention for Trauma in Schools (CBITS) program. *Journal of the American Academy of Child Adolescent Psychiatry, 47*(8), 858–862.

Olin, S., O'Connor, B. C., Storfer-Isser, A., Clark, L. J., Perkins, M., Scholle, S. H., . . . Horwitz, S. M. (2016). Access to care for youth in a state mental health system: a simulated patient approach. *Journal of the American Academy of Child & Adolescent Psychiatry, 55*(5), 392–339.

Olin, S. S., Williams, N., Pollock, M., Armusewicz, K., Kutash, K., Glisson, C., & Hoagwood, K. E. (2014). Quality indicators for family support services and their relationship to organizational social context. *Administration and Policy in Mental Health and Mental Health Services Research, 41*(1), 43–54.

Osher, T., Penn, M., & Spencer, S. A. (2008). Partnerships with families for family-driven systems of care. In B. A. S. G. M. Blau (Ed.), *The system of care handbook: Transforming mental health services for children, youth, and families* (pp. 249–274): Baltimore: Brookes.

Owens, P. L., Hoagwood, K., Horwitz, S. M., Leaf, P. J., Poduska, J. M., Kellam, S. G., & Ialongo, N. S. (2002). Barriers to children's mental health services. *Journal of the American Academy of Child & Adolescent Psychiatry, 41*(6), 731–738.

Palinkas, L. A., Holloway, I. W., Rice, E., Fuentes, D., Wu, Q., & Chamberlain, P. (2011). Social networks and implementation of evidence-based practices in public youth-serving systems: a mixed-methods study. *Implementation Science, 6*(1), 113–123.

Pires, S. (2002). *Building systems of care: A primer.* Washington, DC: National Technical Assistance Center for Children's Mental Health.

Powell, B. J., McMillen, J. C., Proctor, E. K., Carpenter, C. R., Griffey, R. T., Bunger, A. C., . . . York, J. L. (2011). A compilation of strategies for implementing clinical innovations in health and mental health. *Medical Care Research and Review, 69*, 123–157.

Raghavan, R., Bright, C., & Shadoin, A. (2008). Toward a policy ecology of implementation of evidence-based practices in public mental health settings. *Implementation Science, 3*(1), 26.

Raghavan, R., Leibowitz, A. A., Andersen, R. M., Zima, B. T., Schuster, M. A., & Landsverk, J. (2006). Effects of Medicaid managed care policies on mental health service use among a national probability sample of children in the child welfare system. *Children and Youth Services Review, 28*(12), 1482–1496.

Reschly, D. J., & Bergstrom, M. K. (2009). Response to intervention. In T. B. Gutkin & C. R. Reynolds (Eds.), *The handbook of school psychology.* New York: Wiley.

Robbins, V., Johnston, J., Barnett, H., Hobstetter, W., Kutash, K., Duchnowski, A. J., & Annis, S. (2008). *Parent to parent: A synthesis of the emerging literature.* Tampa, FL: University of South Florida.

Saldana, L., Chamberlain, P., Wang, W., & Brown, C. H. (2012). Predicting program start-up using the stages of implementation measure. *Administration and Policy in Mental Health and Mental Health Services Research, 39*(6), 419–425.

Saloner, B., Bandara, S., Bachhuber, M., & Barry, C. L. (2017). Insurance coverage and treatment use under the Affordable Care Act among adults with mental and substance use disorders. *Psychiatric Services, 68*(6), 542–548.

Schoenwald, S. K., Chapman, J. E., Kelleher, K., Hoagwood, K. E., Landsverk, J., Stevens, J., . . . Hlth, R. N. Y. M. (2008). A survey of the infrastructure for children's mental health services: Implications for the implementation of empirically supported treatments (ESTs). *Administration and Policy in Mental Health and Mental Health Services Research, 35*(1–2), 84–97.

Silverman, W. K., & Hinshaw, S. P. (2008). The second special issue on evidence-based psychosocial treatments for children and adolescents: A 10-year update. *Journal of Clinical Child & Adolescent Psychology, 37*(1), 1–7.

Stein, B. D., Jaycox, L. H., Kataoka, S. H., Wong, M., Tu, W., Elliott, M. N., & Fink, A. (2003). A mental health intervention for schoolchildren exposed to violence: A randomized controlled trial. *JAMA, 290*(5), 603–611.

Stein, B. D., Kataoka, S. H., Jaycox, L. H., Wong, M., Fink, A., Escudero, P., & Zaragoza, C. (2002). Theoretical basis and program design of a school-based mental health intervention for traumatized immigrant children: a collaborative research partnership. *Journal of Behavioral Health Services and Research, 29*(3), 318–326.

Stoiber, K. C., & Kratochwill, T. R. (2000). Empirically supported interventions and school psychology: Rationale and methodological issues—Part I. *School Psychology Quarterly, 15*(1), 75–105.

Stroul, B. A., & Friedman, R. M. (1986). *A system of care for severely emotionally disturbed children & youth*. Washington, DC: CASSP Technical Assistance Center.

Sugai, G., & Horner, R. R. (2006). A promising approach for expanding and sustaining school-wide positive behavior support. *School Psychology Review, 35*(2), 245–259.

Thompson, R., Dancy, B. L., Wiley, T. A., Najdowski, C. J., Perry, S. P., Wallis, J., & Knafl, K. A. (2013). African American families' expectations and intentions for mental health services. *Administration and Policy in Mental Health and Mental Health Services Research, 40*(5), 371–383.

United States Department of Health, Education, and Welfare. Office for Civil Rights. (1978). *Section 504 of the Rehabilitation Act of 1973: Fact sheet: Handicapped persons rights under Federal law*. Washington, DC: Dept. of Health, Education, and Welfare, Office of the Secretary, Office for Civil Rights.

U.S. Department of Health and Human Services. (2003). *New Freedom Commission on Mental Health: Achieving the promise: Transforming mental health care in America. Final report*. (SMA-03-3832). Retrieved from Rockville, MD: U.S. Department of Health and Human Services.

Walker, D. K., & Crocker, R. W. (2008). Measuring family systems outcomes. *Evaluating Family Programs: Current Issues in Theory and Policy, 2008*, 153–176.

Wang, P. S., Lane, M., Olfson, M., Pincus, H. A., Wells, K. B., & Kessler, R. C. (2005). Twelve-month use of mental health services in the United States: results from the National Comorbidity Survey Replication. *Archives of General Psychiatry, 62*(6), 629–640.

Weist, M. D. (1997). Expanded school mental health services. In T. H. Ollendick & R. J. Prinz (Eds.), *Advances in clinical child psychology* (pp. 319–352). New York: Springer.

Weist, M. D., Flaherty, L., Lever, N., Stephan, S., Van Eck, K., & Albright, A. (2017). The history and future of school mental health. In B. S. J. Harrison & S. Evans (Eds.), *School mental health services for adolescents* (pp. 3–23). New York: Oxford University Press.

Weist, M. D., Goldstein, A., Morris, L., & Bryant, T. (2003). Integrating expanded school mental health programs and school-based health centers. *Psychology in the Schools, 40*(3), 297–308.

Weist, M. D., Paternite, C. E., Wheatley-Rowe, D., & Gall, G. (2009). From thought to action in school mental health promotion. *International Journal of Mental Health Promotion, 11*(3), 32–41.

Weisz, J. R., Weiss, B., Han, S. S., Granger, D. A., & Morton, T. (1995). Effects of psychotherapy with children and adolescents revisited: A meta-analysis of treatment outcome studies. *Psychological Bulletin, 117*(3), 450–468.

Wells, K. B., Staunton, A., Norris, K. C., Bluthenthal, R., Chung, B., Gelberg, L., . . . Wong, M. (2006). Building an academic-community partnered network for clinical services research: the Community Health Improvement Collaborative (CHIC). *Ethnicity and Disease, 16*(1 Suppl 1), S3–17.

Westin, A. M., Barksdale, C. L., & Stephan, S. H. (2014). The effect of waiting time on youth engagement to evidence based treatments. *Community Mental Health Journal, 50*(2), 221–228.

Wu, P., Hoven, C. W., Bird, H. R., Moore, R. E., Cohen, P., Alegria, M., . . . Narrow, W. E. (1999). Depressive and disruptive disorders and mental health service utilization in children and adolescents. *Journal of the American Academy of Child & Adolescent Psychiatry, 38*(9), 1081–1090.

CHAPTER FOUR

Multitiered Approaches to School-Based Mental Health, Wellness, and Trauma Response

Catherine P. Bradshaw, Sandra K. Williamson, Kimberly Kendziora, Wehmah Jones, and Susan Cole

More than one-fourth of the U.S. population is estimated to experience signs and symptoms of mental and/or behavioral disorders (Kessler, Chia, Demler, & Walters, 2005), with the majority of individuals experiencing the onset of those symptoms prior to age 24 (Kessler, Berglund, Demler, Jin, & Walters, 2005). Moreover, it is estimated that 11 million Americans (i.e., 4.8% of the U.S. population) have a serious mental illness. Given the significant impairment, disability, and disease burden associated with mental illness (Muñoz, Le, Clarke, & Jaycox, 2002), the prevention of mental health problems is a public health priority. Although up to 20% of children and youth experience a mental, emotional, or behavioral disorder (Centers for Disease Control and Prevention, 2015; Perou et al., 2013), nearly half of all children with emotional or behavioral difficulties receive no mental health services (Simon, Pastor, Reuben, Huang, & Goldstrom, 2015). Only 7.4% of young people report any mental health visits in the past year (Merikangas et al., 2010).

Further, considerable health disparities exist within the United States, where a variety of economic, social, and cultural barriers limit access to care. Given the high rate of mental health concerns among children and youth, it is helpful to understand the etiology of those concerns, as this may inform the approaches used to address these concerns in schools.

The current chapter provides an overview of multitiered approaches, which are increasingly used in schools and school-community collaborations to promote mental health, address trauma, and prevent and treat mental health problems, substance use and abuse, suicide, youth violence, and various forms of bullying. We also provide examples of complementary school-based models, such as Positive Behavioral Interventions and Supports, the Integrated Systems Framework, social and emotional learning, and trauma-sensitive approaches, which are aligned with a multitiered system of supports framework. We conclude by identifying recommendations for integrating programming and directions for future research related to the multitiered approach.

Prevalence and Impacts of Exposure to Adverse Childhood Experiences

The high prevalence of potentially traumatic experiences among American youth has become well known in recent years. The National Survey of Children's Exposure to Violence documented that 47.6% of children ages 6–9 years had experienced a physical assault in the past year, 13.8% had experienced maltreatment, 10.7% had witnessed community violence, and 5.8% had witnessed family violence (Finkelhor, Turner, Shattuck, & Hamby, 2015). A groundbreaking study, referred to as the Adverse Childhood Experiences (ACE) Study (Anda, Felitti, et al., 2006; Felitti, Anda, et al., 1998), shed considerable light on the issue of trauma from multiple perspectives. Specifically, the ACE study surveyed participants about their experiences in seven categories of childhood adversity: being subjected to physical, sexual, or psychological abuse; witnessing domestic violence; and living with a parent afflicted with a mental illness or involved in substance abuse or criminal behavior. The ACE study found that high numbers of adults reported abuse and/or challenging family experiences during childhood. For example, more than half the adults stated that they had had experiences in at least one of these categories as children.

There is also an increasing awareness of the various effects of trauma on mental health, behavior, relationships, and learning outcomes. Although not all adverse experiences result in trauma, such experiences greatly increase the risk for disorders such as depression, anxiety, and disruptive behavior (Copeland, Keeler, Angold, & Costello, 2007). The effects of trauma during childhood are vast and cover multiple aspects of the child's development. For example, many traumatized children develop behavioral coping mechanisms that can frustrate educators and evoke exasperated reprisals—reactions that both strengthen the child's expectations of confrontation and danger and reinforce a negative self-image. Many of the effects of traumatic experiences originate from the inability to self-regulate emotions, distorted perceptions of the behaviors and feelings of others, or the inability to process social cues and convey feelings in an appropriate manner (Shields & Cicchetti, 1998).

Children's behavioral and emotional responses to trauma can be confusing to the adults and peers who interact with youth exposed to traumatic events. For example, young children exposed to traumatic events may experience relationship problems because of insecure attachment with parents, which in turn can adversely affect their relationships with peers and other adults, in both the short and long term (Bowlby, 1988). In fact, early attachment experiences influence a host of social-cognitive factors and emotion regulation skills that lay the foundation for interpersonal relationships across the lifecourse (Bradshaw & Garbarino, 2004; Hazan & Campa, 2013). Trauma may also influence self-regulation of attention, emotions, and behavior, language, and communication skills. Trauma can affect executive functions related to planning, inhibition, or delay of gratification, all of which are critical for academic success and workforce readiness. Many of these effects could occur as the result of changes in brain chemistry and circuitry, including the hypothalamic-pituitary-adrenal [HPA] system and neurotransmitter functioning (for a review, see Gunnar & Donzella, 2002; Gunnar, Talge, & Herrera, 2009). Trauma has also been shown to thwart the establishment of a coherent sense of self, compromise the ability to attend to classroom tasks and instructions, interfere with the ability to organize and remember new information, and hinder the comprehension of cause-and-effect relationships—all of which are necessary to process information effectively (Cole, Eisner, Gregory, & Ristuccia, 2013). Not surprisingly, these behavioral, social, and mental health effects often translate into academic and behavioral challenges at school. As such, a public health approach to the prevention of trauma and behavioral and mental health problems more broadly is needed to address these concerns in schools and communities (Jennings, 2019).

A Public Health Approach to Addressing Behavioral and Mental Health Problems

Research from the field of public health has greatly informed our understanding of the variety of risk and protective factors associated with a range of behavioral and mental health concerns and the etiology of those disorders (Mendelson et al., 2012). The public health approach to prevention assumes that the etiology of most mental disorders is multifactorial, with interacting biological, environmental, psychological, and sociocultural components

(Lilienfeld & Lilienfeld, 1980), suggesting the need for multicomponent prevention approaches to target a range of risk and protective factors.

Over the past 20 years, many frameworks have been developed to characterize the public health approach to the continuum from health promotion to treatment (O'Connell, Boat, & Warner, 2009; Weisz, Sandler, Durlak, & Anton, 2005). These models are gaining increased recognition and traction for addressing mental health problems in diverse service settings, including education, juvenile justice, and child welfare, in addition to the more traditional areas of medicine and public health. For example, nearly 85% of children receiving community-based services reported having experienced symptoms of their aggressive behavior problems in the classroom (Zima et al., 2005), and teachers in 10 metropolitan-area schools in the northwestern United States reported that 44% of their elementary students had experienced one or more adverse childhood experience (Blodgett & Lanigan, 2018).

There is a need to bridge the various models identified across fields, both in terms of their focus and setting, as we move toward advancing a model of comprehensive and integrated multitiered system of supports. The movement toward interagency collaboration for prevention and promotion of behavioral and mental health problems in school in partnership with the community further signals the need for better integration of frameworks, common terminology, and implementation.

Multitiered System of Supports Framework

A model for organizing intervention efforts is a multitiered system of supports (MTSS) framework, which builds on existing prevention models and emphasizes integration across both Tiers of service and ecological levels. The MTSS framework accounts for the varying intensity of interventions (i.e., universal, selective, and indicated) through the full continuum from promotion of adaptive skills to maintenance of treatment effects. It also incorporates the multiple agencies and settings within which these interventions are implemented. Thus, MTSS addresses a broad set of risk and protective factors and adopts a positive, developmental framework, with the explicit aim to organize and coordinate among various interventions (see figure 4.1). This coordination means that MTSS also requires greater practitioner collaboration than traditional intervention models, which have historically targeted a single ecological context. The need for greater collaboration has led states and government agencies to adopt a formalized MTSS framework and develop guidelines for practice, particularly collaboration with families, schools, community organizations, and other local service providers (e.g., see Kansas State Department of Education, 2011; University of South Florida, 2011). In the following section of this chapter, we summarize specific information about the MTSS framework in relation to other approaches and

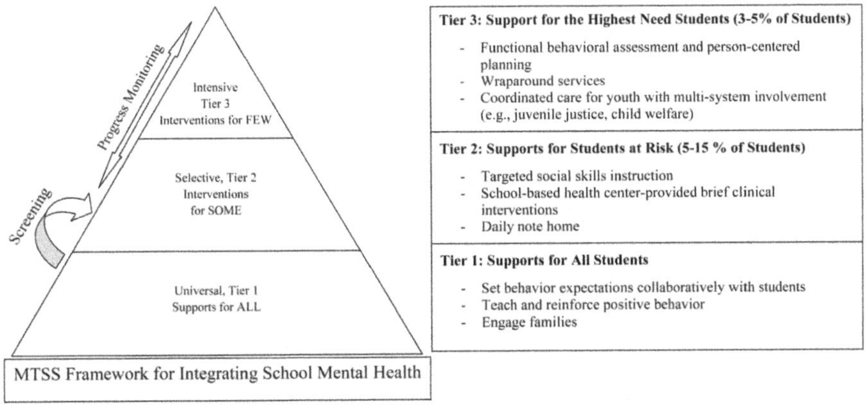

Figure 4.1 MTSS tiers and sample interventions. (Adapted from Bruns, E. J., Duong, M. T., Lyon, A. R., Pullmann, M. D., Cook, C. R., Cheney, D., & McCauley, E. (2016). Fostering SMART partnerships to develop an effective continuum of behavioral health services and supports in schools. *American Journal of Orthopsychiatry*, 86(2), 156–170, page 158.)

models for the delivery of programs and services to address mental health concerns, such as trauma exposure, in schools.

Trauma-Informed and Trauma-Sensitive Approaches in Schools

Schools can play a critical role in supporting students who have been exposed to psychological trauma, including physical or sexual abuse, community or domestic violence, natural disasters, accidents, and other potentially traumatic events (Chafouleas, Johnson, Overstreet, & Santos, 2016; Overstreet & Chafouleas, 2016). Schools can provide safe environments needed to buffer the adverse effects of trauma and can help students return to routines and rituals important to everyday life after trauma exposure (Dorado, Martinez, McArthur, & Leibovitz, 2016; Jennings, 2019; Powell & Bui, 2016).

Researchers explain that the best way to meet students' needs is to create an environment in which all children, including those who have experienced trauma, can be successful (Bloom, 1995; Harvey, 1996). Weaving trauma sensitivity throughout the school day requires that the values of a trauma-sensitive school are reflected in both the schoolwide environment and in services at Tiers 2 and 3. These services should be trauma-informed, integrated as much as possible into the whole school environment, and support academic goals.

Unfortunately, educators often struggle to implement holistic approaches to learning in a system that has been fragmented by individual responses to academics, anti-bullying, social skill development, positive discipline, truancy, dropout prevention, and more. However, schoolwide programs created in response to important but more narrowly defined needs do not always connect to or support one another, and are not often integrated into the culture of the school. Thus, many important initiatives that could make a school safe and supportive often remain stand-alone programs or compete with one another for resources (Grubb, 2012).

The Trauma and Learning Policy Initiative (TLPI) has launched a trauma-sensitive demonstration in five schools using a process of trauma-sensitive culture change (Cole et al., 2013). TLPI's approach is based in part on the observation that using a whole school and whole child trauma-sensitive lens to reflect on practices and programs in place in a school allows educators to find new ways to make the existing programs mutually reinforcing and better meet children's multifaceted, holistic needs. A recent descriptive study of the TLPI work found staff experienced a shift in mindset that led to shifts in practices (e.g., revising discipline and behavior management strategies using a trauma-sensitive lens) and resulted in positive changes to school climate and culture (e.g., improved student behavior, fewer crises, increased student engagement; Jones, Osher, & Berg, 2018). Staff at the University of California, San Francisco developed the Healthy Environments and Response to Trauma in Schools (HEARTS) program, which is a school-based prevention and intervention program for children who have experienced trauma. Dorado and colleagues (2016) produced preliminary support, showing that participation in HEARTS was associated with fewer trauma-related symptoms in children and positive changes in schools' climate and culture (e.g., a decrease in student behavior problems and increased student engagement).

The available research suggests that schools should consider a whole school approach to advancing a trauma-sensitive culture change, focusing on universal trauma sensitivity and integrating initiatives at Tiers 1, 2, and 3. Importantly, schoolwide trauma-sensitivity *requires its own time and space.* For example, educators need training and professional development regarding trauma, its effect on child development and learning, and how it affects their school community. As educators reflect and view their practices through a whole child, trauma-sensitive lens, they should receive support in creating a variety of approaches for addressing the needs in collaborative, schoolwide, integrated ways that infuse and inform the school's multiple initiatives and programs.

Social and Emotional Learning

Social and emotional learning (SEL) approaches provide a framework for developing social and emotional competencies in children using a variety of interventions (Weissberg, Durlak, Domitrovich, & Gullotta, 2015). SEL programming is based on the understanding that: (1) learning is maximized in the context of supportive relationships that make learning appropriately challenging, engaging, and meaningful; (2) social and emotional skills are critical to being a good student, citizen, and worker; and (3) many different risky behaviors (e.g., drug use, violence, bullying, and dropout) can be prevented or reduced when multiyear, integrated efforts are used to develop students' social and emotional skills. At Tier 1, or the universal level, this may be achieved through effective classroom instruction, student engagement in positive activities in and out of the classroom, and broad parent and community involvement in program planning, implementation, and evaluation (Hawkins & Catalano, 2004; Hawkins, Catalano, & Arthur, 2002).

SEL is strengths-focused and aims to actively build assets and positive, prosocial behaviors and attitudes. Many of the individual interventions that teach SEL skills have been rigorously evaluated and found to have positive impacts on student outcomes (Durlak, Weissberg, Dymnicki, Taylor, & Schellinger, 2011; Taylor, Oberle, Durlak, & Weissberg, 2017). Schools are a highly effective setting for teaching SEL skills, but similar activities can also be implemented in afterschool settings (Durlak, Weissberg, & Pachan, 2010). SEL programs are implemented schoolwide (i.e., preschool through high school) in a coordinated manner, and lessons are reinforced in the classroom, during out-of-school activities, and at home. Educators receive ongoing professional development in SEL, and families and schools work together to promote children's social, emotional, and academic success. Many programs related to SEL focus on a single problem or issue (e.g., substance use prevention); however, SEL is an inclusive approach that covers the entire spectrum of social and emotional competencies that help children develop into resilient and successful learners.

Positive Behavioral Interventions and Supports

Positive Behavioral Interventions and Supports (PBIS) is an MTSS approach that explicitly incorporates the three-tiered public health model and aims to prevent and reduce problem behaviors in classrooms and schools by rewarding positive behaviors (Sugai & Horner, 2006). PBIS focuses on developing explicit, simple behavioral expectations and procedures to encourage students to treat themselves and others with respect. Schools are provided with training and tools to collect data, which inform the assessment of needs and targets specific interventions at different Tiers. As with other MTSS applications, PBIS can provide a scaffold for supporting previously adopted interventions or curricula into the prevention framework. Schoolwide PBIS is a useful strategy for preventing school violence, alcohol and drug use, and bullying. The coordination of PBIS is led by a schoolwide team comprising administration, teaching staff, and support personnel and may also include parents and mental health providers from an outside agency. Given that PBIS is being implemented in nearly 26,000 schools across the country, there is additional infrastructure at the local and state education agencies to support the use of the PBIS framework (see Bradshaw & Pas, 2011; Bradshaw et al., 2012).

The universal (Tier 1) component of PBIS emphasizes schoolwide rules, routines, and physical arrangements, as developed and taught by school staff, to prevent initial occurrences of problem behavior. The selective (Tier 2) and indicated (Tier 3) components of PBIS are expected to be evidence-based programs that address individual student and school-based needs (e.g., a school-based team that reviews student referrals for both academic and behavioral issues; see next section). Therefore, SEL programs can be implemented through the PBIS framework in an integrated and coordinated fashion (Bradshaw, Bottiani, Osher, & Sugai, 2014). For example, schools may consider implementing a classroom-based SEL program (Tier 1), such as Promoting Alternative THinking Strategies or Second Step, to provide direct instruction and reinforcement for skill development. Many schools are also using an evidence-based SEL program called Check and Connect (Anderson, Christenson, Sinclair, & Lehr, 2004), which aims to enhance student engagement and attendance and reduce later dropout by providing at-risk students with an adult mentor. The mentors serve as liaisons for the school to the family by offering individualized interventions to students on their caseload and tracking student attendance, behavior, and grades.

Through PBIS, behavioral support teams composed of teachers, administrators, counselors, and parents work to create individualized plans for students, which often involve multiple service systems (Eber, Hyde, & Suter, 2011) using the school-based wraparound process. This process provides care for individual children and families and involves the implementation of community-level collaboration of services and supports, often referred to as a system of care. Intensive interventions may include the family and multi-component interventions, as well as home-based services, respite care, individual group or family therapy, therapeutic foster care, crisis intervention, intensive after-school programs and in-school aides, after-school behavioral support, flexible school days, flexible programming (such as a half-day in public school and a half-day in a day treatment program), or transportation aides. PBIS also has been used in alternative settings (e.g., juvenile justice, special education, residential education; Swain-Bradway, Swoszowski, Boden, & Sprague, 2013). Although the students in these settings are at high risk, the same core positive behavior principles (e.g., reinforcement of positive behavior, clear expectations) are relevant but may need adaptation to fit the needs of the school population (Simonsen & Sugai, 2013).

A series of studies has provided evidence for the effectiveness of PBIS framework as well as specific selective and indicated interventions (e.g., Check-In/Check-Out, a derivation of Check & Connect; Horner, Sugai, & Anderson, 2010; Swoszowski, McDaniel, Jolivette, & Melius, 2013). Two randomized trials testing the effectiveness of the universal elements of PBIS provide evidence of positive outcomes in elementary schools. Specifically, PBIS has been shown to be effective at reducing student office discipline referrals and suspensions, and improving school climate (Bradshaw, Koth, Bevans, Ialongo, & Leaf, 2008; Bradshaw, Koth, Thornton, & Leaf, 2009; Bradshaw, Mitchell, & Leaf, 2010; Bradshaw, Waasdorp, & Leaf, 2011; Horner et al., 2009). Teachers in PBIS schools also rate their students as needing fewer specialized support services, as having fewer behavioral problems (e.g., aggressive behavior, concentration problems, bullying, and rejection) and displaying more prosocial behavior (Bradshaw, Waasdorp, & Leaf, 2012; Waasdorp, Bradshaw, & Leaf, 2012). A separate randomized trial testing the impact of the addition of selective preventive interventions and supports has also demonstrated significant impacts (Bradshaw, Pas, Goldweber, Rosenberg, & Leaf, 2012). Research at the secondary level is also demonstrating positive effects (see Bradshaw, Debnam, et al., 2014).

Interconnected Systems Framework

Most schools do not have the resources in-house to address the needs of students who need relatively more intensive interventions. For such students, school collaborations with community agencies are often necessary. The Interconnected Systems Framework (ISF) was developed to facilitate the links between education and other systems, particularly mental health (Barrett, Eber, & Weist, 2012). The ISF works across all Tiers of support in a school, employs cross-system problem-solving teams, uses data to decide which evidence-based practices to implement, uses progress monitoring for both fidelity and impact, and actively engages youth, families, and other school and community stakeholders.

Table 4.1 shows how the ISF reframes traditional practices so that mental health and other professional services can be coordinated with and integrated into a school system at all levels of intervention. The ISF centralizes and streamlines management, infuses services throughout the school all levels of need, and combines school and community-based staff to provide services and supports collaboratively. The ISF employs blended teams to organize supports around the specific needs of a student and family—not around the service units of different disciplines (Sander, Lane, Vinciquerra, Davis, Perales, & Horner, 2012).

Table 4.1 Interconnected Systems Framework

Traditional Practice	Interconnected Systems Framework Practice
Each school works out their own plan with a mental health or other service agency	The district has a plan for integrating mental health and other services at all buildings based on both school and community data
A counselor is housed in a school building one day a week to provide services to students	A mental health professional participates in teams at all three Tiers
No data are used or available to select or monitor interventions	A professional service provider leads group or individual interventions based on data
School personnel are alone in attempting to "do mental health"	A blended team of school and community providers "divide and conquer" based on strengths of the team

Source: Adapted from Eber, 2014.

Putting It All Together: Integration

As evidence for effective prevention approaches has grown, many schools and communities have implemented individual programs and supports. And as the numbers of programs and supports implemented have grown, schools and communities have faced challenges in implementing them simultaneously. To better manage implementation, schools and communities can integrate their approaches within an MTSS framework because each program and support addresses different issues and Tiers (see table 4.2).

Integrating programs can be challenging, however. It requires schools and child-serving systems to work collaboratively together to change the way they have historically functioned. There are costs involved, as well as a long-term commitment to training, professional development, and data collection. It also requires leadership and a common vision by all stakeholders. To minimize challenges, the natural location to integrate programming is at school. The primary objective of schooling is to improve academic achievement in a safe, supportive learning environment. Such an environment provides the necessary supports for the emotional and behavioral needs of students, so learning can occur. In addition, schools tend to be the primary providers of mental health services for children, often partnering with community-based

Table 4.2 Examples of evidence-based programs that can be integrated in an MTSS framework

Tier 1	**Promoting Alternative THinking Strategies (PATHS)** is a universal, school-based, SEL curriculum that has demonstrated positive effects on elementary school-age children (Greenberg, Kusché, & Mihalic, 1998). Focusing on self-control and emotion-regulation skills, the program has been found to reduce both internalizing and externalizing behavior one year post-intervention (Kam, Greenberg, & Kusché, 2004). A large, multi-site trial of children from high-risk neighborhoods resulted in improved prosocial behavior as well as reduced aggressive disruptive behavior (Conduct Problems Prevention Research Group, 2010).
Tier 1	The **LifeSkills training program** (Botvin, Griffin, & Nichols, 2006) is an interactive, skills-based universal prevention program designed to lower substance use and promote adaptive skills. Trials of LifeSkills demonstrated reductions in substance use and violence among middle school students (Botvin et al., 2006). A recently developed high school version of the program uses developmentally appropriate, collaborative learning strategies to help students achieve competency and has demonstrated promising outcomes on reductions in substance use among high school students.
Tier 1	The **Good Behavior Game (GBG)** is an approach to the management of classroom behavior that rewards children for staying on task during instruction. The class is divided into two teams and a point is given to a team for any inappropriate behavior displayed by any of its members. The team with the fewest points at the game's conclusion wins a group reward. If both teams keep their points below a preset threshold, then both teams participate in the reward. The program was first tested in 1969 (Barrish, Saunders, & Wolf); perhaps better-known are the randomized trials with long-term follow-up conducted in Baltimore beginning in 1985. Kellam et al. (2011) reported that follow-up at age 19–21 found significantly lower rates of drug and alcohol use disorders, smoking, antisocial personality disorder, delinquency, incarceration for violent crimes, suicidal ideation, and use of school-based services among students (particularly aggressive male students) who had played the GBG. Other studies have focused more on academics in conjunction with the GBG and, in turn, yielded significant impacts on academic performance, high school completion, college attendance, and reduced reliance on special education

(continued)

Table 4.2 (continued)

	services (Bradshaw, Zmuda, Kellam, & Ialongo, 2009). Alternate versions of GBG that emphasize student choice and intrinsic rewards (PAX GBG) have been developed and tested as well, with positive effects on students and teachers (e.g., Smith, Osgood, Oh, & Caldwell, 2018).
Tier 2	**Check-In/Check-Out (CICO)** was developed to reduce problem behavior and increase academic engagement (Hawken & Horner, 2003). CICO involves students meeting with a mentor in the morning to discuss behavioral expectations, receive behavioral feedback throughout the day using a daily progress report form, and check-out with a mentor to review performance at the end of the day. CICO combines multiple intervention components that improve student behavior, including the use of increased monitoring and feedback to students about their performance, the use of positive reinforcement, and a home-school component (Dart et al., 2015). CICO has been widely adopted as a Tier 2 intervention within MTSS approaches.
Tier 2	**Check & Connect** (Christenson & Carroll, 1999) uses a systematic monitoring and school engagement procedure to address the needs of individual students and builds capacity within families to assist their children's education performance. Check & Connect is composed of two components: the Check component is designed systematically to monitor youth's behavior for signs of school withdrawal, and the Connect component is designed to respond accordingly and in a timely and efficient fashion to students' needs. A randomized comparative effectiveness trial of Check & Connect (Maynard, Kjellstrand, & Thompson, 2014) found, controlling for pretest performance and all relevant student- and school-level characteristics, that Check & Connect was significantly related to improvements in academic performance and reductions in disciplinary referrals, but not attendance.
Tier 3	The **Coping Power Program** (Lochman & Wells, 2004), a school-based, indicated preventive intervention, has produced significant effects among preadolescent students with aggressive and disruptive behavior problems. This multicomponent program applies a contextual, social-cognitive framework addressing both parenting processes and children's sequential cognitive processing. Delivered to parents and students over the course of an academic year, the intervention addresses the social-cognitive factors and mechanisms involved in aggressive and disruptive behaviors. RCTs of the program have

Table 4.2 (continued)

	demonstrated reductions in substance use and aggression, improved social competence, and significant teacher-rated behavioral improvement (Lochman & Wells, 2004). Although much of the original research on Coping Power focused on upper elementary school students, recent studies have tested adapted versions for middle and high schoolers; these studies are demonstrating similar effects on a range of behavioral, academic, and mental health outcomes (Bradshaw, Lochman, Powell, & Ialongo, 2017).
Tier 3	The **wraparound** process is a frequently implemented comprehensive approach for planning and providing individualized, community-based care for children and adolescents with serious mental health conditions (Walker, Bruns, & Penn, 2008). Bruns, Sather, Pullmann, and Stambaugh (2011) estimated that there were at least 98,000 youth enrolled in more than 800 wraparound initiatives in the United States. Wraparound is a strengths-based approach in which both child or youth and family perspectives are prioritized in determining the primary needs to be addressed, as well as the service and support strategies to be included in the wraparound plan of care (Walker et al., 2008). When services are complete and implemented with fidelity outcomes can be positive (see Suter & Bruns, 2009, for a meta-analysis), but challenges to effective wraparound implementation include family attrition (Yohannan, Carlson, Shepherd, & Batsche-McKenzie, 2017).
Tiers 1, 2, and 3	The **Adolescent Transitions Program** aims to reduce and prevent adolescent substance use and antisocial behavior by incorporating universal, selective, and indicated components. The data-driven process helps guide the provision of different programs and supports based on the families' unique pattern of need. Various versions of the program have shown to reduce aggressive behaviors, school problems, and substance use for adolescents (Dishion & Kavanagh, 2003; Dishion & Stormshak, 2007).

organizations to address student needs (Brenner, Martindale, & Weist, 2000; Burns et al., 1995; Rones & Hoagwood, 2000).

Some schools and communities have successfully integrated various prevention programs and supports across systems. This section of the chapter will describe common elements those schools and communities have used to integrate their promotion/prevention/treatment interventions and supports, including the following (Bazelon Center for Mental Health, 2006; Kutash, Duchnowski, & Lynn, 2006):

- Resource mapping
- Systematically collecting and reviewing school climate and incident data
- Using a selection process to identify evidence-based interventions,
- Training and ensuring that programs and supports are implemented with fidelity
- Facilitating student intervention and support teams
- Participating in community-based interagency partnerships

Resource Mapping

Systems begin by first developing an inventory of existing programs and resources (resource mapping), compiling existing information on the evidence of program effectiveness, identifying gaps or duplication in programs, reviewing school- or system-level survey data and or incident data, and then identifying areas that need to be addressed so resources can be used more efficiently. Using the three-Tiered intervention framework, teams consider what universal preventive interventions they have in place for all students; what selective preventive interventions they have in place for some students; and then what indicated preventive interventions they have in place for a few students. An important aspect of this process is identifying what data are being collected, how they are being collected, and how teams or individuals are using those data to make decisions. This will lead to more efficient use of time and streamline the data collection process. The resource-mapping process examines available services and supports not only in schools but also those provided by other systems and organizations in a community. This can reveal untapped resources or potential new service providers. It will be essential to include key system partners and agency representatives in this process. This process can begin more broadly, focusing on the larger community, or it can begin at the school level.

Schoolwide Teams

These teams establish a systematic process for reviewing individual, classroom, and schoolwide incident data (office referrals, suspensions, absenteeism, and violence incidents), as well as school climate data that may be available from student, staff, or family surveys. This process supports the selection of evidence-based programs as well as a mechanism for periodic reviews of program effectiveness.

Various models frame positive school climate and culture, but the most recent work from the U.S. Department of Education approaches school climate from three major areas that are directly relevant to an MTSS approach related to culture and climate (see Bradshaw, Waasdorp, Debnam & Lindstrom Johnson, 2014):

- Engagement: adult-to-adult, adult-to-student, and student-to-student relationships and feelings of connectedness
- Safety: emotional and physical safety
- Environment: physical, academic, and disciplinary environment, and overall wellness

Schools may have a school-based climate team, a PBIS team, or an MTSS team that has responsibilities to meet its schoolwide goals related to developing a proactive system of identifying needs and providing supports. Schools also may have a response to intervention team looking at individual data and program development. Although both of these functions are needed in schools, it is important for schools to clearly define these roles and intended outcomes.

Schoolwide teams may also focus on developing a continuum of services (based on their resource-mapping process) and gradually shifting their focus to continuous quality improvement over time. This continuous quality improvement role should include reviewing schoolwide data and student group data (i.e., race/ethnicity, grade level, and English language learners), making recommendations to address need areas, enhancing outcomes, and reviewing impact of previous programmatic changes on services. The goal is to build the capacity of a school-based team to routinely review the school data and make recommendations to school leadership, who follow through with implementation throughout the school year. This supports the schoolwide overall climate and culture. As schools develop more services and supports at each Tier, "less restrictive" program options (those that require less time out of the classroom or general education placement) will be more likely to address students' needs, therefore, maximizing instructional time.

Individual Student Teams

Most schools already have groups of staff who meet on a regular basis (weekly or biweekly) to review the needs of individual students and make recommendations to address those needs. Continued professional development of teams that review individual data is essential in order to increase their ability to review behavioral and academic data, make recommendations for interventions, monitor intervention implementation, and then modify services and approaches as needed. For example, a school might include a community-based clinician as a member of the student intervention team on a rotating basis. He or she could be scheduled to participate on the team for approximately one hour (per week, biweekly, monthly, depending on resources available for support), and the team would review and discuss any students who are experiencing social, emotional, or behavioral issues during that time. This also serves as an ongoing, capacity-building approach for school team members. Teams learn what questions to ask and they learn more about resources and supports in the community. If a school does not have an existing relationship with a community-based clinician or agency, those relationships can be developed, often with little or no additional costs to the school or district. Part of the resource-mapping process can help partnerships and collaborations identify community-based clinicians as resources within those partner organizations.

A school team member is designated as a lead to contact the partner agency and discuss the potential role for a clinician. Schools would be looking for a clinician who has experience working with schools and with children and youth within the targeted age-range—someone who could serve in a consultant capacity as part of school-based teams on a routine basis to provide guidance, suggest resources, strategies, or programs within and outside of the school, and make linkages back to the partner agency regarding the types of needs that are being seen in the community. Often, clinicians also serve a valuable professional development role by providing helpful strategies and information directly to teachers, staff, and families during individual student meetings. These clinicians would be employees of a community-based agency. Their time is either covered by the agency, by a negotiated fee structure between the school district and the agency, or through Medicaid dollars (in some states). Districts and agencies usually develop a memorandum of agreement/understanding (MOA/MOU) addressing the role of clinicians, as well as the legal issues involved in sharing student information.

Community Agency Partners

MTSS accounts for the varying intensity of interventions (i.e., universal, selective, and indicated) from promotion to maintenance and incorporates the multiple agencies and settings within which these interventions are implemented. As schools build multitiered supports and interventions, they will need community agency partners. These connections to external agencies can increase the school's capacity to meet the nonacademic needs of students and their families.

It is best to involve multiple stakeholders early in the process. This promotes buy-in among community agencies and allows agencies to determine how they can best streamline services to effectively meet the needs of students. This opportunity also may allow stakeholders (districts, schools, and agencies) to begin thinking about potential barriers to reaching students and identifying ways to address these barriers. There are examples of national initiatives that have focused on partnerships among schools, mental health agencies, and other social service agencies and community providers, such as Safe Schools Healthy Students, Systems of Care, and school-based behavioral health models. These initiatives apply proven, successful strategies to develop those partnerships and increase capacity and resources available in schools for students with social, emotional, and behavioral needs. The school and a community coalition can address issues related to wait lists for services and expand capacity to meet student needs.

Conclusions and Future Directions

MTSS is an extension of the public health framework, which is particularly instructive for examining a variety of behavioral, academic, and mental health concerns, including bullying, substance use, and school violence. Recent efforts to integrate evidence-based models under the MTSS framework hold great promise for informing the next stage of prevention research and programming in communities across the United States and abroad. As summarized in this chapter, the MTSS framework can be implemented across the life course and at various levels of the social ecology, ranging from individual and family to school, workplace, and public health policy. Although there is considerable interest in the application of MTSS, there is also a great need for additional research specifically testing this integrated approach to prevention.

By coordinating the delivery of multiple evidence-based programs into a coherent, integrated system of support, the MTSS model can be intensive and thus potentially challenging to implement with high fidelity (Domitrovich et al., 2010). It is possible that the integration process may actually compromise implementation fidelity of the individual evidence-based programs. Thus, it is critical to develop and test a systematic integration process (Bradshaw et al., 2014). There is also a need for additional research examining the feasibility and acceptability of these multicomponent programs (Domitrovich et al., 2010). Further, separate efforts have produced positive outcomes. The next challenge is to see if coordinating those efforts adds value. The field of implementation science has much to contribute to our understanding of the feasibility and implementation of MTSS. There is great opportunity for further work on these models in both school and community settings. There is also growing interest in these two critical Systems of Care and their ecological impact on youth and families.

References

Alexander, J. (1982). *Functional family therapy.* Monterey, CA: Brooks/Cole.

Anda, R. F., Felitti, V. J., Bremner, J. D., Walker, J. D., Whitfield, C., Perry, B. D., . . . Giles, W. H. (2006). The enduring effects of abuse and related adverse experiences in childhood: A convergence of evidence from neurobiology and epidemiology. *European Archives of Psychiatry and Clinical Neuroscience, 256*(3), 174–186. doi:10.1007/s00406-005-0624-4

Anderson, A. R., Christenson, S. L., Sinclair, M. F., & Lehr, C. A. (2004). Check & Connect: The importance of relationships for promoting engagement with school. *Journal of School Psychology, 42*, 95–113.

Barrett, S., Eber, L., & Weist, M. D. (Eds.). (2012). *Advancing education effectiveness: Interconnecting school mental health and school-wide positive behavior support.* Eugene, OR, and Baltimore: Office of Special Education Programs Center on Positive Behavioral Interventions and Supports and the University of Maryland Center for School Mental Health. Retrieved from http://www.pbis.org/common/cms/files/Current%20Topics/Final-Monograph.pdf

Barrish, H. H., Saunders, M., & Wolf, M. M. (1969). Good Behavior Game: Effects of individual contingencies for group consequences on disruptive behavior in a classroom. *Journal of Applied Behavior Analysis, 2*, 119–124.

Bazelon Center for Mental Health Law. (2006). *Way to go: School success for children with mental health care needs.* Washington, DC: Author.

Blodgett, C., & Lanigan, J. D. (2018). The association between adverse childhood experience (ACE) and school success in elementary school children. *School Psychology Quarterly, 33*(1), 137–146. doi:10.1037/spq0000256

Bloom, S. L. (1995). Creating sanctuary in the school. *Journal for a Just and Caring Education, 1*(4), 403–433. Retrieved from http://www.sanctuaryweb.com

Botvin, G. J., Griffin, K. W., & Nichols, T. R. (2006). Preventing youth violence and delinquency through a universal school-based prevention approach. *Prevention Science, 7*, 403–408.

Bowlby, J. (1988). *A secure base.* London: Routledge.

Bradshaw, C. P., Bottiani, J., Osher, D., & Sugai, G. (2014). Integrating Positive Behavioral Interventions and Supports (PBIS) and social emotional learning. In M. D. Weist, N. A. Lever, C. P. Bradshaw, & J. Owens, J. (Eds.), *Handbook of school mental health: Advancing practice and research* (2nd ed., pp. 101–118). New York: Springer.

Bradshaw, C. P., Debnam, K. J., Lindstrom Johnson, S., Pas, E., Hershfeldt, P., Alexander, A., . . . Leaf, P. J. (2014). Maryland's evolving system of social, emotional, and behavioral interventions in public schools: The Maryland Safe and Supportive Schools Project. *Adolescent Psychiatry, 4*(3), 194–206. doi:10.2174/221067660403140912163120

Bradshaw, C. P., & Garbarino, J. (2004). Social cognition as a mediator of the influence of family and community violence: Implications for intervention. In

J. Devine, J. Gilligan, K. Miczek, R. Shaikh, & D. Pfaff (Guest Eds.), Scientific approaches to youth violence prevention. *Annals of the New York Academy of Sciences, 1036,* 85–105. doi:10.1196/annals.1330.005

Bradshaw, C. P., Koth, C. W., Bevans, K. B., Ialongo, N., & Leaf, P. J. (2008). The impact of school-wide Positive Behavioral Interventions and Supports (PBIS) on the organizational health of elementary schools. *School Psychology Quarterly, 23*(4), 462–473.

Bradshaw, C. P., Koth, C. W., Thornton, L. A., & Leaf, P. J. (2009). Altering school climate through school-wide Positive Behavioral Interventions and Supports: Findings from a group-randomized effectiveness trial. *Prevention Science, 10*(2), 100–115.

Bradshaw, C. P., Lochman, J., Powell, N., & Ialongo, N. (2017). Preventing bullying in middle schoolers by using the coping power program: A targeted group intervention. In C. P. Bradshaw (Ed.), *Handbook on bullying prevention: A lifecourse perspective* (pp. 215–220). New York: National Association of Social Workers Press.

Bradshaw, C. P., Mitchell, M. M., & Leaf, P. J. (2010). Examining the effects of school-wide Positive Behavioral Interventions and Supports on student outcomes: Results from a randomized controlled effectiveness trial in elementary schools. *Journal of Positive Behavior Interventions, 12,* 133–148.

Bradshaw, C. P., & Pas, E. T. (2011). A state-wide scale-up of Positive Behavioral Interventions and Supports (PBIS): A description of the development of systems of support and analysis of adoption and implementation. *School Psychology Review, 40,* 530–548.

Bradshaw, C. P., Pas, E. T., Bloom, J., Barrett, S., Hershfeldt, P., Alexander, A., . . . Leaf, P. (2012). A state-wide collaboration to promote safe and supportive schools: The PBIS Maryland Initiative. *Administration and Policy in Mental Health and Mental Health Services Research, 39*(4), 225–237. doi:10.1007/s10488-011-0384-6

Bradshaw, C. P., Pas, E. T., Goldweber, A., Rosenberg, M., & Leaf, P. (2012). Integrating school-wide Positive Behavioral Interventions and Supports with tier 2 coaching to student support teams: The PBISplus Model. *Advances in School Mental Health Promotion, 5*(3), 177–193.

Bradshaw, C. P., Waasdorp, T. E., Debnam, K. J., & Lindstrom Johnson, S. (2014). Measuring school climate in high schools: A focus on safety, engagement, and the environment. *Journal of School Health, 84*(9), 593–604. https://doi.org/10.1111/josh.12186

Bradshaw, C. P., Waasdorp, T. E., & Leaf, P. J. (2012). Effects of school-wide Positive Behavioral Interventions and Supports on child behavior problems. *Pediatrics, 130*(5), 1136–1145.

Bradshaw, C. P., Zmuda, J. H., Kellam, S. G., & Ialongo, N. S. (2009). Longitudinal impact of two universal preventive interventions in first grade on educational outcomes in high school. *Journal of Educational Psychology, 101*(4), 926–937. doi:10.1037/a0016586

Brenner, N. D., Martindale, J., & Weist, M. D. (2000). Mental health and social services: Results from the School Health Policies and Programs Study 2000. *Journal of School Health, 7*(7), 305–312.

Bruns, E. J., Duong, M. T., Lyon, A. R., Pullmann, M. D., Cook, C. R., Cheney, D., & McCauley, E. (2016). Fostering SMART partnerships to develop an effective continuum of behavioral health services and supports in schools. *American Journal of Orthopsychiatry, 86*(2), 156–170. doi:10.1037/ort0000083

Bruns, E. J., Sather, A., Pullmann, M. D., & Stambaugh, L. F. (2011). National trends in implementing wraparound: Results from the state wraparound survey. *Journal of Child and Family Studies, 20*, 726–735. doi:10.1007/s10826-011-9535-3

Bruns, E. J., Walker, J. S., & The National Wraparound Initiative Advisory Group. (2008). Ten principles of the wraparound process. In E. J. Bruns & J. S. Walker (Eds.), *The resource guide to wraparound*. Portland, OR: National Wraparound Initiative, Research and Training Center for Family Support and Children's Mental Health. Retrieved from https://nwi.pdx.edu/NWI-book/Chapters/Bruns-2.1-(10-principles-of-wrap).pdf

Burns, B. J., Costello, E. J., Angold, A., Tweed, D., Stangl, D., Farmer, E. M., & Erkanli, A. (1995). Children's mental health service use across service sectors. *Health Affairs, 14*(3), 149–159.

Chafouleas, S. M., Johnson, A. H., Overstreet, S., & Santos, N. M. (2016). Toward a blueprint for trauma-informed service delivery in schools. *School Mental Health, 8*, 144–162. doi:10.1007/s12310-015-9166-8.

Christenson, S. L., & Carroll, E. B. (1999). Strengthening the family–school partnership through "Check and Connect." In E. Frydenberg (Ed.), *Learning to cope: Developing as a person in complex societies* (pp. 248–273). New York: Oxford University Press. doi:10.1093/med:psych/9780198503187.003.0012

Cole, S. F., Eisner, A., Gregory, M., & Ristuccia, J. (2013). *Helping traumatized children learn II: Creating and advocating for trauma-sensitive schools*. Boston: Massachusetts Advocates for Children, Trauma, and Learning Policy Initiative.

Collaborative for Academic, Social, and Emotional Learning. (2008). *Social and emotional learning and student benefits: Implications for the Safe School/Healthy Students core elements*. Newton, MA: National Center for Mental Health Promotion and Youth Violence Prevention, Education Development Center.

Conduct Problems Prevention Research Group. (2010). The effects of a multi-year universal social-emotional learning program: The role of student and school characteristics. *Journal of Consulting and Clinical Psychology, 78*, 156–168.

Copeland, W. E., Keeler, G., Angold, A., & Costello, E. J. (2007). Traumatic events and posttraumatic stress in childhood. *Archives of General Psychiatry, 64*(5), 577–584.

Dart, E. H., Furlow, C. M., Collins, T. A., Brewer, E., Gresham, F. M., & Chenier, K. H. (2015). Peer-mediated check-in/check-out for students at-risk for internalizing disorders. *School Psychology Quarterly, 30*(2), 229–243. doi:10.1037/spq0000092

Dishion, T. J., & Kavanagh, K. (2003). *Intervening in adolescent problem behavior: A family-centered approach.* New York: Guilford Press.

Dishion, T. J., & Stormshak, E. (2007). *Intervening in children's lives: An ecological, family-centered approach to mental health care.* Washington, DC: APA Books.

Domitrovich, C. E., Bradshaw, C. P., Greenberg, M. T., Embry, D., Poduska, J., & Ialongo, N. S. (2010). Integrated models of school-based prevention: Theory and logic. *Psychology in the Schools, 47*(1), 71–88.

Dorado, J., Martinez, M., McArthur, L., & Leibovitz, T. (2016). Healthy environments and response to trauma in schools (HEARTS): A whole-school, multi-level, prevention and intervention program for creating trauma-informed, safe and supportive schools. *School Mental Health, 8*, 163–176.

Durlak, J. A., Weissberg, R. P., Dymnicki, A. B., Taylor, R. D., & Schellinger, K. B. (2011). The impact of enhancing students' social and emotional learning: A meta-analysis of school-based universal interventions. *Child Development, 82*, 405–432.

Durlak, J. A., Weissberg, R. P., & Pachan, M. (2010). A meta-analysis of after-school programs that seek to promote personal and social skills in children and adolescents. *American Journal of Community Psychology, 45*(3–4), 294–309.

Eber, L. (2014, November). *Integrating mental health and other community partners into the PBIS framework.* Paper presented at the 10th Annual New England Positive Behavior Support Forum: PBIS: Research to Practice. Norwood, MA. Retrieved from https://www.mayinstitute.org/presentation/A%20PBIS%202014%20-%20Eber%20Mulit-Tiered%20Behaviroal%20Systems.pdf

Eber, L., Hyde, K., & Suter, J. C. (2011). Integrating wraparound into a school-wide system of positive behavioral supports. *Journal of Child and Family Studies, 20*, 782–790.

Felitti, V. J., Anda, R. F., Nordenberg, D., Williamson, D. F., Spitz, A. M., Edwards, V., . . . Marks, J. S. (1998). Relationship of childhood abuse and household dysfunction to many of the leading causes of death in adults: The Adverse Childhood Experiences (ACE) Study. *American Journal of Preventive Medicine, 14*(4), 245–258. doi:10.1016/S0749-3797(98)00017-8

Finkelhor, D., Turner, H. A., Shattuck, A., & Hamby, S. L. (2015). Prevalence of childhood exposure to violence, crime, and abuse: Results from the National Survey of Children's Exposure to Violence. *JAMA Pediatrics, 169*(8), 746–754. doi: 10.1001/jamapediatrics.2015.0676.

Gordon, R. S. (1983). An operational classification of disease prevention. *Public Health Reports, 98*, 107–109.

Greenberg, M. T., Kusché, C., & Mihalic, S. F. (1998). *Blueprints for violence prevention, book ten: Promoting Alternative THinking Strategies (PATHS)*. Boulder, CO: Center for the Study and Prevention of Violence.

Grubb, W. N. (2012). Narrowing the multiple achievement gaps in the United States: Eight goals for the long haul. In T. B. Timar & J. Maxwell-Jolly (Eds.), *Narrowing the achievement gap: Perspectives and strategies for challenging times* (pp. 57–76). Cambridge, MA: Harvard Education Press.

Gunnar, M. R., & Donzella, B. (2002). Social regulation of the cortisol levels in early human development. *Psychoneuroendocrinology, 27*(1–2), 199–220.

Gunnar, M. R., Talge, N. M., & Herrera, A. (2009). Stressor paradigms in developmental studies: What does and does not work to produce mean increases in salivary cortisol. *Psychoneuroendocrinology, 34*(7), 953–967.

Harvey, M. R. (1996). An ecological view of psychological trauma and trauma recovery. *Journal of Traumatic Stress, 9*(1), 3–23.

Hawken, L. S., & Horner, R. H. (2003). Evaluation of a targeted intervention within a schoolwide system of behavior support. *Journal of Behavioral Education, 12*(3), 225–240. doi:10.1023/A:1025512411930

Hawkins, J. D., & Catalano, R. F. (2004). *Communities that care: Prevention strategies guide*. South Deerfield, MA: Channing Bete.

Hawkins, J. D., Catalano, R. F., & Arthur, M. W. (2002). Promoting science-based prevention in communities. *Addictive Behaviors, 27*, 951–976.

Hazan, C., & Campa, M. (2013). *Human bonding: The science of affectional ties*. New York, Guilford.

Horner, R. H., Sugai, G., & Anderson, C. M. (2010). Examining the evidence base for schoolwide positive behavior support. *Focus on Exceptional Children, 42*(8), 1–14.

Horner, R. H., Sugai, G., Smolkowski, K., Eber, L., Nakasato, J., Todd, A. W., & Esperanza, J. (2009). A randomized, wait-list controlled effectiveness trial assessing school-wide Positive Behavior Support in elementary schools. *Journal of Positive Behavior Interventions, 11*, 133–144.

Jennings, P. (2019). *The trauma-sensitive classroom: building resilience with compassionate teaching*. New York: Norton.

Jones, W., Osher, D., & Berg, J. (2018). *TLPI trauma sensitive schools descriptive study: Final report*. Washington, DC: American Institutes for Research.

Kam, C., Greenberg, M. T., & Kusché, C. A. (2004). Sustained effects of the paths curriculum on the social and psychological adjustment of children in special education. *Journal of Emotional and Behavioral Disorders, 12*, 66–78.

Kansas State Department of Education. (2011). *Kansas multi-tier system of supports (MTSS): Academic structuring guide*. Topeka, KS: Project SPOT–Supporting Program Outcomes and Teachers.

Kellam, S. G., MacKenzie, A. C. L., Brown, C. H., Poduska, J. M., Wang, W., Petras, H., & Wilcox, H. C. (2011). The Good Behavior Game and the future of prevention and treatment. *Addiction Science and Clinical Practice, 6*(1), 73–84.

Kessler, R., Berglund, P., Demler, O., Jin, R., & Walters, E. E. (2005). Lifetime prevalence and age-of-onset distributions of DSM-IV disorders in the National Comorbidity Survey Replication. *Archives of General Psychiatry, 62*, 593–602.

Kessler, R., Chia, W. T., Demler, O., & Walters, E. E. (2005). Prevalence, severity, and comorbidity of 12-month DSM-IV disorders in the National Comorbidity Survey Replication. *Archives of General Psychiatry, 62*, 617–627.

Kutash, K., Duchnowski, A. J., & Lynn, N. (2006). *School-based mental health: An empirical guide for decision-makers.* Tampa, FL: University of South Florida, The Louis de la Parte Florida Mental Health Institute, Department of Child & Family Studies., Research and Training Center for Children's Mental Health.

Lilienfeld, A. M., & Lilienfeld, D. E. (1980). *Foundations of epidemiology* (2nd ed.). New York: Oxford University Press.

Lochman, J. E., & Wells, K. C. (2004). The Coping Power program for preadolescent aggressive boys and their parents: Outcome effects at the one-year follow-up. *Journal of Consulting and Clinical Psychology, 72*, 571–578.

Mendelson, T., Pas, E. T., Bradshaw, C. P., Leis, J., Leaf, P. J., & Rebok, G. (2012). The logic and practice of prevention. In W. Eaton (Ed.), *Public mental health* (pp. 459–509). New York: Oxford.

Merikangas, K. R., He, J. P., Burstein, M., Swanson, S. A., Avenevoli, S., Cui, L., . . . Swendsen J. (2010). Lifetime prevalence of mental disorders in U.S. adolescents: Results from the National Comorbidity Survey Replication—Adolescent Supplement (NCS-A). *Journal of the American Academy of Child and Adolescent Psychiatry, 49*, 980–989. doi:10.1016/j.jaac.2010.05.017

Muñoz, R. F., Le, H., Clarke, G., & Jaycox, L. (2002). Preventing the onset of major depression. In I. H. Gotlib & C. L. Hammen (Eds.), *Handbook of depression* (pp. 343–359). New York: Guilford.

O'Connell, M. E., Boat, T., & Warner, K. E. (2009). *Preventing mental, emotional, and behavioral disorders among young people: Progress and possibilities.* Washington, DC: National Academies Press.

Perou, R., Bitsko, R. H., Blumberg, S. J., Pastor, P., Ghandour, R. M., & Huang, L. N. (2013). Mental health surveillance among children—United States, 2005–2011. *Morbidity and Mortality Weekly Report, 62*, 1–35. Retrieved from http://www.cdc.gov/mmwr/preview/mmwrhtml/su6202a1.htm?s_cid=su6202a1_w

Powell, T. M., & Bui, T. (2016). Supporting social and emotional skills after a disaster: Findings from a mixed methods study. *School Mental Health*, 8(1), 106–119. http://dx.doi.org/10.1007/s12310-016-9180-5

Read, N. W., & Lampron, S. (2012). *Supporting student achievement through sound behavior management practices in schools and juvenile justice facilities: A spotlight on positive behavioral interventions and supports (PBIS).* Washington, DC: National Evaluation and Technical Assistance Center for Children and

Youth Who Are Neglected, Delinquent, or At-Risk (NDTAC). Retrieved from http://www.neglected-delinquent.org/nd/docs/SupportingStudentAchievement.pdf

Rones, M., & Hoagwood, K. (2000). School-based mental health services: A research review. *Clinical Child & Family Psychology Review, 3*(4), 223–241.

Sanchez, A. L., Cornacchio, D., Poznanski, B., Golik, A. M., Chou, T., & Comer, J. S. (2018). The effectiveness of school-based mental health services for elementary-aged children: A meta-analysis. *Journal of the American Academy of Child & Adolescent Psychiatry, 57*(3), 153–165. doi:10.1016/j.jaac.2017.11.022

Sander, M., Lane, K., Vinciquerra, M., Davis, J., Perales, K., & Horner, R. (2012). The district/community role in advancing the Interconnected Systems Framework. In S. Barrett, L. Eber, & M. D. Weist (Eds.), *Advancing education effectiveness: Interconnecting school mental health and school-wide positive behavior support* (pp. 73–82). Eugene, OR and Baltimore: Office of Special Education Programs Center on Positive Behavioral Interventions and Supports and the University of Maryland Center for School Mental Health. Retrieved from http://www.pbis.org/common/cms/files/Current%20Topics/Final-Monograph.pdf

Shields, A., & Cicchetti, D. (1998). Social information-processing patterns partially mediate the effect of early physical abuse on later conduct problems. *Journal of Abnormal Psychology, 104*, 632–643.

Simon, A. E., Pastor, P. N., Reuben, C. A., Huang, L. N., & Goldstrom, I. D. (2015). Use of mental health services by children ages six to 11 with emotional or behavioral difficulties. *Psychiatric Services, 66*(9), 930–937. doi:10.1176/appi.ps.201400342

Simonsen, B., & Sugai, G. (2013). PBIS in alternative education settings: Positive support for youth with high-risk behavior. *Education and Treatment of Children, 36*, 3–14.

Smith, E. P., Osgood, D. W., Oh, Y., & Caldwell, L. C. (2018). Promoting after-school quality and positive youth development: Cluster randomized trial of the PAX Good Behavior Game. *Prevention Science*, 19(2), 159–173. doi: 10.1007/s11121-017-0820-2.

Substance Abuse and Mental Health Services Administration. (2010). *Results from the 2009 National Survey on Drug Use and Health: Mental health findings*. Rockville, MD: Author.

Sugai, G., & Horner, R. (2006). A promising approach for expanding and sustaining school-wide positive behavior support. *School Psychology Review, 35*, 245–259.

Suter, J. C., & Bruns, E. J. (2009). Effectiveness of the wraparound process for children with emotional and behavioral disorders: A meta-analysis. *Clinical Child and Family Psychology Review, 12*, 336–351. doi:10.1007/s10567-009-0059-y

Swain-Bradway, J., Swoszowski, N. C., Boden, L. J., & Sprague, J. R. (2013). Voices from the field: Stakeholder perspectives on PBIS implementation in alternative educational settings. *Education and Treatment of Children, 36*, 31–46.

Swoszowski, N. C., McDaniel, S. C., Jolivette, K., & Melius, P. (2013). The effects of tier 2 Check-In/Check-Out including adaptation for non-responders on the off-task behavior of elementary students in a residential setting. *Education and Treatment of Children, 36*, 63–79.

Taylor, R. D., Oberle, E., Durlak, J. A., & Weissberg, R. P. (2017). Promoting positive youth development through school-based social and emotional learning interventions: A meta-analysis of follow-up effects. *Child Development, 88*(4), 1156–1171. doi:10.1111/cdev.12864

University of South Florida. (2011). *Implementing a multi-tiered system of support for behavior: A practical guide.* Tampa: Florida's Positive Behavior Support Project.

Waasdorp, T. E., Bradshaw, C. P., & Leaf, P. J. (2012). The impact of School-wide Positive Behavioral Interventions and Supports (SWPBIS) on bullying and peer rejection: A randomized controlled effectiveness trial. *Archives of Child and Adolescent Medicine, 116*(2), 149–156.

Walker, J. S., Bruns, E. J., & Penn, M. (2008). Individualized services in systems of care: The wraparound process. In B. A. Stroul & G. M. Blau (Eds.), *The system of care handbook: Transforming mental health services for children, youth, and families* (pp. 127–153). Baltimore: Brookes Publishing.

Weissberg, R. P., Durlak, J. A., Domitrovich, C. E., & Gullotta, T. P. (2015). *Social and emotional learning: Past, present, and future.* In J. A. Durlak, C. E. Domitrovich, R. P. Weissberg, & T. P. Gullotta (Eds.), *Handbook of social and emotional learning: Research and practice* (pp. 3–19). New York: Guilford.

Weisz, J. R., Sandler, I. N., Durlak, J. A., & Anton, B. S. (2005). Promoting and protecting youth mental health through evidence-based prevention and treatment. *American Psychologist, 60*(6), 628–648.

Yohannan, J., Carlson, J. S., Shepherd, M., & Batsche-McKenzie, K. (2017). Exploring attrition, fidelity, and effectiveness of wraparound services among low-income youth of different racial backgrounds. *Families, Systems, & Health, 35*(4), 430–438. doi:10.1037/fsh0000313

Zima, B. T., Hurlburt, M., Knapp, P., Ladd, H., Tang, L., Duan, N., . . . Wells, K. B. (2005). Quality of publicly-funded outpatient specialty mental health care for common childhood psychiatric disorders in California. *Journal of the American Academy of Child & Adolescent Psychiatry, 44*, 130–144.

PART 2

Valuing and Addressing Diversity

CHAPTER FIVE

Race, Ethnicity, and Socio-Emotional Health

Deborah Rivas-Drake, Robert J. Jagers, and Kenneth J. Martinez

Current projections indicate that the United States will cross over to become a "minority-majority" nation in less than three decades (Census, 2014). Yet, racial and ethnic inequalities in the education, health, and life chances of youth of color in the United States threaten the nation's capacity fully realize the promise of these imminent changes. The preponderance of research on the life circumstances and life prospects for U.S. students of color (African Americans, Latino, and Asian American youth) highlights an array of overlapping vulnerabilities and challenges. For example, compared to whites, African Americans, Latinos, and some Asian subgroups are overrepresented among the poor and working poor (Shapiro, Meschede, & Osoro, 2013). Such concentrated poverty and low-income status tend to restrict access to high-quality educational experiences and to increase risk for mental health problems, especially among Latino youth (Centers for Disease Control and Prevention, 2014; Johnston, O'Malley, Miech, Bachman, & Schulenberg, 2015).

Unfortunately, many children and youth of color experience early negative trajectories and disparities and disproportionality in schools at the very beginning of their careers. One particularly problematic phenomenon is known as the school-to-prison or cradle-to-prison pipeline, and it begins with disparities in discipline at very young ages. For example, black preschoolers are three to five times more likely to be expelled than their white, Latino, or Asian American peers. Among all students in school, K–12 black students are suspended and expelled at a rate three times greater than white students (U.S. Department of Education, 2014b). While black students represent 16% of total student enrollment, they represent 27% of students referred to law enforcement and 31% of all school-related arrests (U.S. Department of Education, 2014b). In addition, youth of color also appear to demonstrate lower levels of more conventional civic knowledge, political attitudes, and forms of political participation (e.g., voting or contacting elected officials) than white youth (Levinson, 2007; Syvertsen, Wray-Lake, Flanagan, Osgood, & Briddell, 2011).

Against this backdrop, this chapter illuminates how several *racial and ethnic processes* help or hinder youths' socio-emotional health in an increasingly diverse yet socially stratified U.S. context. To begin this discussion, we provide a note of clarification regarding the terms race, ethnicity, and culture. Race was once thought to be a biological construct; however, most scholars now conceptualize race as a socio-political construct used historically and currently to justify differential access to desired psychological and material resources (e.g., Bonilla-Silva, 2006). Culture and ethnicity are related terms that are often used interchangeably with each other and with race. Ethnicity is typically used to characterize groups in terms of national, regional, and tribal origin or affiliations; culture typically refers to highly variable systems of shared meaning that are learned and transmitted from generation to generation (Rohner, 1984). According to Triandis and colleagues (1980), cultures include physical and subjective dimensions. Physical culture includes things such as buildings and technological devices. Subjective culture is reflected in prescribed social norms, beliefs, values, and behaviors, such as gender and familial roles, communication patterns, affective styles, and values regarding the nature of personal control, individualism, collectivism, spirituality, and religiosity (Triandis et al., 1980).

As further context, we clarify what we mean when we refer to racial and ethnic processes in youth development. Simply, these are the mechanisms by which race and ethnicity make their way into the daily, lived experiences of young people. There are many such processes, and here we focus on ones that have been widely theorized and studied in regard to youth development (cf. Neblett, Rivas-Drake, & Umaña-Taylor, 2012). Specifically, this chapter sheds light on how youth (1) experience and respond to stress associated with discrimination and acculturation; (2) make meaning around their ethnic and racial group identities; (3) form and enact cultural values and orientations; and (4) develop socio-political dispositions. As we will discuss, each of these processes have been shown to inform socio-emotional health outcomes among youth of color. Socio-emotional health in this chapter refers to social competencies and behaviors as well as psychological outcomes, including self-esteem, depressive symptoms, anxiety, and well-being. Our primary goal is to provide a selective review regarding the aforementioned racial and ethnic processes to illustrate what we know about how they inform these various indicators of socio-emotional health. We organize the review by first discussing what are known as *cultural stressors*, in this case, discrimination and acculturation stress, which are challenges due to race or ethnicity that undermine youths' capacity for socio-emotional health (Rivas-Drake & Stein, in press). We then discuss what are known as *cultural assets*, which in this chapter refer to identity, values, and socio-political development processes that support resilience in the face of cultural stressors. These assets align with what Neblett and colleagues (2012) described as racial and ethnic promotive and protective factors in that they have the potential to promote positive outcomes or attenuate risk exposure (e.g., due to cultural stressors) among youth of color. Following our discussion of cultural stressors and assets, we then explain the implications of the literature reviewed for prevention and intervention work that seeks to be culturally sensitive.

Cultural Stressors

Discrimination and Microaggressions

Treatment that is unfair or meant to subordinate a given ethnic or racial group is one of the primary cultural stressors associated with minority status (Neblett et al., 2012; Umaña-Taylor, 2016). Exposure to discrimination, which is often a fact of life for many youth of color, occurs at multiple levels: in the context of interpersonal interactions and in the ways in which youth are systematically and differentially treated by social institutions (Fisher, Wallace, & Fenton, 2000; Rosenbloom & Way, 2004; Wong, Eccles, & Sameroff, 2003). These experiences can take many forms and can include, among other things: treating youth rudely or disrespectfully, calling them names or harassing them, following them and treating them suspiciously, acting as though one is afraid or intimidated by them, and speaking to them in a condescending manner (e.g., Fisher, Wallace, & Fenton, 2000, 2000; Sellers, Copeland-Linder, Martin, & Lewis, 2006). In addition to explicit, unambiguous discrimination, youth are also exposed to microaggressions, which refer to seemingly innocuous daily interactions and exchanges meant to undermine their humanity, dignity, and social status, for example, being "ignored at a store counter as attention is given to a customer (of a different ethnic group from you) behind you" or being told "you talk too loud" (Hyunh, 2012). Microaggressions such as these are associated with more depressive and somatic symptoms among youth of color (e.g., Hyunh, 2012).

Umaña-Taylor (2016) recently noted that the prevalence of ethnic and racial discrimination appears to increase during adolescence relative to childhood, and that such increasing exposure is reported among diverse groups, including African American, Latino, Asian American, and Native American youth across the United States (see, e.g., Behnke, Plunkett, Sands, & Bámaca-Colbert, 2010; Benner & Graham, 2011; Benner & Kim, 2009; Niwa, Way, & Hughes, 2014 Rivas-Drake, Hughes, & Way, 2008; Seaton et al., 2008). One reason for the increasing salience of discrimination in adolescence may be that, as a number of studies have shown, interpersonal discrimination during this period is not only perpetrated by adults but also other youth (e.g., Greene, Way, & Pahl, 2006; Niwa et al., 2014 Rivas-Drake et al., 2008). There is also some evidence, though mixed, that exposure to discrimination persists or increases between adolescence and young adulthood, and thus, has potentially long-term implications for youths' well-being and adjustment (Brody et al., 2014; Greene et al., 2006; Witherspoon, Seaton, & Rivas-Drake, 2016).

More exposure to discrimination in adolescence is linked to a host of negative socio-emotional health outcomes, including lower self-esteem and more anger, depression, perceived stress, delinquency, conduct problems, and substance use (Fuller-Rowell, Cogburn, Brodish, Peck, Malanchuk, & Eccles, 2012; Gibbons et al., 2007; Greene et al., 2006; Niwa et al., 2014 Rivas-Drake et al., 2008; Sellers et al., 2006; Simons et al., 2003; Wong et al., 2003). Studies of the psychophysiology of discrimination among youth suggest that some part of the link between discrimination exposure and negative socio-emotional health outcomes may be due to its role on physical health, including sleep and stress reactivity. For example, youth who encounter more discrimination exhibit lower quality sleep patterns over time (Yip, 2015; Zeiders, Updegraff, Kuo, Umaña-Taylor, & McHale, 2016). More discrimination and poorer sleep, in turn, take a significant toll on youth, as youth who reported both phenomena tended to exhibit increased depression and decreased self-esteem over the course of adolescence (Yip, 2015). Zeiders and colleagues (2014) found that a diverse sample of young adults of color—including African Americans, Latinos, and Asian Americans—who experienced more discrimination evinced a pattern of neuroendocrine activity (i.e., related to cortisol levels) that is thought to be linked to chronic stress exposure and, consequently, to negative health outcomes. In a study of Mexican American adolescents, specifically, Zeiders and colleagues (2012) found that more discrimination was associated with greater overall output of cortisol—the hormone associated with stress—among this group.

Acculturative Stress

For immigrant-origin youth, another important cultural stressor is the phenomenon known as acculturative stress, which occurs when youth encounter competing or conflicting expectations and norms between their host (e.g., United States) and immigrant (heritage) cultural contexts that they experience as stressful (Gil, Vega, & Dimas, 1994; Gil, Wagner, & Vega, 2000; Rodriguez, Flores, Flores, Myers, & Vriesema, 2015; Romero & Roberts, 2003). These conflicts may arise due to the process of learning the ways of the "new land" (Suárez-Orozco, Suárez-Orozco, & Todorova, 2008) in combination with exposure to discrimination and social exclusion by host nationals (e.g., U.S.-born youth) due to youths' ethnic or immigrant origins (Sirin, Ryce, Gupta, & Rogers-Sirin, 2013). Moreover, acculturative stress can occur in the context of family situations in which children's preferences for, or adoption of, heritage and host values and language are misaligned or are in conflict with those of their parents (Cervantes & Cordova, 2011; Schwartz et al., 2015; Smokowski, Rose, & Bacallao, 2010; Stein & Polo, 2014; Telzer, 2011). Thus, given its more varied nature and that it is a construct that theoretically only applies to immigrant-origin youth, the literature on acculturative stress is closely related but distinct from that on other minority status stressors such as discrimination, as discussed above.

The stresses associated with acculturation affect youth of myriad ethnic heritages across the United States (e.g., Cervantes, Padilla, Napper, & Goldbach, 2013; Sirin et al., 2013; Thomas & Choi, 2006; Tummala-Narra, Deshpande, & Kaur, 2016). For instance, in a study focused on Latinos in multiple cities (i.e., Los Angeles, Miami, El Paso, and Boston), Cervantes and colleagues (2013) found that one of the most common acculturation stressors for immigrants and children of immigrants was the expectation of their parents to adhere to traditional customs and values; for immigrant youth only, other important stressors reflected ones pertaining more specifically to the immigration experience, such as having to leave people behind in their home country and starting over in a new country. Tummala-Narra and colleagues' (2016) study of acculturative stress among South Asian youth living in the Northeast found that youth encountered such stress across family and contexts.

Not surprisingly, experiencing acculturative stress has been associated with a number of maladaptive behaviors and mental health problems among diverse immigrant-origin youth (e.g., Sirin et al., 2013). For example, Rodriguez and colleagues (2015) found that Mexican-origin adolescents who reported greater conflict in choosing between Latino and American cultural practices experienced lower self-control and less psychological well-being overall. Hurwich-Reiss and Gudiño (2016) similarly found that experiencing more acculturation stress was associated with more conduct problems (e.g., fights, stealing) among Latino adolescents, and the association was present for both youth who were immigrants themselves and those who were children of immigrant parents. In a three-year prospective study of immigrant-origin adolescents in New York City of Latino, Asian, and African origins, Sirin and his colleagues (2013) found that youth who were exposed to greater exposure to acculturative stress also tended to exhibit more withdrawn, somatic, and anxious/depressed symptoms over time. Finally, in studies of Arab American youth, findings indicate that acculturative stress, alone and in tandem with exposure to racism, was associated with more psychological distress and internalizing symptoms, respectively (Ahmed, Kia-Keating, & Tsai, 2011; Goforth, Pham, Chun, Castro-Olivo, & Yosai, 2016).

Cultural Assets

Ethnic or Racial Identity

Ethnic or racial identity (ERI) refers to the importance and meaning associated with ethnic or racial group membership and the processes by which youth arrive at such meaning (Rivas-Drake et al., 2014; Umaña-Taylor et al., 2014). The importance and meaning of ERI is typically thought of as its content, whereas meaning-making efforts are considered the process by which ERI develops, usually as an age-graded and thus developmental phenomenon. ERI content refers to a range of beliefs and feelings, including beliefs about the importance of ethnicity or race to their sense of self as a person (centrality), feelings about their group and group membership (private regard/affirmation), and beliefs about how other groups view one's group (public regard). The primary aspects of ERI process, by contrast, focus on the extent to which youth have explored the meaning of their group membership (exploration) and have developed a sense of clarity about its role in their lives (resolution). Together, the various aspects of ERI increase in relevance from childhood through adolescence, with a number of studies showing that the adolescent to young adult years are a time in which various aspects of ERI increase among youth of color (e.g., French, Seidman, Allen, & Aber, 2000, 2006; Rivas-Drake & Witherspoon, 2013). For example, Rivas-Drake and Witherspoon (2013) found that the centrality of ERI increased significantly among African American youth between 11th grade and three years post high school. Youths' ERI is thus multifaceted, going well beyond their simple identification with an ethnic or racial group, and it becomes of increasing salience over the course of adolescence (Umaña-Taylor et al., 2014).

Recent meta-analyses and narrative reviews have established the importance of ERI for the psychological and academic adjustment of youth (Miller-Cotto & Byrnes, 2016; Rivas-Drake, Seaton, et al., 2014; Rivas-Drake, Syed, et al., 2014). For example, in a meta-analysis of an ERI measure that combined both affirmation and exploration, Smith and Silva (2011) found that this composite was associated with psychological and mental health outcomes (e.g., self-esteem, depressive symptoms) more strongly in youth (e.g., adolescence) than among older adults. In a second meta-analysis of ERI based on 46 studies of positive ethnic or racial affect among African American, Latino, Asian American and Pacific Islander, and American Indian youth (average age = 14 years old), the overall pattern of results indicates that the more positively youth felt about their ethnicity or race the fewer depressive symptoms and emotional and behavior problems they exhibited, and they also demonstrated more positive social interactions and better self-esteem, well-being, academic achievement, and attitudes toward school and academics (Rivas-Drake, Seaton, et al., 2014). These patterns were similar among African American, Latino, Asian American, and Native American and across elementary, middle, and high school aged samples included in the study. Miller-Cotto and Byrnes' (2016) meta-analysis of 47 studies of ERI and academic outcomes, in particular, lend further support for considering ERI processes in youth; they found that, in addition to positive personal affect toward one's ethnic or racial group, engaging in more ERI exploration was associated with higher academic achievement among diverse youth. In addition to these meta-analyses, recent laboratory-based research suggests that ERI moderated individuals' physiological responses to experiences of racism (Neblett & Roberts, 2013). They found support for the idea that among African American young adults, having higher levels of private regard may help to "insulate against physiological challenge or threat responses in the face of racial adversity" (p. 950). In short, ERI matters for the health, psychological well-being, and academic success of many youth of color.

ERI is also thought to shape individuals' capacities to navigate their social world (cf. Camacho, Bañales, Cross, Marchand, & Rivas-Drake, 2017; Rivas-Drake & Umaña-Taylor, 2019), and social relationships are indeed vital to ERI development. For example, Rivas-Drake and Witherspoon (2013) found that youth who resided in neighborhoods characterized as relatively unsafe but also as a source of positive interpersonal connections in the community as early adolescents tended to report high and increasing levels of private regard toward African Americans in later adolescence and young adulthood. In the aforementioned meta-analysis by Rivas-Drake and her colleagues (2014), positive affect toward their ethnic or racial group was positively related to youths' peer competencies and acceptance by peers. Similarly, Newman (2005) reported that American Indian youth who expressed more interest in learning about their culture tended to also report more prosocial and less aggressive behaviors with peers, and Phinney and her colleagues (2007) found that diverse adolescents who had thought about and formed a positive sense of ERI tended to also feel more positively about befriending peers from other ethnic or racial groups. Moreover, recent studies indicate that youths' friendships are an important context in and of themselves for the development of their ERI (Rivas-Drake, Umaña-Taylor, Schaefer, & Medina, in press; Santos, Kornienko, & Rivas-Drake, in press). For instance, Rivas-Drake and colleagues (in press) recently found that middle-school boys who had more clarity about their ERI tend to have more diverse friends later on, and having more diverse friends prompts all kids (boys and girls) to explore their identities more over time. Thus, consideration of youths' social relationships, especially with peers, may be vital to understanding the role of ERI in socio-emotional health.

Cultural Values

Another important cultural asset that has been highlighted in adolescent development literature concerns cultural traditions and values associated with one's ethnic or racial group (Neblett et al., 2012). Cultural values are related to ERI conceptually (Neblett et al., 2012) and empirically (e.g., Kiang & Fuligni, 2009; Knight, Carlo, Mahrer, & Davis, 2016; Stein, Rivas-Drake, & Camacho, 2017). However, the distinct literature on cultural values provides a closer look at the contributions of this complementary aspect of group membership on youth outcomes. Cultural values include a sense of deference to and mutual support in one's family (i.e., familism), filial piety, and Africentrism (Kiang, Andrews, Stein, Supple, & Gonzalez, 2013; Lieber, Nihira, & Mink, 2004; Neblett & Carter, 2012; Stein, Cupito, Mendez, Prandoni, Huq, & Westerberg, 2014). Cultural values are pertinent to myriad ethnic and racial groups, including Latino (Knight et al., 2010; see Stein et al., 2014, for a review), Asian American (Kiang et al., 2013; Shen, Kim, & Wang, 2016), and African American youth (Neblett & Carter, 2012), among others. A common theme across groups is a communalistic orientation toward one's family, ethnic or racial group, and community, more generally.

Adhering to communalistic cultural values has been shown to support positive socio-emotional outcomes in adolescence, such as reduced feelings of distress, positive family functioning, better emotional well-being (e.g., fewer depressive symptoms), greater emotional persistence, less risky behavior, and more emotional engagement with school (McHale, Updegraff, Kim, & Cansler, 2009; Rivas-Drake & Marchand, 2016; Schwartz et al., 2015; Stein, Gonzalez, Cupito, Kiang, & Supple, 2015; Telzer, Yuen, Gonzales, & Fuligni, 2016). In a study that followed Mexican American youth from 5th to 7th to 10th grade, Knight and colleagues (2016) found that adolescents' endorsement of familism as 7th graders was associated with their prosocial helping behaviors as 10th graders in varied situations, such as when someone is upset, when help is explicitly requested by someone else, and when there is a crisis. In addition, neuroimaging research suggests that familistic behaviors may activate neural reward systems in the brain among Latinos; on an experimental task in the laboratory setting, Latinos obtained rewards when helping to contribute to their families, whereas white youth obtained such rewards when making personal monetary gains (Telzer, Masten, Berkman, Lieberman, & Fuligni, 2010). In research with African American young adults, Neblett and Carter (2012) found that Africentric values—defined as nonmaterialistic, holistic, and communal orientations—showed salutary physiological benefits for this group. They found that strong endorsement of such values attenuated the link between racial discrimination and blood pressure. Finally, among Mexican American adolescents, youth who more strongly endorsed Mexican American cultural values—including familism and respect for elders—exhibited less internalizing and externalizing behaviors (Berkel et al., 2010). Thus, endorsement and enactment of cultural values is shown to promote positive outcomes and to have the potential to protect youth from the sequelae of exposure to cultural stressors.

Civic Engagement

Another potential cultural asset is youths' agency as civic actors who positively impact their ethnic and racial communities. Youth civic development encompasses a range of knowledge, values, attitudes, and behaviors related to involvement in one's local community and broader society. For example, youth of color have been shown to express positive civic dispositions through various prosocial behaviors, including provision of family financial assistance, participation in community service via religious organizations, and engagement in politically motivated artistic expression, such as poetry and hip-hop (Ginwright, 2010; Smetana & Metzger, 2005; Watts & Flanagan, 2007).

Civic engagement has become an important developmental outcome in its own right, as civically engaged youth are critical to maintaining and improving local, national, and global communities (Lerner, Wang, Champine, Warren, Erickson, & Lerner, 2004; Weissberg, Durlak, Domitrovich & Gullotta, 2015). With regard to the particular forms of civic development pertinent to adolescents, Westheimer and Kahne (2004) distinguish among efforts that focus on personally responsible, participatory, and justice-oriented citizenship. In brief, the personally responsible citizen is thought to exemplify good character by displaying prosocial attitudes and behaviors, and promote the common good (e.g., by being helpful in their local community in a general sense). The participatory citizen is actively involved in civic life through particular local clubs, traditional clubs and civic organizations, social institutions, and political activities. Finally, justice-oriented citizenship is concerned with institutional and system change efforts in pursuit of a fairer, more equitable society. It is possible that, for youth of color, civic development reflects another way to manifest communalistic cultural values, as discussed above.

For some youth, civic development goes beyond communalism and is intertwined with their socio-political development. Watts and Flanagan (2007) argued for the expansion of civic development scholarship to include socio-political development, in order to attend to justice-oriented modes of civic engagement. Socio-political development and related notions, such as critical consciousness and empowerment, focus on advancing human rights and social equality. Socio-political development considers the individual and contextual factors through which youth gain an understanding of inequality and become involved in personal or collective actions that promote meaningful community and societal change (Hope & Jagers, 2014; Watts & Guessous, 2006). Socio-political action is thus intended to empower and gain control over one's life circumstances. Such behaviors can include personal and collective actions that are either internal or external to one's benefactors (Watts & Hipolito-Delgado, 2015). Hope and Jagers (2014) used data from the *Black Youth Project* Youth Survey to examine factors associated with a subset of socio-political behaviors of a national probability sample of 15- to 25-year-old African American youth. Across younger and older youth, political discussions were the most frequent form of behavior followed by community service, boycotting, sending communications to politicians, and signing petitions. Perceived institutional discrimination, having taken a civics course, and a sense of political efficacy predicted greater levels of such behaviors.

One pivotal aspect of socio-political development is an evolving understanding of how economic, political, and cultural systems shape and sustain society, or what is referred to as critical social analysis. Such an analysis involves collective identities (e.g., race, gender, class) and attention to the ways in which local and societal institutions and processes impact on individual and group statuses and experiences (Watts, Diemer, & Voight, 2011). Among adolescents, critical social analysis has been conceptualized in terms of (dis)belief in the world as a just and fair place (Watts & Guessous, 2006), mistrust of political systems (Hope & Jagers, 2014), and other systemic causes for social inequities (Watts, Diemer & Voight, 2011). Although understanding youths' critiques of oppression within larger socio-political systems are apt, their critiques of oppression in relation to group status and identity may also play an important role in shaping their civic behavior. For example, Lozada and her colleagues (2016) found that among African American adolescent boys, having an oppression analysis (i.e., seeing commonality between African Americans and other oppressed groups, together with racial centrality and private regard) and experiencing school-based discrimination had direct positive effects on prosocial behaviors. In addition, an oppression analysis had an indirect effect on prosocial behaviors through youths' social-emotional skills.

A final aspect of socio-political development is political efficacy, which refers to an individual's belief in their own capacity to use knowledge and skills to act socially and politically; it reflects youths' personal belief that they have the capacity to bring about community change through their actions (Beaumont, 2010). The fundamental assumption of this component of socio-political development is that people take action when they believe that their efforts can make a difference. In addition to the work of Hope and Jagers (2014) mentioned above, other empirical work supports this theoretical assumption. For example, Rubin (2007) found a link between perceived discrimination and increased efficacy for future civic behavior. Watts and Guessous (2006) found that for youth of color, experiences of agency in previous community or political projects moderated the relationships between their belief in a just world and their commitment to future civic activities.

Our discussion thus far suggests that cultural assets, which in this chapter refer to identity, values, and socio-political development processes, are critical for promoting resilient outcomes among youth who encounter cultural stressors. Such assets play a pivotal role in youths' socio-emotional health. Next, we consider what it means to take a cultural assets approach to prevention and promotion efforts with youth of color. As we discuss below, the approaches we consider explicitly or implicitly build on or foster the development of youths' cultural assets in schools.

Implications of a Cultural Assets Approach for Prevention and Intervention in Schools

Given the amount of time youth spend in school, we consider what it means to take a cultural assets approach in schools. Enrollment in grades K–12 is approximately 50.4 million (U.S. Department of Education, 2014a), and over 50% of those children and youth enrolled in public school are children of color (U.S. Department of Education, 2014a). Moreover, public schools are the major providers of mental health services for school-aged children (Foster, Rollefson, Doksum, Noonan, Robinson, & Teich, 2005). In recent years, there has been increased interest in social emotional learning (SEL) among teachers, school administrators, families, researchers, and policy makers (Weissberg et al., 2015). There has been particular attention to the need for high-quality universal programs, which are offered to all students regardless of their risk status. The assumption is that SEL supplements the traditional focus on academic outcomes and thereby offers a more holistic approach to the education process. Such programs can make targeted and indicated programs more efficient.

The broad reach and potential to impact youth of color makes schools a key setting in which to promote a cultural assets approach to strengthening socio-emotional health, especially for children of color, through promotion, prevention, and early intervention programs. There have been several meta-analyses that suggest that school-based SEL can contribute to desirable outcomes for children and youth. For example, in Durlak et al.'s (2011) review of 213 studies, they found that SEL programs that were structured, active, focused, and explicit (SAFE) increased various academic, social, and emotional outcomes for children and youth. The Center for Health and Health Care in Schools (2014) conducted a meta-analysis of 157 studies between

2001 and 2013 that indicated universal school-based behavioral health interventions were not only associated with improved academic achievement, such as increases in school grades, standardized test scores, grade point averages, and teacher-rated academic competence, but there was also improvement in decreased rates of absenteeism and suspensions. The same meta-analysis found that students who received behavioral health interventions showed greater resilience and emotional functioning as evidenced by increased academic motivation, self-efficacy, commitment to school, and stability during grade-level transitions. At the school level, intervention sites reported less violence, bullying, and other problem-behaviors among students (Center for Health and Health Care in Schools, 2014).

To be clear, neither of the aforementioned meta-analyses addresses issues related to cultural asset promotion. Thus, despite mounting evidence about the benefits of SEL generally, questions remain about the effectiveness and appropriateness of universal SEL programs for students from diverse backgrounds (e.g., Castro-Olivo, 2014; Jagers, 2016). Central concerns of such critiques include whether guiding frameworks, program content and delivery, and related assessments adequately reflect, cultivate, and leverage the cultural assets of youth of color. The cultural grounding of SEL programs seems like a worthy pursuit, as such efforts have shown promise in improving youth engagement and outcomes in health promotion programs (Kreuter, Lukwago, Bucholtz, Clark, & Sanders-Thompson, 2003) and in academic content (Aronson & Laughter, 2016).

The capacity to deliver culturally attentive SEL certainly implies cultural competence among adults within the context of schools, which is defined as the ability to successfully teach students who come from cultures other than our own. It entails developing certain personal and interpersonal awareness and sensitivities, developing certain bodies of cultural knowledge, and mastering a set of skills that, taken together, underlie effective cross-cultural teaching (Diller & Moule, 2005). A cultural assets approach is inherently culturally competent, since it is focusing on cultural strengths including values, beliefs, rituals, and traditions associated with one's ethnic or racial group, such as those discussed throughout this chapter. The literature reviewed thus far suggests that it is important for practitioners working with children and youth of color to use approaches that are culturally and linguistically competent in order to build on or foster youths' cultural assets.

One major goal of focusing on cultural competence is to eliminate racial and ethnic disparities and disproportionality in schools and communities; improve access, quality, and outcomes of behavioral health services; and reduce placement of students of color in the most restrictive or inappropriate settings. Focusing on cultural competence also serves to acknowledge and respond to the history of trauma many youth and families of color experience as well as to address racism, power, ethnocentrism, privilege, stigma, discrimination, and injustice. Addressing cultural competence also fosters development of culturally appropriate and effective promising and best practices and programs, also called practice-based evidence (Isaacs, Huang, Hernandez, & Echo-Hawk, 2005) and community-defined evidence (Martínez, Callejas, & Hernandez, 2010).

Promoting Cultural Assets via Culturally Responsive Teaching

One widely touted approach is culturally responsive teaching (Gay, 2010, as cited in Gay, 2013). According to Gay (2013), culturally responsive teaching focuses on creating learning communities where culturally different individuals and heritages are valued; cultural knowledge of ethnically diverse cultures, families, and communities is used to guide curriculum development, classroom climates, instructional strategies, and relationships with students. Culturally responsive teaching also challenges racial and cultural stereotypes, prejudices, racism, and other forms of intolerance, injustice, and oppression. It encourages being change agents for social justice and academic equity; mediates power imbalances in classrooms based on race, culture, ethnicity, and class; and assumes cultural responsiveness is endemic to educational effectiveness in all areas of learning for students from all ethnic groups (Gay, 2013). The cultural backgrounds of students are utilized as a vehicle for learning (Ladson-Billings, 1995).

Further, Hanley and Noblit (2009) state that culturally responsive pedagogy can be used to promote racial identity, resilience, and achievement by (1) inviting active participation of family members and the community because they can be valuable in informing educators about the needs and resources of the students whom they know better than educators and (2) using culture to promote racial identity through adaptations in instructional practice, classroom organization, motivational management, curricula, and espoused values. They emphasize having the program focus on developing strategies to use the culture to construct a positive racial identity that promotes resilience and success in social institutions. Culturally responsive teaching sees cultural differences as assets, because it uses behavioral expressions of knowledge, beliefs, and values to recognize the importance of racial and cultural diversity while also improving the performance of underachieving ethnically and racially diverse students (Gay, 2013). Below we offer a sampling of scholarship that helps to advance the cultural grounding of SEL with regard to ERI, cultural values, and civic development.

In terms of ERI, Loyd and Williams (2017) offer a conceptual framework and review literature on programmatic efforts to promote the ERI of African American youth. Conceptually, they posit that a culture-specific program philosophy informs the selection of materials and interpersonal interactions that reflect positive racial socialization messages and behaviors. The influence of these program factors is contingent on both individual and context factors of participating youth. A review of literature on youth development programs targeting African American youth identified 14 programs that addressed ERI and other youth outcomes. Further examination pointed to nine programs that explicitly sought to improve ERI of participating adolescents. Six of these nine programs reported positive effects on ERI; two of them were school-based (i.e., NTU: Substance Abuse Prevention and Young Empowered Sisters programs; Loyd & Williams, 2017).

One of the two aforementioned school-based programs is NTU, an Africentric program designed to reduce risk behaviors (e.g., by reducing tolerance of substance use) and increase protective factors, including racial identity, among African American early adolescents who were considered at high risk for substance use (e.g., children of substance users) (Cherry, Belgrave, Jones, Kennon, Gray, & Phillips, 1998). Among the multiple components of the intervention was a Rites of Passage program based on the Nguzo Nane (Seven Principles of Kwanzaa) and Heshema (Respect), which was designed to enhance adolescents' cultural awareness, development of healthy values, resiliency, and social skills (p. 324). In a quasi-experimental study, the researchers found that 5th graders in the intervention group, as compared to the comparison group, more strongly endorsed Africentric values and reported feeling more positively about being black and believing that being black is a positive attribute.

In another review of culturally sensitive risk behavior prevention programs for black youth, Metzger and colleagues (2013) identified five school-based programs that included ERI in their theoretical orientation, program activities, and/or evaluation. These programs varied with regard to methodological approach (e.g., qualitative, quantitative) and rigor (e.g., sample size, use of randomization), yet several reported positive program effects including increased ERI. Our scan revealed fewer applied studies on the promotion of ERI among Latino youth, in particular. In one recent study, Umaña-Taylor and colleagues (2017) report on an efficacy trial of the Identity Project, a classroom-based intervention designed to promote ERI exploration and resolution of diverse adolescents. While youth of color reported higher exploration and resolution over time, they report expected program effects on identity exploration for all youth. These studies offer evidence that school-based programs can help foster ERI among black and Latino youth. However, to date there appears to be little evidence that such improvements can lead to subsequent prevention or reduction in risk behaviors or the growth of other desired social emotional outcomes.

With regard to cultural values, there have been several recent efforts to illuminate the ways in which cultural values can be deployed in prevention and promotion programs. For example, Kreuter and colleagues (2003) offer five cultural integration strategies: (1) *peripheral*, the use of colors, images, fonts, pictures, or images that overtly convey relevance to those in the group; (2) *evidential*, which includes providing some form of data demonstrating that a given problem affects members of the target group; (3) *linguistic*, which employs the dominant or preferred language of the group to make program activities or materials more familiar and accessible; (4) *socio-cultural*, which integrates the cultural norms, values, beliefs, and behaviors of the group into program activities and materials, and (5) *constituent-involving*, which seeks to benefit from the experience and knowledge of the group's members in the development, delivery, and evaluation of the intervention.

The socio-cultural strategies are most relevant to the focus of this chapter. Jagers, Mustafaa, and Noel (2017) employed Kreuter and colleagues' (2003) definitions of these cultural integration strategies to examine programs that support African American empowerment in the areas of health and education. The programs reviewed ranged with regard to whether the various cultural infusion strategies were used alone or in combination, program setting (family, school, community) and rigor of evaluation design. However, several reviewed programs infused cultural values in their theoretical orientation, program content, and program delivery. Further, a number of programs that included a school component or were school-based were found to have positive program effects on health and academic outcomes. Metzger and colleagues (2013) reported similar findings in their review of risk behavior prevention programs for black youth.

With regard to Latino youth, programs such as Keepin' it Real (Hecht et al., 2003), a substance use prevention program, offer culturally appropriate curricula for Latino, black, and multicultural middle-school contexts. Efficacy trials with Latino youth yielded reduced substance use attitudes and improved resistance strategies to avoid use. However, our cursory review of this body of literature revealed that there was limited attention to assessing the ways in which youth cultural values might impact on program processes or outcomes.

Conditions that Support Civic Engagement as a Cultural Asset

There is a small but growing body of applied research on how schools might foster civic engagement. This makes sense, as schools and classrooms can be construed as communities in which youth can learn how to debate, negotiate, cooperate, and the like. The literature on the role of schooling in civic engagement suggests that caring and productive classroom communities are built through teachers' cultivating students' participatory citizenship skills such as open and respectful dialogue about diverse opinions and shared decision-making. This focus on student voice and choice conveys fairness and supportiveness, and it lends itself to desirable civic development outcomes among students (Godfrey & Grayson, 2014). For example, an open classroom climate has been linked to civic knowledge and commitment to voting (Campbell, 2008; Torney-Purta et al., 2001, 2007), intentions to be an informed voter and appreciation for the role of conflict in democracy (Campbell, 2008), and student beliefs regarding their ability to impact issues in their school, community, and society.

Jagers, Lozada, Rivas-Drake, and Guilluame (2017) examined whether and in what ways the democratic classroom practices associated with the Developmental Designs (DD) approach might contribute to civic beliefs attitudes and behaviors among black and Latino middle-school students. DD is a multifaceted approach that features a homeroom advisory structure; individual and classroom goal-setting and social contracts; modeling and practicing of classroom routines; empowering teacher language; planning and reflection on student products; collaborative problem-solving among students; and balanced discipline strategy that highlights student self-control (Kwame-Ross et al., 2011). Jagers and colleagues (2017) found that all components of civic engagement were increased by community-building in homeroom and classroom settings. This finding suggests that such practices support participatory citizenship. It is also noteworthy that having a sense that one's school supports fair treatment of diverse groups also emerged as a predictor of concurrent and later civic engagement in the Jagers and colleagues (2017) study.

There are also several lines of research aimed at the promotion of justice-oriented citizenship. For example, some recent research suggests that civics education programs such as Facing History and Ourselves (FHAO) can enhance civic outcomes for diverse youth. FHAO is integrated into regular Social Studies and Language Arts instruction, and it employs historical examples of conflict, injustice, and discrimination to teach tolerance, social skills, and civic responsibility. The program also targets teaching practices and classroom climate. A quasi-experimental trial (pre-post, non-randomized controls) involving predominantly white urban and suburban 8th grade classrooms demonstrated significant impacts on students psychosocial competence and (decreased) racist attitudes as well as marginal effects on students' fighting behavior, but not civic awareness or moral reasoning (Schultz, Barr, & Selman, 2001). Barr and colleagues (2015) found that compared to controls, 9th and 10th grade students taught a Holocaust unit by their teachers reported a greater sense of an open classroom climate, more engagement with civic issues greater civic self-efficacy and more political tolerance at post-test. In addition, teachers in the FHAO condition reported greater self-efficacy regarding civic instruction, personal accomplishment, and professional engagement and growth. Although the student sample was substantial, largely from under-resourced backgrounds and racially and ethnically diverse, analyses were not reported based on these factors.

Seider and colleagues (2017) add complexity to efforts to understand how schools might foster justice-oriented citizenship. They used a mixed-method approach to compare the contributions of progressive and "no nonsense" schools to the developing socio-political consciousness of roughly 450 youth of color from under-resourced backgrounds. Progressive schools promote caring and collaboration and highlight social justice through inquiry-based learning. On the other hand, no nonsense schools emphasize strict discipline and teaching traditional math and literacy skills in order to close the "achievement gap." Surveys, interviews, and observations were used to examine possible changes in consciousness of both racial and social class inequities in the United States among students from the beginning of 9th grade through the end of 10th grade year. Results indicated that progressive school students had greater growth in racial consciousness than their counterparts attending a no nonsense school. However, no nonsense school students indicated greater growth in consciousness of social-class inequities. Seider and colleagues (2017) posit that all educational methods have the potential to foster socio-political conscious and point to the content of specific school courses and initiatives to help to explain this pattern of findings.

Finally, there has been considerable attention to the benefits of youth participatory action research (YPAR) to cultivate justice-oriented civic engagement of youth. While much of this work has been done in out-of-school (OST) settings (Murray & Milner, 2015), there are several studies that describe YPAR efforts in elementary, middle, and high school settings. The connections of YPAR to school-based academic pursuits have also been articulated (Ozer, 2016). A cursory scan of published studies indicates that regardless of setting, there is a focus on group processes and collective action of participating youth. Ozer and Douglas (2013) report on one of the few experimental studies of YPAR that includes multiple assessments of individual-level psychological empowerment across the school year. Participating students were predominately youth of color (93%, with 35% Asian and 31% Latino) from five high schools. At least two classes at each school were assigned to the YPAR or the peer-mentoring comparison condition. Compared to their peers, students taking part in YPAR indicated greater socio-political skills, more motivation to influence school and community, and more participatory behavior.

The Disparities Impact Statement: Another Cultural Assets Approach

Unfortunately, individuals of color, especially children and youth of color, are impacted by disparities in access to, utilization, and quality of behavioral health services, as well as from poorer treatment outcomes (U.S. Health and Human Services Department, 2011). Disparities in access and outcomes are often attributed to challenges such as transportation barriers, stigma, and cost. With few exceptions (e.g., Cummings, Ponce, & Mays, 2010), racial and ethnic disparities also exist among youth receiving school-based mental health services.

One way practitioners are attempting to address disparities and disproportionality in schools and communities is through the development and implementation of a Disparities Impact Statement (DIS) and accompanying strategies to reduce disparities. The DIS emanated from the *HHS Action Plan to Reduce Racial and Ethnic Health Disparities: A Nation Free of Disparities in Health and Health Care* (U.S. Health and Human Services Department, 2011), which asked U.S. Department of Health and Human Services (HHS) agencies to address health and behavioral health disparities among its funded programs. In 2013, the Substance Abuse and Mental Health Services Administration (SAMHSA), an HHS agency responsible for most behavioral health program funding, required a DIS as a special condition of award in most of their grants/cooperative agreements, which asks grantees to disaggregate race/ethnicity data, identify populations of focus who are experiencing behavioral health disparities and disproportionalities, and describe how they will reduce them among those populations.

The SAMHSA DIS has a strategic focus on reducing behavioral health disparities among racial and ethnic populations and individuals who are lesbian, gay, bisexual, and transgender (LGBT). It addresses three specific domains: (1) access to services/programs/interventions; (2) use (utilization) of the same; and (3) behavioral health outcomes. The DIS is based on a data-informed quality improvement approach that requires regular monitoring, reviewing, and revising of the methods, data analysis, strategies, and benchmark goals to ensure that quality is maintained and progress is made through continuous data review and updating. The DIS has brought awareness about the existence of disparities and disproportionalities in many communities around the country through the grants/cooperative agreements that SAMHSA issues. For instance, many for the first time are disaggregating data for racial/ethnic and LGBT populations and addressing behavioral health disparities and disproportionalities that prior to the DIS requirement had not been addressed.

Conclusion

In this chapter, we provided a selective review of the literature on cultural stressors and assets as well as illustrative examples of practice and policy that take a cultural assets approach. More research is needed to better understand how prevention and intervention that takes a cultural assets approach conveys benefits to youth by leveraging assets themselves. School settings, in particular, present an unparalleled opportunity to improve the socio-emotional health of our children and youth of color. They allow educators to develop culturally and linguistically competent curriculum and teaching methods, and apply evidence informed prevention and early intervention practices and programs that can improve the trajectory of all children and youth, especially those of color. Behavioral health promotion, prevention, and early intervention practices and programs in schools that focus on cultural assets have the potential for significant positive impact on children and youth of color. In addition, strategies such as the Disparities Impact Statement address the disparity challenges communities face. By highlighting and applying cultural assets as intervention strategies for disparities, ethnic and racial identity, and child and community well-being can be improved.

References

Ahmed, S. R., Kia-Keating, M., & Tsai, K. H. (2011). A structural model of racial discrimination, acculturative stress, and cultural resources among Arab American adolescents. *American Journal of Community Psychology, 48*, 181–192. doi:10.1007/s10464-011-9424-3

Aronson, B., & Laughter, J. (2016). The theory and practice of culturally relevant education: A synthesis of research across content areas. *Review of Educational Research, 86*(1), 163–206.

Beaumont, E. (2010). Political agency and empowerment: Pathways for developing a sense of political efficacy in young adults. In L. Sherrod, J. Torney-Purta, & C. Flanagan (Eds.), *Handbook of research on civic engagement in youth* (pp. 525–558). Hoboken, NJ: John Wiley.

Behnke, A. O., Plunkett, S. W., Sands, T., & Bámaca-Colbert, M. Y. (2010). The relationship between Latino adolescents' perceptions of discrimination, neighborhood risk, and parenting on self-esteem and depressive symptoms. *Journal of Cross-Cultural Psychology, 42*, 1179–1197. doi:10.1177/0022022110383424

Benner, A. D., & Graham, S. (2011). Latino adolescents' experiences of discrimination across the first 2 years of high school: Correlates of influence on educational outcomes. *Child Development, 82*, 508–519.

Benner, A. D., & Kim, S. Y. (2009). Experiences of discrimination among Chinese American adolescents and the consequences for socioemotional and academic development. *Developmental Psychology, 45*, 1682–1694. doi:10.1037/ a0016119

Berkel, C., Knight, G., Zeiders, K. H., Tein, J., Roosa, M. W., Gonzales, N. A., & Saenz, D. (2010). Discrimination and adjustment for Mexican American adolescents: A prospective examination of the benefits of culturally related values. *Journal of Research on Adolescence, 20*(4), 893–915.

Betancourt, H., & Lopez, S. R. (1993). The study of culture, ethnicity, and race in American psychology. *American Psychologist, 48*(6), 629–637.

Bonilla-Silva, E. (2006). *Racism without racists: Color-Blind racism and the persistence of racial inequality in the USA*. Lanham, MD: Rowman & Littlefield.

Brody, G. H., Lei, M. K., Chae, D. H., Yu, T., Kogan, S. M., & Beach, S. R. H. (2014). Perceived discrimination among African American adolescents and allostatic load: A longitudinal analysis with buffering effects. *Child Development, 85*, 989–1002. doi:10.1111/cdev.12213

Camacho, T., Bañales, J., Cross, F., Marchand, A., & Rivas-Drake, D. (2017). Psychological aspects of ethnic identity and their associations with social behavior. In A. Blume (Ed.), *Social issues in living color: Challenges and solutions from the perspective of ethnic minority psychology* (pp. 165–188). Santa Barbara, CA: Praeger.

Campbell, D. E. (2008). Voice in the classroom: How an open classroom climate fosters political engagement among adolescents. *Political Behavior, 30*(4), 437–454. https://doi.org/10.1007/s11109-008-9063-z

Castro-Olivo, S. M. (2014). Promoting social-emotional learning in adolescent Latino ELLs: A study of the culturally adapted Strong Teens Program. *School Psychology Quarterly, 29*(4), 567–577.

Center for Health and Health Care in Schools. (2014). *The impact of school-connected behavioral and emotional health interventions on student academic performance: An annotated bibliography of research literature*. Washington, DC. Retrieved from http://hsrc.himmelfarb.gwu.edu/cgi/viewcontent.cgi?article=1759&context=sphhs_policy_facpubs

Centers for Disease Control and Prevention. (2014). *Youth risk behavior surveillance—United States, 2013*. Atlanta, GA: U.S. Department of Health and Human Services.

Cervantes, R. C., & Cordova, D. (2011). Life experiences of Hispanic adolescents: Developmental and language considerations in acculturation stress. *Journal of Community Psychology, 39*(3), 336–352.

Cervantes, R. C., Padilla, A. M., Napper, L. E., & Goldbach, J. T. (2013). Acculturation-related stress and mental health outcomes among three generations of Hispanic adolescents. *Hispanic Journal of Behavioral Sciences, 35*(4), 451–468.

Chae, D., Takeuchi, D., Barbeau, E., Bennett, G., Lindsey, J., & Krieger, N. (2008). Unfair treatment, racial/ethnic discrimination, ethnic identification, and smoking among Asian Americans in the National Latino and Asian American Study. *American Journal of Public Health, 98*(3), 485–492. doi:10.2105/ajph.2006.102012

Cherry, V. R., Belgrave, F. Z., Jones, W., Kennon, D. K., Gray, F. G., & Phillips, F. (1998). NTU: An Africentric approach to substance abuse prevention among African American youth. *The Journal of Primary Prevention, 18*(3), 319–339.

Cummings, J. R., Ponce, N. A., & Mays, V. M. (2010). Comparing racial/ethnic differences in mental health service use among high-need subpopulations across clinical and school-based settings. *Journal of Adolescent Health, 46*(6) 603–606.

Diller, J. V., & Moule, J. (2005). *Cultural competence: A primer for educators*. Belmont, CA: Thomson/Wadsworth.

Durlak, J. A., Weissberg, R. P., Dymnicki, A. B., Taylor, R. D., & Schellinger, K. B. (2011). The impact of enhancing students' social and emotional learning: a meta-analysis of school-based universal interventions. *Child Development*, 82(1), 405–32. doi:10.1111/j.1467-8624.2010.01564.x

Fisher, C. B., Wallace, S. A., & Fenton, R. E. (2000). Discrimination distress during adolescence. *Journal of Youth and Adolescence, 29*, 679–695. doi:10.1023/A.1026455906512

Foster, S., Rollefson, M., Doksum, T., Noonan, D., Robinson, G., & Teich, J. (2005). *School mental health services in the United States, 2002–2003* (DHHS Pub. No. (SMA) 05-4068). Rockville, MD: Center for Mental Health Services, Substance Abuse and Mental Health Services Administration.

French, S. E., Seidman, E., Allen, L., & Aber, J. L. (2000). Racial/ethnic identity, congruence with the social context, and the transition to high school. *Journal of Adolescent Research, 15*(5), 587–602. doi:10.1177/07435 58400155004

French, S. E., Seidman, E., Allen, L., & Aber, J. L. (2006). The development of ethnic identity during adolescence. *Developmental Psychology, 42*(1), 1–10.

Fuller-Rowell, T. E., Cogburn, C. D., Brodish, A. B., Peck, S. C., Malanchuk, O., & Eccles, J. S. (2012). Racial discrimination and substance use: Longitudinal associations and identity moderators. *Journal of Behavioral Medicine, 35*, 581–590. doi:10.1007/s10865-0119388-7

Gay, G. (2013). Teaching to and through cultural diversity. *Curriculum Inquiry, 43*, 48–70. doi:10.1111/curi.12002

Gibbons, F. X., Hsiu-Chen, Y., Gerrard, M., Cleveland, M. J., Cutrona, C., Simons, R. L., & Brody, G. H. (2007). Early experience with racial discrimination and conduct disorder as predictors of subsequent drug use: A critical period hypothesis. *Drug and Alcohol Dependence, 88S*, S27–S37.

Gil, A., Vega, W., & Dimas, J. (1994). Acculturative stress and personal adjustment among Hispanic adolescent boys. *Journal of Community Psychology,* 22(1), 43–54. doi:10.1002/1520-6629(199401)22:1<43::aid-jcop22902 20106>3.0.co;2-t

Gil, A., Wagner, E., & Vega, W. (2000). Acculturation, familism, and alcohol use among Latino adolescent males: Longitudinal relations. *Journal of Community Psychology, 28*(4), 443–458. doi:10.1002/1520-6629(200007)28:4 <443::aid-jcop6>3.0.co;2-a

Ginwright, S. (2010). *Black youth rising: Activism and radical healing in urban America*. New York: Teacher's College Press.

Godfrey, E. B., & Grayman, J. K. (2014). Teaching citizens: The role of open classroom climate in fostering critical consciousness among youth. *Journal of Youth and Adolescence*, 43(11), 1801–1817, http://dx.doi.org/10.1007 /s10964-013-0084-5.

Goforth, A. N., Pham, A. V., Chun, H., Castro-Olivo, S. M., & Yosai, E. R. (2016). Association of acculturative stress, Islamic practices, and internalizing symptoms among Arab American adolescents. *School Psychology Quarterly, 31*(2), 198–212.

Greenberg, M. T., Domitrovich, C. E., Graczyk, P. A., & Zins, J. E. (2005). *The study of implementation in school-based preventive interventions: Theory, research, and practice* (Vol. 3; DHHS Pub. No. SMA). Rockville, MD: Center for Mental Health Services, Substance Abuse and Mental Health Services Administration.

Greenberg, M. T., Weissberg, R. P., Utne O'Brien, M., Zins, J. E., Fredericks, L., Resnik, H., & Elias, M. J. (2003). Enhancing school-based prevention and youth development through coordinated social, emotional, and academic learning. *American Psychologist, 58*, 466–474.

Greene, M., Way, N., & Pahl, K. (2006). Trajectories of perceived adult and peer discrimination among black, Latino, and Asian American adolescents: Patterns and psychological correlates. *Developmental Psychology, 42*(2), 218–238. doi:10.1037/0012-1649.42.2.218

Hanley, M. A., & Noblit. G. W. (2009). Cultural responsiveness, racial identity and academic success: A review of the literature. Retrieved from http://www.heinz.org/userfiles/library/culture-report_final.pdf

Hecht, M. L., Marsiglia, F. F., Elek, E., Wagstaff, D. A., Kulis, S., Dustman, P., & Miller-Day, M. (2003). Culturally grounded substance use prevention: An evaluation of the Keepin' it R.E.A.L. curriculum. *Prevention Science, 4*(4), 233–248.

Hope, E. C., & Jagers, R. J. (2014). The role of sociopolitical attitudes and civic education in the civic engagement of black youth. *Journal of Research on Adolescence, 24*(3), 460–470. doi:10.1111/jora.12117

Hurwich-Reiss, E., & Gudiño, O. G. (2016). Acculturation stress and conduct problems among Latino adolescents: The impact of family factors. *Journal of Latina/o Psychology, 4*(4), 218–231.

Hussey, D., & Guo, S. (2003). Measuring behavior change in young children receiving intensive school-based mental health services. *Journal of Community Psychology, 31*, 629–639.

Hyunh, V. (2012). Ethnic microaggressions and the depressive and somatic symptoms of Latino and Asian American adolescents. *Journal of Youth and Adolescence, 41*(7), 831–846. https://doi.org/10.1007/s10964-012-9756-9

Isaacs, M. R., Huang, L. N., Hernandez, M., & Echo-Hawk, H. (2005). *The road to evidence: The intersection of evidence-based practices and cultural competence in children's mental health.* Washington, DC: National Alliance of Multi-Ethnic Behavioral Health Associations. Retrieved from https://pdfs.semanticscholar.org/aadd/7fae2a3309b02c353e602911975aecf58dcc.pdf?_ga=2.191846754.97321378.1494867279-1253870691.1494615007

Jagers, R., Lozada, F., Rivas-Drake, D., & Guillaume, C. (2017). Classroom and school predictors of civic engagement patterns among Black and Latino middle school youth. *Child Development*, 88(4), 1125–1138.

Jagers, R. J. (2016). Framing social and emotional learning among African-American youth: Toward an integrity-based approach. *Human Development, 59*, 1–3.

Jagers, R. J., Mustafaa, F., & Noel, B. (2017). Cultural integrity and African American empowerment. In M. A. Bond, C. B. Keys, & I. Serrano-García (Eds.), *Handbook of community psychology* (pp. 459–474). Washington, DC: American Psychological Association.

Jennings, J., Pearson, G., & Harris, M. (2000). Implementing and maintaining school-based mental health services in a large, urban school district. *Journal of School Health, 70*(5), 201–205.

Johnston, L. D., O'Malley, P. M., Miech, R. A., Bachman, J. G., & Schulenberg, J. E. (2015). *Monitoring the Future national survey results on drug use: 1975–2014: Overview, key findings on adolescent drug use.* Ann Arbor: Institute for Social Research, The University of Michigan.

Kiang, L., Andrews, K., Stein, G. L., Supple, A. J., & Gonzalez, L. M. (2013). Socioeconomic stress and academic adjustment among Asian American adolescents: The protective role of family obligation. *Journal of Youth and Adolescence, 42*, 837–847. doi:10.1007/s10964-013-9916-6

Kiang, L., & Fuligni, A. J. (2009). Ethnic identity and family processes among adolescents from Latin American, Asian, and European backgrounds. *Journal of Youth and Adolescence, 38*(2), 228–241.

Knight, G. P., Carlo, G., Mahrer, N. E., & Davis, A. N. (2016). The socialization of culturally related values and prosocial tendencies among Mexican-American adolescents. *Child Development, 87*(6), 1758–1771.

Knight, G. P., Gonzales, N. A., Saenz, D. S., Bonds, D. D., Germán, M., Deardorff, J., . . . Updegraff, K. A. (2010). The Mexican American cultural values scales for adolescents and adults. *Journal of Early Adolescence, 30*, 444–481. doi:10.1177/0272431609338178

Kreuter, M. W., Lukwago, S. N., Bucholtz, D. C., Clark, E. M., & Sanders-Thompson, V. (2003). Achieving cultural appropriateness in health promotion programs: Targeted and tailored approaches. *Health Education and Behavior, 30*, 133–146.

Kwame-Ross, T., Crawford, L., & Krug, E. (2011). Developmental Designs: A description of the approach and implementation in schools. *Middle Grades Research Journal, 6*, 145–162.

Ladson-Billings, G. (1995). Toward a theory of culturally relevant pedagogy. *American Educational Research Journal, 32*(3), 465–491.

Lerner, R. M., Wang, J., Champine, R. B., Warren, D. J. A., & Erickson, K. (2014). Development of civic engagement: Theoretical and methodological issues *International Journal of Developmental Science, 8*(3–4), 69–79. doi: 10.3233/DEV-14130

Levinson, M. (2007, January). *The civic achievement gap* (CIRCLE working paper 51). College Park, MD: Center for Information and Research on Civic Learning and Engagement.

Lieber, E., Nihira, K., & Mink, I. (2004). Filial piety, modernization, and the challenges of raising children for Chinese immigrants: Quantitative and qualitative evidence. *Ethos, 32*(3), 324–347. doi:10.1525/eth.2004.32.3.324

Loyd, A. B., & Williams, B. V. (2017). The potential for youth programs to promote African American youth's development of ethnic and racial identity. *Child Development Perspectives, 11*(1), 29–38.

Lozada, F., Jagers, R. J., Smith, C., Banales, J., & Hope, E. (2016). Prosocial development of black boys: An application of the sociopolitical development model. *Journal of Black Psychology*. doi:10.1177/0095798416652021

Martínez, K. J., Callejas, L., & Hernandez, M. (2010). Community-defined evidence: A bottom-up behavioral health approach to measure what works in communities of color. *Report on Emotional and Behavioral Disorders in Youth, 10*(1), 11–16.

McHale, S. M., Updegraff, K. A., Kim, J. Y., & Cansler, E. (2009). Cultural orientations, daily activities, and adjustment in Mexican American youth. *Journal of Youth and Adolescence, 38*(5), 627–641. doi:10.1007/s10964-008-9321-8

Metzger, I., Cooper, S. M., Zarrett, N., & Flory, K. (2013). Culturally sensitive risk behavior prevention programs for African American adolescents: A systematic analysis. *Clinical Child Family Psychology Review, 16*, 187–212.

Miller-Cotto, D., & Byrnes, J. P. (2016). Ethnic/racial identity and academic achievement: A meta-analytic review. *Developmental Review, 41*, 51–70.

Murray, I. & Milner, H. (2015). Toward a pedagogy of sociopolitical consciousness in outside of school programs. *The Urban Review, 47*. doi:10.1007/s11256-015-0339-4

Neblett, E., & Carter, S. (2012). The protective role of racial identity and Africentric worldview in the association between racial discrimination and blood pressure. *Psychosomatic Medicine, 74*(5), 509–516. doi:10.1097/psy.0b013e3182583a50

Neblett, E., & Roberts, S. O. (2013). Racial identity and autonomic responses to racial discrimination. *Psychophysiology, 50*, 943–953.

Neblett, E. W., Rivas-Drake, D., & Umaña-Taylor, A. J. (2012). The promise of racial and ethnic protective factors in promoting ethnic youth development. *Child Development Perspectives, 6*(3), 295–303. doi:10.1111/j.1750-8606.2012.00239.x

Newman, D. L. (2005). Ego development and ethnic identity formation in rural American Indian adolescents. *Child Development, 76*, 734–746.

Niwa, E. Y., Way, N., & Hughes, D. L. (2014). Trajectories of ethnic-racial discrimination among ethnically diverse early adolescents: Associations with psychological and social adjustment. *Child Development, 85*(6), 2339–2354.

Ozer, E. J. (2016). Youth-led participatory action research: Developmental and equity perspectives. In S. S. Horn, M. D. Ruck, & L. S. Liben (Eds.), *Equity and justice in developmental sciences: Theoretical and methodological issues* (pp. 189–207). New York: Oxford University Press.

Ozer, E. J., & Douglas, L. (2013). The impact of participatory research on urban teens: An experimental evaluation. *American Journal of Community Psychology, 51*. doi:10.1007/s10464-012-9546-2

Phinney, J. S., Jacoby, B., & Silva, C. (2007). Positive intergroup attitudes: The role of ethnic identity. *International Journal of Behavioral Development, 31*, 478–490.

Rivas-Drake, D., Hughes, D., & Way, N. (2008). A closer look at peer discrimination, ethnic identity, and psychological well-being among urban Chinese American sixth graders. *Journal of Youth and Adolescence, 37*(1), 12–21.

Rivas-Drake, D., & Marchand, A. (2016). Academic socialization among Latino families: Exploring the complementary role of cultural processes. *Research in Human Development, 13*, 225–240.

Rivas-Drake, D., Seaton, E. K., Markstrom, C., Quintana, S., Syed, M., Lee, R. M., . . . Yip, T. (2014). Ethnic and racial identity in adolescence: Implications for psychosocial, academic, and health outcomes. *Child Development, 85*(1), 40–57. doi:10.1111/cdev.12200

Rivas-Drake, D., & Stein, G. L. (in press). Multicultural developmental experiences: Implications for resilience in transitional age youth with mental illness. *Child and Adolescent Psychiatric Clinics, 26*, 271–281.

Rivas-Drake, D., Syed, M., Umaña-Taylor, A., Markstrom, C., French, S., Schwartz, S. J., & Lee, R. (2014). Feeling good, happy, and proud: A meta-analysis of positive ethnic-racial affect and adjustment. *Child Development, 85*(1), 77–102. doi:10.1111/cdev.12175

Rivas-Drake, D., & Umaña-Taylor, A. J. (2019). *Below the surface: Talking with Teens about race, ethnicity, and identity*. Princeton, NJ: Princeton University Press.

Rivas-Drake, D., Umaña-Taylor, A., Schaefer, D., & Medina, M. (2017). Ethnic-racial identity and friendships in early adolescence. *Child Development, 88*(3), 710–724.

Rivas-Drake, D., & Witherspoon, D. (2013). Racial identity from adolescence to young adulthood: Does prior neighborhood experience matter? *Child Development, 84*(6), 1918–1932.

Rodriguez, N., Flores, T., Flores, R. T., Myers, H. F., & Vriesema, C. C. (2015). Validation of the Multidimensional Acculturative Stress Inventory on adolescents of Mexican origin. *Psychological Assessment, 27*(4), 1438–1451.

Rohner, R. P. (1984). Toward a conception of culture for cross-cultural psychology. *Journal of Cross-Cultural Psychology, 15*, 111–138.

Romero, A. J., & Roberts, R. E. (2003). Stress within a bicultural context for adolescents of Mexican descent. *Cultural Diversity and Ethnic Minority Psychology, 9*, 171–184. doi:10.1037/1099-9809.9.2.171

Rones, M., & Hoagwood, K. (2000). School-based mental health services: A research review. *Clinical Child and Family Psychology Review, 3*, 223–241.

Rosenbloom, S. R., & Way, N. (2004). Experiences of discrimination among African American, Asian American, and Latino adolescents in an urban high school. *Youth & Society, 35*(4), 420–451.

Rubin, B. (2007). "There's still not justice": Youth civic identity development amid distinct school and community contexts. *Teachers College, 109*(2), 449–481.

Rudolph, B. (2005). Filial responsibility among Mexican American college students: A pilot investigation and comparison. *Journal of Hispanic Higher Education, 4*(1), 64–78. doi:10.1177/1538192704271667

Santos, C., Kornienko, C., & Rivas-Drake, D. (2017). Peer network influence on ethnic-racial identity development: A multi-site investigation. *Child Development, 88*(3), 725–742.

Schultz, L. H., Barr, D. J., & Selman, R. L. (2001). The value of a developmental approach to evaluating character development programmes: An outcome study of Facing History and Ourselves. *Journal of Moral Education, 20*(1), 3–27.

Schwartz, S. J., Unger, J. B., Baezconde-Garbanati, L., Zamboanga, B. L., Córdova, D., Lorenzo-Blanco, E. I., . . . Villamar, J. A. (2015). Testing the parent–adolescent acculturation discrepancy hypothesis: A five-wave longitudinal study. *Journal of Research on Adolescence, 26*(3), 567–586. doi:10.1111/jora.12214

Seaton, E. K., Caldwell, C. H., Sellers, R. M. & Jackson, J. S. (2008). The prevalence of perceived discrimination among African American and Caribbean Black youth. *Developmental Psychology, 44,* 1288–1297.

Seider, S., Graves, D., El-Amin, A., Soutter, M., Tamerat, J., Jennett, P., Clark, S., Malhotra, S., & Johannsen, J. (2017). Developing sociopolitical consciousness of race and social class inequality in adolescents attending progressive and no excuses urban secondary schools. *Applied Developmental Science.* doi: 10.1080/10888691.2016.1254557Shapiro, T., Meschede, T., & Osoro, S. (2013). *The roots of the widening racial wealth gap: Explaining the black-white economic divide.* Waltham, MA: Institute on Assets and Social Policy, Brandeis University.

Sellers, R. M., Copeland-Linder, N., Martin, P. P., & Lewis, R. L. (2006). Racial identity matters: The relationship between racial discrimination and psychological functioning in African American adolescents. *Journal of Research on Adolescence, 16*(2), 187–216.

Shen, Y. S., Kim, S. Y., & Wang, Y. J. (2016). Intergenerational transmission of educational attitudes in Chinese American families: Interplay of socioeconomic status and acculturation. *Child Development, 87*(5), 1601–1616. doi:10.1111/cdev.12545

Simons, R. L., Simons, L. G., Stewart, E. A., Chen, Y., & Brody, G. (2003). Incidents of discrimination and risk for delinquency: A longitudinal test of strain theory with an African American sample. *Justice Quarterly, 20,* 501–528.

Sirin, S., Ryce, P., Gupta, T., & Rogers-Sirin, L. (2013). The role of acculturative stress on mental health symptoms for immigrant adolescents: A longitudinal investigation. *Developmental Psychology, 49*(4), 736–748.

Smetana, J., & Metzger, A. (2005). Family and religious antecedents of civic involvement in middle class African American late adolescents. *Journal of Human Behavior in the Social Environment, 19*(2), 196–212.

Smith, T. B., & Silva, L. (2011). Ethnic identity and personal well-being of people of color: A meta-analysis. *Journal of Counseling Psychology, 58*(1), 42–60. doi:10.1037/a0021528

Smokowski, P. R., & Bacallao, M. L. (2006). Acculturation and aggression in Latino adolescents: A structural model focusing on cultural risk factors and assets. *Journal of Abnormal Child Psychology, 34*(5), 657–671. doi:10.1007/s10802-006-9049-4

Smokowski, P. R., Rose, R. A., & Bacallao, M. (2010). Influence of risk factors and cultural assets on Latino adolescents' trajectories of self-esteem and internalizing problems. *Child Psychiatry and Human Development, 41*, 133–155. doi:10.1007/s10578-009-0157-6

Stein, G. L., Cupito, A., Mendez, J., Prandoni, J., Huq, N., & Westerberg, D. (2014). Familism through a developmental lens, *Journal of Latina/o Psychology*, 2(4), 224–250. doi:10.1037lat0000025

Stein, G. L., Gonzalez, L. M., Cupito, A. M., Kiang, L., & Supple, A. J. (2015). The protective role of familism in the lives of Latino adolescents. *Journal of Family Issues*, *36*(10), 1255–1273. doi:10.1177/0192513X13502480

Stein, G. L., & Polo, A. J. (2014). Parent–child cultural value gaps and depressive symptoms among Mexican American youth. *Journal of Child and Family Studies*, 23(2), 189–199.

Stein, G. L., Rivas-Drake, D., & Camacho, T. (2017). Ethnic identity and familism among Latino college students: A test of prospective associations. *Emerging Adulthood*, 5(2), 106–115. doi:10.1177/2167696816657234

Strozer, J., Juszczak, L., & Ammerman, A. (2010). *School-based health center census*. Washington, DC: National Assembly on School-Based Health Care. Retrieved from http://censusreport.sbh4all.org/

Syvertsen, A. K., Wray-Lake, L., Flanagan, C. A., Osgood, D. W., & Briddell, L. (2011). Thirty year trends in U.S. adolescents' civic engagement: A story of changing participation and educational differences. *Journal of Research on Adolescence*, *21*(3), 586–594.

Telzer, E. H. (2011). Expanding the acculturation gap-distress model: An integrative review of research. *Human Development*, *53*(6), 313–340. doi:10.1159/000322476

Telzer, E. H., Masten, C., Berkman, E., Lieberman, M., & Fuligni, A. (2010). Gaining while giving: An fMRI study of the rewards of family assistance among white and Latino youth. *Social Neuroscience*, *5*(5–6), 508–518. doi:10.1080/17470911003687913

Telzer, E. H., Yuen, C., Gonzales, N., & Fuligni, A. J. (2016). Filling gaps in the acculturation gap-distress model: Heritage cultural maintenance and adjustment in Mexican-American families. *Journal of Youth and Adolescence*, *45*(7), 1412–1425. doi:10.1007/s10964-015-0408-8

Thomas, M., & Choi, J. B. (2006). Acculturative stress and social support among Korean and Indian immigrant adolescents in the United States. *Journal of Sociology & Social Welfare*, *33*, 123–143.

Torney-Purta, J., Amadeo, J.-A., & Richardson, W. K. (2007). Civic service across the life course. In A. M. McBride & M. Sherraden (Eds.), *Civic service worldwide: Impacts and inquiry* (pp. 95–132). New York: M.E. Sharpe.

Torney-Purta, J., Lehmann, R., Oswald, H., & Schulz, W. (2001). *Citizenship and education in twenty-eight countries: Civic knowledge and engagement at age 14*. Amsterdam, Netherlands: IEA.

Triandis, H., Lambert, W., Berry, J., Lonner, W., Heron, A., Brislin, R., & Draguns, J. (Eds.). (1980). *Handbook of cross-cultural psychology* (Vols. 1–6). Boston: Allyn & Bacon.

Tummala-Narra, P., Deshpande, A., & Kaur, J. (2016). South Asian adolescents' experiences of acculturative stress and coping. *American Journal of Orthopsychiatry*, *86*(2), 194–211.

Umaña-Taylor, A. J. (2016). A post-racial society in which ethnic-racial discrimination still exists and has significant consequences for youths' adjustment. *Current Directions in Psychological Science, 25*(2), 111–118.

Umaña-Taylor, A. J., Quintana, S. M., Lee, R. M., Cross, W. E., Rivas-Drake, D., Schwartz, S. J., . . . Seaton, E. (2014). Ethnic and racial identity during adolescence and into young adulthood: An integrated conceptualization. *Child Development, 85*(1). doi:10.1111/cdev.12196

U.S. Census Bureau. (2014). *2014 National population projections—People and households*. Retrieved from http://www.census.gov/population/projections/data/national/2014.html

U.S. Department of Education. (2014a). *National Center for Educational Statistics*. Retrieved from https://nces.ed.gov/fastfacts/display.asp?id=372

U.S. Department of Education. (2014b). *Office of Civil Rights Data Snapshot*. School Discipline Issue Brief No.1 (March). Retrieved from http://ocrdata.ed.gov/Downloads/CRDC-School-Discipline-Snapshot.pdf

U.S. Health and Human Services. (2011). *Department action plan to reduce racial and ethnic health disparities: A nation free of disparities in health and health care*. Retrieved from https://minorityhealth.hhs.gov/npa/files/Plans/HHS/HHS_Plan_complete.pdf

Watts, R., Diemer, M., & Voight, A. (2011). Critical consciousness: Current status and future directions. In C. A. Flanagan & B. D. Christens (Eds.), *Youth civic development: Work at the cutting edge* (Vol. 134). San Francisco: Josey-Bass.

Watts, R., & Guessous, O. (2006). Sociopolitical development: The missing link in research and policy on adolescents. In S. Ginwright, P. Noguera, & J. Cammarota (Eds.), *Beyond resistance! Youth activism and community change: New democratic possibilities for practice and policy for America's youth* (pp. 59–80). New York: Routledge.

Watts, R. J., & Flanagan, C. (2007). Pushing the envelope on youth civic engagement: A developmental and liberation psychology perspective. *Journal of Community Psychology, 35*, 779–792.

Watts, R. J., & Hipolito-Delgado, C. P. (2015). Thinking ourselves to liberation?: Advancing sociopolitical action in critical consciousness. *Urban Review: Issues and Ideas in Public Education*, *47*(5), 847–867.

Weissberg, R. P., Durlak, J. A., Domitrovich, C. E., & Gullotta, T. P. (2015). Social and emotional learning: Past, present and future. In J. A. Durlak, C. E. Domitrovich, R. P. Weissberg and, T. P. Gullotta (Eds.), *Handbook of social and emotional learning: Research and practice* (pp. 3–19). New York, NY: Guilford Press.

Westheimer, J., & Kahne, J. (2004). What kind of citizen? The politics of educating for democracy. *American Educational Research Journal*, *41*(2), 237–269. doi: 10.3102/00028312041002237.

Witherspoon, D., Seaton, E., & Rivas-Drake, D. (2016). Neighborhood characteristics and expectations of racially discriminatory experiences among African American adolescents. *Child Development*, *87*(5), 1367–1378.

Wong, C., Eccles, J., & Sameroff, A. (2003). The influence of ethnic discrimination and ethnic identification on African American adolescents' school and socioemotional adjustment. *Journal of Personality*, *71*(6), 1197–1232.

Yip, T. (2015). The effects of ethnic/racial discrimination and sleep quality on depressive symptoms and self-esteem trajectories among diverse adolescents. *Journal of Youth and Adolescence*, *44*, 419–430.

Zeiders, K. H., Doane, L. D., & Roosa, M. W. (2012). Perceived discrimination and diurnal cortisol: Examining relations among Mexican American adolescents. *Hormones and Behavior*, *61*(4), 541–548.

Zeiders, K. H., Hoyt, L. T., & Adam, E. K. (2014). Associations between self-reported discrimination and diurnal cortisol rhythms among young adults: The moderating role of racial-ethnic minority status *Psychoneuroendocrinology*, *50*, 280–288.

Zeiders, K. H., Updegraff, K., Kuo, S., Umaña-Taylor, A, McHale, S. (2017). Perceived discrimination and Mexican-origin young adults' sleep duration and variability: The moderating role of cultural orientations. *Journal of Youth and Adolescence*, *46*(8), 1851–1861. doi:10.1007/s10964-016-0544-9.

Zins, J., Weissberg, R., Wang, M., & Walberg, H. (2004). *Building academic success on social and emotional learning: What does the research say?* New York: Teachers College Press.

CHAPTER SIX

Gender Identity and Sexual Orientation

Tracey G. Scherr and Shannon D. Snapp

LGBTQ Youth's Experiences of Unsafe School Climates

Recent polls suggest roughly 4% of the U.S. population (9 million people) identifies as lesbian, gay, bisexual, transgender, queer, or questioning (LGBTQ; Gates, 2011). Although we do not have census data to document the number of LGBTQ school-aged youth, the 2015 Youth Behavior Risk Survey included questions about sexual identity. Eight percent of respondents in 9th–12th grades indicated they identify as LGB (Kann et al., 2016). There is clear and consistent evidence that LGBTQ youth experience verbal and physical harassment due to their actual or perceived sexual orientation or gender identity (SOGI). To that end, 67% of LGBTQ students (ages 13–21) report significantly higher rates of biased-based bullying that has been attributed to their sexual orientation and gender expression (approximately 60%) compared to their straight peers (14% and 18%, respectively; Greytak, Kosciw, Villenas, & Giga, 2016). Further, a meta-analysis with 18 independent studies and over 50,000 middle and high school students found similar results: across all studies, sexual non-majority students reported higher levels of school-based harassment compared to straight students (Toomey & Russell, 2016). While reports of perceived school safety have improved for LGBTQ students compared to a decade ago

(Greytak et al., 2016), LGBTQ youth have continued to experience disproportionate rates of harassment and violence (Goodenow, Watson, Adjei, Homma, & Saewyc, 2016).

Homophobia and transphobia from school staff are among the reported reasons for disproportionate rates of SOGI harassment and bullying among LGBTQ students. Approximately 15% of students, regardless of SOGI status, reported hearing homophobic comments from their teachers, and 13% of students heard teachers make negative statements about transgender individuals (Greytak et al., 2016). In addition to demonstrated bias from school staff, students have indicated teachers regularly fail to intervene in SOGI-based bullying (Snapp, Burdge, Licona, Moody, & Russell, 2015), a non-intervention that condones and normalizes such behavior.

Bullying, harassment, and the implications of such behavior should be of concern to educators and policy makers. We now have consistent evidence, supported by Meyer's (2003) minority stress theory, that LGBTQ individuals experience unique stressors due to rejection, discrimination, and homophobia (which often becomes internalized), and these stressors make LGBTQ people vulnerable to mental and physical health issues.

While LGBTQ students face disproportionate victimization based on gender identity, expression, and sexual orientation, youth also have multiple identities that intersect to affect their life experiences and levels of risk and resilience. In a 2015 joint resolution about SOGI diversity, the American Psychological Association (APA) and National Association of School Psychologists (NASP) specified that LGBTQ youth "with intersecting identities face additional challenges to their psychological well-being as a result of the negative consequence of discrimination" (APA & NASP, 2015, p. 5). For example, LGBTQ youth may face discrimination based on race or ethnicity, religion, country of origin, and physical or psychological disabilities, among other characteristics. For instance, in the most recent national GLSEN (formerly the Gay, Lesbian & Straight Education Network) climate study, LGBTQ students who were also Asian/South or Asian/Pacific Islander were least likely to be victimized based on gender expression or sexual orientation and White/European American LGBTQ students were least likely to be victimized based on race or ethnicity (Kosciw et al., 2016). The previously mentioned APA/NASP resolution identified low SES and living in less diverse smaller towns and rural areas as additional potential stressors (2015). The latter was corroborated in the GLSEN climate study as being due to more victimization and less access to supportive resources (Kosciw et al., 2016). Scholars in child and youth development have begun to attend to the issues of students with intersecting identities and have developed frameworks to study intersectionality and reduce inequities among diverse young people (for examples, see Bauer, 2014; Cole, 2009; Russell, 2016).

Outcomes Related to Harmful School Experiences

SOGI-based harassment and bullying can have severe consequences for young people's physical and mental health as well as their future success. There is a consistent body of research that has documented the mental health disparities among LGBTQ youth and young adults (for review, see Russell & Fish, 2016). For example, LGBTQ youth experience depression, eating disorders, suicidality, and suicide ideation at disproportionately higher rates than their straight peers (Fergusson, Horwood, Ridder, & Beautrais, 2005; Kann et al., 2016; Marshal, Dietz, Friedman, Stall, & Smith, 2011). One of the predominant risk factors for mental health issues among LGBT youth is discrimination and stigma, negative views of their intersecting identities, often found in social institutions that are meant to protect young people, such as schools (Russell & Fish, 2016). Youth who experience SOGI-based victimization also report higher rates of depression, suicide ideation and attempts, and substance use compared to those who face non-bias-based victimization (Russell, Sinclair, Poteat, & Koenig, 2012).

The implications for SOGI-based harassment do not stop at compromised health. Youth who are bullied due to their SOGI often skip or miss school because they feel unsafe (Russell et al., 2012). More recently, evidence has also demonstrated LGBTQ youth are disproportionately disciplined in school compared to their peers (Chmielewski, Belmonte, Stoudt, & Fine, 2016; GLSEN, 2016; Himmelstein & Bruckner, 2011; Poteat, Scheer, & Chong, 2016) despite the fact that they do not engage in more punishable acts (Himmelstein & Bruckner, 2011; Poteat et al., 2016). One of the reasons youth are disciplined is because they are truant, typically due to feeling unsafe in school (Snapp, Hoenig, Fields, & Russell, 2015). Similarly, LGBTQ youth are disciplined for fighting back when they have experienced SOGI-based victimization and have often resorted to self-protection because school staff did not intervene (Snapp et al., 2015). LGBTQ youth are already vulnerable to disengagement in school due to lack of belonging, exclusivity, and harassment (Watson & Russell, 2014). When they are disciplined, they are particularly susceptible to school pushout and the school-to-prison pipeline, and this risk can be especially heightened for LGBTQ youth of color (Burdge, Licona, & Hyemingway, 2014; Poteat et al., 2016; Snapp & Licona, 2016; Snapp, Hoenig, et al., 2015). In sum, when youth are not in school either because they are afraid or because they have been pushed out through unresponsive or harmful policies and practices, their potential to learn and be successful in the future is clearly at risk.

Strategies to Support LGBTQ Youth in School and Build Protective Factors

Researchers have focused much effort on risk among LGBTQ youth and less on resilience. Although LGBTQ students face many challenges that can result in mental health difficulties and obstacles to academic achievement, the minority stress model (Meyer, 2003) also suggests protective factors can serve as a firewall to some of the vulnerabilities LGBTQ people experience. In response, nearly a decade ago, researchers pointed to four strategies schools could take to improve school safety for LGBTQ youth: (1) enumerated anti-bullying policies that ban SOGI-based discrimination and harassment; (2) supportive, trained teachers; (3) supportive LGBTQ-affiliated clubs such as Gay Straight Alliances (GSAs); and (4) access to inclusive and responsive curricula (Russell, Kosciw, Horn, & Saewyc, 2010). Since then, multiple strategies have been examined to promote resilience, improve learning and safety, and reduce disproportionate discipline among LGBTQ youth, such as the elimination of punitive discipline and high stakes testing (for additional strategies, see Snapp & Licona, 2016; Snapp & Russell, 2016). In addition, several professional organizations in child development, psychology, and education have developed resolutions, position statements, and policy reports about providing safe and responsive school environments for LGBTQ students (e.g., APA, NASP, and Society for Research in Child Development). In what follows, we briefly illustrate the evidence behind those original four strategies and add additional strategies, including the use of supportive language in school as well as support services and school readiness assessments.

Enumerated Anti-Bullying Policies and Inclusive and Supportive Policies

Students in schools with harassment and anti-bullying policies that include specific language enumerating types of prohibited bullying (i.e., actual or perceived gender identity, gender expression, sexual orientation, and other possible characteristics) feel safer than those in schools with non-enumerated policies (APA & NASP, 2015; Kull, Kosciw, & Greytak, 2015; Russell et al., 2010). Further, students in the most recent GLSEN climate study who attended schools with comprehensive bullying policies were less likely to hear negative comments about gender expression or sexual orientation, were more likely to report staff intervened when anti-LGBT remarks were made, were less likely to experience anti-LGBT victimization at school, and were more likely to report victimization to staff, who they were more likely to believe would respond effectively (Kosciw et al., 2016). Additionally, a study of lesbian and gay 11th grade students in Oregon revealed inclusive anti-bullying policies were related to significantly reduced risk for suicide attempts within the past year, even after controlling for sex, race or ethnicity, and exposure to peer victimization (Hatzenbuehler & Keyes, 2013).

As of 2011, 70.5% of all 13,181 U.S. school districts had anti-bullying policies. Yet, of all school districts, only 1 in 10 enumerated both gender identity/expression and sexual orientation in their anti-bullying policies (Kull et al., 2015). Further, in the GLSEN climate survey no change was reported between 2013 and 2015 in percent of students indicating their school had a comprehensive anti-bullying policy, despite this being a relatively direct way schools can improve safety, climate, and student well-being (Kosciw et al., 2016). Districts and schools that wish to develop an enumerated anti-bullying policy may find GLSEN's model policies and related commentary and resources helpful (available at https://www.glsen.org/article/model-laws-policies). GLSEN also has a state legislation model available for those who wish to advocate for such.

It is insufficient to have a policy if students are unaware of it, though. In the Kull and colleagues (2015) study, 34% of LGBT students in schools that enumerated sexual orientation were aware of this declaration and 18% of LGBT students were aware when their schools specified gender identity/expression in their policies. Awareness of enumerated policies contributed to LGBT students being more likely to report bullying incidents to school staff, who responded more effectively; greater perceived and actual safety; more supportive staff; and stronger feelings of belonging (Kull et al., 2015).

All students can be negatively affected by school policies and practices that are punitive and discriminatory. Examples of such practices include being disciplined for public affection, being discouraged or prohibited from wearing clothing deemed inappropriate for their assigned sex, discussing or writing about LGBTQ topics in assignments or during extracurricular activities, attending an event with a student of the same gender, advertising or forming a GSA, wearing clothing and accessories in support of LGBTQ issues, using their affirmed name or pronouns, using bathrooms or locker rooms consistent with their affirmed gender, and playing sports based on their LGBTQ status. The majority of LGBTQ students (66%) have reported they had been subject to at least one of the aforementioned policies or practices (Kosciw et al., 2016).

Most (71%) LGBTQ students in the GLSEN climate study reported attending schools that engaged in segregated and binary gender practices such as with graduation regalia, prom or homecoming courts, and school pictures (Kosciw et al., 2016). The APA and NASP, in their 2014 joint resolution, asserted school administrators should allow "all students, staff, and teachers to have access to the sex-segregated facilities, activities, and programs that are consistent with their gender identity" (p. 9). Further, gender segregation should be avoided for uniforms, dances, and other extracurricular activities (APA & NASP, 2015). Gender Spectrum's (2015) guide to supporting transgender students includes specific guidance and explanations for recommended policies about dress codes, restrooms, locker rooms, overnight field trips, competitive sports, health and physical education classes, and school dances. GLSEN and the National Center for Transgender Equality's (2016) Model Policy on Transgender and Gender Nonconforming Students also contains language and explanations for recommended policies on traditionally gender-segregated activities and facilities as well as for several other topics that have been addressed in this chapter.

Further, disciplinary policies that punish students for nonviolent acts such as public displays of affection toward a same-gender peer and dress code violations are part of the reason discipline disparities exist among the LGBTQ community (Snapp, Hoenig, et al., 2015). Schools should adopt alternatives to zero tolerance practices such as restorative justice (Snapp & Russell, 2016) and related positive practices such as access to school counselors, referrals to supportive programs, and conflict resolution, all of which have been associated with fewer reports of SOGI-related bullying (Day, Snapp, & Russell, 2016) and lower rates of suspension among LGBTQ students (Snapp, Day, & Russell, 2017).

Teacher Support and Training

Foremost, school personnel must not, themselves, discriminate against students. It is not enough for teachers not to cause harm; they must also intervene when it is present (APA & NASP, 2015; Russell et al., 2010). Yet, only 20% of U.S. school districts required accountability in the form of reporting bullying incidents to district administration or state agencies (Kull et al., 2015). Despite the aforementioned effectiveness of enumerated antibullying policies in improving safety and school climate for LGBT students, accountability requirements for reporting bullying to district administration or state agencies did not seem to significantly affect LGBT students' school experiences according to Kull and colleagues (2015). As the authors concluded, districts may not have followed through with accountability requirements or may not have implemented them in ways that effectively addressed safety of LGBT students (Kull et al., 2015).

Further, when students do report harassment or assault at school, staff do not always respond. For example, 64% of all students in the GLSEN climate study who reported an incident indicated school staff either did nothing in response or told them to ignore the problem, and 58% of LGBTQ students who had been victimized in school indicated they did not report the problem to school staff because they did not believe anything helpful would be done in response or feared the problem might worsen as a result (Kosciw et al., 2016). Requirements for accountability for reporting about harassment, assault, and bullying must be established, yet they will only be helpful if staff follow them and are trained in appropriate, effective responses to reports.

School psychologists and other educators can support LGBTQ students by "modeling ethical practice through accepting and affirming attitudes, language, and behaviors in daily interactions with all students and staff" (NASP, 2011, p. 4). Virtually all respondents to the GLSEN climate survey indicated they knew of at least one supportive school staff member, yet only 64% could identify six or more supportive adults at school. In addition, less than half (40%) viewed their school's administration as supportive (Kosciw et al., 2016). Safe space identifiers, such as posters and stickers, can signal the presence of a supportive adult to LGBTQ students and allies (NASP, 2016).

In order for teachers to be responsive and supportive, they must be trained. Educators need training in "the full range of sex development, gender expression, gender identity, and sexual orientation" and the needs of LGBTQ students, in particular, in order to best understand and support them (APA & NASP, 2015, p. 8). Results of some studies indicate providing professional development for teachers about LGBTQ topics contributes to improvements in teacher intervention in related bullying, harassment, and discrimination (NASP, 2011; Russell et al., 2010). Specifics such as content and number and length of sessions should be determined by data from needs assessments and climate surveys of particular schools and by consideration of district resources, including whether training can be provided by qualified student services personnel or by community providers (e.g., local or national LGBTQ advocacy agencies).

Specific training regarding challenges faced by many LGBTQ students and how to best support LGBTQ students must occur in college and university teacher preparation programs and be offered by public school district employers in order to be comprehensive, ongoing, and relevant. Professional development should include affirmative, non-binary, evidence-based methods of protecting and supporting students' mental health and academic achievement. Policies and procedures that deny, squelch, or oppose the range of identities and expressions negatively affect students' mental health and contribute to school climates and community cultures that feed bullying and other forms of discrimination. Further, such educational opportunities should extend beyond school personnel to students, parents, and the larger community (APA & NASP, 2015). Despite the importance of this type of professional development, only 20% of U.S. school districts have required such training (Kull et al., 2015).

Gender and Sexuality Alliances

Supportive educators might serve as faculty advisors for Gender and Sexuality Alliances (GSAs). Student organizations that have been commonly referred to as Gay Straight Alliances are more often being called GSAs to better capture that gender diverse students are welcome to participate in addition to students with diverse sexual orientations and allies (NASP, 2016; Savage, 2017). Fifty-four percent of students aged 13–21 years have reported their school has a GSA (Kosciw et al., 2016).

The presence of GSAs appears to be a powerful influence as their existence alone has been found to be related to both perceived and actual safety and less discrimination for LGBTQ students and their peers (APA & NASP, 2015; Poteat, 2017; Poteat, Heck, Yoshikawa, & Calzo, 2017). LGBTQ students with GSAs heard less negative language about gender expression, less homophobic comments, and were more likely to report school staff intervened regarding such comments (still only 21%; Kosciw et al., 2016). Students in schools with GSAs have reported greater perceived and actual safety, missed less school due to safety concerns, identified more supportive staff, and felt more connected to their schools than those in schools without GSAs (Kosciw et al., 2016; Poteat, 2017). Supportive resources, especially GSAs, are not as accessible to middle school students compared to those in high schools, according to Kosciw and colleagues (2016). Also, middle schoolers have reported hearing more negative language about gender expression and sexual orientation, and being victimized more often (Kosciw et al., 2016).

Sensitive and Inclusive Curricula

Children need to feel safe in school physically, emotionally, and regarding their identities and they need to see themselves represented in curricula in order to thrive emotionally and academically (Snapp & Russell, 2016; Snapp, Burdge, et al., 2015). Marginalized youth often report feeling invisible in school curricula (Cammarota, 2007; Tintiangco-Cubales et al., 2015). Invisibility sends messages about societal values, which, in turn, can affect feelings of self-esteem, belonging, and safety (Grant & Zwier, 2011; Ladson-Billings, 2009; Sleeter, 2011).

When LGBTQ people, history, or events were taught, 18% of LGBTQ students have indicated the information was positive and 22% indicated they were taught negative depictions (Kosciw et al., 2016). History lessons should include pioneers in LGBTQ rights work and materials that feature famous LGBTQ athletes should be available in school libraries and sports facilities, for instance. Further, LGBTQ topics need to be addressed across the curricula. For example, heteronormative sex education excludes many groups of students. Research has indicated sex education that includes LGBTQ issues results in reduced risk-taking among LGBTQ students (Russell et al., 2010). Further, LGBTQ students who attended schools with inclusive curricula have heard less negative language about gender expression and sexual orientation, felt safer, were less likely to miss school, were more positive about graduation and post-secondary education, perceived peers as more accepting, and felt more connected to their schools (Kosciw et al., 2016; Snapp, Burdge, et al., 2015; Snapp, McGuire, Sinclair, Gabrion, & Russell, 2015). The NASP (2011) position statement describes additional ways to integrate LGBTQ issues into curricula, including reading books authored by LGBTQ writers, introducing theories of gender identity development in science classes, and analyzing LGBTQ demographic data in math classes, among others (for additional teaching materials about LGBTQ topics, see Gender Spectrum, Welcoming Schools, and Teaching Tolerance).

Inclusive and Supportive Language

Use of non-presumptive language regarding gender helps create inclusive classrooms for all students. For example, instead of the gender binary use of "boys" and "girls" when addressing a class, one might refer to a group of students as "first grade scholars" (Savage, 2017). Instead of inquiring whether an older student or faculty member has a "boyfriend, girlfriend, wife, or husband," one could inquire about their "significant other or partner." Acronyms also attempt to capture the range of diversity in gender identity and expression and sexual orientation. Preferred acronyms change, responsively, over time as well. In this chapter, the authors have used the LGBTQ acronym, yet NASP has been using the LGBTQI2-S acronym more recently to include intersex and two spirit individuals. Educators should always follow the lead of individuals themselves regarding how they identify. Also, school forms should be inclusive in multiple respects, including allowing for multiple gender, ethnicity, and family structure options as well as the option not to specify any of these.

In addition, there is some more specific terminology that should be avoided. For example, transgender is an adjective, not a noun or verb (Savage, 2017). People are transgender. They are not "a transgender," or many "transgenders," nor are they "transgendered." Someone who is transgender may decide to transition. "Sex change" has been replaced with "sex affirmation surgery" or the broader "transition" to help better convey the purpose of aligning body and mind (Savage, 2017). Further, "queer" is a term that has been reclaimed by many individuals of non-majority sexual orientations and gender identities. However, to many in older generations, and if used spitefully, this term may be inappropriate for the cisgender, heterosexual person to use unless the person to whom they are referring identifies this way (Savage, 2017). At the student level, use of affirmed or declared (instead of assigned) names and pronouns, as requested by students, and without demanding the indignity of medical "proof" communicates care and support (Savage, 2017).

Simultaneously, confidentiality about students' SOGI is essential due to the physical safety (i.e., increased potential for violent victimization) and social-emotional risks (e.g., social rejection, rejection from family resulting in foster care placement or homelessness, trauma) attached to outing someone without their consent. According to NASP (2014), for example, school psychologists are bound by the organization's Principles for Professional Ethics to maintain confidentiality of SOGI of students, parents, and school personnel. School psychologists are ethically bound to respect individuals' need for control of this sensitive information about themselves. In their work in schools, supportive services professionals and educators must adhere to the ethical codes of their professional organizations and simultaneously comply with related federal, state, and local laws. Resources for assistance with clarifying, defending, and advocating for the rights of LGBTQ students include school district legal counsel, state departments of public instruction, Lambda Legal, the American Civil Liberties Union, and the Southern Poverty Law Center.

Supportive Services for LGBTQ Students

LGBTQ students may benefit from counseling inside or outside of school, especially when they have experienced bullying and when they need support regarding others' responses to them as gender diverse individuals or to their sexual orientation (NASP, 2016). LGBTQ students are at elevated risk for a variety of challenges to their mental health as described at the beginning of this chapter. Risk can be particularly heightened as students "come out," or reveal their identities to others (Scherr, 2011; Scherr & Mayer, 2018). Supportive services professionals may help students develop related plans. For transgender students, the *Schools in Transition* guide contains templates for developing support plans and transition plans for individual students (Gender Spectrum, 2015). Should social-emotional assessment become necessary, supportive services professionals may decide to interpret results based on combined norms if available, based on norms consistent with a student's affirmed identity if binary, or based on both female and male norms and compare corresponding decision differences (Westheimer et al., 2016). When students experience suicidal ideation, also an elevated risk among LGBTQ youth, risk assessments are imperative so that corresponding treatment occurs (Scherr, 2011).

To avoid unnecessarily pathologizing and further stigmatizing transgender students, some key facts must be understood. Gender dysphoria appears in the current *Diagnostic and Statistical Manual of Mental Disorders* (American Psychiatric Association, 2013). However, "current research confirms that feeling a mismatch between one's biological sex and gender identity is not psychopathology, though persons may experience clinical levels of anxiety, depression, and stress due to genetic predisposition or environmental factors related to acceptance" (Westheimer, Persinger, Cannava, & Klotz, 2016, p. 3).

As with all students, schools may or may not be able to meet LGBTQ students' mental health needs on their own. Thus, supportive services professionals should collaborate with community programs that support LGBTQ students and families (NASP, 2011, 2016). In addition, supportive services professionals should be aware of various treatment options, including those that have been most successful in helping students and families and those that have been damaging in order to best advise families and make useful referrals. For instance, use of hormone blockers to prevent puberty has been shown to be related to improved mental health for many transgender students (Westheimer et al., 2016). Conversely, many professional organizations (e.g., APA, NASP) have expressed opposition to the damaging effects of conversion therapies that attempt to alter SOGI (Just the Facts Coalition, 2008) and some states have passed legislation outlawing such damaging practices.

Conclusions

The evidence from the past two decades on LGBTQ youth is clear: LGBTQ youth face disproportionate bullying and harassment in schools (Toomey & Russell, 2016), and now we also know they experience higher rates of punitive discipline (Chmielewski et al., 2016; Himmelstein & Bruckner, 2011; Kosciw et al., 2016; Poteat et al., 2016). The minority stress (Meyer, 2003) they experience due to this discrimination by both peers and school staff often has severe implications for their emotional and physical well-being that could deter their future success, possibly over their life course (Hatzenbuehler, 2009). The onus to create safe, optimal learning environments that support all students must be shouldered by schools and policy makers.

Advocating for inclusive, supportive schools can be daunting due to the scope of systemic change needed and the potential for encountering resistance from stakeholders. One way schools can start is by conducting a readiness assessment to see where they stand first. Readiness assessment tools can help advocates highlight school strengths and areas in need of improvement in a more formal, objective manner that might be received by stakeholders interested in reducing liability at minimum and improving students' lives at best. For example, Savage, Springborg, and Lagerstrom (2016) developed the *School Building Transgender & Gender Diverse Readiness Assessment*. The assessment allows teams to systematically identify strengths and weaknesses in multiple areas and prioritize how quickly to address identified deficiencies. For those desiring a briefer assessment, Gender Spectrum (n.d.) published the *Gender Inclusive Schools Assessment* available on the organization's website.

Similarly, schools are also encouraged to collect data on students' experiences with school climate, especially regarding LGBTQ topics. Data allow schools to identify areas in need of improvement and assess changes following improvement efforts, and create opportunities for LGBTQ youth to be represented in both science and policy (Snapp, Russell, Arredondo, & Skiba, 2016). For example, they might opt to use the online GLSEN Local School Climate Survey (available at http://localsurvey.glsen.org/).

Much attention in this chapter has been focused on the importance of providing enumerated anti-bullying policies that ban SOGI-based discrimination and harassment. As Kull and colleagues (2015) suggested, stakeholders can advocate for LGBTQ anti-bullying laws and amendments, professional development for educators about why and how to intervene, reporting accountability, and funding for local districts to implement established mandates. This advocacy can be applied to state-, district-, and school-level policy development and implementation as well (Kull et al., 2015).

Not only must school staff not discriminate against students, but they must also intervene to stop harassment, assault, and bullying of students, including those who are LGBTQ. In order to do so effectively and to be supportive of diverse students, school staff require training in their university preparation programs and through professional development opportunities throughout their careers. Supportive educators might serve as faculty advisors for GSAs, student organizations that have been shown to improve safety and well-being for students, especially those who are LGBTQ. In addition, students need access to inclusive and responsive curricula that features LGBTQ people and topics in favorable ways.

Several punitive and discriminatory school policies and practices have been described in this chapter along with suggestions about avoiding them and implementing more inclusive practices. For example, segregated and gender binary methods can be replaced with practices more inclusive and affirming of gender diversity. Further, disproportionate discipline among LGBTQ youth can be decreased or eliminated by implementing supportive, not punitive, disciplinary policies and practices.

Given LGBTQ youth's experiences of unsafe school climates and negative outcomes related to harmful school experiences, supportive services personnel are needed to advocate for better practices at universal and individual levels to help LGBTQ students build resiliency. Counseling, social-emotional assessments, risk assessments, and referrals to mental health and other supportive community agencies are examples of services these professionals may provide. Hence, supportive services professionals must be aware of treatment options that have demonstrated the greatest success in helping LGBTQ youth.

Finally, these changes cannot happen without both top-down and bottom-up collaboration (Snapp & Russell, 2016). All vested stakeholders have an obligation to support the well-being and success of all students, especially the most vulnerable. The strategies described here are clear, doable, and have been consistently documented as relevant and effective. It is past time to move beyond the repeated documentation of strategies schools *should* take to support LGBTQ youth and instead make the commitment to "make it better" for youth now.

References

American Psychiatric Association. (2013). *Diagnostic and statistical manual of mental disorders* (5th ed.). Washington, DC: Author.

American Psychological Association & National Association of School Psychologists. (2015). *Resolution on gender and sexual orientation diversity in children and adolescents in schools*. Retrieved from http://www.apa.org/about/policy/orientation-diversity.aspx

Bauer, G. R. (2014). Incorporating intersectionality theory into population health research methodology: Challenges and the potential to advance health equity. *Social Science & Medicine, 110*, 10–17. doi:10.1016/j.socscimed.2014.03.022

Burdge, H., Licona, A. C., & Hyemingway, Z. T. (2014). *LGBTQ youth of color: Discipline disparities, school push-out, and the school-to-prison pipeline.* San Francisco: Gay-Straight Alliance Network; Tucson, AZ: Crossroads Collaborative at the University of Arizona.

Cammarota, J. (2007). A social justice approach to achievement: Guiding Latina/o students toward educational attainment with a challenging, socially relevant curriculum. *Equity & Excellence in Education, 40*, 87–96. doi:10.1080/10665680601015153

Chmielewski, J., Belmonte, K., Stoudt, B., & Fine, M. (2016). Intersectional inque(e)ries: Participatory research on discipline disparities at the race/sexuality/gender nexus. In R. J. Skiba, K. Mediratta, & M. K. Rausch (Eds.), *Inequality in school discipline: Research and practice to reduce disparities* (pp. 171–188). New York: Palgrave MacMillan.

Cole, E. R. (2009). Intersectionality and research in psychology. *American Psychologist, 64*, 170–180. doi:10.1037/a0014564

Day, J. K., Snapp, S. D., & Russell, S. T. (2016). Supportive, not punitive, practices reduce homophobic bullying and improve school connectedness. *Psychology of Sexual Orientation and Gender Diversity, 3*, 416–425.

Fergusson, D. M., Horwood, L. J., Ridder, E. M., & Beautrais, A. L. (2005). Sexual orientation and mental health in a birth cohort of young adults. *Psychological Medicine, 35*, 971–981.

Gates, G. J. (2011). *How many people are lesbian, gay, bisexual, and transgender?* Los Angeles: Williams Institute. Retrieved from https://williamsinstitute.law.ucla.edu/wp-content/uploads/Gates-How-Many-People-LGBT-Apr-2011.pdf

Gender Spectrum. (2015). *Schools in transition: A guide for supporting transgender students in K-12 schools.* Oakland, CA: Author. Retrieved from https://www.genderspectrum.org/staging/wp-content/uploads/2015/08/Schools-in-Transition-2015.pdf

Gender Spectrum. (n.d.). *Gender Inclusive Schools Assessment.* Oakland, CA: Author. Retrieved from https://www.genderspectrum.org/blog/creating-gender-inclusive-schools-qa/

GLSEN & National Center for Transgender Equality. (2016, February). *Model district policy on transgender and gender nonconforming students.* Retrieved from https://www.glsen.org/article/transgender-model-district-policy

Goodenow, C., Watson, R. J., Adjei, J., Homma, Y., & Saewyc, E. (2016). Sexual orientation trends and disparities in school bullying and violence-related experiences, 1999–2013. *Psychology of Sexual Orientation and Gender Diversity, 3*, 386–396. doi:doi:10.1037/sgd0000188

Grant, C., & Zwier, E. (2011). Intersectionality and student outcomes: Sharpening the struggle against racism, sexism, classism, ableism, heterosexism, nationalism, and linguistic, religious, and geographical discrimination in teaching and learning. *Multicultural Perspectives, 13*, 181–186. doi:10.1080/15210960.2011.616813

Greytak, E. A., Kosciw, J. G., Villenas, C., & Giga, N. M. (2016). *From teasing to torment: School climate revisited: A survey of U.S. secondary school students and teachers.* New York: GLSEN. Retrieved from https://www.glsen.org/article/teasing-torment-school-climate-revisited-survey-us-secondary-school-students-and-teachers

Hatzenbuehler, M. L. (2009). How does sexual minority stigma "get under the skin"? A psychological mediation framework. *Psychological Bulletin, 135*, 707–730. doi:10.1037/a0016441

Hatzenbuehler, M. L., & Keyes, K. M. (2013). Inclusive anti-bullying policies and reduced risk of suicide attempts in lesbian and gay youth. *Journal of Adolescent Health, 53*, 521–526. doi:10.1016/j.jadohealth.2012.08.010

Himmelstein, K., & Bruckner, H. (2011). Criminal justice and school sanctions against nonheterosexual youth: A national longitudinal study. *Pediatrics, 127*, 49–57. doi:10.1542/peds.2009-2306

Just the Facts Coalition. (2008). *Just the facts about sexual orientation and youth: A primer for principals, educators and school personnel.* Washington, DC: American Psychological Association. Retrieved from http://www.apa.org/pi/lgbt/resources/just-the-facts.pdf

Kann, L., Olsen, E. O., McManus, T., Harris, W. A., Shanklin, S. L., Flint, K. H., . . . Zaza, S. (2016, August). Sexual identity, sex of sexual contacts, and health-related behaviors among students in grades 9–12—United States and selected sites, 2015. *Centers for Disease Control and Prevention, Morbidity and Mortality Weekly Report, 65*(9). Retrieved from https://www.cdc.gov/mmwr/volumes/65/ss/pdfs/ss6509.pdf

Kosciw, J. G., Greytak, E. A., Giga, N. M., Villenas, C., & Danischewski, D. J. (2016). *The 2015 National School Climate Survey: The experiences of lesbian, gay, bisexual, transgender, and queer youth in our nation's schools.*

New York: GLSEN. Retrieved from https://www.glsen.org/article/2015-national-school-climate-survey

Kull, R. M., Kosciw, J. G., & Greytak, E. A. (2015). *From statehouse to schoolhouse: Anti-bullying policy efforts in U.S. states and school districts.* New York: GLSEN. Retrieved from https://www.glsen.org/article/state-and-school-district-anti-bullying-policies

Ladson-Billings, G. (2009). Race still matters: Critical race theory in education. In M. W. Apple, W. Au, & L. A. Gandin (Eds.), *The Routledge international handbook of critical education* (pp. 110–122). New York: Routledge.

Marshal, M. P., Dietz, L. J., Friedman, M. S., Stall, R., & Smith, H. A. (2011). Suicidality and depression disparities between sexual minority and heterosexual youth: A meta-analytic review. *Journal of Adolescent Health, 49*, 115–23. doi:10.1016/j.jadohealth.2011.02.005

Meyer, I. H. (2003). Prejudice, social stress, and mental health in lesbian, gay, and bisexual populations: Conceptual issues and research evidence. *Psychological Bulletin, 129*, 674–697. doi:10.1037/0033-2909.129.5.674

National Association of School Psychologists (NASP). (2011). *Lesbian, gay, bisexual, transgender, and questioning (LGBTQ) youth* [Position Statement]. Bethesda, MD: Author. Retrieved from https://www.nasponline.org/research-and-policy/professional-positions/position-statements

National Association of School Psychologists (NASP). (2014). *Safe schools for transgender and gender diverse students* [Position statement]. Bethesda, MD: Author. Retrieved from https://www.nasponline.org/research-and-policy/professional-positions/position-statements

National Association of School Psychologists (NASP). (2016). *School climate: #ConnectTheDots brief: Safe and supportive schools for LGBTQ+ students.* Bethesda, MD: Author. Retrieved from https://www.nasponline.org/research-and-policy/advocacy-tools-and-resources/communications-strategies-and-resources/school-climate%E2%80%94connectthedots/safe-and-supportive-schools-for-lgbtq-students

Poteat, V. P. (2017). Gay-Straight Alliances: Promoting student resilience and safer school climates. *American Educator, 40*, 10–14.

Poteat, V. P., Heck, N. C., Yoshikawa, H., & Calzo, J. P. (2017). Gay-Straight Alliances as settings to discuss health topics: Individual and group factors associated with substance use, mental health, and sexual health discussions. *Health Education Research, 32*, 258–268. doi:10.1093/her/cyx044

Poteat, V. P., Scheer, J. R., & Chong, E. S. K. (2016). Sexual orientation-based disparities in school and juvenile justice discipline: A multiple group comparison of contributing factors. *Journal of Educational Psychology, 108*, 229–241. doi:10.1037/edu0000058

Russell, S. T. (2016). Social justice, research, and adolescence. *Journal of Research on Adolescence, 26*, 4–15. doi:10.1111/jora.12249

Russell, S. T., & Fish, J. N. (2016). Mental health in lesbian, gay, bisexual, and transgender (LGBT) youth. *Annual Review of Clinical Psychology, 12*, 465–487. doi:10.1146/annurev-clinpsy-021815-093153

Russell, S. T., Kosciw, J., Horn, S., & Saewyc, E. (2010). Safe schools policy for LGBTQ students. *Society for Research in Child Development Social Policy Report, 24*(4), 1–25. Retrieved from https://www.srcd.org/sites/default/files/documents/spr_24_4_final.pdf

Russell, S. T., Sinclair, K. O., Poteat, V. P., & Koenig, B. W. (2012). Adolescent health and harassment based on discriminatory bias. *American Journal of Public Health, 102*, 493–495.

Savage, T. A. (2017, March). *Gender diversity 2.0: Strategies for supporting transgender and gender diverse students in schools.* Workshop presented at the Wisconsin School Psychologists Fall Pre-Convention, Appleton, WI.

Savage, T. A., Springborg, H., & Lagerstrom, L. (2016). *District and school transgender and gender diverse readiness assessment form.* Minneapolis: Authors. Retrieved from http://www.nasponline.org

Scherr, T. G. (2011). Addressing the needs of marginalized youth at school. In S. R. Jimerson, A. B. Nickerson, M. J. Mayer, & M. J. Furlong (Eds.), *The handbook of school violence and safety: International research and practice* (pp. 105–116). New York: Routledge.

Scherr, T. G., & Mayer, M. J. (2018). Supporting at-risk and marginalized students. In M. J. Mayer & S. R. Jimerson (Eds.), *School safety and violence prevention: Science, practice, and policy driving change* (pp. 121–147). Washington, DC: American Psychological Association.

Sleeter, C. E. (2011). The academic and social value of ethnic studies: A research review. Washington, DC: National Education Association. Retrieved from http://www.nea.org/assets/docs/NBI-2010-3-value-of-ethnic-studies.pdf

Snapp, S., Burdge, H., Licona, A. C., Moody, R., & Russell, S. T. (2015). Students' perspectives on LGBTQ-inclusive curriculum. *Equity and Excellence in Education, 48*, 249–265. doi:10.1080/10665684.2015.1025614

Snapp, S., Day, J., & Russell, S. T. (2017, April). *Preventing pushout: The role of supportive versus punitive practices for LGBT youth of color.* Paper presentation at the Society for Research in Child Development, Austin, TX.

Snapp, S., Hoenig, J., Fields, A., & Russell, S. T. (2015). Messy, butch, and queer: LGBTQ youth and the school-to-prison pipeline. *Journal of Adolescent Research, 30*, 57–82. doi:10.1177/0743558414557625

Snapp, S., & Licona, A. C. (2016). The pipeline population: Interrogating the patterns and practices of its production. In S. T. Russell & S. Horn (Eds.), *Sexual orientation, gender identity, and schooling: The nexus of research, practice, and policy* (pp. 126–142). New York: Oxford University Press.

Snapp, S., McGuire, J., Sinclair, K., Gabrion, K., & Russell, S. T. (2015). LGBTQ-inclusive curricula: Why supportive curricula matters. *Sex Education: Sexuality, Society, & Learning*, 1–17. doi:10.1080/14681811.2015.1042573

Snapp, S., & Russell, S. T. (2016). Discipline disparities for LGBTQ youth: Challenges that perpetuate disparities and strategies to overcome them. In R. J. Skiba, K. Mediratta, & M. Karega Rausch (Eds.), *Inequality in school discipline: Research and practice to reduce disparities* (pp. 207–223). London: Palgrave-Macmillan.

Snapp, S., Russell, S. T., Arredondo, M., & Skiba, R. (2016). A right to disclose: LGBTQ youth representation in data, science, and policy. In S. Horn, M. Ruck, & L. Liben (Eds.), *Equity and justice in developmental sciences: Theoretical and methodological issues* (pp. 135–159). London: Elsevier.

Tintiangco-Cubales, A., Kohli, R., Sacramento, J., Henning, N., Agarwal-Rangnath, R., & Sleeter, C. (2015). Toward an ethnic studies pedagogy: Implications for K-12 schools from the research. *The Urban Review, 47*, 104–125.

Toomey, R. B., & Russell, S. T. (2016). The role of sexual orientation in school-based victimization: A meta-analysis. *Youth & Society, 48*, 176–201. doi:10.1177/0044118X13483778

Watson, R. J., & Russell, S. T. (2014). Disengaged or bookworm: Academics, mental health, and success for sexual minority youth. *Journal of Research on Adolescence, 26*, 159–165. doi:10.1111/jora.12178

Westheimer, K., Persinger, L., Cannava, A., & Klotz, M. B. (2016). *Frequently asked questions: Safe and inclusive learning environments for transgender and gender expansive students.* San Leandro, CA: Gender Spectrum; Bethesda, MD: National Association of School Psychologists. Retrieved from http://www.nasponline.org

CHAPTER SEVEN

Understanding and Practicing Cultural Competence in Helping Youth Thrive

Roberto C. Rivera and JuanCarlos Arauz

The Cultural Disconnect between Educators and Youth

Youth who have been historically deemed as "at-risk" or full of deficiencies and even labeled liabilities can demonstrate that they are in fact "at-opportunity" and full of assets even capable of becoming agents of change if engaged in culturally competent ways. Noguera (2008) suggests that academic achievement of students of color can be predicted by the level of culturally responsive pedagogy that their teachers use. This topic of cultural competence and relevant engagement is particularly salient in U.S. public schools today where, according to the National Center for Education Statistics (McFarland et al., 2018) analysis of data, suggests that over 82.5% of teachers are white while more than 50.3% are students of color. This racial and cultural disparity between educators and youth is also reflected in a variety of youth development and health service fields (Betancourt, Green, Carrillo, & Park, 2005). While efforts have been taken to increase and diversify educators and staff across sectors, additional efforts in fostering cultural competence in individuals and organizations are needed to ensure the needs of youth and their families from diverse backgrounds are being effectively met.

Ladson-Billings (1994) defines cultural competence in education as the ability to help students appreciate and celebrate their cultures of origin while also gaining knowledge of or fluency in at least one other culture. The Center for Advanced Research on Language Acquisition defines the term "Culture" as shared patterns of behavior and interactions, cognitive constructs, and understandings that are learned by socialization (Zimmerman, 2017). Culture goes beyond practices and values influenced by race or ethnicity and can include characteristics such as age, gender, sexual orientation, socioeconomic status, geographical location, education, profession, or religion. Culture is influenced by numerous factors such as race, class, and gender and must always be contextualized within a social construct. Thus, keeping these diverse characteristics in mind, cultural competence is an ongoing practice as opposed to finite accomplishment. Culturally responsive or relevant teaching is pedagogy where educators display cultural competence in teaching in a multicultural or cross-cultural setting (Gay, 2010; Ladson-Billings, 1995b). This approach enables each student to connect course content to his or her cultural context. Further, Paris and Alim (2017) describe *culturally sustaining pedagogies* in education as a process to sustain different cultural ways of being, teaching students to be resilient and to persevere, and to empower youth to accept and honor their cultural backgrounds. Overall, the process of developing cultural competence is also an evolving, dynamic process that takes time and applies to educators and organizations, just as it does to individuals and cohorts of students.

Whether in social service, educational, or out-of-school institutions, culturally competent institutions require a willingness to listen to and learn from members of other cultures. Cultural competence as exhibited in institutions shares information and services in appropriate languages, at appropriate literacy levels, with respect to the context of the individual and collective cultural beliefs and practices of those being served (Cross, Bazron, Dennis, & Isaacs, 1989). According to the U.S. Department of Health and Human Services (Betancourt et al., 2016), a culturally competent organization (1) engages in practices that continually assess organizational diversity; (2) invests in building capacity for cultural competency and inclusion; (3) practices strategic planning that incorporates community culture and diversity; (4) implements strategies using culture and diversity as a resource; and (5) assesses and evaluates the incorporation of cultural competence continuously. For the purposes of this chapter, we will share a framework for thriving that includes a culturally relevant application that we have developed from our collective praxis in schools, out-of-school programs, and engagement with communities. As researchers and practitioners, it is important that we demonstrate how culturally competent efforts to support thriving can play out pedagogically in classrooms, through community programs, and in strategic plans that include youth and families from diverse backgrounds in decision-making.

A special focus will be taken to examine these efforts in light of the realities of inequitable outcomes for these populations in areas of health, education, and well-being. The review of literature and the case studies that follow confront issues of institutional racism and systemic oppression while also highlighting impediments to well-being that can be overcome by cultural competence. Finally, we will offer examples of how educators, students, and communities can mobilize assets and cultural capital to promote cultural resilience, empowerment, and improve individual and collective forms of well-being.

Redefining Youth Engagement and Thriving: From Deficits to an Asset Perspective

Many social science scholars and practitioners believe that prevention and intervention programs designed to engage youth from diverse backgrounds are ineffective because these methods are overly focused on remediating student "deficits" rather than promoting student assets (Scales, Benson, Leffert, & Blyth, 2000; Weissberg, Kumpfer, & Seligman, 2003). Others have argued that instead of seeing youth as problems needing to be "fixed," youth should be viewed as asset-rich agents capable of making positive change (Ginwright & James, 2002; Pittman & Fleming, 1991). They called for the adoption of a positive youth development (PYD) model for working with youth that stops asking "what is wrong" with them and starts asking, "what is right" with them? This movement introducing positive psychology into school and after-school programs through a positive youth development framework was further developed as researchers documented how the promotion of youth "assets" increased student academic achievement, improved physical and emotional well-being, and subsequently decreased risky behaviors (Benson, Scales & Syvertsen, 2011.

Through the research of scholars at the Search Institute, 40 developmental assets were identified as contributing to the thriving of youth on both proximal outcomes during the course of adolescence as well as more distal outcomes of early adulthood (Scales & Leffert, 1999). From these 40 internal and external assets, 7 thriving indicators emerged which included: (1) leadership, (2) school success, (3) helping others, (4) maintenance of physical health, (5) delay of gratification, (6) valuing diversity, and (7) overcoming adversity. The work was developed further by Scales, Benson, and Roehlkepartain's (2011) study, which suggested that adolescent thriving could be connected to three essential strengths. These three strengths were: (1) relationships with adults other than parents; (2) the presence of Sparks, strengths, or interests; and (3) having a Voice or an ability to contribute to the things that matter to them. Their research suggests that youth who have all three of these strengths do better on every academic, social and emotional, psychological, and behavioral outcome that they have studied. However, their findings with a national sample of 1,817 youths (representative of youth from all demographics in the United States) suggest that less than 10% of 15-year-old youth score high on all three strengths. These efforts of engaging youth, particularly youth of color, in strength-based ways is a great start, and can be enhanced by including culturally competent and relevant ways of engaging youth.

Toward this end, Ginwright and Cammarota (2002) have argued for a theory of Social Justice Youth Development (SJYD) that combines a strength-based approach with the impetus for cultural relevance and emergence of critical consciousness. Critical consciousness is a term that originates from the work of Paulo Freire and da Veiga Coutinho (1970), who posits that critical consciousness is the result of engaging people in dialogue and the praxis of combining theory and action.

In continuation of this critical education legacy, SJYD theory highlights three additional components needed to bridge youth development research with application to demographics of students of color. These components include an emphasis on: (1) personal praxis (looking at self-awareness, social awareness, and global awareness); (2) praxis through youth culture (including being culturally relevant and incorporating the use of hip-hop culture); and (3) healing as an outcome and not just settling for resilience but promoting growth through hardship. Some scholars have begun to operationalize how this theory can be applied to helping empower high school students to cultivate their critical consciousness in after school hip-hop programs (Ginwright, Noguera, Cammarota, 2006; Slaten, Rivera, & Shemwell, 2016). However, there is a need to revisit the positive youth development framework around youth thriving with a lens that emphasizes cultural competence and promotes a critically conscious model of thriving that can be applied to a variety of settings.

A Culturally Competent Model for Promoting Thriving among Diverse Youth

We build off of the framework of Scales, Benson, and Roehlkepartain (2011) emphasizing the importance of Relationships, Sparks, and Voice and include also the components of cultural competence and social justice described by Ginwright and Cammarota (2002) to create a more robust model of youth thriving that can be operationalized in a variety of contexts with youth from diverse backgrounds. This model presented by Scales, Benson, and Roehlkepartain (2011) includes: (1) establishing relationships that exercise personal praxis by fostering strong cultural identities and cultivating critical consciousness in adults and youth; (2) identifying and cultivating Sparks in culturally competent ways; and (3) activating youth voice by promoting cultural resilience and positive social change. In the spirit of praxis (combining research, reflection, and practice), we will illustrate the research base for this culturally competent model of thriving and will further illustrate how this model can be operationalized in various contexts through case studies from our work in schools and out-of-school contexts.

Relationships That Foster Cultural Identity and Critical Consciousness

The research of Scales et al. (2011) suggests that adolescents need positive developmental relationships with adults other than parents in order to thrive. Search Institute (2018) defines a positive developmental relationship as taking place in the life of a young person when an adult expresses care, promotes growth, provides support, shares power, and expands possibilities by connecting youth to people and places that broaden their world. These types of relationships are no doubt critically important and valuable; however, in order for youth of color to thrive, they also need these adults to be culturally competent in supporting them in the development of a positive cultural identity and critical consciousness. Critical consciousness is a way of being that focuses on achieving an in-depth understanding of the world, allowing for the perception and exposure of social, cultural, and political contradictions. Critical consciousness also includes taking action against the oppressive elements in one's life that are illuminated by that understanding. To foster this kind of critical consciousness in youth, it has to start first in the lives of the adults. This process can begin by adults understanding how racism affects youth of color individually and institutionally. One way to ascertain a deeper understanding of how racism can be institutionalized and reproduced through systems is through critical race theory (Delgado & Stefacic, 2017).

Critical Race Theory (CRT) is the study of the relationship among race, racism, and power and can become a powerful lens for mentors and educators to utilize in understanding the experiences of students of color. CRT considers the intersections of economic structure, national history, culture, and conscious and unconscious feelings and examines the larger social structure that enables the status quo. Its focus is less on how and why students identify ethnically and racially and more about the ways in which the school responds to those identities and how this influences students' educational experiences. CRT provides a foundational language to help mentors and educators to take into account the implicit and explicit ways in which the dominant culture unconsciously or consciously creates advantages and disadvantages that are often played out in the education system. Yosso, Smith, Ceja, and Solórzano (2009) offer four themes to summarize the foundations of CRT: (1) CRT maintains a commitment toward social justice by offering transformative solutions to racial, gender, and class oppression; (2) CRT utilizes the interdisciplinary knowledge of law, education, ethnic and women's studies, history, and sociology to better comprehend the experiences of people of color; (3) CRT separates race and racism from the analysis of gender and class (critical race theorists postulate that racism has a micro and a macro component; this means that it emerges institutionally and individually on both an unconscious and conscious level and impacts both the individual and the group); (4) CRT challenges the assumptions of the dominant ideology by questioning mainstream beliefs regarding culture, intelligence, and capability. Adults committed to ensuring that every child can thrive and maximize his or her potential can embrace CRT as a basis for cultivating critical consciousness and healthy ethnic, racial, and cultural identities.

The connection with healthy identity development is based on the understanding that youth who have these qualities experience less emotional distress and increased well-being. For example, Dukes, Martinez, and Stein (1997) note that stronger ethnic identities weaken the impact of negative stereotypes and social denigration in individuals by giving access to a broadened understanding for the self that includes access to other sources of identity. Thus, positive developmental relationships between adults and youth of color need to nurture positive cultural identities and cultivate critical consciousness in order for them to decrease emotional distress and cultivate the individual and cultural power to thrive.

Fostering Culturally Relevant Sparks

Scales et al. (2011) suggest that another core strength youth need to foster is their "sparks" or areas of passion. The research suggests that only 60% of youth in their sample knew they had a spark and significantly fewer youth knew how to cultivate this. From our observation, one of the major contributing factors to youth not finding their passions is that sparks can be embedded in cultures or traditions that are different than the educator or the adult. This along with deficit models of viewing youth can lead to many students not discovering or cultivating their sparks. It is therefore important that mentors and educators take a culturally relevant approach when identifying and nurturing sparks of passion in their youth. Advocates of culturally responsive pedagogy strongly favor positioning students' cultural knowledge at the core of instruction in order to engage student learning. This means, for working with students of color to achieve academic excellence, it is important to develop programs that use the characteristics of culturally responsive pedagogy to build upon on students' strengths in promoting their racial identity and socialization.

Gay (2010 defines culturally responsive teaching as using the cultural knowledge, prior experiences, frames of reference, and performance styles of ethnically diverse students to make learning encounters more relevant and effective for them. It teaches to and through the strengths of these students. Gay (2010 highlights the characteristics of culturally responsive teaching as being: (1) validating and affirming as it acknowledges the strengths of students from diverse backgrounds; (2) comprehensive in using the cultural resources to teach knowledge, values, skills, and attitudes; (3) multidimensional as it applies multicultural theory to the classroom environment, teaching methods, and evaluation; (4) liberating as it is directed toward liberating students from oppressive ideologies and realities; (5) empowering by giving students opportunities to excel in the classroom and beyond; (6) transformative as educators and students must often challenge education traditions that maintain the status quo. The results of an extensive literature review covering over 2,800 sources conducted by Hanley and Noblit (2009) indicate that culturally responsive approaches contribute to positive racial identity, resilience, and achievement. Hanley and Noblit conclude that an established link exists between culturally responsive pedagogy and achievement for students of color. These researchers also found that making this approach systemic also helps in confronting issues of racism and deficit thinking. Consistent with this finding, several cultural researchers contend that youth culture represents an unofficial dimension of pedagogical space where youth from diverse backgrounds are provided with protective factors for facing oppressive realities such as institutional racism (Freedman & Ball, 2004; Hull & Nelson, 2005).

Further, youth culture has historically provided youth with the cultural tools necessary for the production of counter-narratives to the official dimension of classroom learning. Thus, researchers like Hull and Zacher (2010) view out-of-school times as the space where literacy is most active and indicate that student performances through the material production of poetry and rap are more authentic indicators of youth literacy, identity development, and social practice. In examining the potential of hip-hop culture, Rose (1994) expresses that "rap music, more than any other form of black cultural expression, articulates the chasm between black urban lived experience and dominant, 'legitimate'. . . ideologies regarding equal opportunity and racial inequality" (p. 102). Hip-hop based education (Petchauer, 2009) has become a popular and powerful way to engage youth sparks through the utilization of a model that acknowledges the sparks evident in the elements of hip-hop. It provides a lens by which youth sparks can be seen as manifestations of multiple intelligences with graffiti expressing visual intelligence, rap or spoken word expressing verbal intelligence, street entrepreneurship expressing numeric intelligence, breaking or popping expressing kinesthetic intelligence, promotion expressing interpersonal intelligence, street smarts expressing environmental intelligence, and expression of the blues narratives as manifesting intra-personal intelligence, the expression of the gospel narratives of redemption and hope manifesting spiritual intelligence (Gardner, 2011). By becoming students of students, we can learn what our students' sparks are and use the classroom or youth development programs as opportunities to further cultivate these sparks and also bring content to life in culturally relevant and transformative ways.

Youth Voice: Promoting Cultural Resilience and Authentic Youth Empowerment

Scales et al. (2011) suggests that the final core strength required for youth to thrive is to foster a youth voice. They define youth voice as developing the confidence, skills, and opportunities to express and influence what's important to you. It is an important part of becoming active in community and civic life. However, their findings suggest that only 22% of all 15-year-olds—across all demographic groups—score high on the Teen Voice Index. Part of what is missing from this thriving model is understanding what youth voice is from the perspectives of youth and helping them to not only define but also develop the agency to embody this definition. An alternative definition of youth voice (as defined by youth) is "an expression of the human spirit that is shown in different forms such as art, words, poetry, and music. Engaging in the creation of your own opportunities to SPEAK OUT to authority. . . . Believing and putting our voices into practice so youth can be taken seriously" (Morrell, 2008). What is being explicated in this definition is that youth desire multidimensional, authentic, and transformative ways of being engaged that impact individuals and institutions. It is toward these topics that we will now shift our attention.

Youth Voice Expressed Intra-personally and Inter-personally through Cultural Resilience

Resilience has been defined as the ability to thrive in the face of adverse circumstances and often the focus is on how an individual's characteristics contribute to his or her resilience (Gordon & Coscarelli, 1996). Resilience emphasizes humans' remarkable ability to recover from adversity. Most of the research into this phenomenon focuses on trauma victims. However, Ginsberg (2011) proposes that children can be raised in a safe environment and still develop resilience. In a broader sense, resilience enables children to rise above difficult situations if adults believe in them unconditionally and hold them to high expectations. Consequently, Ginsberg (2011) has expanded Lerner's 5 C's model and has offered what he calls the "Seven C's" to help adults guide their youth's recognition of their own abilities and inner resources: Competence, Confidence, Connection, Character, Contribution, Coping, and Control (Lerner, Almerigi, Theokas, Gestsdottir; & Smith, 2005). Clauss-Ehlers (2004) takes this view of resilience further, expanding the definition to include "cultural resilience"—how a person's "cultural background supports, values, and environmental experience help facilitate the process of overcoming adversity towards a culturally-focused resilient adaptation" (p. 28). Therefore, cultural values can influence the "child's cultural script for resilience" (p. 36). This enables us to perceive culture as a resource that children can access in the way that Ginsberg (2011) theorizes and then identify ways for communities and families to utilize it as an asset to promote resilience among children. By nurturing resilience among students, they are able to adapt well to adversity, trauma, tragedy, and threats in order to better manage the stress and feelings of anxiety and uncertainty. Through the development of cultural resilience, students are able to recognize and identify in themselves the competencies to cope with such experiences.

Resilience-focused research observes that individuals who successfully overcome challenges develop similar skills in adapting quickly to new circumstances, thriving amid constant change, and, most important, "bouncing back" (Ginsberg, 2011). Yet advocates of cultural resilience argue that more than individual strengths and characteristics are needed to enable individuals and communities to cope with, and overcome, adversity. Although adapting to changing environments can be challenging, proficiency in cultural resilience can help individuals transfer skills even across different environments. Cultural resilience has been correlated to competencies by E3: Equity, Excellence, and Education as competencies (also considered as inner strengths) acquired through diverse life experiences that are either positive or negative. High levels of these competencies have been observed in students of color from low-income families and in undocumented youth (Arauz, 2007). Seen through a strengths-based and culturally competent lens, students can learn to translate their cultural resilience into opportunities for authentic youth empowerment.

Youth Voice Expressed Institutionally in Organizations and Schools

The level of youth voice and leadership that is embodied by an organization, program, or initiative is evident in the language and practice it uses to engage them. A critical examination of the language and practice of youth-serving organizations and programs reveals a continuum of youth voice and engagement strategies starting from a prevention model to a collective empowerment model that impacts systemic change. The spectrum of youth engagement starts with the youth service approach being the least engaging, progresses to youth development, youth leadership, and civic engagement, and ends with youth organizing as the most effective method. In a youth services approach, the language used describes youth as clients that receive services to deal with individual problems and pathologies. This approach defines programs with terms like treatment, prevention, or intervention. Needless to say, these programs have the lowest level of youth engagement and authentic youth voice. A step up from this is a youth development approach, which provides support and services to youth that allows them access to safe spaces and caring adults. This approach meets young people where they are and offers them opportunities for growth and development. It focuses on building competencies, offering age appropriate support, emphasizes positive identity, and enhances youth and adult partnerships.

A step up from a youth development approach is a youth leadership model that includes components of youth development but also builds in authentic youth leadership within the programming and organization structure. It helps youth develop a deeper historical and cultural understanding of their individual experiences and community issues. It builds capacity in youth to become youth decision-makers and problem-solvers involved in community projects. A step up from this is civic engagement, which includes elements from youth development and youth leadership models but also includes developing a deeper analysis of power structures and the impacts on one's identity formation. This approach builds a collective identity as change agents. It engages youth to become advocates on a variety of levels including, but not limited to, political advocacy and negotiation. Following this model, youth organizing is a term used to describe what many deem as the epitome of authentic youth voice.

Youth organizing embodies many of the elements youth leadership and civic engagement exemplifies, it also includes building a membership base, involves youth operating as part of a core staff, engages them as taking the lead in developing alliances and coalitions, and supports in transforming their external world both politically and creatively. This kind of approach can also be described as creating "youth driven spaces," where youth are actively involved in programming and organization decisions. It is important for all youth, particularly youth of color, to have opportunities to develop their cultural resilience and cultivate a sense of voice and ownership in the programs, policies, and practices of their youth-serving organizations, schools, and community.

Case Study Introduction: Combining Theory and Practice

In this section of the chapter, we now demonstrate how the ideas expressed in this model for culturally relevant thriving can be applied in schools and out-of-school time work with youth. In these case studies, you will also see how these ideas have been transformative both to youth and to us as educators and organization leaders. These stories are not meant to be prescriptive but descriptive on how these ideas can be integrated into education and youth work. In both instances, we were asked to partner with schools as outside consultants. This gave us an advantage of being able to have some administrative freedom in implementing these ideas. In both cases, however, buy in from administration, educators, and youth was absolutely necessary. We include youth here because often times a top-down approach leaves them out of the discussion.

Hip-Hop(e): A Culturally Relevant Example of Thriving in Communities and Schools *by Roberto C. Rivera*

Some community leaders and I were in shock when teens in our after-school hip-hop leadership program came in and told us that they felt like absolute failures at school. The disillusionment came about because these were the same youth who were presenting at regional conferences with members of Congress, opening up for international hip-hop acts, having magazine articles written about their work, and becoming regular guests on radio and television programs. These young people, primarily young men of color, were telling us that they were treated like they were stupid at school, and constantly singled out and disciplined unjustly. One young man told me, "I feel like I have been marked as a failure by teachers and the school as a whole, and they won't stop attacking me unless I either drop out or lose any sense of who I really am and accept this as the 'truth.'" Questions began to emerge for us like: How could students who were so engaged in one area of their lives be so disengaged in another? What would the impacts be if what we have been doing in after-school could be implemented during the school day? What was the relationship between the hopelessness that our young men were experiencing in school and the opportunity gap? How could we create an environment where these youth could thrive and cultivate the fruit of transformative hope?

These questions continued to come up until some colleagues and I wrote a proposal and finally received the funds to create a hip-hop leadership curriculum that could be implemented during the school day. In the true fashion of hip-hop, we remixed our experiences working with youth in out-of-school times with Social and Emotional Learning, Positive Youth Development, and Culturally Relevant Pedagogy while designing the curriculum we later called Fulfill the Dream to be used during the school day. We felt inspired by the work of Paulo Freire, who helped us to define something that would help our students both acknowledge their concrete realities while also actively working toward the dreams of what is still possible (Freire, 2014). We realized that this critical, creative, and competent hope could not be schooled in our youth but it had to be educated and drawn out. We realized that there was no better way to engage this generation than to utilize the very culture they were immersed in. We decided to use hip-hop culture as the vehicle to engage youth and help them and their schools realize that they are an essential asset in changing the culture of the school. We called this pedagogy Hip-Hope, and after implementing our approach over the last 10 years, we have seen small alternative high schools with 100 students have 100% graduate rates after one year of implementation using school data comparing numbers of youth who started the school year as seniors and ended the school year as seniors who graduated. In addition, we have seen GPAs go up as much as full points in as little as 10 weeks examining report card data comparing third quarter data to fourth quarter with 90 students in 3 classes. We have conducted quantitative inquiries and documented hope increasing, anger decreasing, and critical consciousness elevated to significant levels. What follows is how we first got started with Hip-Hope, and the essential lessons that we learned along the way can engage youth in ways that call them out as our greatest school assets capable of igniting new climates of hope.

Our opportunity came when the school district we were courting was labeled as being in "crisis" by articles coming out of the state newspaper. Seeing our opportunity, we approached the superintendent, who seemed like he would be open to a new approach to student engagement. He explained, "We have tried every intervention under the sun, but we haven't tried this Hip-hop stuff, let's see what that can do." With his blessing we were sent into the "worst school" in the district. We met with the principals and were able to ascertain that the majority of issues were coming from four classes in the school, in which we realized they were warehousing their students of color. These students had been given every label under the sun from Emotional Behavior Disorder, Attention Deficit Disorder, Attention Deficit and Hyperactivity Disorder, to Oppositional Defiant Disorder. The last thing these youth needed was another intervention or prevention, what they needed was invention; which was to experience themselves in a new way that didn't focus on their deficits. We decided that framing the purpose of the program to all of the students was important so we hosted an all-school assembly. We brought in local hip-hop artists, we spoke and announced that we were launching a hip-hop leadership program to a few classes of elite youth. This was on a Friday; on the following Monday, we showed up to the four classes and the youth were astounded we chose them. We told them that they had tremendous influence in the school and that we wanted them to use that influence to have a positive impact on the school. We explained that they had things they were passionate about and we wanted them to grow in these areas until they felt like they could make a positive contribution to the school culture. We held our program during homeroom once a week for about 45 minutes and gave the teachers follow-up lessons on the days we weren't there. We required all teachers on the days we were there to engage with the students in the activities and discussions. About three weeks into it, we also started meeting with the youth after school to focus on creative skill development. This took place after the third lesson focused on assessing student passions and forms of multiple intelligences.

We facilitated discussions examining the difference between hip-hop culture and hip-hop industry. We explained that hip-hop culture had a long history of youth empowerment, with practitioners seeing themselves as producers capable of wielding the power to change their realities. We contrasted this with showing video clips that demonstrated how hip-hop industry was more focused on having power over young people, shaping them to see themselves as consumers, and ultimately stripping them of their power to change reality by keeping them believing fantasy and myths about themselves. We encouraged youth to think critically about the media and music they were ingesting, and similar to how hip-hop deejays sampled from classic hit records to create new sounds, encouraged them to start being intentional about "sampling" from the examples of people who lived purposefully that they knew. Instead of mimicking these elders, we encouraged them to "remix" these examples into ways that were authentic to who they are and what they are passionate about. As facilitators, we got to be open about our own lives and shared our own personal historical records of what we felt proud of and experiences that were painful. One teacher opened up and shared an experience about losing her father just the previous summer, and in tears said she being a teacher was one way she felt like she made him proud. We encouraged students to consider their own legacies and to realize that whether they acknowledged it or not, the young students in the school were being influenced by their examples for better or worse. We then challenged them to think about what kind of "sounds" they wanted the music of their lives to make, and how they wanted that to move people.

Instead of asking "are" they smart, we encouraged youth to ask "how" are they smart. We explained that just as they exhibited passion in the elements of hip-hop culture (dance, visual art, music, poetry, rap, etc.), they were also demonstrating multiple forms of intelligence (Gardner, 2011), and that like a physical muscle, this intelligence could be strengthened (Delpit, 2006). This meant they could not only exercise their passions and expressions after school but also in applying these creative muscles to achieving academically. We encouraged them to be a good "crew" to one another, which not only meant calling out one another's spark of passion (Benson, 2008), but encouraging one another to taking positive risks to fan these sparks into flame. Youth were challenged to look at the untapped resources of their school and find creative ways to use these fires to change the culture and climate of the schools.

We helped youth realize that they had a voice in not only sharing their "blues" stories and developing social awareness and self-management skills in the process but also that they could listen deeply to the stories of others and cultivate deeper social awareness and empathy. The voicing of personal struggle and the dialogues that took place moved the group to create a deeper critical consciousness about their realities and a beloved community where radical healing could take place (Ginwright, 2010), and it nurtured an awareness that they could use their voices to make a difference. Radical healing is a healing process where healing occurs on the individual, community, and broader societal levels by creating spaces where youth engage in healing activities and exercise their imagination about how their political realities can change. Youth decided that they wanted to help reinvigorate the school talent show and used it as a platform to unleash their newfound hope on the school and community at-large.

Our youth were not only the masters of ceremony of the event but also participated in skits about racism in the school, shared poems about struggle, and performed raps about transformation and hope. One chorus in their song went:

> It is not a new but an old thing
> We are working hard man trying to let our soul bling
> We're not concerned what your gold brings
> We got a purpose and it is more than trying to hold things
> You serving them death I'm serving them life
> You serving them wrong I am serving them right
> You are either part of the problem or the solution
> So let's solve our problems and start a movement.

The youth got a standing ovation, and fortunately the data also stood out as we saw GPAs went up half a point on average in the four classes, attendance improved, and behavior issues went down. Interviews with principals included stories of these youth being involved in creative conflict resolution and some even breaking up fights. Upon sharing this data with the superintendent, he called for a town-hall meeting where we shared the pre- and post-data but also had an opportunity for the youth to share their stories. One young man said, "My brother is in a gang and I have been planning to join later this year, but I am not anymore because now I realize I have a dream and can see how school connects to me fulfilling that dream." Another young man said he "used to smoke weed every day after school but now I stopped because I can say I have hope." Upon hearing this, the Chief of Staff probed him and asked: "What kind of hope is this, hope you have today and is gone tomorrow?" He looked her firmly in the eye and said, "This is a hope I will have for the rest of my life." These young men of color involved with the group went on to get on the honor roll and became the agents of change that later made this leadership program schoolwide, allowing us to do cultural competence training with the entire school and later other schools in the district. This training began with educators building their social and emotional and cultural competence personally first; and then continued on to how they could apply this pedagogically in engaging youth. We found that starting at the personal level in cultivating competencies was an important foundation for teachers then leveraging this competence in their engagement of students. This foundation later served as our launch pad to do work across the nation and world.

Connecting the Case Study to a Model of Culturally Competent Thriving

Operationalizing a culturally relevant application of thriving, we saw how relationships are formulated when people see the assets in each other and build trust. What if we saw our youth not as problems to be fixed but as solutions waiting to be unleashed? Had we come into the school with another intervention seeking to "fix" students, we would have never had seen the same level of progress. What our youth were hungry for was the *invention* of new opportunity to experience themselves in a different light. We needed to see them not as being full of deficits but full of assets and sparks of passion. They needed to know that their passions were indeed manifestations of multiple forms of intelligence. Yes, even if they were into graffiti, this was really a manifestation of visual intelligence that could be recognized, cultivated, and applied to enhance achievement. Lastly, these youth needed to have a voice and be given the opportunity to contribute to the school, we realized that they singlehandedly had greater ability to change the climate and culture in the school than anyone else. The solutions that these young people unleashed were unmatched by any other person in authority at either the school or district level. They just needed an opportunity to take a positive risk and apply their ideas. In the words of Dr. King, "Society will tell you that you are a thermometer, but in fact you are a thermostat." What if the key to transforming the culture and climate of public education was through the igniting of hip-hope in our youth who are most marginalized and deemed at-risk?

Changing One Practice That Changes Beliefs: A Case Model for Culturally Responsive Pedagogy *by JuanCarlos Arauz*

Having established a nonprofit organization designed to support educators in becoming more effective in reaching a diverse student population, it became increasingly evident that the so-called student achievement gap is more like a *teacher-belief-in-student gap*. Consequently, I intended to find a way to speed up the process that institutionalized critical reflection in which educators would see the brilliance in every student. Realizing that changing the mind of teachers to see brilliance in a historically marginalized student population was difficult if not impossible, a group of us developed an asset-based culturally responsive assessment that translated the lived experiences of students into 21st century skills. These 21st century skills were based on seven survival skills by Wagner (2010) and the four C's from Kay and Greenhill (2013). Our guiding framework for cultural resilience applied these concepts in a strength-based and culturally relevant way to specifically reach adolescents from diverse backgrounds.

Our Cultural Resilience Assessment tool became a tool for educators, with a wide variety of cultural competence, to use in better engaging their students. The first step was to provide them with an ability to first recognize their students' cultural strengths and brilliance. In addition, the tool allowed the teachers a way to assess and become more reflective of their own practice of engaging youth in culturally responsive ways. For those who were already culturally responsive, this tool enhanced their effectiveness with students by giving them a metric to use to see gains in student skills. For those who were not culturally responsive educators, their lack of cultural competence did not become a barrier—rather through their training and utilization of the tool, their mindset shifted as they began to better recognize the brilliance in students in a similar way that culturally responsive educators could.

The instrument developed has been named the Educational Strengths Assessment Tool or (ESAT). The E3 inventory named (ESAT) can best be classified as a targeted biographical data (bio data) assessment. Bio data assessments are a relatively common and long-standing assessment approach within the applied world. Generally speaking, bio data measures include items about past events and behaviors reflecting personality attributes, attitudes, experiences, interests, skills, and abilities validated as predictors of overall performance. Specific to the ESAT, the expectation is that the assessment is predictive of a targeted performance dimension, based on five competencies; innovation, adaptability, critical analysis, cross-cultural analysis, and teamwork, which we collectively define as cultural resilience.

Once teachers implement the ESAT, they demonstrate a stronger willingness to critically reflect on their own practice. As stated by the Freire Institute, the process of developing a critical awareness of one's social reality is through reflection and action. Action is fundamental because it is the process of changing the reality. We all acquire social myths that have a dominant tendency, and so learning is a critical process that depends upon uncovering real problems and actual needs. However, it is not enough for people to come together in dialogue in order to gain knowledge of their social reality. Critical praxis is when they act together upon their environment in order critically to reflect upon their reality and so transform it through further action and critical reflection.

So my case study is of a school community that exemplifies these concepts and emulates the concept of cultural resiliency as well as the definition of critical praxis, cultural humility diversity, and culturally responsive teaching. I recall entering this K–8 school community of 250 relatively ethnically diverse students with about 70% of students of color representing countries from Haiti, England, Korea, Philippines, and a dozen Spanish-speaking countries as well as diversity of income levels. In addition, there is a diversity of socioeconomic classes of people who own their own homes and second homes as well as those renting apartments with another family. Finally, there is diversity of language, as well as diversity of political thoughts, in this school community.

While there were amazing results that the school has demonstrated, the process was a mutual transformational for our organization as well as the educators. For example, not only did the school demonstrate student achievement but more important the teachers expressed an increase in belief in the capabilities of students over the course of the school year. This school community taught us that regurgitation of content knowledge on cultural competency is not as powerful as the practice of culturally responsive strategies. Therefore, the traditional approach to train educators in learning how to be culturally responsive is not the methodology we utilized as a way to institutionalize culturally responsive practices.

As the narrative goes in a very stereotypical fashion, a white-led faculty was teaching students of color and a low-income community that utilized a banking method-deficit approach. There were teachers who would request English only in this classroom or students teasing each other for having different accents in speaking English. When the school leadership requested our assistance, several teachers could not see the challenges and responded with "English is the official language why are we not just teaching English to all of our students." I recall one of the educators sharing with me that everything is black-and-white to which I agreed that it's both. I responded by sharing that English is important to teach and that it is also important to be multilingual. I then asked the educator why we would want to limit students to only one language. She did not have a response and it was the beginning of expanding the teacher's approach to culturally responsive pedagogy.

The first step was to take the leadership under training in how to implement culturally responsive tools. These tools focused on identifying the brilliance of students, developing engagement strategies for students, and creating lesson plans that were culturally inclusive to the student population. This did not mean we bypassed the educators who did not have a culturally responsive approach to their teachers, rather the focus was to ask these educators to implement the equitable teaching practices. This included specifically asking educators to pilot the E3 assessment tool that translates the life experiences of students into 21st-century competencies. In turn, educators did not focus on the struggles of students, but rather the strengths that they brought and in a way educators could understand. Another specific implementation tool was to pilot the engagement identification tool, in which educators look at data as indicators to focus on engagement strategies. Through these two examples, the educators were more engaged to learn how to teach to students whose data demonstrated they had strengths as opposed to getting stuck on how hard it was to motivate students who had low test scores or behavior challenges.

As a result, the buy-in by educators became much easier as the results came in after the first year. For example, 3rd grade reading is widespread as a benchmark to identify how well students are doing in school. In this school community, the students on average did better than the state average. More important, the top quartile of students who already met reading levels had increased their reading level at a higher percentage than the rate of the state average. On the other end of the spectrum, the lowest quartile of students who were below grade level in their reading level and met 3rd grade reading level compared to the state average. After several years of these results, this led the faculty and leadership team to buy into believing that their students were brilliant because they had spent an entire year practicing these culturally responsive practices. As a result of faculty buy-in, there has been an ongoing practice of critical reflection from lesson plans to overall school policy. The weekly professional learning communities established in faculty meetings look at student achievement as indicators for how they are teaching rather than indicators of a student's capability. In fact, at the recent graduation ceremony, they celebrated the event by speaking in multiple languages. This was quite a turnaround given the fact that some of those same teachers were resistant to teaching anything more than English in their schools. Some of those same teachers introduced diplomas in the native language of the student's family. By no means is this school community an exemplar of cultural competency, but it is representative of many schools and it is a prototype of how other educational institutions can focus some of their energy on changing practices to be more culturally responsive rather than changing beliefs of educators. I end with one of the highlights of a testimony from one of the educators:

> E3 has developed tools that will forever impact how institutions see our young people of color and more importantly how young people see themselves. Instead of being labeled as broken, they can see their true assets, strength and incredible resilience. The gifts our young people hold, just may be the answer to a world that has lost its way. Our policies, systems and institutions were constructed under an inequitable narrative and indoctrination that has labeled incorrectly so many. Had I taken his assessments in my youth, I might not have spent so many years thinking I was broke, but rather I had something incredible to offer the world, and I may have offered it up sooner. I was blown away at how a tool and process could have such an impact on the outcomes for young people. Powerful!

Conclusion

Creating organizations, programs, and classrooms that allow all youth to thrive can seem daunting at first glance, but this need not be the case. As we have highlighted in this chapter, cultural competence can be woven into the development of relationships that cause youth to think critically, identify their sparks and cultural forms of expression, and foster a sense of authentic voice that promotes personal healing and social change. An initial step in getting this process underway is to begin to assess and identify the cultural strengths and assets that are already present in a given situation. As Roberto discusses in his case study, it took identifying the key administration and teaching staff that was willing to champion a culturally competent and strength-based approach to engaging the youth who were disengaged to begin to shift the narrative about the under-performing youth. From our collective experience, we have seen that every organization, school, and community has champions (even if it is only one or two) that are willing to engage youth in culturally relevant and strength-based ways, and are looking for an opportunity. Starting with this cohort of champions is key to demonstrating the power of cultivating cultural competence in the programs, pedagogy, and policies that follow. Another way to begin to recognize the champions in a school is to administer a culturally relevant assessment among the teachers. As Ladson-Billings and others have suggested, this can be a great way to see who already has cultural competency, to understand where the cultural blind spots are, and to begin to develop a plan of action for professional development that meets the needs of the school or organization.

As Juan Carlos highlights in his case study, assessments can also be administered to youth to help them recognize their own cultural resilience while also allowing educators a way to reflect on their own pedagogy and practice. From our vantage point, no human being ever reached his or her optimal performance by focusing solely on what they were not good at. By engaging youth in strength-based ways that highlight their own 21st-century skills and cultural capital, this momentum can be transferred to a variety of activities that can enhance cognitive, emotional, and social well-being. As JuanCarlos's case study suggests, assessing the cultural strengths youth already possess inter-personally, intra-personally, and as they navigate institutions can cultivate their positive cultural identity development, bolster confidence, and increase their academic self-efficacy. However, as the examples that were discussed show, developing a strategy and plan for cultural competence training is also suggested. This can take place in three ways: (1) identifying someone in the school or district that is highly skilled in the area of cultural competence and organizing a training with them; (2) identifying someone at a local university or college who demonstrates a history of facilitating cultural competence and/or equity training; and (3) connecting to national organizations and experts who provide cultural competence and equity training. In all the examples above, the efforts should build capacity in the local champions so that they can take the lead in assessing, implementing, reflecting, and improving these efforts. Developing a culture of improvement and structured professional learning communities can enhance impact and ensure sustainability.

Beyond engaging local staff and educators to increase their cultural competence and ability to engage youth in culturally relevant ways, efforts should be taken to increase voice and choice for youth and others in their community. The thriving of young people in culturally competent ways is an undertaking that cannot be done in isolation. Again, assessments and data can become tools to help parents and community leaders understand the level of thriving that students are experiencing. Approaches like appreciative inquiry allow for, once strengths have been identified, the engagement of the community in conversations to dream about how to leverage these strengths to improve youth and community outcomes (Whitney & Trosten-Bloom, 2010).

Once stakeholders express their desire to create impact, outcomes can be identified, and actions steps and accountability structures can be implemented. Engaging youth and communities in processes influenced by learning sciences and design thinking can be extremely valuable in creating culturally competent communities of improvement (Buchanan, 1992). Youth can be and should become important participants in these school climate, organization, and community improvement groups. As we have discussed in this chapter, authentic youth participation and voice engagement is an important goal to identify and work toward. Engaging with the "end user" that the curriculum, programs, and policies are designed to serve can ensure that root issues are identified and the full assets and sparks of students are included in the creation of viable solutions. For example, engaging youth and community in developing solutions to increase attendance, increasing classroom participation, and improved disciplinary outcomes in schools is key to increasing student engagement and disrupting the school-to-prison pipeline.

Finally, creating the context where all young people can thrive requires both top-down and bottom-up collaboration (Snapp, Russell, Arredondo, & Skiba, 2016). This "tree-top" and "grass-roots" collaboration is necessary and essential for the final process of collective healing as expressed by Laenui (2000). While not all educators will understand or agree that our educational institutions are designed to obtain the results that are statistically predictable, the collective healing journey that each of us must engage in is the ultimate process for all students to thrive. Youth thriving has a reciprocally transformative impact on the well-being outcomes of organizations and the community. Thus, it takes the full obligation of all vested stockholders to create culturally competent conditions for youth to thrive, especially for youth of color who are most vulnerable. The framework highlighted here was designed to be clear, doable, and consistently documented across disciplines. It is now time to move from discussion and documentation about cultural competence and equity to instead making the commitment and taking the action to create the conditions by which all youth can thrive under our care.

References

Adams, M., Lee, A., & Griffin, P. (1997). *Teaching for diversity and social justice.* New York: Routledge.

Arauz, J. (2007). *Jaula de Oro: Growing up as an undocumented Latin@ immigrant in the United States* (Doctoral Dissertations 145). Ed.D. diss., University of San Francisco, San Francisco. Retrieved from https://repository.usfca.edu/diss/145

Benson, P. L. (2008). *Sparks: How parents can ignite the hidden strengths of teenagers.* San Francisco, CA: John Wiley.

Benson, P. L., Scales, P. C., & Syvertsen, A. K. (2011). The contribution of the developmental assets framework to positive youth development theory and practice. In *Advances in Child Development and Behavior, 41*, 197–230.

Betancourt, J. R., Green, A. R., Carrillo, J. E., & Owusu Ananeh-Firempong, I. I. (2016). Defining cultural competence: A practical framework for addressing racial/ethnic disparities in health and health care. Public health reports. https://www.ncbi.nlm.nih.gov/pmc/articles/PMC1497553/pdf/12815076.pdf

Betancourt, J. R., Green, A. R., Carrillo, J. E., & Park, E. R. (2005). Cultural competence and health care disparities: Key perspectives and trends. *Health Affairs, 24*(2), 499–505.

Buchanan, R. (1992). Wicked problems in design thinking. *Design Issues, 8*(2), 5–21.

Clauss-Ehlers, C. (2004). Social-cultural factors, resilience, and coping: Support for a culturally sensitive measure of resilience. *Journal of Applied Developmental Psychology, 29*(3), 197–212.

Clauss-Ehlers, C. S. (2010). Cultural resilience. In C. S. Clauss-Ehlers (Ed.), *Encyclopedia of cross-cultural school psychology.* Boston: Springer.

Cross, T., Bazron, B. J., Dennis, K. W., & Isaacs, M. R. (1989). *Toward a culturally competent system of care.* Washington, DC: Georgetown University Child Development Center.

Delgado, R. (1989). Storytelling for oppositionists and others: A plea for narrative. *Michigan Law Review, 87*(8), 2411–2441.

Delgado, R., & Stefancic, J. (2017). *Critical race theory: An introduction.* New York and London: NYU Press.

Delpit, L. (2006). *Other people's children: Cultural conflict in the classroom.* New York, NY: New Press.

Diller, A., Houston, B., Pauly Morgan, K., & Ayim, M. (1996). *The gender question in education: Theory, pedagogy, and politics*. New York, NY: Westview Press.

Dukes, R. L., Martinez, R. O., & Stein, J. A. (1997). Precursors and consequences of membership in youth gangs. *Youth & Society, 29*(2), 139–165.

Freedman, S. W., & Ball, A. (2004). Ideological becoming: Bakhtinian concepts to guide the study of language. In *Literacy, and Learning* (pp. 3–33). New York: Cambridge University Press.

Freire, P. (1970). *Pedagogy of the oppressed* (M. B. Ramos, trans.). New York: Continuum, 2007.

Freire, P. (2014). *Educação como prática da liberdade*. Editor Paz and Terra. Retrieved from http://www.dhnet.org.br/direitos/militantes/paulofreire/livro_freire_educacao_pratica_liberdade.pdf

Freire, P., & da Veiga Coutinho, J. (1970). *Cultural action for freedom* (pp. 476–521). Cambridge: Harvard Educational Review.

Gardner, H. (2011). *Frames of mind: The theory of multiple intelligences*. Hachette, UK: Basic Books.

Gay, G. (2010). *Culturally responsive teaching: Theory, research, and practice*. New York and London: Teachers College Press.

Ginwright, S., & Cammarota, J. (2002). New terrain in youth development: The promise of a social justice approach. *Social Justice, 29*(4), 82–95.

Ginwright, S., & James, T. (2002). From assets to agents of change: Social justice, organizing, and youth development. *New Directions for Student Leadership, 2002*(96), 27–46.

Ginwright, S. A. (2010). Peace out to revolution! Activism among African American youth: An argument for radical healing. *Young, 18*(1), 77–96.

Gordon, K., & Coscarelli, W. (1996). Recognizing and fostering resilience. *Performance & Instruction, 35*(9), 14–17.

Hanley, M. S., & Noblit, G. W. (2009). *Cultural responsiveness, racial identity and academic success: A review of literature*. Retrieved from http://www.heinz.org/UserFiles/Library/Culture-Report_FINAL.pdf

Hull, G. A., & Nelson, M. E. (2005). Locating the semiotic power of multimodality. *Written Communication, 22*(2), 224–261.

Hull, G. A., & Zacher, J. (2010). What is after-school worth? Developing literacy and identity out of school. *Building Smart Education Systems, 20*.

Kay, K., & Greenhill, V. (2013). *The leader's guide to 21st century education*. Boston, MA: Pearson.

Ladson-Billings, G. (1994). *The dreamkeepers: Successful teaching for African-American students*. San Francisco, CA: Jossey-Bass Publishers.

Ladson-Billings, G. (1995a). But that's just good teaching! The case for culturally relevant pedagogy. *Theory into Practice, 34*(3), 159–165.

Ladson-Billings, G. (1995b). Toward a theory of culturally relevant pedagogy. *American Educational Research Journal, 32*(3), 465–491.

Laenui, P. (2000). Processes of decolonization. *Reclaiming Indigenous Voice and Vision*, 150–160.

Lerner, R. M., Brentano, C., Dowling, E. M., & Anderson, P. M. (2002). Positive youth development: Thriving as the basis of personhood and civil society. *New Directions for Student Leadership, 2002*(95), 11–34.

McFarland, J., Hussar, B., Wang, X., Zhang, J., Wang, K., Rathbun, A., Barmer, A., Forrest Cataldi, E., & Bullock Mann, F. (2018). *The condition of education 2018* (NCES 2018-144). U.S. Department of Education. Washington, DC: National Center for Education Statistics. Retrieved from https://nces.ed.gov/pubsearch/pubsinfo. asp?pubid=2018144

Morrell, E. (2008). Six summers of YPAR. In J. Cammarota & M. Fine (Eds.), *Revolutionizing education: Youth participatory action research in motion* (pp. 155–184). New York and London: Routledge.

Noguera, P., Cammarota, J., & Ginwright, S. (2013). *Beyond resistance! Youth activism and community change: New democratic possibilities for practice and policy for America's youth*. New York: Routledge.

Noguera, P. A. (2008). Creating schools where race does not predict achievement: The role and significance of race in the racial achievement gap. *Journal of Negro Education*, 77, 90–103.

Paris, D., & Alim, H. S. (2017). *Culturally sustaining pedagogies: Teaching and learning for justice in a changing world*. New York: Teacher's College Press.

Petchauer, E. (2009). Framing and reviewing hip-hop educational research. *Review of Educational Research, 79*(2), 946–978.

Pittman, K. J., & Fleming, W. E. (1991). *A new vision: Promoting youth development*. Testimony of Karen Johnson Pittman, Vice President, Academy for Educational Development, Director Center for Youth Development and Policy Research before the House Select Committee on Children Youth and Families.

Rose, T. (1994). *Black noise: Rap music and black culture in contemporary America* (Vol. 6). Middletown, CT: Wesleyan University Press.

Scales, P. C., Benson, P. L., Leffert, N., & Blyth, D. A. (2000). Contribution of developmental assets to the prediction of thriving among adolescents. *Applied Developmental Science, 4*(1), 27–46.

Scales, P. C., Benson, P. L., & Roehlkepartain, E. C. (2011). Adolescent thriving: The role of sparks, relationships, and empowerment. *Journal of Youth and Adolescence, 40*(3), 263–277.

Scales, P. C., & Leffert, N. (1999). *Developmental assets: A synthesis of the scientific research on adolescent development*. Minneapolis, MN: Search Institute.

Search Institute. (2018). Retrieved from https://www.search-institute.org/developmental-relationships/developmental-relationships-framework/, accessed June 12, 2018.

Slaten, C. D., Rivera, R. C., Shemwell, D., & Elison, Z. M. (2016). Fulfilling their dreams: Marginalized urban youths' perspectives on a culturally sensitive social and emotional learning program. *Journal of Education for Students Placed at Risk (JESPAR), 21*(2), 129–142.

Smith, W. A., Hung, M., & Franklin, J. D. (2011). Racial battle fatigue and the miseducation of black men: Racial microaggressions, societal problems, and environmental stress. *Journal of Negro Education, 80*, 63–82.

Snapp, S. D., Russell, S. T., Arredondo, M., & Skiba, R. (2016). A right to disclose: LGBTQ youth representation in data, science, and policy. *Advances in Child Development and Behavior, 50*, 135–159.

Solorzano, D., Allen, W. R., & Carroll, G. (2002). Keeping race in place: Racial microaggressions and campus racial climate at the University of California, Berkeley. *Chicano-Latino Law Review, 23*, 15–112.

Sue, D. W., Capodilupo, C. M., Torino, G. C., Bucceri, J. M., Holder, A., Nadal, K. L., & Esquilin, M. (2007). Racial microaggressions in everyday life: Implications for clinical practice. *American Psychologist, 62*(4), 271–285.

Wagner, T. (2010). *The global achievement gap—Why even our best schools don't teach the new survival skills our children need, and what we can do about it.* New York: Basic Books.

Weissberg, R. P., Kumpfer, K. L., & Seligman, M. E. (2003). Prevention that works for children and youth: An introduction. *American Psychological Association, 58*(6–7), 425–432.

Whitney, D. D., & Trosten-Bloom, A. (2010). *The power of appreciative inquiry: A practical guide to positive change*. San Francisco, CA: Berrett-Koehler Publishers.

Yosso, T., Smith, W., Ceja, M., & Solórzano, D. (2009). Critical race theory, racial microaggressions, and campus racial climate for Latina/o undergraduates. *Harvard Educational Review, 79*(4), 659–691.

Zimmerman, K. (2017, July 12). What is culture? *Live Science*. Retrieved from https://www.livescience.com/21478-what-is-culture-definition-of-culture.html

PART 3

Building Capacity

CHAPTER EIGHT

Developing Social and Emotional Skills and Attitudes and Ecological Assets

Maurice J. Elias, Marc A. Brackett, Rose H. Miller, Stephanie M. Jones, Jennifer Kahn, Joseph L. Mahoney, Roger P. Weissberg, and SooYun Chung

There is an emerging consensus that areas of research and intervention described variously as social and emotional learning (SEL), character education and development, 21st-century learning, life skills training, prosocial education, and positive youth development are tapping into competencies and characteristics essential for human health, accomplishment, and well-being (Brown, Corrigan, Higgins-D'Allesandro, 2012; Durlak, Domitrovich, Weissberg, & Gullotta, 2015; Farrington et al., 2012). Among the various ways this domain has been defined, two conclusions can be stated with confidence. First, there is a recent and substantial body of evidence demonstrating positive effects of interventions and practices in this domain on academic, interpersonal, and mental health outcomes. Second, among these approaches, those focused on SEL appear to have the largest and most rigorously evaluated body of supporting evidence (Jones & Bouffard, 2012).

What Are the Skills?

Broadly speaking, SEL refers to the process through which individuals learn and apply a set of social, emotional, behavioral, and character skills required to succeed in schooling, the workplace, relationships, and citizenship. Looking across a variety of disciplines, organizing systems, and correlational and evaluation research, there are at least a dozen specific social and emotional skills that are relevant for both students and the adults who teach and care for them, including those in clinical and counseling roles (Jennings & Greenberg, 2009). These skills can be grouped into three interconnected domains:

1. *Cognitive regulation* can be thought of as the basic skills required to direct behavior toward the attainment of a goal. This set of skills includes executive functions such as working memory, attention control and flexibility, inhibition, and planning, as well as beliefs and attitudes that guide one's sense of self and approaches to learning and growth. Children use cognitive regulation skills whenever faced with tasks that require concentration, planning, problem-solving, coordination, conscious choices among alternatives, or overriding a strong internal or external desire (Diamond & Lee, 2011)—all key skills for behavioral and academic success.
2. *Emotional competencies* are a set of skills and understandings that help children recognize, express, and regulate their emotions, as well as engage in empathy and perspective-taking around the emotions of others. Emotional skills allow children to recognize how different situations make them feel and to address those feelings in prosocial ways. Consequently, they are often fundamental to positive social interactions and critical to building relationships with peers and adults.
3. *Social and interpersonal skills* support children and youth to interpret other people's behavior accurately, navigate social situations effectively, and interact positively with peers and adults. Social and interpersonal skills build on emotional knowledge and processes; children must learn to recognize, express, and regulate their emotions before they can be expected to interact with others who are engaged in the same set of processes. Children must be able to use these social and interpersonal processes effectively in order to work collaboratively, solve social problems, and coexist peacefully with others.

We fully expect readers to notice overlap in these areas and to identify at least a few skills or attributes they would prefer to see explicated. However defined, drawing on evidence from a range of disciplines and perspectives, social and emotional skills develop in a complex system of contexts, interactions, and relationships (Capella, Blair, & Aber, 2016; Jones & Bouffard, 2012; Nagaoka, Farrington, Ehrlich, & Heath, 2015). As such, the development of SEL skills is influenced by multiple environmental factors and systems, including culture and climate. When these factors and systems are aligned for positive contributions, they can be considered ecological assets to healthy development; when they are not, they can be considered ecological impediments.

Contexts influence the development and expression of SEL skills in many ways. First, the physical and human resources available to a child may facilitate (or challenge) their SEL. Research shows that children who have positive, contextually and developmentally appropriate, reciprocal, reliable, and flexible relationships with adults, typically have more access to interactions that support SEL (Brion-Meisels & Jones, 2012). Similarly, children who have access to developmentally appropriate and engaging learning tools such as books, games, and toys also benefit from these resources.

Correspondingly, students experiencing frequent acute or chronic adverse events must overcome these developmental barriers to achieve at the same level as their more advantaged peers. Second, specific settings can be more or less likely to influence the ease with which a child accesses and expresses SEL skills that he or she already possesses, particularly among young children. For example, children are more likely to be able to pay attention to their teacher and their schoolwork in a classroom community where they are not simultaneously worried about or distracted by peer aggression. Finally, contexts send messages to youth that shape their attitudes, expectancies, and character in many ways. Some schools communicate to subgroups of children that adults do not expect them to learn to the same degree as their peers; some communities convey a differential appreciation for social and institutional participation among certain populations; and attitudes internalized by parents about their children's potential for achieving particular career paths or educational outcomes become communicated in households. Because these influences are transactional, a developmental-systems approach is necessary to ensure all children have equitable access to learning social-emotional competencies.

Although more research is required in this area, a growing body of evidence suggests two overarching features of how SEL skills emerge and change over the first 10 years of life. First, some skills act as building blocks: they serve as a foundation for more complex skills that emerge later in life. This suggests that children must develop certain basic SEL competencies before they can master others. Second, some skills are stage-salient: they enable children and youth to meet the demands of a particular developmental stage or setting. In other words, as the environmental contexts in which children learn, grow, and play change, so do the demands placed on children to be successful, and some SEL skills are variably important at these different times of development. There is reason to believe, then, that certain SEL skills should be taught before others, and within specific grades or age ranges.

Links to Mental Health Outcomes

A substantial and rigorous body of evidence shows that across the school years, social and emotional skills are related to positive academic, social, and mental health outcomes. This makes eminently good sense. Children with strong social skills are more likely to make and sustain friendships, initiate positive relationships with teachers, participate in classroom activities, and be positively engaged in learning. Children with stronger social and emotional competencies are also more likely to enter and graduate from college, succeed in their careers, have positive work and family relationships, better mental and physical health, reduced criminal behavior, and to become engaged citizens (Greenberg et al., 2017; Moffitt et al., 2011; Weissberg et al., 2015). Deficiencies in the ability to correctly label and manage strong emotions, listen carefully and accurately to others, and problem solve effectively appear highly relevant to a range of interpersonal difficulties, as well as behavioral and emotional disorders (Elias, 2004; Elias, Gara, Rothbaum, Reese, & Ubriaco, 1987). It should not be surprising that interventions focused on improving children's social and emotional skills have produced reductions in aggression, depression, and anxiety (Jones, Barnes, Bailey, & Doolittle, 2017).

In addition, social and emotional skills serve as important protective factors in the face of negative life events or chronic stressors (Buckner, Mezzacappa & Beardslee, 2003, 2009) and support general well-being—including job and financial security, and physical and mental health—through adulthood (Jones, Greenberg & Crowley, 2015; Moffitt et al., 2011). A longitudinal study following more than 1,000 children found that early self-control predicted a range of long-term outcomes, including better physical health and personal finances, and lower substance dependence and criminal activity (Duckworth & Seligman, 2005; Moffitt et al., 2011). Likewise, the inability to cope effectively with stress or regulate one's emotions is associated with numerous diseases that influence the physiological response system. This is particularly relevant for children exposed to chronic stress often associated with poverty, violence, and substance abuse, conditions that have long-lasting consequences for learning, behavior, and general physical and mental well-being (Center on the Developing Child, 2007; Jones & Kahn, 2017; Thompson, 2014).

A meta-analysis by Taylor, Oberle, Durlak, and Weissberg (2017) reviewed 82 school-based, universal SEL interventions published through 2014 that involved 97,406 children in grades K–12. The study was grounded in a combined SEL-positive youth development perspective that focuses both on strengths and asset promotion, and protection from negative outcomes. A major aim was to determine whether such interventions sustain their initial findings through analysis of follow-up effects on multiple positive and negative indicators of well-being.

Examining follow-up periods ranging from 56 to 195 weeks, Taylor and colleagues (2017) found that SEL participants were significantly better adjusted in all seven categories of outcomes considered: social and emotional skills; attitudes toward self, others, and school; positive social behaviors; academic performance; conduct problems; emotional distress; and substance use (effect size ranging .13 to .33 across categories). This held for all demographic subgroups considered (i.e., white students, students of color, diverse student populations, low-income vs. middle-to-high income). Moreover, interventions conducted within or outside of the United States showed comparable, positive effects. Looking just at individual studies with long-term follow-ups through adolescence and young adulthood, participants in SEL interventions continued to show significantly more positive adjustment in areas such as graduating from high school, attending college, fewer arrests, and fewer placements in special education, although the statistical effect sizes for these long-term benefits were small.

Taken together, supporting positive social and emotional development is highly valuable for the success and well-being of individuals, schools, and society at large. Reductions in violence, drug use, delinquent behavior, and mental health problems—as a result of stronger social and emotional skills and competencies—are likely to lead to decreased need for government services, and ultimately, less expenditure of public money (Jones, Greenberg, Crowley, 2015; Jones & Kahn, 2017). Importantly, interventions designed to build social and emotional skills have been shown to be effective for all children and youth, regardless of geographical setting (e.g., urban, suburban, rural) or socio-demographic background (Bridgeland, Bruce, & Hariharan, 2013; DePaoli et al., 2015; Durlak, Weissberg, Dymnicki, Taylor, & Schellinger, 2011; Jones & Kahn, 2017; Taylor et al., 2017). Importantly, this work is especially relevant for supporting students who are low-income or experience other risk factors, providing them with a set of skills that can buffer exposure to adverse experiences or difficulty in school (Aber et al., 2003; Capella et al., 2016).

Numerous studies identify benefits from SEL programming, with most sharing a social-ecological developmental perspective (Durlak et al., 2011; Taylor et al., 2017; see detailed listings at http://www.casel.org). The Collaborative for Academic, Social, and Emotional Learning (CASEL) has taken a lead role in understanding the differences among these programs to help schools match a particular approach to the context and population for which it will be implemented. For example, some SEL programs focus on the integration of social and emotional skills into the curriculum, others incorporate lessons that are separate from school-day activities. In addition, some SEL programs focus on social justice issues to teach positive attitudes and openness, whereas others rely on students' individual experiences to guide lessons and practices. Regardless, there is wide agreement that the effectiveness of programs is related less to their SEL content and more to the structural features of those programs (e.g., that they map onto the acronym SAFE by being sequenced, active, focused, and explicit, CASEL, 2017), and the extent to which they are implemented in contexts that are congruent with the messages being conveyed in those programs and provide opportunities for students to authentically enact what is being learned.

Osher and colleagues (2016) laid out a framework for a well-designed SEL program, namely that a program is: developmentally appropriate, culturally relevant, systemic, comprehensive, evidence-based, and forward thinking. Whether or not a program is developmentally appropriate might hinge on how many grade levels are incorporated into a program, and whether materials corresponding to these differentiations account for variations in learning styles of students of different ages. Cultural relevance can be judged based on how a program is designed to reach students of different backgrounds in a socially responsible manner—an instance where values positions, noted earlier, are especially salient and require explicit attention. Comprehensiveness refers to the extent to which a particular SEL approach is deeply rooted in theory and inclusive of more, rather than fewer, SEL competencies. How systemic a program is hinges on how widely its practices reach adults and other stakeholders in the larger community and then are carried through into the life of the school. Evidence-based refers to the research that has demonstrated the effectiveness of the SEL program. Finally, a forward-thinking program is one that encapsulates the changing cultural tides in which the program exists and prepares students for new and forthcoming opportunities in the larger world.

Next, we review the theoretical orientations, practices, and efficacy of six widely adopted yet distinct approaches to SEL. These programs were chosen for the extent to which their theory of action explicitly connects their SEL content and instruction to mental health outcomes. We present them alphabetically in order to avoid the appearance of favoring one program over another.

SEL Programs and Approaches

4Rs

The 4Rs (Reading, Writing, Respect, and Resolution) Program uses developmentally appropriate literature to teach students in pre-kindergarten through 5th grade classrooms social and emotional skills focused on interpersonal relationships and conflict resolution. The target skills of the program include actions like handling anger, listening, cooperating, being assertive, celebrating differences, countering bias, and building community (Brown, Jones, LaRusso, & Aber, 2010). The program's theory of change focuses on altering underlying processes that are related to aggressive behaviors during key developmental periods so as to create lasting change (Jones, Brown, & Aber, 2011). Specifically, the program targets students' tendency to have an aggressive response to socially neutral stimuli (i.e., hostile attributional biases, aggressive interpersonal negotiation strategies). 4Rs also aims to lessen students' display of affective symptomatology (i.e., depressive, and ADHD-related).

4Rs uses children's literature as a jumping-off point for building supportive, emotionally aware students, schools, and communities with a guideline of at least one 20- to 60-minute lesson per week. Each teaching unit focuses on a single book and is made up of three sequenced parts: Read Aloud, Book Talk, and Applied Learning (Jones et al., 2017). Every book is carefully chosen based on its relevance to an SEL theme, and then is read aloud as a class before being discussed by the group to highlight the major themes, and increase understanding of the connection it has to the students' lives. Finally, each unit concludes 3–6 applied learning activities that allow students to practice skills related to the lesson's theme (The 4Rs Program, 2016).

One randomized controlled trial of 82 3rd grade classrooms from 18 urban public schools found that 4Rs had a positive impact on teachers' perceived emotional skills, which directly impacted the emotional and instructional quality of the classroom at the end of the year. Results indicated that at the end of the school year, classrooms that had incorporated 4Rs had higher independent observer ratings of social processes than control classrooms, even when controlling for teacher ratings of social-emotional functioning (Brown et al., 2010). Another experimental investigation into the impact of 4Rs on the same cohort of classrooms found that students in 4R classrooms had lower rates of hostile attributional bias and aggressive interpersonal negotiation strategies, and a greater decline in ADHD and depressive symptoms than children in the control classrooms. In terms of academic functioning, the study found that students who demonstrated more behavioral risk factors at baseline showed greater improvements in their math and reading achievement scores compared to students whose baseline behavioral risk was lower (Jones et al., 2011).

Facing History and Ourselves

Facing History and Ourselves is an SEL program designed to be infused into an academic classroom setting in English, History, or Social Studies courses at the secondary school level. The program uses relevant academic content to promote understanding about intergroup conflict, racism, religious intolerance, and general prejudice. This civic learning approach strives to educate students in a supportive classroom environment that melds historical knowledge with social- and self-awareness and respect for diversity, along with perspective taking and conflict resolution (Facing History and Ourselves, 2017).

At the center of the program's pedagogical approach is a focus on three major components: intellectual rigor, emotional engagement, and ethical reflection. Facing History uses self-exploration of individuals and groups to answer the questions "who am I?" and "who are we?" Examining and discussing case studies taken from both historical and literary contexts, students are encouraged to delve deeply into ideas about personal and group responsibility, and to complete individual projects in which they explore the emotional and intellectual facets of openness and tolerance (Facing History and Ourselves, 2017).

A 2015 randomized controlled trial of Facing History found that the program had a significant positive impact on teacher self-efficacy and engagement, and a moderate positive impact on students' civic self-efficacy and feeling that the classroom was a respectful, open, and tolerant environment. These results were especially notable given that only half of the teachers reported full fidelity to implementation of the program (Barr et al., 2015). Another study showed that eighth graders in classrooms where the program was implemented demonstrated increases in relationship maturity levels as well as decreases in racist attitudes throughout the year (Schultz, Barr, & Selman, 2001).

PATHS

Promoting Alternative THinking Strategies (PATHS) focuses on the reduction of problem behaviors and promotion of emotional and social skills in classrooms for children in grades K–6. Originally developed for use with deaf children, PATHS now aims to teach all elementary-aged children emotional literacy, self-control, and social competence (PATHS Curriculum, 2012). Designed to be taught 2–3 times a week for at least 20–30 minutes per session, the PATHS program relies on high-quality implementation that focuses on emotion knowledge, emotion expression, and interpersonal skill development (Jones et al., 2017). PATHS covers five main domains of social and emotional development: self-control, emotional understanding, positive self-esteem, relationships, and interpersonal problem-solving through sequenced lessons that build upon one another with increasing developmental difficulty. PATHS follows an affective-behavioral-cognitive-dynamic (ABCD) model of development that focuses on active integration of affective and cognitive processes as they relate to social and emotional competence (Greenberg & Kusché, 1993). The ABCD model takes into account that emotional development occurs prior to most cognitive developmental processes. Therefore, the model focuses on integrating affective processes into cognitive and linguistic understanding in a developmentally appropriate manner (Kam, Greenberg, & Kusché, 2004). The PATHS program is also compatible with and has been proven effective for Head Start classrooms (PATHS Program Objectives and Goals, 2017).

A randomized controlled trial of PATHS in 14 schools examined teacher- and self-reports of different student social information processing (SIP) and social behavior outcomes. Students in the PATHS condition exhibited less aggressive behavior and fewer conduct problems than students in the control condition, in addition to showing stability in SIP outcomes while control students' behaviors trended more negatively (Crean & Johnson, 2013).

A separate study examining the efficacy of PATHS found significant positive effects of the intervention on levels of aggression, prosocial behavior, and academic engagement, although the main effects of the intervention were dependent on both student and school characteristics. Specifically, the intervention showed greater impact in more disadvantaged schools (Bierman et al., 2010). Another study implemented a pilot version of PATHS for a sample of 133 students with special needs in the 1st to 3rd grades. Researchers found that the PATHS curriculum had a significant impact on children's externalizing and internalizing behaviors, as well as on their self-reported depression symptoms (Kam et al., 2004). The authors also found that these positive impacts were sustained up to two years after implementation of the intervention.

Responsive Classroom

Responsive Classroom (RC) is an evidence-based SEL teaching approach for students in grades K–8 that focuses on four key facets: engaging students in academics, positive community building, effective classroom management, and developmental awareness (Rimm-Kaufman et al., 2014). Using structured classroom activities such as Morning Meetings, Energizers, Quiet Time, and Closing Circles, RC places a high emphasis on building students' attentional control and fostering positive interpersonal relationships (Jones et al., 2017). RC focuses on teacher effectiveness and provides educators the resources to encourage students to make meaningful choices about their learning, to establish autonomy in class, and to create a sense of joyful community and shared purpose in their school community. RC has six guiding principles that set the tone for the program, most prominently that SEL learning is as important as academic learning, and that the *way* material is taught is as important as *what* material is taught. Additionally, the program implies that social interaction promotes cognitive change, that belief in positive expectations about students informs how students act and are treated, and that families contribute meaningfully to social and emotional growth (Rimm-Kaufman et al., 2014).

In one quasi-experimental three-year longitudinal examination of the efficacy of the RC approach, researchers found that students of teachers who implemented more RC practices had higher social awareness and academic competence than students of teachers who used fewer RC practices. The use of RC practices also positively impacted children's perceptions of their classrooms' emotional climates, such that children's perceptions of their classroom mediated the relationship between the use of RC practices and their social and academic outcomes. In other words, students in classrooms that implemented more RC practices had a more favorable view of their school in general, and these positive views, in turn, impacted their social and academic gains for the better (Brock, Nishida, Chong, Grimm, & Rimm-Kaufman, 2008).

Results from a three-year longitudinal, randomized controlled trial found that RC practices link positively with achievement, and unexpectedly high implementation fidelity of RC practices negatively impacted students' math scores. This suggests that the nature of the implementation is highly important, such that RC practices be equally distributed among classroom lessons so as not to detract resources or time from other academic lessons (Rimm-Kaufman et al., 2014). An earlier study posited that RC implementation practices positively impacted fifth graders' self-efficacy related to math and science, thereby reducing their anxiety around performance in those subjects (Griggs, Rimm-Kaufman, Merritt, & Patton, 2013). Together, these results suggest that the quality and quantity of RC lessons together affect student outcomes.

RULER

RULER is an empirically based approach to SEL rooted in both emotional intelligence (EI, Salovey, & Mayer, 1990) and ecological systems theory (Bronfenbrenner & Morris, 1998). RULER teaches students and adults the skills to Recognize, Understand, Label, Express and Regulate their emotions, which represent the RULER acronym (Brackett, Elbertson, & Rivers, 2015). RULER implies that it is not enough to simply teach skills—the classroom and school environment must be supportive to foster positive outcomes among students and adults (Brackett et al., 2015). A third theoretical component of RULER is the focus on helping adults and students develop a "growth" rather than a "fixed" mindset regarding the development of emotion skills and building classroom and school communities (Dweck, 2000).

RULER uses a phased approach, with the first phase aimed at garnering support from adults and stakeholders in the educational community at hand. Using a train-the-trainer model, phase one of RULER aims at professional development for adults. The second phase focuses on teaching skills and strategies to students and families. The third phase focuses on integrating RULER principles into broader policy efforts, including behavior management systems. RULER teaches emotional intelligence through four sequentially taught Anchor Tools known as the Charter, the Mood Meter, the Meta-Moment, and the Blueprint. By way of example, the Mood Meter provides a framework for understanding emotions, building both self- and social-awareness as educators and students practice checking in with their bodies and minds to accurately identify their emotional experiences and learn strategies to manage them effectively. At the elementary and middle school levels, RULER also embeds a Feeling Words Curriculum that focuses on developing students' self- and social-awareness, responsible decision-making, and emotion regulation skills.

A 2013 randomized controlled trial of RULER's efficacy that was completed across 5th and 6th grade classrooms in 62 schools found that RULER schools had stronger emotional climates present in their classrooms than control schools after one year (Rivers, Brackett, Reyes, Elbertson, & Salovey, 2013). A second study found that shifts in emotional climate were maintained after two years, and that by the end of the second year of implementation instructional and organizational climate of a school was positively impacted (Hagelskamp, Brackett, Rivers, & Salovey, 2013). In one quasi-experimental study of fifth and sixth graders from three different schools, evidence was found that students who received instruction in RULER had higher end-of-year academic performance as well has higher teacher-rated social and emotional competence (Brackett, Rivers, Reyes, & Salovey, 2012). One study investigating the training and implementation quality of 28 teachers' delivery of RULER found that for teachers who were high- or moderate-quality implementers (i.e., demonstrated openness to the program and taught material accurately) who attended more training and coaching sessions had students with higher social problem-solving and emotional literacy scores than low-quality implementers who attended the same number of trainings (Reyes, Brackett, Rivers, Elbertson, & Salovey, 2012).

Second Step

Second Step is a pre-kindergarten to 8th grade program designed to help students develop skills to manage their emotions and behaviors so as to reduce aggression and violence. For elementary school students, Second Step is divided into four major modules: Skill for Learning, Empathy, Emotion Management, and Problem-Solving (Second Step, 2017). Each grade level has a separate set of curricula to encourage developmentally appropriate lessons that are relevant for each age group. Second Step provides teachers with a variety of teaching materials to help make lessons interactive and engaging.

Optional training involves workshops and coaching for parents, faculty, and school staff who provide instruction on all major domains of the program in the year prior to schoolwide implementation (Jones, 2017).

A 2015 randomized control trial of Second Step in 61 schools across five districts found that the benefits of Second Step were most pronounced for students who began the program with their competence scores in the bottom half of the range for their age groups. Students whose baselines scores for conduct problems and aggressive behavior were higher, and whose teacher-rated scores of emotion management and problem-solving skills were lower showed the most improvement in their competencies over the course of the school year (Low, Cook, Smolkowski, & Buntain-Ricklefs, 2015).

A separate study of 4th and 5th grade classrooms found that students showed improvements across main areas of the program (i.e., anger management, impulse control, empathy) at post-test (Edwards, Hunt, Meyers, Grogg, & Jarrett, 2005). A study of the program's efficacy after one year of implementation in 11 Norwegian schools showed that fifth and sixth graders demonstrated improvements in social competence and rates of externalizing behaviors and hyperactivity. Another study of 1,253 2nd and 4th grade students found that students in Second Step classrooms demonstrated more explicit prosocial goals and behavior than other students (Frey, Nolen, Edstrom, & Hirschstein, 2005).

SEL programs vary in their pedagogical approaches to teaching students and adults. Overall, most programs share similar priorities, namely striving to help adults teach students the skills they need to succeed inside and outside of the classroom. Most SEL programs include explicit teaching of skills, regardless of whether lessons are integrated into a language-arts course, a history course, or stand alone as a separate curriculum. Even sharing similar goals, when revisiting the six major criteria of which effective SEL programming should be composed, one might notice that some programs address some benchmarks and not others. For example, 4Rs aims to tailor its lessons and choice of literature based on the needs and experiences of students of different ages, making it a developmentally appropriate program for each of its target audiences. A program such as Facing History hits the benchmark for cultural relevance in incorporating discussions about social justice and other topical issues heavily into SEL instruction. PATHS' focus on the ABCD theory of development shows a commitment to comprehensiveness, while RULER's demonstrated ability to hold up in the face of rigorous experimental evaluation and focus on all stakeholders demonstrates its systemic approach to teaching SEL. Each SEL program has a unique pedagogical approach, but all aim to equip students with the same sets of skills in order to set them up for success. Covering a wide range of competencies, these differing SEL approaches all have qualities that have value and foster academic, social, and emotional growth for students.

In discussing these, or any, programs as examples of SEL implementation, it is important to acknowledge several points made earlier. First, virtually every SEL program has had instances of failure as well as success; in Gager and Elias's (1997) analysis of examples of SEL-related programs carried out statewide in New Jersey, implementation factors were necessary, if not sufficient, conditions for success among programs with empirical support of the kind noted in the six examples just cited. Further, whether programs were sustainable over multiple years was similarly determined by implementation and contextual factors (Elias, 2010).

Second, a meta-analysis of SEL studies (Durlak et al., 2011) supports the idea that the most reliable gains from SEL programs come from multiyear, systematic implementation. However, the majority of empirical studies, including RCTs, are no more than one year in duration. This speaks to the larger issue of the extent to which empirical supports of SEL adequately discuss the context of implementation, including when in the history of relationship of program consultants and host settings a study is carried out. Three of the programs noted above—Facing History, RULER, and RC—are perhaps best not thought of as discrete programs implementing SEL-related skill lessons. They have a different relationship to their host environment. Facing History must be adopted into existing Social Studies curriculum and instruction; RULER requires strong systemic commitment prior to implementation, including staff preparation and support; and RC focuses on changing pedagogy as well as increasing student voice in the classroom. Typically, it is implemented in units, such as grade levels or entire schools, which also provide a community of support for those carrying out the approach.

It would be most accurate to say that successful, multiyear, sustained SEL represents a confluence of program and instructional factors, cultural and developmental tailoring, and contextual implementation support (Wigelsworth et al., 2016). More and more, although the empirical base of SEL is located in its studies of theory-guided relationships and impact of programs, the practice base is holistically connected to settings larger than classrooms (Berman, Chaffee, & Sarmiento, 2018). That is, SEL in practice is a school-level intervention within which classrooms and other school settings are embedded; considering the impact of programs separate from their context is unwise (Gager & Elias, 1997). Notably, three of the six SEL approaches just described (Facing History, RULER, and RC) are not at all best characterized as "programs." Each defines its context of use differently, and implicitly or explicitly calls for significant preparation necessary for implementation, including commitments at the school level. There are processes involved in creating consensus and an overall facilitative environment within which SEL becomes implemented.

The Role of Teachers and Parents

Attention increasingly turns to the influence of children's teachers, including their first teachers (i.e., parents), in systematic attempts to improve children's social-emotional competence. Bar-On (2003), while focusing on teachers, makes the point that there is a cycle of competence that begins with having emotionally and socially intelligent individuals educating others in becoming more emotionally and socially intelligent: "It is logical to assume that these people will be the best teachers . . . [and] if we succeed in raising and educating more emotionally and socially intelligent children, we will contribute to building more effective and productive organisations, communities and societies" (Bar-On, 2003, p. 13).

There is a small, but growing, body of evidence supporting this perspective. Interventions addressing teacher-specific social and emotional competencies result in improvements in a variety of indicators of teacher well-being including reductions in stress and burnout, which can reduce rates of teacher and administrator turnover. Teachers also report greater job satisfaction when their students are more engaged and successful, and student motivation and engagement are linked to experiences with instructional content and approaches that reflect students' social and emotional worlds. Williford and Wolcott (2015) made the point that engaged teachers, in turn, engage students in both learning and in positive relationships in schools and classrooms. Although evidence is still preliminary, it seems reasonable that in such contexts, SEL skills will also be more likely to thrive (Cantor, Osher, Berg, Steyer, & Rose, 2018). Thus, there seems to be a movement toward school-based interventions for teachers that promote their mindfulness and stress management; however, research on these topics is in its early stages, with a paucity of long-term studies.

From an ecological-developmental-systems perspective, the challenges of being an effective teacher are many, and the likelihood of simple interventions being effective is small (Cantor et al., 2018). Teachers' well-being is directly or indirectly influenced by their effectiveness in a number of areas: (a) using instructional practices and classroom management; (b) school scheduling; (c) relationships with diverse students, professional peers, support staff, and administrators; and (d) communication and contact with parents. Also relevant are the overall climate of their buildings, involvement of community members and leaders, and macro-systemic factors such as attitudes and resources provided to teachers. We also should not ignore the hassles discussed daily in teachers' lounges: availability of safe and accessible parking, functioning of microwaves at lunchtime, and the quality of climate control in classrooms and buildings. Relying on individual coping in the context of so many systemic factors seems to be an error of logical typing and risks "blaming the victim" with regard to why teachers are not functioning "better" and thereby imparting more knowledge and SEL to their students.

Similarly, the same perspective is helpful for understanding the role of parents. As Eli Bower (1972) pointed out, among the many socializing influences on the development of children, parents are most critical. Many decisions made by the time a child reaches school at age 3, 4, or 5 set into motion powerful trajectories. These include with whom to partner to have a child (with its genetic implications), how to live, where to live, maternal lifestyle before and after the child's birth, and access to and use of the health care system throughout. One way of understanding parents' influence from an ecological perspective (Belsky, 1984) is to consider how they navigate their children's relationships through all the microsystems that are most directly influential on their development and which serve as arenas for the growth of SEL skills: households, childcare, playgroups, camps, after-school activities, religious settings, health care systems, to name a few. Parents' own social-emotional competencies—as well as the nature of, access to, and resources within those microsystems—strongly determine the nature of children's experiences within them. So it is not unreasonable to say that there would be a strong relationship between the social-emotional competence parents display each day in contexts highly salient to their children, and the corresponding skills their children develop through modeling and indirect instruction (Stern & Elias, 2007).

We are living in times of change in family composition and diversity (McGoldrick, Giordano, & Garcia-Preto, 2006). There is increasing inequity, resulting in stress due to such ongoing processes as racial prejudice, socioeconomic disadvantage, family disruption, immigration threat, and inadequate access to quality health care. These processes frame the ecological and developmental context described above and create a functional imperative for parent-school partnerships to foster children's social-emotional competence.

There is some empirical evidence that the social and emotional skills, drive, and competencies of parents and families can greatly affect outcomes. If, for instance, parents lack efficacy in terms of their ability to help their children, they may be less likely to be involved in their children's education and in promoting their children's social, emotional, and behavioral outcomes (Cantor et al., 2018; Garbacz, Swanger-Gagné, & Sheridan, 2015; Hoover-Dempsey, Bassler, & Brissie, 1992; Osher et al., 2016). Home environment, or more specifically the extent to which learning is stimulated in the home, significantly affects students' academic and social development, including prevention of—or promotion of—problem behaviors (Elias, Bryan, Patrikakou, & Weissberg, 2003).

For these reasons, Garbacz, Swanger-Gagné, and Sheridan's (2015) evaluation of SEL programs that actively engage families and promote a school-family partnership is particularly salient. SEL programs that "work" seem to foster positive social and emotional outcomes (i.e., self-management, social awareness, responsible decision-making) through meaningful family engagement (i.e., partnership-centered meetings and consultations between teachers and parents or caregivers, schoolwide modules that engage parents and children in activities at home). Patrikakou and Weissberg (2007) recommended selecting SEL approaches that systematically include parents. Specifically, they suggested educators look for interventions that feature:

1. Communication between home and school: two-way communication between home and school is the most important factor promoting children's social competence.
2. Parent involvement at home: CASEL Select Programs provide specific strategies and support through which teachers can involve parents, such as activities and materials that reinforce and extend classroom learning at home.
3. Parent involvement at school: Given the demands of modern life, involving families at school presents greater challenges than involvement at home. Often, both parents work extended hours and struggle to attend school meetings or activities. Nevertheless, accessible invitations should be made, including meetings that accommodate diverse parent schedules, and a clear sense of welcome and participation must be communicated.

Because each child and family's path to social and emotional competence has innumerable influences, systematic intervention with parents related to SEL has been fleeting and, when present, difficult to prove potent or to empirically derive the most salient elements. Nevertheless, there is some strong consensus from the practice literature regarding parenting practices, ideally in concert with the school but not necessarily, most likely to foster students' social-emotional and character development. They include parental self-reflection, to improve modeling, parental observation, to improve parent-child interaction, and contextual considerations, including the role of culture (Whitcomb & Elias, in press).

Table 8.1 summarizes the reflective questions parents can ask to build both awareness of and competence in SEL. Parents can ask a parallel set of questions when observing and interacting with their children. For example, for self-awareness: How does your child experience emotions? How well, and with how much variety and nuance, is your child able to name feelings or describe them? What seems to trigger your children's strongest emotions? How well are they able to explain their feelings when you ask about them?

There are many contextual considerations, including developmental, ability and disability, sibling issues, and family, school, and community context and culture (Cantor et al., 2018). Hence, there are many factors that make it challenging for parents to be the sole primary role models and SEL teachers of their children, particularly in a globalized world. This creates an imperative for the idea of parent-school-community partnership for building SEL in

Table 8.1 Parental self-reflection on social and emotional learning

- ***Self-awareness.*** How do you experience strong emotions, physically (e.g., joy, anger)? When do you find that you experience certain emotions, typically? What things do your children do that trigger strong feelings in you? What thoughts accompany these strong feelings?
- ***Self-management.*** How do you respond to your strong emotions, particularly when negative? Do you model ways you want your child to learn? How organized are you, in general and with your children? Do you set goals and make and keep plans to reach them?
- ***Social awareness.*** How much do you notice others' facial expressions, tone of voice, body posture, and other signs of their feelings? Are you typically accurate about how others are feeling, and do you understand why they may be behaving the way they do?
- ***Relationship skills.*** How do you make friends and interact informally with colleagues, neighbors, others you may not know well? What helps you to maintain relationships with others? Are you more comfortable or effective in a group or one-on-one, or as a leader or team member?
- ***Responsible decision-making.*** How do you go about thinking through big decisions? How do you resolve conflicts or arguments? Are you able to assert yourself? Do you consider others? Are you able to make healthy and good decisions?

upcoming generations as being, de facto, how those skills will be developed (Patrikakou & Weissberg, 2007). The challenge that remains largely unaddressed, both in practice as well as in research, is how to do this effectively across contexts and in ways that will reach all parents equitably.

Conclusion and Future Directions

Supporting positive social and emotional development is highly valuable for the success and well-being of individuals, schools, and society at large. Reductions in violence, drug use, delinquent behavior, and mental health problems—as a result of stronger social and emotional skills and competencies—are likely to lead to decreased need for government services, and ultimately, less expenditure of public money (Jones et al., 2015). Importantly, interventions designed to build social and emotional skills have been shown to be effective for all children and youth, regardless of geographical setting (e.g., urban, suburban, rural) or socio-demographic background (Bridgeland et al., 2013; DePaoli et al., 2015; Durlak et al., 2011; Taylor et al., 2017). This work is especially relevant for supporting low-income or at-risk students, providing them with a set of skills that can buffer exposure to adverse experiences or difficulty in school (Aber et al., 2003; Capella et al., 2016). There also has been a strong convergence around what might be considered best practices, including, as noted earlier, the need to shift from a program perspective more to schools as ecological contexts, themselves nested in wider ecologies, in which SEL skills are continuously developed (Berman et al., 2018).

That said, the strength of empirical, longitudinal, developmental, and cross-contextual evidence for these contentions varies. As noted earlier, Rowe and Trickett (2017) pointed out the stark imbalance of research conducted with what might be labeled advantaged, majority groups, versus others. Although the theoretical base is strong, the nomological net has not been extended empirically to all the contexts in which implementation of SEL is taking place in practice, or is being called for. For the future, two key recommendations are to (1) expand the focus on populations and settings being studied; and (2) begin to bring SEL into new settings using the best available evidence from current practice and taking an action-research approach to make modifications in a spirit of continuous improvement (Elias & Leverett, 2011).

An additional continuing challenge is the organization of research. Although there are now many follow-up studies showing sustained effects of SEL programs, the significance of a developmental approach to programming itself involving continuous and integrated SEL from pre-kindergarten through young adulthood has received only modest attention. The methodological conundrum is that the programming rigor and continuity required of the strongest, "gold standard" research designs is least likely to be attainable in the maelstrom of under-resourced school contexts over extended periods of time. Further, the general model of individual researcher-initiated and grant-funded efforts is likely to result in a continued hodgepodge of findings and significant gaps in coverage of populations and settings. The SEL field will need to address the research future in concert with funders, journal editors, and large research labs and organizations, and create associations and affiliations with cadres of relevant individual research and research teams to allow for coordinated investigations.

There are other research issues, beyond what we can address here, that create limits to both existing findings and future work, particularly with regard to assessment. However, the final issue we will raise is the relative neglect in research, theory, and intervention of the ways in which what we might refer to as a moral compass relates to specific competencies. The SEL field uses words such as character, values, and virtues to a limited degree. Some efforts have begun to explicate these concerns, under the rubric of social-emotional and character development and prosocial education (Brown et al., 2012; Elias, 2009, 2013; Hatchimonji, Linsky, & Elias, 2017). This is a necessary step, because the SEL field implicitly assumes SEL skills give positive direction and energy to learning, mental health, and general social functioning and competence. However, this is not an inevitability. SEL skills, as skills for competence, can be used for ill as well as for good—with those terms being open to subjective interpretation. Although the SEL field has long relied on detailed analyses of consequences—short and long term, for self and others, direct and indirect—to lead to prosocial actions, this is an assumption that is no longer viable in a culturally sensitive, diverse world, in which the role of school-parent-community partnerships is seen as essential. The future of SEL is connected to the direction that the moral compass is pointing, and that should be the subject of explicit future theorizing, research, and practice.

References

Aber, J. L., Brown, J. L., & Jones, S. M. (2003). Developmental trajectories toward violence in middle childhood: Course, demographic differences, and response to school-based intervention. *Developmental Psychology, 39*(2), 324.

Bar-On, R. (2003). How important is it to educate people to be emotionally and socially intelligent, and can it be done? *Perspectives in Education, 214*, 3–16.

Barr, D. J., Boulay, B., Selman, R. L., McCormick, R., Lowenstein, E., Gamse, E., . . . Leonard, M. B. (2015). A randomized controlled trial of professional development for Interdisciplinary civic education: Impacts on humanities teachers and their students. *Teachers College Record, 117*, 2–52.

Belsky, J. (1984). The determinants of parenting: A process model. *Child Development, 55*, 83 96.

Berman, S., Chaffee, S., & Sarmiento, J. (2018). *The practice base for how we learn—Supporting students' social, emotional, and academic development: Consensus statements of practice from the Council of Distinguished Educators.* Washington, DC: Aspen Institute's National Commission on Social, Emotional, and Academic Development.

Bierman, K. L., Coie, J. D., Dodge, K. A., Greenberg, M. T., Lochman, J. E., McMahon, R. J., & Pinderhughes, E. (2010). The effects of a multiyear universal social-emotional learning program: The role of student and school characteristics. *Journal of Consulting and Clinical Psychology, 78*, 156–168. doi:10.1037/a0018607

Bouffard, S. M. (2017). Riding the turnover wave. Usable Knowledge. Retrieved from https://www.gse.harvard.edu/ news/uk/17/08/riding-turnover-wave

Bower, E. (1972). Education as a humanizing process. In S. Golann & C. Eisdorfer (Eds.), *Handbook of community mental health* (pp. 37–50). New York: Appleton-Century-Crofts.

Brackett, M. A., Elbertson, N. E., & Rivers, S. E. (2015). Applying theory to the development of approaches to SEL. In J. A. Durlak, C. E. Domitrovich, R. P. Weissberg, & T. P. Gullotta (Eds.), *Handbook of social and emotional learning* (pp. 20–32). New York: Guilford Press.

Brackett, M. A., Rivers, S. E., Reyes, M. R., & Salovey, P. (2012). Enhancing academic performance and social and emotional competence with the RULER feeling words curriculum. *Learning and Individual Differences, 22*, 218–224. doi:10.1016/j.lindif.2010.10.002

Bridgeland, J., Bruce, M., & Hariharan, A. (2013). *The missing piece: A national teacher survey on how social and emotional learning can empower children and transform schools* (A report for CASEL). Washington, DC: Civic Enterprises.

Brion-Meisels, G., & Jones, S. M. (2012). Learning about relationships. In S. Roffey (Ed.), *Positive relationships: Evidence based practice across the world* (pp. 55–72). New York: Springer.

Brock, L. L., Nishida, T. K., Chong, C., Grimm, K. J., & Rimm-Kaufman, S. E. (2008). Children's perceptions of the classroom environment and social and academic performance: A longitudinal analysis of the contribution of the Responsive Classroom approach. *Journal of School Psychology, 46*, 129–149. doi:10.1016/j.jsp.2007.02.004

Bronfenbrenner, U., & Morris, P. A. (1998). The ecology of developmental processes. In W. Damon & R. M. Lerner (Eds.), *Handbook of child psychology* (pp. 993–1028). Hoboken, NJ: John Wiley.

Brown, J. L., Jones, S. M., LaRusso, M. D., & Aber, J. L. (2010). Improving classroom quality: Teacher influences and experimental impacts of the *4Rs* program. *Journal of Educational Psychology, 102*, 153–167. doi:10.1037/a0018160

Brown, P. M., Corrigan, M. W., & Higgins-D'Allesandro, A. (Eds.). (2012). *The handbook of prosocial education* (pp. 767–800). Blue Ridge Summit, PA: Rowman and Littlefield.

Buckner, J., Mezzacappa, E., & Beardslee, W. (2003). Characteristics of resilient youths living in poverty: The role of self-regulatory processes. *Developmental Psychopathology, 15*(1), 139–162.

Buckner, J., Mezzacappa, E., & Beardslee, W. (2009). Self-regulation and its relations to adaptive functioning in low income youths. *American Journal of Orthopsychiatry, 79*(1), 19–30.

Cantor, P., Osher, D., Berg, J., Steyer, L., & Rose, T. (2018). Malleability, plasticity, and individuality: How children learn and develop in context. *Applied Developmental Science.* doi:10.1080/10888691.2017.1398649

Capella, E., Blair, C., & Aber, L. A. (2016). Outcomes beyond test scores, what is social-emotional learning? *Steinhardt White Paper.* Retrieved from https://steinhardt.nyu.edu/e/i2/edsolutions/201609/2SELOutcomesBeyondTestScores.pdf

Center on the Developing Child. (2011). *Building the brain's "air traffic control" system: How early experiences shape the development of executive function*

(Working paper no. 11). Retrieved from https://developingchild.harvard.edu/wp-content/uploads/2011/05/How-Early-Experiences-Shape-the-Development-of-Executive-Function.pdf

Collaborative for Academic, Social, and Emotional Learning. (2013). *Effective social and emotional learning programs—Preschool and elementary school edition*. Chicago: CASEL.

Cooke, M. B., Ford, J., Levine, J., Bourke, C., Newell, L., & Lapidus, G. (2007). The effects of city-wide implementation of "Second Step" on elementary school students' prosocial and aggressive behaviors. *Journal of Primary Prevention, 28*, 93–115. doi:10.1007/s10935-007-0080-1

Crean, H. F., & Johnson, D. B. (2013). Promoting Alternative THinking Strategies (PATHS) and elementary school aged children's aggression: Results from a cluster randomized trial. *American Journal of Community Psychology, 52*, 56–72.

DePaoli, J. L., Fox, J. H., Ingram, E. S., Maushard, M., Bridgeland, J. M., & Balfanz, R. (2015). *Building a grad nation: Progress and challenge in ending the high school dropout epidemic* (Annual Update 2015). Washington, DC: Civic Enterprises.

Diamond, A., & Lee, K. (2011). Interventions shown to aid executive function development in children 4 to 12 years old. *Science, 333*(6045), 959–964.

Duckworth, A. L., & Seligman, M. E. (2005). Self-discipline outdoes IQ in predicting academic performance of adolescents. *Psychological Science, 16*(12), 939–944.

Durlak, J. A., Domitrovich, C. E., Weissberg, R. P., & Gullotta, T. P. (Eds.). (2015). *Handbook of social and emotional learning: Research and practice*. New York: Guilford Press.

Durlak, J. A., Weissberg, R. P., Dymnicki, A. B., Taylor, R. D., & Schellinger, K. B. (2011). The impact of enhancing students' social and emotional learning: A meta-analysis of school-based universal interventions. *Child Development, 82*, 405–432. doi:10.1111/j.1467-8624.2010.01564.x

Dweck, C. S. (2000). *Self-theories: Their role in motivation, personality, and development*. New York: Taylor & Francis.

Edwards, D., Hunt, M. H., Meyers, J., Grogg, K. R., & Jarrett, O. (2005). Acceptability and student outcomes of a violence prevention curriculum. *Journal of Primary Prevention, 26*, 401–418. doi:10.1007/s10935-005-0002-z

Elias, M. J. (2004). The connection between social-emotional learning and learning disabilities: Implications for intervention. *Learning Disability Quarterly, 27*(1), 53–63.

Elias, M. J. (2009). Social-emotional and character development and academics as a dual focus of educational policy. *Educational Policy, 23*, 831–846.

Elias, M. J. (2010). Sustainability of social-emotional learning and related programs: Lessons from a field study. *The International Journal of Emotional Education, 2*(1), 17–33.

Elias, M. J. (2013). The character of schools, the character of individuals, and the character of society: Creating educational policy to reflect this inextricable interconnection. *Korean Journal of Educational Policy, 10*(3), 141–149.

Elias, M. J., Bryan, K., Patrikakou, E., & Weissberg, R. P. (2003). Challenges in creating effective home-school partnerships in adolescence: Promising paths for collaboration. *School Community Journal, 13*(1), 133–153.

Elias, M. J., Gara, M., Rothbaum, P., Reese, A., & Ubriaco, M. (1987). A multivariate analysis of factors differentiating behaviorally and emotionally dysfunctional children from other groups in school. *Journal of Clinical Child Psychology, 16*, 107–112.

Elias, M. J., & Leverett, L. (2011). Consultation to urban schools for improvements in academics and behavior: No alibis. No excuses. No exceptions. *Journal of Educational and Psychological Consultation, 21*, 1–17.

Facing History and Ourselves. (n.d.). Retrieved from https://www.facinghistory.org/

Farrington, C. A., Roderick, M., Allensworth, E., Nagaoka, J., Keyes, T. S., Johnson, D. W., & Beechum, N. O. (2012). *Teaching adolescents to become learners. The role of noncognitive factors in shaping school performance: A critical literature review.* Chicago: University of Chicago Consortium on Chicago School Research.

Frey, K. S., Nolen, S. B., Edstrom, L. V., & Hirschstein, M. K. (2005). Effects of a school-based social-emotional competence program: Linking children's goals, attributions, and behavior. *Journal of Applied Developmental Psychology, 26*, 171–200. doi:10.1016/j.appdev.2004.12.002

Gager, P. J., & Elias, M. J. (1997). Implementing prevention programs in high-risk environments: Application of the resiliency paradigm. *American Journal of Orthopsychiatry, 67*, 363–373.

Garbacz, S. A., Swanger-Gagné, M. S., & Sheridan, S. M. (2015). The role of school-family partnership programs for promoting student SEL. In J. A. Durlak, C. E. Domitrovich, R. P. Weissberg, & T. P. Gullotta (Eds.), *Handbook of social and emotional learning* (pp. 244–259). New York: Guilford.

Greenberg, M. T., Domitrovich, C. E., Weissberg, R. P., & Durlak, J. A. (2017). Social and emotional learning as a public health approach to education. *The Future of Children, 27*(1), 13–32. Retrieved from http://www.jstor.org/stable/44219019

Greenberg, M. T., Katz, D. A., & Klein, L. C. (2015). The potential effects of SEL on biomarkers and health outcomes: A promissory note. In J. A. Durlak, C. E. Domitrovich, R. P. Weissberg, T. P. Gullotta, & J. Comer (Eds.), *Handbook of social and emotional learning: Research and practice* (pp. 81–96). New York: Guilford Press.

Greenberg, M. T., & Kusché, C. A. (1993). *Promoting social and emotional development in deaf children: The PATHS Project.* Seattle: University of Washington Press.

Gregory, A., & Fergus, E. (2017). Social and emotional learning and equity in school discipline. *The Future of Children, 27*, 117–136.

Griggs, M. S., Rimm-Kaufman, S. E., Merritt, E. G., & Patton, C. L. (2013). The Responsive Classroom approach and fifth grade students' math and science anxiety and self-efficacy. *School Psychology Quarterly, 28*, 360–373. doi:10.1037/spq0000026

Hagelskamp, C., Brackett, M. A., Rivers, S. E., & Salovey, P. (2013). Improving classroom quality with the RULER approach to social and emotional learning: Proximal and distal outcomes. *American Journal of Community Psychology, 51*, 530–543. doi:10.1007/s10464-013-9570-x

Hatchimonji, D. R., Linsky, A. V., & Elias, M. J. (2017). Cultivating noble purpose in urban middle schools: A missing piece in school transformation. *Education, 138*(2), 162–178.

Hecht, M. L., & Shin, Y. S. (2015). Culture and social emotional competencies. In J. A. Durlak, C. E. Domitrovich, R. P. Weissberg, & T. P. Gullotta (Eds.), *Handbook of social and emotional learning: Research and practice* (pp. 50–64). New York: Guilford Press.

Holsen, I., Smith, B. H., & Frey, K. S. (2008). Outcomes of the social competence program Second Step in Norwegian elementary schools. *School Psychology International, 29*, 71–88. doi:10.1177/0143034307088504

Hoover-Dempsey, K. V., Bassler, O. C., & Brissie, J. C. (1992). Explorations in parent-school relations. *Journal of Educational Research, 85*, 297–294.

Introducing the PATHS Program and SEL. (n.d.). Channing Bete. Retrieved from https://www.channing-bete.com/prevention-programs/paths/introducing-paths.html

Jennings, P. A., Frank, J. L., Snowberg, K. E., Coccia, M. A., & Greenberg, M. T. (2013). Improving classroom learning environments by Cultivating Awareness and Resilience in Education (CARE): Results of a randomized controlled trial. *School Psychology Quarterly, 28*(4), 374–390.

Jennings, P. A., & Greenberg, M. T. (2009). The prosocial classroom: Teacher social and emotional competence in relation to student and classroom outcomes. *Review of Educational Research, 79*(1), 491–525.

Jennings, P. A., Snowberg, K. E., Coccia, M. A., & Greenberg, M. T. (2011). Improving classroom learning environments by cultivating awareness and resilience in education (CARE): Results of two pilot studies. *Journal of Classroom Interaction, 46*, 37–48.

Jones, D. J., Greenberg, M. T., & Crowley, M. (2015). The economic case for SEL. In J. A. Durlak, C. E. Domitrovich, R. P. Weissberg, T. P. Gullotta, & J. Comer (Eds.), *Handbook of social and emotional learning: Research and practice* (pp. 97–113). New York: Guilford Press.

Jones, S. M., Barnes, S. P., Bailey, R., & Doolittle, E. J. (2017). Promoting social and emotional competencies in elementary school. *The Future of Children, 27*, 49–72.

Jones, S. M., & Bouffard, S. M. (2012). Social and emotional learning in schools: From programs to strategies. *Society for Research in Child Development Social Policy Report, 26*(4), 1–33. Retrieved from http://files.eric.ed.gov/fulltext/ED540203.pdf

Jones, S. M., Brown, J. L., & Aber, J. L. (2011). Two-year impacts of a universal, school-based social-emotional and literacy intervention: An experiment in translational developmental research. *Child Development, 82*, 533–554. doi:10.1111/j.1467-8624.2010.01560.x

Jones, S. M., Brush, K., Bailey, R., Brion-Meisels, G., McIntyre, J., Kahn, J., . . . Stickle, L. (2017). *Navigating SEL from the inside out.* Boston: Harvard Graduate School of Education.

Jones, S. M., & Kahn, J. (2017). The evidence base for how we learn: Supporting students' social, emotional, and academic development. Retrieved from https://assets.aspeninstitute.org/content/uploads/2018/03/FINAL_CDS-Evidence-Base.pdf

Kam, C.-M., Greenberg, M. T., & Kusché, C. A. (2004). Sustained effects of the PATHS curriculum on the social and psychological adjustment of children in special education. *Journal of Emotional and Behavioral Disorders, 12*, 66–78. doi:10.1177/10634266040120020

Low, S., Cook, C. R., Smolkowski, K., & Buntain-Ricklefs, J. (2015). Promoting social-emotional competence: An evaluation of the elementary version of Second-Step. *Journal of School Psychology, 53*, 463–477. doi:10.1016/j.jsp.2015.09.002

McGoldrick, M., Giordano, J., & Garcia-Preto, N. (Eds.). (2006). *Ethnicity and family therapy* (3rd ed.). New York: Guilford.

Moffitt, T. E., Arseneault, L., Belsky, D., Dickson, N., Hancox, R. J., Harrington, H., & Sears, M. R. (2011). A gradient of childhood self-control predicts health, wealth, and public safety. *Proceedings of the National Academy of Sciences, 108*(7), 2693–2698.

Nagaoka, J., Farrington, C. A., Ehrlich, S. B., & Heath, R. D. (2015). *Foundations for young adult success: A developmental framework* (Concept Paper for Research and Practice). Chicago: University of Chicago Consortium on Chicago School Research.

Osher, D., Kidron, Y., Brackett, M., Dymnicki, A., Jones, S., & Weissberg, R. P. (2016). Advancing the science and practice of social and emotional learning: Looking back and moving forward. *Review of Research in Education, 40*, 644–681. doi:10.3102/0091732X16673595

Patrikakou, E. N., & Weissberg, R. P. (2007). School-family partnerships to enhance children's social, emotional, and academic learning. In R. Bar-On, J. Maree, & M. J. Elias (Eds.), *Educating people to be emotionally intelligent* (pp. 60–68). Westport, CT: Praeger.

Reyes, M. R., Brackett, M. A., Rivers, S. E., Elbertson, N. A., & Salovey, P. (2012). The interaction effects of program training, dosage, and implementation quality on targeted student outcomes for the RULER approach to social and emotional learning. *School Psychology Review, 41*, 82–99.

Rimm-Kaufman, S. E., Larsen, R. A. A., Baroody, A. E., Curby, T. W., Ko, M., Thomas, J. B., . . . DeCoster, J. (2014). Efficacy of the responsive classroom approach: Results from a 3-Year, longitudinal randomized controlled trial. *American Educational Research Journal, 51*, 567–603. doi:10.3102/0002831214523821

Rivers, S. E., Brackett, M. A., Reyes, M. R., Elbertson, N. A., & Salovey, P. (2013). Improving the social and emotional climate of classrooms: A clustered randomized controlled trial testing the RULER approach. *Prevention Science, 14*, 77–87. doi:10.1007/s11121-012-0305-2

Roeser, R. W., Schonert-Reichl, K. A., Jha, A., Cullen, M., Wallace, L., Wilensky, R., & Harrison, J. (2013). Mindfulness training and reductions in teacher stress and burnout: Results from two randomized, waitlist-control field trials. *Journal of Educational Psychology, 105*(3), 787–804.

Rowe, H. L., & Trickett, E. J. (2017). Student diversity representation and reporting in universal school-based social and emotional learning programs: Implications for generalizability. *Educational Psychology Review, 30*, 1–25. doi:10.1007/s10648-017-9425-3

Schultz, L. H., Barr, D. J., & Selman, R. L. (2001). The value of a developmental approach to evaluating character development programmes: An outcome study of Facing History and Ourselves. *Journal of Moral Education, 30*, 3–27. doi:10.1080/03057240120033378

Stern, R., & Elias, M. J. (2007). Emotionally intelligent parenting. In R. Bar-On, J. Maree, & M. J. Elias (Eds.), *Educating people to be emotionally intelligent* (pp. 37–48). Westport, CT: Praeger.

Taylor, R. D., Oberle, E., Durlak, J. A., & Weissberg, R. P. (2017). Promoting positive youth development through school-based social and emotional learning interventions: A meta-analysis of follow-up effects. *Child Development, 88*, 1156–1171. doi:10.1111/cdev.12864

Thompson, R. A. (2014). Stress and child development. *The Future of Children, 24*(1), 41–59.

Weissberg, R. P., Durlak, J. A., Domitrovich, C. E., & Gullotta, T. P. (2015). Social and emotional learning: Past, present, and future. In J. A. Durlak, C. E. Domitrovich, R. P. Weissberg, T. P. Gullotta, & J. Comer (Eds.), *Handbook of social and emotional learning: Research and practice* (pp. 3–19). New York: Guilford Press.

Whitcomb, S. A., & Elias, M. J. (in press). Social and emotional learning: Helping handout for home. In G. G. Bear & K. Minke (Eds.), *Helping handouts: Supporting students at school and home*. Bethesda, MD: National Association of School Psychologists.

Wigelsworth, M., Lendrum, A., Oldfield, J., Scott, A., Bokkel, I., Tate, K., & Emory, C. (2016). The impact of trial stage, developer involvement and international transferability on universal social and emotional learning programme outcomes: A meta-analysis. *Cambridge Journal of Education, 46*, 347–376. doi: 10.1080/0305764X.2016.1195791

Williford, A. P., & Wolcott, C. S. (2015). SEL and student-teacher relationships. In J. A. Durlak, C. E. Domitrovich, R. P. Weissberg, T. P. Gullotta, & J. Comer (Eds.), *Handbook of social and emotional learning: Research and practice* (pp. 229–243). New York: Guilford Press.

CHAPTER NINE

Creating the Working Conditions to Enhance Teacher Social and Emotional Well-Being

Patricia A. Jennings, Angela Minnici, and Nick Yoder

Teaching is a demanding profession. Education scholar Lee Shulman (2004) once described teaching as "perhaps the most complex, most challenging and most demanding, subtle, nuanced, and frightening activity that our species has ever invented" (p. 258). The job of a teacher has significantly changed since Shulman made that statement over a decade ago—from the needs that students bring to schools to the ongoing advances in technology, learning science, and human development. Furthermore, classrooms are much more culturally diverse, requiring that teachers develop a greater degree of cultural responsiveness. These changes are constantly shaping our understanding of and approach to teaching and learning, and increasing the intellectual and emotional demands on teachers.

Given the changing nature of teaching and learning, it is even more important to understand the skills and competencies, in addition to the content knowledge, that teachers need to effectively engage students in learning. In fact, teachers make thousands of decisions with students on a daily basis (Danielson, 1996; Jackson, 1990), in which teachers' emotion and emotion regulation play a critical role in how teachers' process information (Lerner, Li, Valdesolo, & Kassam, 2014). Emotions and emotion regulation influence cognitive and motivational processing, including one's working memory capacity and problem-solving skills, which are critical as teachers make decisions in complex environments and implement instruction to support all of their students' social, emotional, and academic development in a culturally responsive way (Emmer & Stough, 2001; Fried, 2011).

Although teaching has become one of the most stressful and emotionally laden professions that currently exist within the United States, research, policy, and practice are only recently beginning to focus on teacher social and emotional well-being and development and the teaching (or working) conditions that support teacher job satisfaction, stress reduction, and overall well-being (Greenberg, Brown, & Abenavoli, 2016; Kraft & Papay, 2013). When schools support and teachers develop necessary social and emotional competencies (SEC), including emotion regulation, teachers are more apt to manage their behavior, be more fully attentive to the learning environment, develop more positive relationships with students, support student outcomes (e.g., academic achievement, prosocial behaviors, and SECs), and create a more productive and engaging environment (Fried, 2011; Jennings & Greenberg, 2009).

Teacher-reported daily stress is among the highest (46% of teachers reported great daily stress) of all occupational groups, including nurses (46%) and physicians (45%; Gallup, 2014). In a recent survey of a demographically representative sample of K–12 public school teachers conducted by MetLife, researchers found that 59% of teachers reported being under great stress compared to only 35% of teachers in 1985 (Markow, Macia, & Lee, 2013). Similarly, researchers from the MetLife survey found a significant decrease in teacher-reported job satisfaction from 62% (in 2008) to 39% (in 2012).

When teachers experience high levels of stress (and negative emotions) on a continuous basis, negative consequences can occur for the teachers' overall well-being (e.g., mental and physical health), the students (e.g., behavior and academic performance), and the teaching profession as whole (for a review, see Greenberg et al., 2016; Jennings et al., 2017). For example, research demonstrates that a relationship exists between chronic self-reported stress and physiological indicators of stress among teachers (e.g., Katz, Greenberg, Klein, & Jennings, 2016). Similarly, teacher stress influences their interactions with students, potentially affecting their disciplinary strategies (Osher et al., 2007) and how teachers engage students in learning activities. This may be especially true when teachers experience toxic or prolonged stress, which can disrupt the chemical makeup of the brain (Osher, Cantor, Berg, Steyer, & Rose, 2017). Indeed, research on how stress affects decision-making has found that when individuals are experiencing high levels of stress, they tend to rely on habitual or automatic processes, such as implicit biases, due to diminished activity in the prefrontal executive control regions of the brain and exaggerated activity in subcortical reactive emotion regions (Yu, 2016). Furthermore, the teaching profession as a whole is impacted by consistent teacher stress, in which teachers are more likely to burn out, and potentially leave the profession or switch schools due to teacher dissatisfaction and poor working conditions (Ingersoll, 2011). Although not all teachers leave the profession due to occupational stress, teacher attrition costs the profession up to $2.2 billion annually (Haynes, Maddock, & Goldrick, 2014).

Given its negative effects, it is critical to understand the sources of teacher stress. Greenberg and colleagues (2016) state there are four critical factors that cause teacher stress, including the following:

1. *School organization, including the leadership of the building, and the collaborative culture within the building.* This also includes the relational trust that educators have with their colleagues and with their administrators, and the conditions needed to support relational trust in schools (Bryk & Schneider, 2002);
2. *Job demands, such as high-stakes testing, threats of termination, and managing student behaviors.* This also includes the high demands of information that teachers attend to during instruction, which they use to make informed instructional shifts and moves in the classroom to keep a lesson engaging and useful for students (Huberman, 1996), and to ensure that lessons are within each student's zone of proximal development (see Osher, Kidron, Brackett, Dymnicki, Jones, & Weissberg, 2016, for a review);
3. *Work resources*, such as lack of autonomy or job control, can cause teachers to feel greater levels of stress and lack of ownership within their day-to-day work; and
4. *Teacher's SEC* (e.g., intra- and interpersonal skills), including the ways in which educators are able to manage their own stress, form positive relationships with their students and colleagues, and make good decisions during instruction.

There are both organizational structures and individual-level skills and competencies that influence stress levels of teachers and ways in which teachers manage the stressors they face on a regular basis. It is critical that state education agencies, districts, schools, and higher education begin to deliberately focus on teachers' SECs and well-being as an overall retention strategy, given that teacher stress is at an all-time high and teacher shortages have increased recently (Sutcher, Darling-Hammond, & Carver-Thomas, 2016).

In the current chapter, we argue that in order to reduce teacher stress and improve teacher overall well-being and effectiveness, research, policy, and practice need to take a comprehensive systems approach that includes both

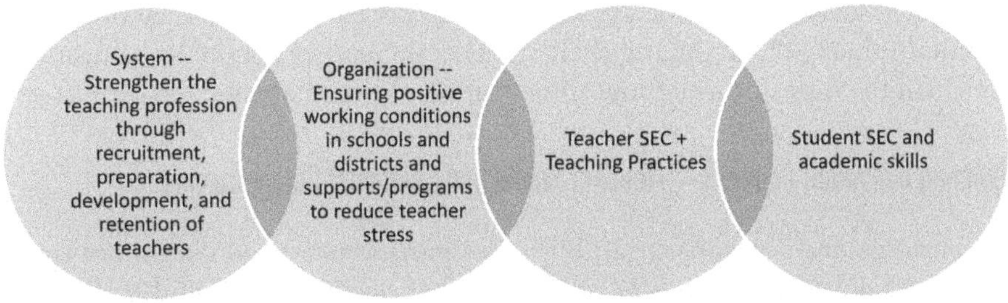

Figure 9.1 Intersection of individual and organizational changes

organizational- and individual-level change (see figure 9.1). Typically, researchers, policy makers, and educators look at either the organization or the individual (or classroom), rarely at the intersection of the two, or how teachers navigate their environment, and the organizational structures in which they are situated. Thus, it is important to understand how educators make sense of the policies and organizations in which they work, the ways in which policies and organizations influence the work teachers do, and the skills and competencies teachers must have in order to successfully navigate the teaching and learning environment to support student learning (Rigby, Woulfin, & Marz, 2016).

Specifically, in this chapter, we apply a systems approach proposing that the most effective strategy is to promote practices and policies that ensure the conditions under which teachers work in are supportive and productive, in addition to building teachers' capacity to mitigate and deal with stress through approaches such as mindfulness (Jennings et al., 2017) and strengthening teacher SEC (Jennings & Greenberg, 2009; Yoder, 2014). Additionally, a systems approach requires us to think beyond strategies aimed at improving just organizations (e.g., school districts or schools) or just individuals (e.g., teachers or administrators) to those strategies that can ultimately strengthen the profession. We suggest an organizational approach be twofold, in which states, districts, and schools place a strategic focus on the development of positive teaching conditions, as well as implement policies and practices that enhance the system to create a more effective teacher and administrator workforce to enhance the conditions within a school. Those approaches would include the thoughtful and strategic recruitment of people into the profession who are well suited to work with children and adolescents (state and district role), the preparation of candidates to build the SEC they will need to navigate the profession (higher education role), and building the capacity of district and school leaders to manage both the development of positive teaching conditions as well as teacher and student SEC (district and school role). Through creating both organizational and individual level change, the system can support educators as they build and maintain their SEC, reducing their stress and creating conducive conditions for them to work in throughout the duration of their career.

Building Individual Capacity—Teacher Social and Emotional Competencies

Jennings and Greenberg (2009) presented the prosocial classroom theoretical model (see figure 9.2) proposing that teachers' SEC and well-being support teachers' ability to cope with the demands of teaching. The model proposes that there are five SECs, as defined by the Collaborative for Academic, Social, and Emotional Learning (CASEL) framework. The five core competencies include self-awareness, self-management, social awareness, relationship skills, and responsible decision-making (http://www.casel.org). High levels of these skills are also required to recognize and overcome individual biases and institutional and structural inequities that are associated with racial and gender disparities in school discipline (Gregory & Fergus, 2017).

Social and Emotional Competencies Required for Effective Teaching

Teachers' SECs are key skills teachers need to create a positive teaching and learning environment. See table 9.1 for a description of the SEC that

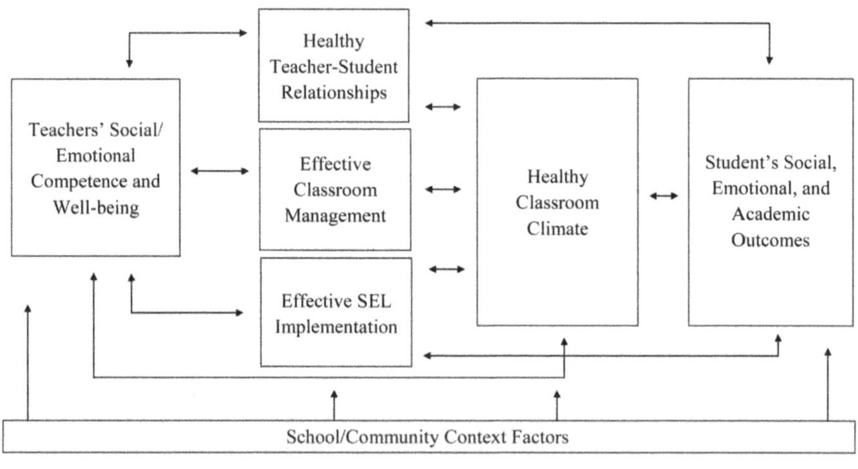

Figure 9.2 Prosocial classroom model (A Model of Teacher Well-Being and Social and Emotional Competence, Support, and Classroom and Student Outcomes. From Jennings, P. A., & Greenberg, M. T. (2009). The prosocial classroom: Teacher social and emotional competence in relation to student and classroom outcomes. *Review of Educational Research*, 79, 491–525. Reprinted with permission from SAGE Publications, Inc.)

Table 9.1 Definition of teacher social and emotional competencies

- *Self-awareness*: Teachers with high degrees of self-awareness recognize their emotional states and how strong emotions interfere with their perceptions and may provoke unintended reactions in their students.
- *Self-management*: Teachers require high degrees of self-management to regulate their emotions effectively in a context where student behaviors may be challenging and where they have no privacy. Teachers' strong emotions can trigger defiance or fear in their students that can lead to power struggles and a deteriorating classroom climate. However, simply suppressing emotional reactions can impair teachers' physical health (Gross, 2002).
- *Social awareness*: To function well, teachers need to be socially aware of the classroom dynamics of their classroom (Audley-Piotrowski, Singer, & Patterson, 2015) so that they can support healthy peer relationships.
- *Relationship skills*: They also need strong relationship skills, as there is strong evidence that supportive teacher-student relationships are critical to student academic engagement (Hamre & Pianta, 2005).
- *Responsible decision-making*: Finally, these competencies support teachers' ability to make responsible decisions that take into account students' developmental needs and their home contexts.

teachers need to navigate the profession successfully. Teachers with high levels of SECs can cope well with the demands of the classroom, build supportive relationships with their students, manage their classrooms effectively, and teach students these competencies through modeling and direct instruction, resulting in a classroom climate that supports student learning. The trust they are able to engender may reduce biases among peers (Lin & Packer, 2017). In contrast, when teachers lack SECs, their well-being may erode, leading to a deterioration of the classroom climate and triggering a "burnout cascade" in which teachers feel a great deal of stress on a regular basis (Jennings & Greenberg, 2009, p. 492).

Research supports the prosocial classroom model as defined by Jennings and Greenberg (2009), demonstrating the importance of teacher SEC on classroom instruction. For example, as part of the Head Start REDI program, teachers learn an SEL curriculum that emphasizes the importance of generalization of learning through extension activities, including classroom management strategies. In a randomized controlled trial of the Head Start REDI program, researchers found that preschool teachers who participated in the program and engaged in weekly mentoring demonstrated improvements in emotional supportiveness, as measured by the Classroom Assessment Scoring System (CLASS; Pianta, La Paro, & Hamre, 2008), compared to teachers assigned to the control group (Domitrovich, Gest, Gill, Bierman, Welsh, & Jones, 2009). In another example, teachers participated in the RULER SEL program, which provides instruction on SECs for both teachers and students. In a cluster randomized controlled trial of the RULER program, researchers found statistically significant program impacts after two years on all three domains of the CLASS—emotional, organizational, and instructional support (Hagelskamp, Brackett, Rivers, & Salovey, 2013).

Intervention Approaches

A variety of interventions have been developed to promote teacher well-being and the SECs required to promote an effective learning environment and to cope with the ongoing demands of teaching. The three approaches with the most promising evidence are workplace wellness programs, SEL programs for students that include professional learning for teachers, and mindfulness-based interventions (MBIs). Given that MBIs are most likely to explicitly target teacher SEC and well-being, we will provide three examples of MBI programs for teachers.

Workplace Wellness Programs

Workplace wellness programs are systems-wide approaches designed to promote teacher health and well-being by focusing on health promotion practices. These programs focus on health risk appraisals, nutrition, weight management, and physical activity. Between 2000 and 2014, the percentage of schools offering wellness programs increased dramatically; however, only 26% of schools offered stress management services in 2014—a decline of 10% since 2000 (Centers for Disease Control and Prevention, 2015).

There is some evidence that school workplace wellness programs improve physical health. One study examined a workplace wellness program over the course of one year. The program included behavior change campaigns and insurance incentives (e.g., lower co-pay and deductibles). Of the employees who participated, 65.6% lowered blood glucose, 46% lowered body mass index, 38.7% lowered total cholesterol, and 34.7% lowered systolic blood pressure (Merrill & Sloan, 2014). While these biomarkers are associated with stress, this study did not address occupational stress specifically. In another study, teachers who reported greater engagement with a wellness program reported lower levels of emotional exhaustion (as measured by the emotional exhaustion dimension of the Maslach Burnout Inventory), but there was no relationship with overall burnout (Lawrence, 2016). Taken together, there is initial evidence that engagement in workplace wellness programs improve physical and mental health of adults; however, more research is needed to understand the influence such programs have on teacher stress and job satisfaction.

Social and Emotional Learning Programs

While most SEL programs were designed to promote student SEC—and not necessarily designed to develop teacher SEC—many programs are beginning to recognize the importance of adult SEC in the implementation of those programs (Jennings & Frank, 2015). Research has found that SEL programs are effective for promoting student outcomes such as SEC, positive attitudes, prosocial behaviors, and academic achievement and decreasing negative attitudes and behaviors; and these effects are even greater when teachers implement SEL programs with fidelity (Durlak, Weissberg, Dymnicki, Taylor & Schellinger, 2011). In addition to the positive effect that SEL programs have on students, some studies have found that teachers trained to deliver SEL programs report reduced anxiety and depression (Tyson, Roberts, & Kane, 2009), improved teacher engagement (Castillo-Gualda, Herrero, Rodríguez-Carvajal, Brackett, & Fernández-Berrocal, 2018), and perceived job control (Zhai, Raver, & Li-Grining, 2011). Thus, it is important to consider how engagement in professional learning for SEL programs for students relates to teacher SEC, well-being, and stress.

For example, teachers who engaged in PATHS to PAX, a training that combined two school-based prevention programs, a behavior management program (PAX Good Behavior Game), and a SEL curriculum (Promoting Alternative THinking Strategies; PATHS) (Domitrovich et al., 2016) reported better attitudes than teachers who did not engage in the training. Specifically, in the randomized controlled trial of 350 K–5 teachers from 27 schools, the teachers who were engaged in PATHS to PAX reported higher levels of personal accomplishment (a subscale of the Maslach Burnout Inventory assessing teachers' feelings of competence and successful occupational achievement) compared to controls. Furthermore, teachers who were assigned to the PATHS to PAX program, compared to teachers assigned to PAX GBG alone, had significantly higher levels of SEL efficacy, behavior management efficacy and the interpersonal dimension of a social and emotional competence measure. The study also found that teachers trained to deliver the curriculum also reported greater efficacy for successfully managing student behavior.

Mindfulness-Based Interventions

One approach for reducing stress and promoting SEC is through engaging in mindful awareness practices. MBIs combine various mindful awareness practices to reduce distress and promote well-being. MBIs have become popularized by Jon Kabat-Zinn, who developed the Mindfulness-Based Stress Reduction (MBSR) program (Kabat-Zinn, 1982). Kabat-Zinn (2003) defined mindfulness as "the awareness that emerges through paying attention on purpose, in the present moment, and nonjudgmentally to the unfolding of experience moment by moment" (p. 144). Bishop and colleagues (2004) offered a definition for research purposes that conceptualized mindfulness as involving two primary dimensions: (1) intentionally directing one's attention to the present moment, while (2) cultivating a curious and accepting orientation to one's experience.

Recent reviews of the research have shown that MBIs reduce stress, anxiety, and depression and increase well-being (Eberth & Sedlmeier, 2012; Khoury et al., 2013; Sharma & Rush, 2014). Other research has examined the underlying neurophysiological mechanisms involved in mindfulness and how they relate to improvements in emotion regulation (Corcoran, Farb, Anderson, & Segal, 2010). In one notable study, researchers found that, compared to controls, participants in an eight-week MBSR program demonstrated increases in grey matter and neuron density in the hippocampus, an area of the brain critical to emotion regulation (Hölzel et al., 2011, 2013; Tang, Hölzel, & Posner, 2015).

Research is beginning to demonstrate causal relationships between MBIs and stress reduction among teachers (Crain, Schonert-Reichl, & Roeser, 2016; Jennings et al., 2013; Kemeny et al., 2012; Roeser et al., 2013) and improvements in classroom interaction quality (Jennings et al., 2017). Because MBIs promote adaptive emotion regulation and coping, mindful awareness practices may help teachers develop the SEC they need to manage the demands of teaching, reduce stress and burnout, and increase teachers' energy and self-reinforcing resources such as joy, job satisfaction, and efficacy. Teachers can then invest their resources in developing supportive teacher-student interactions that promote student learning (Roeser, 2016; Roeser, Skinner, Beers, & Jennings, 2012; Skinner & Beers, 2016). Several mindfulness-based professional learning programs have been developed to promote teachers' SEC and reduce teacher stress. Below we describe three such programs that have been examined in randomized controlled trials and found to be promising along with their associated research.

The CARE Program. One comprehensive professional learning program designed to reduce teachers' stress and promote their SEC is Cultivating Awareness and Resilience in Education (CARE). The program integrates emotion skills instruction and mindful awareness and compassion practices through didactic, experiential, and interactive learning processes. Teachers learn a set of mindful awareness practices including breath awareness practice, mindful walking and stretching, listening and compassion practices, and activities to promote emotional awareness and regulation (for more extensive descriptions of the CARE program model, see Jennings et al., 2011; Jennings et al., 2013; and Jennings, 2016).

The program is typically delivered in 30 hours over five training days spread out over the course of several months. Breaks between sessions are intended to provide opportunities for teachers to apply the practices to their teaching. Between sessions, teachers typically participate in coaching phone calls to help them reflect on their development of self-care practices and applications of CARE practices to their teaching.

Several studies have been conducted to examine the efficacy of CARE (Jennings, Frank, Snowberg, Coccia, & Greenberg, 2013; Jennings, Snowberg, Coccia, & Greenberg, 2011). The most recent and most rigorous was a cluster randomized controlled trial involving 36 New York City elementary schools located in the Bronx and Upper Manhattan with 224 teachers and their 5,200 students (Jennings et al., 2017). Teachers who participated in the CARE program (compared to those in the wait-list control group) demonstrated significant improvements in four out of the five outcomes originally hypothesized to improve. Participation in CARE resulted in significant reductions in psychological distress and time urgency and significant improvements in adaptive emotion regulation and mindfulness. Teachers trained in CARE showed continued benefits one year later in psychological distress, mindfulness, and adaptive emotion regulation (Jennings et al., 2017). There was no significant impact on efficacy; however, teachers scored quite high on this measure at baseline, which may have resulted in ceiling effects.

In addition, teachers who participated in CARE also had significant positive impacts on the emotional support domain of the *CLASS* (reflected by impacts on the dimensions of teacher sensitivity and positive climate), and a trend effect on the domain of classroom organization (and a significant improvement in the dimension of productivity).

Finally, students in CARE classrooms were rated by their teachers as more engaged than students in control group classrooms. The study found that both student and teacher risk moderated the effects of CARE on students. Students in CARE classrooms who were rated low in social skills improved in teacher reported reading competence and these students with teachers who were low on mindfulness at baseline improved in motivation and reading competence (Brown et al., 2017).

These results suggest that the CARE program has positive impacts on teachers' SEC and that these improvements may support teachers' ability to promote classroom interactions that are conducive to learning. Furthermore, they suggest that the program may have direct positive impacts on student outcomes, especially for students and teachers who are at most risk.

The SMART Program. Several studies have examined another MBI program designed for teachers, the Stress Management and Relaxation Techniques in Education (SMART) program. (Benn, Akiva, Arel, & Roeser, 2012; Crain et al., 2016; Roeser et al., 2013). The 8-week, 11-session program was delivered after school for a total of 36 contact hours. The program combines lecture and various experiential activities including mindfulness, self-compassion, and yoga practices and application of these practices through discussion and small group activities.

The largest and most rigorous trial of this program involved 113 (one sample each from the United States and Canada) of elementary and secondary teachers (Roeser et al., 2013). Researchers found that the teachers who received SMART (compared to those in the wait-list control group) showed significant decreases in occupational stress and burnout and increases in mindfulness and self-compassion after engagement in the intervention. Canadian teachers' executive functioning was assessed and those who participated in SMART showed improvements in attention and working memory. There were no significant impacts of the intervention on the physiological indicators of stress. Researchers also assessed teachers three months post-intervention. Researchers found that improvements in mindfulness and self-compassion found at post-intervention, mediated SMART teachers' stress, burnout, anxiety, and depression at three-month follow-up. Researchers also found that SMART teachers reported improvements in sleep and mood at work and home, and group differences in mindfulness and rumination at post-SMART partially mediated the reductions in negative mood and increases in sleep quality at three-month follow-up (Crain et al., 2016).

These findings suggest that the SMART intervention helps reduce teacher stress and improve physiologically symptoms after the intervention is complete and has continued effects three months after the intervention.

The CALM Professional Learning Program. The Community Approach to Living and Learning Mindfully (CALM) professional development program for teachers is a unique program designed to combine the advantages of a place-based, workplace wellness program with mindfulness- and yoga-based approaches. CALM is a brief daily school-based intervention designed to promote teachers' SEC and well-being by teaching gentle yoga and mindful awareness practices focused on preparing teachers for the day.

A pilot study of the program involved 64 educators from two middle schools randomly assigned to CALM or wait-list control condition (Harris, Jennings, Katz, Abenavoli, & Greenberg, 2016). The CALM program was offered before school, 4 days per week for 16 weeks. Teachers assigned to receive CALM reported significant increases in mindfulness, efficacy for classroom management, positive affect, distress tolerance, and significant decreases in physical symptoms and blood pressure. Furthermore, the study showed that CALM protected against stress-related disruptions in physiology. While the educators assigned to the control condition showed a disruption in their awakening response over the course of the school year (from pre- to post-intervention), the CALM educators did not.

Improving Teacher SEC and Well-Being during Teacher Preparation

Professional learning programs specifically designed for teachers show promise for reducing teachers' occupational stress, promoting SEC, reducing the negative physiological effects of stress, and improving the quality of their classroom interactions. While this work is primarily focused on in-service support, an important question is how to prepare students during pre-service education. While teachers experience occupational stressors on a regular basis, for student teachers, these stressors are buffered by the supervising teachers in their practicum sites. Typically, student teachers are assigned to outstanding teachers who have strong classroom management skills. While it's important for student teachers to be placed with well-qualified teachers so they can observe good teaching, this practice may not allow them to experience the typical stressors of managing a classroom until they begin their first year of teaching. Therefore, it may be difficult for them to recognize and understand the importance and value of developing social and emotional competencies to prepare for these stressors and prevent early career burnout. Indeed, Jennings et al. (2011) found that the CARE program showed less efficacy among student teachers than in-service teachers, likely because the students had not experienced the stressors that the program was designed to address.

One innovative approach to preparing students for the stressors of the classroom is simulated classroom environments. A number of university teacher preparation programs have experimented with technology that presents a simulation of the classroom including students who engage in a variety of behaviors that teachers commonly report as challenging (Bradley & Kendall, 2014; Kaufman & Ireland, 2016). While this approach has promise, few studies examined its efficacy and the current state of the technology presents a number of challenges including the lack of realism and the costs associated with the repetition necessary for students to acquire competence (Baidee & Kaufman, 2015).

Beyond Teacher SEC

Although professional learning and targeted supports help reduce teacher stress and increase the skills teachers need to navigate the profession, individual-level interventions alone are not sufficient to decrease teacher stress (Greenberg et al., 2016). There are multiple contextual factors that contribute to teacher stress and it is important to mitigate those stressors to a degree if possible, in addition to providing teachers the skills they need to handle their daily stressors. Similarly, it is important to understand how teachers perceive their working environment and how the working environment influences the quality of teachers' work (Rigby et al., 2016). The following section examines the critical role of building capacity at the organizational level primarily by improving teaching conditions to support teacher well-being.

Building Capacity at the Organizational Level—Improving Teaching Conditions

Teachers work in varying settings and circumstances, under different conditions and with students who come from vastly different backgrounds. A teacher's typical day may look very different in Marlington, West Virginia, than Culver City, California, or even Houston, Texas. For example, some teachers may only have a 30-minute break in an 8-hour day, as they are required to eat with their students. Some teachers have opportunities to regularly collaborate with their peers and provide substantive input into the decision-making processes in their schools while others don't. Some teachers have classrooms of 35 students or more. Some teachers may spend hours grading papers every evening while other teachers have time during the school day to grade student work. Why do such different and uneven conditions under which teachers work exist? Inequitable funding often caused by differences in local tax bases (Baker, Farrie, Johnson, Luhm, & Sciarra, 2017), inability to attract and retain quality school leaders (Hull, 2012), and a lack of policies and institutional practices to ensure positive teaching conditions (Center for Teacher Quality, 2007) are just a few reasons why teachers work in environments that vary significantly in quality and support. This variability of environmental quality or "teaching conditions" impacts teacher stress levels (Greenberg et al., 2016), a teacher's ability to be effective in their job (Johnson, Kraft, & Papay, 2012), and ultimately influences the quality of students' educational experiences (Ferguson & Hirsch, 2014a).

What Are Teaching Conditions?

Teaching conditions go beyond traditional elements of working conditions such as pay and benefits. They include the critical aspects of a teacher's working environment that influence a teacher's ability to be successful in their job such as organizational leadership, the quality of peer to peer interactions, opportunities to collaborate with peers, the extent to which student behavior is well managed at the school level, and the influence teachers have on school- and classroom-based decisions to name a few. Several frameworks currently exist to define, assess, and improve teaching conditions in practice (e.g., see Susan Moore Johnson's comprehensive definition of teaching conditions in table 9.2)

The various definitions, frameworks, and standards set out to define the important features of the teaching environment that matter to student

Table 9.2 Definition of working conditions

Working conditions include the following:

- The *physical features* of buildings, equipment, and resources, which serve as a platform for teachers' work
- The *organizational structures* that define teachers' formal positions and relationships with others in the school, such as lines of authority, workload, autonomy, and supervisory arrangements
- The *sociological features* that shape how teachers experience their work, including their roles, status, and the characteristics of their students and peers
- The *political features* of their organization, such as whether teachers have opportunities to participate in important decisions
- The *cultural features* of the school as a workplace that influence teachers' interpretation of what they do and their commitment, such as values, traditions, and norms
- The *psychological features* of the environment that may sustain or deplete them personally, such as the meaningfulness of what they do day-to-day or the opportunities they find for learning and growth
- The *educational features*, such as curriculum and testing policies that may enhance or constrain

Source: Johnson, Susan Moore. 2006. *The workplace matters: Teacher quality, retention and effectiveness*. Washington, DC: National Education Association. Reprinted with permission of the National Education Association (c) 2006. All rights reserved.

achievement, teacher retention, teacher satisfaction, efficacy, and stress (see table 9.3). Each framework contains critical ingredients within the working environment that are influenced by school-, district-, and state-level policies, as well as relationships with families and community members. In other words, teaching conditions frameworks represent action-oriented steps that education leaders and policy makers can take to improve the working environment for staff, and ultimately for students. As the former governor of North Carolina Mike Easley stated, "Teacher working conditions are student learning conditions" (Hirsch & Emerick, 2007, p. vii).

Why Do Teaching Conditions Matter?

Teachers are only as effective as the environment in which they work. While outstanding teachers may be effective despite poor teaching conditions and high stress levels, the majority of teachers need a positive environment to thrive in in order to be effective (Ferguson & Hirsch, 2014b). Teachers are more effective with their students when the conditions are

Table 9.3 Relationship between working conditions and important outcomes

Working Condition	Influence on Student Achievement	Influence on Teacher Retention	Influence on Teacher Satisfaction and Efficacy	Teacher Stress and Burnout
Student behavior	✓[1, 2]	✓[1, 2, 3]	✓[1, 2]	✓[4]
School administration and leadership	✓[1, 2, 5]	✓[1, 2, 3]	✓[1, 2]	✓[4]
Teacher influence, empowerment, and autonomy	✓[1, 2]	✓[1, 2]	✓[1, 2]	✓[4]
Staff relationships and cohesion		✓[9, 10]		✓[4]
Facilities and resources		✓[11]	✓[12]	✓[4]
Professional learning	✓[7]	✓[9]	✓[13]	
School safety		✓[1]		
Teaching assignments		✓[14]	✓[14]	
Teacher induction and mentoring		✓[15]	✓[15]	
Time	✓[5]	✓[2]	✓[8]	✓[4]

Note: Example references per condition and outcome: [1] Boyd et al., 2011; [2] Ladd, 2011; [3] Ingersoll, 2001; [4] Leithwood, 2006; [5] Hirsch & Emerick, 2007; [6] Allensworth, Ponisciak, & Mazzeo, 2009; [7] Allen, Pianta, Gregory, Mikami, & Lun, 2011; [8] Allen, 2005; [9] Berry & Fuller, 2007; [10] Johnson, Berg, & Donaldson, 2005; [11] Loeb, Darling-Hammond, & Luczak, 2005; [12] Buckley, Schneider, & Shang, 2005; [13] McLaughlin & Talbert, 2001; [14] Johnson & Birkeland, 2003; [15] Johnson, 2006.

supportive, and teaching conditions may even hinder or promote a teacher's future effectiveness. For example, Kraft and Papay (2013) found that a positive working environment helped explain why some teachers improve during a three-year period of time compared with teachers working in less positive environments. In particular, teaching conditions such as student behavior, school administration and leadership; and teacher influence, empowerment, and autonomy have shown a positive relationship to improving student achievement (Hirsch & Emerick, 2007; Johnson, Kraft, & Papay, 2012).

Teaching conditions also support teacher retention—ultimately creating more stable environments for students. Teachers are more likely to stay in schools in which they perceive more positive and supportive environments, particularly in urban environments (Almy & Tooley, 2012; Berry & Fuller, 2007). Conversely, teachers are more likely to leave their school or the profession when they experience poor working conditions (Boyd et al., 2011). When schools experience high rates of teacher turnover, there is often a negative relationship with student achievement as it is more difficult for teachers and students to create substantive and long-term relationships, and the instructional cohesion within the school decreases (Ronfeldt, Loeb, & Wyckoff, 2013). Turnover is a significant concern in low-performing schools that often serve high percentages of traditionally disadvantaged students such as low-income and minority students, English language learners, and special education students (Allensworth, Ponisciak, & Mazzeo, 2009; Hemphill & Nauer, 2009).

The significant relationship between teaching conditions and teacher attrition is also related to teacher stress. For example, Collie, Shapka, and Perry (2012) found that teacher's perceptions of the availability of school resources and input in decision-making were negatively associated with two types of stress, their workload stress and stress related to student behavior. In another study, Bakker, Hakanen, Demerouti, and Xanthopoulou (2007) found that job resources (e.g., supervisory support and organizational climate) helped teachers cope with the demands of teaching, specifically helping manage difficult students. Conversely, the prosocial classroom model (see figure 9.2) by Jennings and Greenberg (2009) predicts that there are school and community contextual factors that influence teacher's SEC and the relationship teacher SEC has on the classroom interactions, suggesting that the teaching conditions and associated policies can limit or enhance teacher SEC.

Taken together, the research suggests that teaching conditions have a significant influence on a wide range of school outcomes, including student achievement, teacher attrition, and teacher stress and well-being. When schools and districts create working conditions, in which there is a strong leader who encourages teacher autonomy and empowers teachers, has clear systems and structures to manage student behavior, and uses time wisely, they will have an easier time attracting teachers, especially more effective teachers, and creating environments that are more conducive to teaching and learning (Almy & Tooley, 2012; Horng, 2005).

Improving Teaching Conditions

Individual teachers alone can do very little to improve conditions in the schools in which they work. Therefore, it's imperative that states and districts intervene and take several steps to improve their working conditions. These steps include identifying the important teaching conditions necessary for teacher and student success, developing strategies to measure and assess the extent to which these conditions exist in districts and especially schools, using the information from these assessments to identify policies and practices to improve the conditions, and engaging in a cycle of continuous improvement through monitoring progress and adjusting course as necessary. In addition to improving the conditions within schools, states and districts can create policies and practices that enhance the educational system, specifically policies and practices that ensure the education workforce provides teachers and administrators the necessary skills to create the learning and teaching conditions, respectfully, that ultimately allow students to be successful in school.

Organizational Strategies to Support Working Conditions

Many states and districts across the country are working toward systemic approaches to improve the conditions under which teachers work. For example, North Carolina has been engaging in a systematic approach to improve the teaching and learning conditions since 2002 (Hirsch & Emerick, 2007). This work initially began in the Office of the Governor as part of the Governor's Teacher Working Conditions Initiative (2002–2008) and is now housed in the North Carolina Department of Public Instruction, in which staff voluntarily take a survey of teaching conditions biennially. The data are used as part of North Carolina's collaborative school and district improvement plan, and can be used as artifacts in educator and administrator evaluations (New Teacher Center, n.d.). Research involving the North Carolina Teaching Conditions survey demonstrates that better teaching conditions are associated with improved student achievement and teacher retention, and that the teaching conditions in schools in North Carolina have improved continuously since the survey was initiated. Specifically, researchers found that working conditions were more likely to improve when schools were actually using the teaching conditions data for improvement and paid particular attention to those areas in which teachers and administrators were perceiving the teaching conditions differently (Hirsch & Emerick, 2007).

In the next section, we discuss a call to action, identifying ways in which to create policies and practices that support improving teaching conditions, as well as teacher and student SEC and overall well-being.

Call to Action

It is difficult to create meaningful change without considering how the organization and the individual intersect and influence one another (Rigby et al., 2016). This is particularly true when considering the SECs teachers need to successfully engage with their environment to support student learning. Piecemeal approaches to supporting teachers and developing their SEC are likely to have limited success if working conditions are poor. We suggest that a comprehensive systems approach that focuses on building capacity at the organization and individual level is needed to ensure that teachers work in healthy environments and have the SEC necessary to manage their stress and engage students in rigorous instruction.

Creating Systems to Support Educator Effectiveness

To ensure that teachers are working in supportive environments that will keep their stress levels low so they can create and maintain learning environments that support students, we will need to adopt a comprehensive approach that includes improving organizational systems (e.g., communities and schools) and individual skills and competencies adapted to local contexts. There are multiple ways key education stakeholders (e.g., U.S. Department of Education, state education agencies, teacher preparation programs, districts, and schools) can address the needs we have identified, across the full spectrum from individual to organization. Without systematic approaches for supporting teachers, school systems will likely suffer from growing teacher burnout and attrition, contributing to the growing teacher shortages (Greenberg et al., 2016).

Education leaders and educators can create policies, practices, and procedures at each juncture of the spectrum of needs to build individual and organizational capacity aimed at supporting educators to be successful with their students. For example, teacher preparation programs could be more strategic about who they recruit into the profession and look for certain skills or competencies (e.g., SECs) that are better aligned to working with children and adolescents, particularly those who come from low-income families, have been exposed to trauma and other adverse experiences. State education agencies could also ensure through the process of program approval that teacher and principal preparation programs include a focus on building educator SEC, and specifically for principals, the knowledge and skills needed to create positive and supportive school conditions. And once teachers enter the profession, there are a host of policies and practices that could be enacted by districts and schools to continue to build teacher SEC and improve working conditions. Local district principal evaluation systems could include (and even prioritize) a principal's ability to promote positive working conditions and create opportunities to build teacher SEC. Below we identify a few examples of potentially high leverage action items for key stakeholders to enact to begin the process of building a strong *system* of support for educator SEC, positing teaching and learning conditions, and overall effectiveness. When key stakeholders create systems of support, they are creating policies and

Table 9.4 Example of systems level approach

The Cleveland Metropolitan School District (CMSD) has implemented a Humanware initiative to support the conditions for learning and conditions for teaching that will support the adults in the building in helping their students succeed in school and in life (CMSD, 2017). To do this, CMSD developed a scope and sequence, which provides the social and emotional skills teachers should focus on per grade per quarter. In addition, CMSD administers the condition for learning survey for students three times per year and has administered a conditions for teaching survey for teachers to better understand the conditions within each school that support teachers and students. CMSD further supports a series of policies, interventions, and practices to provide teachers and students the tools to navigate their daily stressors and challenges, and to be successful in their current environments.

Table 9.5 National efforts to support social and emotional learning

With the passage of the Every Student Succeeds Act (ESSA) in December 2015, policy makers are placing a greater emphasis on developing the social and emotional skills of students through, for example, creating positive conditions for teaching and learning, supporting a well- rounded education, and continuing to make connections between in-school and out-of-school time Aspen Education & Society Program and the Council of Chief State School Officers, 2016). To successfully support the implementation of social and emotional learning (SEL) policies and practices, policy makers and educators can leverage the SEL work that many states, districts, and schools have underway (Dusenbury, Newman, Weissberg, Goren, Domitrovich, & Mart, 2015; Kendziora & Yoder, 2016; Yoder, 2015), as well as that of national efforts to support SEL implementation, such as CASEL's Collaborative States Initiative (CSI) and Collaborative Districts Initiative (CDI), and the Aspen Institute's National Commission on Social, Emotional, and Academic Development.

practices that afford educators opportunities to sustain the work and ensure that SEL and conditions are intertwined in everyday teaching and learning. For an example of how a school district has implemented some of the practices below, see table 9.4. To learn more about national efforts that support student and adult SEC, see table 9.5.

High-Leverage Action Item One—Social and Emotional Learning Goals. Many states and districts have developed or are developing social and emotional learning standards or learning goals. SEL goals provide developmental benchmarks about the social and emotional skills and competencies that youth, and some cases adults, develop across the lifespan in a culturally responsive way. SEL goals are meant to provide goals for students to accomplish, but they are not meant to be one and done skills, and are meant to be exhibited and understood through a student's cultural lens. SEL goals support educators in understanding the skills individuals need to be successful in school, work, and life, in which social and emotional skills are contextually and culturally dependent, and meant to be learned and relearned across the lifespan (Yoder & Dusenbury, 2017).

High-Leverage Action Item Two—Teacher and Principal Preparation Programs. Teacher and principal preparation programs should take more active roles in developing the necessary teacher and administrator skills to enact this work. Teacher preparation programs should include more explicit instruction on SEL and on teacher and student SEC (Schonert-Reichl, Kitil, & Hanson-Peterson, 2017). As noted previously, teacher preparation programs might want to include more simulated classroom experiences that allow them to practice using and reflecting upon their own SEC. Similarly, principal preparation programs should include coursework that teaches principals how to create positive working conditions for their staff including how to create opportunities for and allocate resources to support distributive leadership and collaboration, stress reduction, and building staff social emotional competency.

High-Leverage Action Item Three—Hiring and Onboarding Processes. School districts and schools should embed knowledge of SEL and conditions for teaching and learning within hiring and onboarding processes. For example, schools districts may want to include knowledge of SEL in job descriptions and ask potential candidates about their knowledge of SEL-related practices, child development, and the development of a positive learning environment. Similarly, schools can include SEL and teaching and learning conditions within the onboarding materials for the school, such as ways in which teachers demonstrate autonomy and leadership within the school, the SEL-related policies and practices (e.g., discipline policies, school improvement plans, observations, and feedback processes). By providing these materials upfront to potential candidates and new hires, it demonstrates the importance the school places on the adult culture within the school.

High-Leverage Action Item Four—Continued Professional Learning and Growth. The evidence reviewed in this chapter supports a call for schools and districts to include workplace wellness programs that include mindfulness-based approaches to stress reduction and well-being promotion in their professional learning programming. To ensure quality program delivery, it requires schools and districts to create the necessary conditions for this work to occur. For example, implementing these approaches requires additional time and financial resources to be allocated to these activities. The recently enacted federal Every Student Succeeds Act provides funding through many sources such as Title I, IIA, and IVA that could support educator evidence-based professional learning geared toward improving teacher knowledge and skills. Similarly, educators need the time to process and reflect upon their own social and emotional competencies, and time to engage in collaborative conversations with their peers about the social and emotional environment in the school (Kendziora & Yoder, 2016; Yoder, 2014). In addition, the evidence reviewed in this chapter suggests that schools and districts should incorporate SEL programs for students (and related professional learning experiences), as these programs may have the added benefit of supporting both students and teachers.

High-Leverage Action Item Five—Using Data for Continuous Improvement. To effectively implement a systems level approach to support teacher social and emotional well-being, it is important to collect data to monitor implementation of efforts and determine the outcomes of the efforts. For example, districts and schools may want to assess teaching and learning conditions on a regular basis. This will help identify areas of focus and areas of strength in the school and in the district to improve the environment of the school. Similarly, districts and schools want to collect data on teacher and student SECs and well-being to determine if any new policies or practices result in the intended outcomes.

Conclusion

In this chapter, we reviewed research that suggests when schools have a focus on SEL—in which teachers feel comfortable with teaching SEL—teacher's teaching efficacy and job satisfaction improve, and teacher stress decreases. This research suggests that when we have a targeted focus on SEL within buildings, it not only helps students, but also teachers' well-being (Collie et al., 2012). To support teacher social and emotional development, as well as students' SEC, we suggested that it is important to take a systems approach that addresses organizational- and individual-level needs, as both must be addressed to improve educator effectiveness.

While the approaches reviewed here to support student and adult SEC, as well as teaching conditions, are promising, further research is required to understand how these approaches work in isolation and in combination with one another. For programs and interventions that support teacher SEC, we need to determine how best to scale these programs and whether they can be disseminated broadly with high fidelity and efficacy. Because these programs combine various elements, it is impossible to discern which are contributing to the programs' positive outcomes. Further research will be required to determine which elements are most effective for various populations of teachers, under various circumstances. For example, the CARE program demonstrated efficacy for teachers working in high-poverty urban schools. Further research will be required to determine whether the program has similar effects in suburban and rural contexts.

Similarly, a great deal of research has analyzed the relationship between working conditions and teacher and student outcomes; however, there have been few rigorous research studies examining the practices or interventions that are most likely to improve the teaching conditions. Because one of the primary approaches to improve teaching conditions is through the use of data, it will be important to explore and rigorously test the interventions that schools use to improve their teaching conditions, and those practices that are most important to create an environment that allows a teacher to teach and students to learn. Furthermore, future research should begin to look at the intersection of those practices that support teaching conditions and those that support teacher and student SEC.

References

Allen, J. P., Pianta, R. C., Gregory, A., Mikami, A. Y., & Lun, J. (2011). An interaction-based approach to enhancing secondary school instruction and student achievement. *Science, 333,* 1034–1037.

Allen, M. B. (2005). *Eight questions on teacher recruitment and retention: What does the research say? A summary of the findings.* Denver: Education Commission of the States. Retrieved from https://files.eric.ed.gov/fulltext/ED489332.pdf

Allensworth, E., Ponisciak, S., & Mazzeo, C. (2009). *The schools teachers leave: Teacher mobility in Chicago Public Schools.* Chicago: University of Chicago Consortium on Chicago School Research. Retrieved from http://ccsr.uchicago.edu/sites/default/files/publications/CCSR_Teacher_Mobility.pdf

Almy, S., & Tooley, M. (2012). *Building and sustaining talent: Creating conditions in high-poverty schools that support effective teaching and learning.* Washington, DC: The Education Trust. Retrieved from http://www.edtrust.org/sites/edtrust.org/files/Building_and_Sustaining_Talent.pdf

Aspen Education & Society Program and the Council of Chief State School Officers. (2016). *Advancing equity through ESSA: Strategies for state leaders.* Washington, DC: Authors. Retrieved from https://www.aspeninstitute.org/publications/advancing-equity-essa-strategies-state-leaders/

Audley-Piotrowski, S., Singer, A. & Patterson, M. (2015). The role of the teacher in children's peer relations: Making the invisible hand intentional. *Trans-*

lational Issues in Psychological Science, 1, 192–200. doi:10.1037/tps0000038

Baidee, F., & Kaufman, D. (2015). Design evaluation of a simulation for teacher education. *Sage Open, 5*, 1–10. doi:10.1177/2158244015592454

Baker, B., Farrie, D., Johnson, M., Luhm, T., & Sciarra, D. G. (2017). *Is school funding fair? A national report card* (6th Edition). Newark, NJ: Education Law Center.

Bakker, A. B., Hakanen, J. J., Demerouti, E., & Xanthopoulou, D. (2007). Job resources boost work engagement, particularly when job demands are high. *Journal of Educational Psychology, 99,* 274–284. http://dx.doi.org/10.1037/0022-0663.99.2.274

Benn, R., Akiva, T., Arel, S., & Roeser, R. W. (2012). Mindfulness training effects for parents and educators of children with special needs. *Developmental Psychology, 48*, 1476–1487. doi:10.1037/a0027537

Berry, B., & Fuller, E. (with Williams, A.). (2007). *Stemming the tide of teacher attrition: How working conditions influence teacher career intentions and other key outcomes in Arizona.* Carrboro, NC: Center for Teaching Quality. Retrieved from http://www.teachingquality.org/sites/default/files/AZ2007final.pdf

Bishop, S. R., Lau, M., Shapiro, S., Carlson, L., Anderson, N. D., Carmody, J., . . . Devins, G. (2004). Mindfulness: A proposed operational definition. *Clinical Psychology: Science and Practice, 11*, 230–241. doi:10.1093/clipsy.bph077

Boyd, D., Grossman, P., Ing, M., Lankford, H., Loeb, S., & Wyckoff, J. (2011). The influence of school administrators on teacher retention decisions. *American Educational Research.* Retrieved from https://cepa.stanford.edu/sites/default/files/Admin%20Teacher%20Retention.pdf

Bradley, E. G., & Kendall, B. (2014). A review of computer simulations in teacher education. *Journal of Educational Technology Systems, 43*, 3–12. doi:10.2190/ET.43.1.b

Brown, J. L., Jennings, P. A., Cham, H., Rasheed, D., Frank, J. L., Doyle, S., Oh, Y., DeWeese, A., & Greenberg, M. T. (March, 2017). CARE for Teachers: Direct and mediated effects of a mindfulness-based professional development program for teachers on teachers' and students' social and emotional competencies. In (J. Downer, Chair) *Social and Emotional Learning in Educational Settings Invited Symposium Role of Teacher Well-Being & Stress in the Classroom.* Presented at the Society for Research on Educational Effectiveness (SREE) Annual Conference, Washington, DC.

Bryk & Schneider (2002) *Trust in schools: A core resource for improvement.* New York, NY: Russell Sage.

Buckley, J., Schneider, M., & Shang, Y. (2005). Fix it and they might stay: School facility quality and teacher retention in Washington, DC. *Teachers College Record, 107,* 1107–1123.

Castillo-Gualda, R., Herrero, M., Rodríguez-Carvajal, R., Brackett, M. A., & Fernández-Berrocal, P. (2018). The role of emotional regulation ability, personality, and burnout among Spanish teachers. *International Journal of Stress Management.* Advance online publication. http://dx.doi.org/10.1037/str0000098

Center for Teacher Quality. (2007). *Teaching and learning conditions improve high school reform efforts* [Author]. Retrieved from https://dschool-old.stanford.edu/sandbox/groups/k12/wiki/f329e/attachments/0fdad/Team1%20hsconditions-1.pdf?sessionID=8cbdfc6129ceb041dbad2247ffc9d0112fd0ebce

Centers for Disease Control and Prevention. (2015). *School health policies and practices study, trends over time: 2000–2014.* Washington, DC: U.S. Department of Health and Human Services.

CMSD. (n.d.). *Humanware.* Retrieved from http://www.clevelandmetroschools.org/Page/398

Collie, R. J., Shapka, J. D., & Perry, N. E. (2012). School climate and social-emotional learning: Predicting teacher stress, job satisfaction, and teaching efficacy. *American Psychological Association, 104,* 1189–1204.

Collomp, K., Baillot, A., Forget, H., Coquerel, A., Reith, N., & Vabarel-Rebot, N. (2016). Altered diurnal pattern of steroid hormones in relation to various behaviors, external factors and pathologies: A review. *Psychology & Behavior, 164A,* 68–85. doi:10.1016/j.physbeh.2016.05.039

Corcoran, K. M., Farb, N., Anderson, A., & Segal, Z. V. (2010). Mindfulness and emotion regulation: Outcomes and possible mediating mechanisms. In A. M. Kring & D. M. Sloan (Eds.), *Emotion regulation and psychopathology: A transdiagnostic approach to etiology and treatment* (pp. 339–355). New York: Guilford.

Crain, T. L., Schonert-Reichl, K. A., & Roeser, R. W. (2016). Cultivating teacher mindfulness: Effects of a randomized controlled trial on work, home, and sleep outcomes. *Journal of Occupational Health Psychology.* Advance online publication. doi:10.1037/ocp0000043

Danielson, C. (1996). *Enhancing professional practice: A framework for teaching.* Alexandria, VA: Association for Supervision and Curriculum Development.

Domitrovich, C. E., Bradshaw, C. P., Berg, J. P., Pas, E. T., Becker, K. D., Musci, R., & Ialongo, N. (2016). How do school-based prevention programs impact teachers? Findings from a randomized trial of an integrated classroom management and social-emotional program. *Prevention Science, 17,* 325–337.

Domitrovich, C. E., Gest, S. D., Gill, S., Bierman, K. L., Welsh, J., & Jones, D. (2009). Fostering high quality teaching in Head Start classrooms: Experimental evaluation of an integrated curriculum. *American Education Research Journal, 46,* 567–597. doi:10.3102/0002831208328089

Durlak, J. A., Weissberg, R. P., Dymnicki, A. B., Taylor, R. D., & Schellinger, K. B. (2011). The impact of enhancing students' social and emotional learning: A meta-analysis of school-based universal interventions. *Child Development, 82,* 405–432. doi:10.1111/j.1467-8624.2010.01564.x

Dusenbury, L. A., Newman, J. Z., Weissberg, R. P., Goren, P., Domitrovich, C. E., & Mart, A. K. (2015). The case for preschool through high school state learning standards for SEL. In J. A. Durlak, C. E. Domitrovich, R. P. Weissberg, & T. P. Gullotta (Eds.), *Handbook of social and emotional learning: Research and practice* (pp. 532–548). New York: Guilford Press.

Eberth, J., & Sedlmeier, P. (2012). The effects of mindfulness meditation: A meta-analysis. *Mindfulness, 3*, 174–189. doi:10.1007/s12671-012-0101-x

Emmer, E. T., & Stough, L. M (2001). Classroom management: A critical part of educational psychology, with implications for teacher education. *Educational Psychologist, 36*, 103–112. doi:10.1207/S15326985EP3602_5

Ferguson, R., & Hirsch, E. (2014b). How working conditions predict teaching quality and student outcomes. In T. J. Kane, K. A. Kerr, & R. C. Pianta (Eds.), *Designing teacher evaluation systems: New guidance from the Measures of Effective Teaching project* (pp. 332–364). San Francisco: Jossey-Bass.

Fried, L. (2011). Teaching teachers about emotion regulation in the classroom. *Australian Journal of Teacher Education, 36*(3). doi:10.14221/ajte.2011v36n3.1

Gallup, Inc. (2014). *State of America's schools: A path to winning again in education.* Washington, DC: Author. Retrieved from http://www.gallup.com/services/178709/state-america-schools-report.aspx?ays=n

Greenberg, M. T., Brown, J. L., & Abenavoli, R. M. (2016). *Teacher stress and health effects on teachers, students and schools.* Edna Bennett Pierce Prevention Research Center, Pennsylvania State University. Retrieved from http://www.rwjf.org/en/library/research/2016/07/teacher-stress-and-health.html

Gregory, A., & Fergus, E. (2017). Social-emotional learning and equity in school discipline. In S. M. Jones, E. Doolittle, & S. McLanahan (Eds.), *The Future of Children, 27*, special issue on Social-Emotional Learning, 117–136.

Gross, J. J. (2002). Emotion regulation: Affective, cognitive, and social consequences. *Psychophysiology, 39*, 281–291. doi:10.1017/S0048577201393198

Hagelskamp, C., Brackett, M. A., Rivers, S. E., & Salovey, P. (2013). Improving classroom quality with the RULER approach to social and emotional learning: Proximal and distal outcomes. *American Journal of Community Psychology, 51*, 530–543. doi:10.1007/s10464-013-9570-x

Hamre, B. K., & Pianta, R. C. (2005). Can instructional and emotional support in the first-grade classroom make a difference for children at risk of school failure? *Child Development, 76*, 949–967. doi:10.1111/j.1467-8624.2005.00889.x

Harris, A. R., Jennings, P. A., Katz, D. A., Abenavoli, R. M., & Greenberg, M. T. (2016). Promoting stress management and well-being in educators: Feasibility and efficacy of the CALM intervention. *Mindfulness, 7*, 143–154. doi:10.1007/s12671-015-0451-2

Haynes, M., Maddock, A., & Goldrick, L. (2014). *On the path to equity: Improving the effectiveness of beginning teachers.* Washington, DC: Alliance for Excellent Education. Retrieved from http://all4ed.org/wp-content/uploads/2014/07/PathToEquity.pdf

Hemphill, C., & Nauer, K. (2009). *The new marketplace: How small-school reforms and school choice have reshaped New York City's high schools*. New York: Center for New York City Affairs, The New School for Management and Urban Policy.

Hirsch, E., & Emerick, S. (with Church, K., & Fuller, E.). (2007). *Teacher working conditions are student learning conditions: A report on the 2006 North Carolina teacher working conditions survey*. Hillsborough, NC: Center for Teaching Quality. Retrieved from https://ncteachingconditions.org/uploads/File/NC14_TWC%20stds%20and%20con%20fac%20guide_final.pdf

Hölzel, B. K., Carmody, J., Vangel, M., Congleton, C., Yerramsetti, S. M., Gard, T., & Lazar, S. W. (2011). Mindfulness practice leads to increases in regional brain gray matter density. *Psychiatry Research: Neuroimaging, 191*, 36–43. doi:10.1016/j.pscychresns.2010.08.006

Hölzel, B. K., Hoge, E. A., Greve, D. N., Gard, T., Creswell, J. D., Brown, K. W., . . . Lazar, S. (2013). Neural mechanisms of symptom improvements in generalized anxiety disorder following mindfulness training. *Neuroimage: Clinical, 2*, 448–458. doi:10.1016/j.nicl.2013.03.011

Horng, E. (2005). Poor working conditions make urban schools hard-to-staff. UCACCORD Public Policy Series. Retrieved from https://ucaccord.gseis.ucla.edu/publications/pdf/pb-010-0305.pdf

Huberman, M. (1996). Focus on research: Moving mainstream: Taking a closer look at teacher research. *Language Arts, 73*, 124–140.

Hull, J. (2012). *The principal perspective: Full report*. Alexandria, VA: Center for Public Education. Retrieved from http://www.centerforpubliceducation.org/principal-perspective (site discontinued).

Ingersoll, R. (2001). Teacher turnover and teacher shortages: An organizational analysis. *American Educational Research Journal, 38*, 499–534.

Ingersoll, R. (2011). Do we produce enough mathematics and science teachers? *Phi Delta Kappan, 92*(6), 37–41.

Jackson, P. W. (1990). *Life in classrooms*. New York: Teachers College Press.

Jennings, P. A. (2016). CARE for Teachers: A mindfulness-based approach to promoting teachers' well-being and improving performance. In K. Schonert-Reichl & R. Roeser (Eds.), *The handbook of mindfulness in education: Emerging theory, research, and programs* (pp. 133–148). New York: Springer-Verlag.

Jennings, P. A., Brown, J. L., Frank, J. L., Doyle, S., Oh, Y., Davis, R., . . . Greenberg, M. T. (2017). Impacts of the CARE for Teachers program on teachers' social and emotional competence and classroom interactions. *Journal of Educational Psychology*. Advance online publication. doi:10.1037/edu0000187

Jennings, P. A., & Frank, J. L. (2015). In-service preparation for educators. In J. Durlak, R. Weissberg, & T. Gullota (Eds.), *Handbook of Social and Emotional Learning* (pp. 422–437). New York: Guilford.

Jennings, P. A., Frank, J. L., Snowberg, K. E., Coccia, M. A., & Greenberg, M. T. (2013). Improving classroom learning environments by cultivating awareness and resilience in education (CARE): Results of a randomized controlled trial. *School Psychology Quarterly, 28*, 374–390. doi:10.1037/spq0000035

Jennings, P. A., & Greenberg, M. T. (2009). The prosocial classroom: Teacher social and emotional competence in relation to student and classroom outcomes. *Review of Educational Research, 79*, 491–525. doi:10.3102/0034654308325693

Jennings, P. A., Snowberg, K. E., Coccia, M. A., & Greenberg, M. T. (2011). Improving classroom learning environments by cultivating awareness and resilience in education (CARE): Results of two pilot studies. *Journal of Classroom Interactions, 46*, 27–48.

Johnson, S. M. (2006). *The workplace matters: Teacher quality, retention and effectiveness* (NEA Best Practices Working Paper). Washington, DC: NEA.

Johnson, S. M., Berg, J. H., & Donaldson, M. L. (2005). *Who stays in teaching and why: A review of the literature on teacher retention*. Cambridge, MA: Project on the Next Generation of Teachers, Harvard Graduate School of Education.

Johnson, S. M., & Birkeland, S. E. (2003). Pursuing a "sense of success": New teachers explain their career decisions. *American Educational Research Journal, 40*, 581–617.

Johnson, S. M., Kraft, M. A., & Papay, J. P. (2012). How context matters in high-need schools: The effects of teachers' working conditions on their professional satisfaction and their students' achievement. *Teachers College Record, 114*(10), 1–39.

Kabat-Zinn, J. (1982). An outpatient program in behavioral medicine for chronic pain patients based on the practice of mindfulness meditation: Theoretical considerations and preliminary results. *General Hospital Psychiatry, 4*, 33–47. doi:10.1016/0163-8343(82)90026-3

Kabat-Zinn, J. (2003). Mindfulness-based interventions in context: Past, present, and future. *Clinical Psychology: Science and Practice, 10*, 144–156. doi:10.1093/clipsy/bpg016

Katz, D. A., Greenberg, M. T., Klein, L. C., & Jennings, P. A. (2016). Associations between salivary α-amylase, cortisol, and self-report indicators of health and wellbeing among educators. *Teacher and Teacher Education, 54*, 98–106.

Kaufman, D., & Ireland, A. (2016). Enhancing teacher education with simulations, *TechTrends, 60*, 260–267. doi:10.1007/s11528-016-0049-0

Kemeny, M. E., Foltz, C., Cavanagh, J. F., Giese-Davis, J., Jennings, P. A., Rosenberg, E. L., . . . Ekman, P. (2012). Contemplative/emotion training reduces negative emotional behavior and promotes prosocial responses. *Emotion, 12*, 338–350. doi:10.1037/a0026118

Kendziora, K., & Yoder, N. (2016). *When districts adopt social and emotional learning: Findings from an ongoing evaluation of districtwide implementation of social and emotional learning*. Washington, DC: Education Policy Center at the American Institutes for Research. Retrieved from https://www.air.org/resource/when-districts-support-and-integrate-social-and-emotional-learning-sel

Khoury, B., Lecomte, T., Fortin, G., Masse, M., Therien, P., Bouchard, V., . . . Hofmann, S. G. (2013). Mindfulness-based therapy: A comprehensive meta-analysis. *Clinical Psychology Review, 33*, 763–771. doi:10.1016/j.cpr.2013.05.005

Kraft, M. A., & Papay, J. P. (2013). *Can professional environments in schools promote teacher development? Explaining heterogeneity in returns to teaching experience.* Cambridge, MA: Harvard University, Center for Education Policy Research. Retrieved from http://scholar.harvard.edu/files/mkraft/files/kraft_papay_-_prof_env_teacher_development_eepa_full.pdf

Ladd, H. (2011). Teachers' perceptions of their working conditions: How predictive of planned and actual teacher movement. *Educational Evaluation and Policy Analysis, 33*, 235–261.

Lawrence, M. W. (2016). *Preserving our greatest resources: A quantitative study to better understand the role that worksite wellness programs may have in mediating the symptoms of teacher burnout* (Dissertation). Retrieved from http://search.proquest.com/docview/1847984144

Leithwood, K. (2006). *Teacher working conditions that matter: Evidence for change.* Ontario, Canada. Elementary Teachers' Federation of Ontario. Retrieved from https://www.edcan.ca/wp-content/uploads/EdCan-2007-v47-n2-Leithwood.pdf

Leithwood, K., Louis, K. S., Anderson, S., & Wahlstrom, K. (2004). *How leadership influences student learning.* New York: Wallace Foundation. Retrieved from http://www.wallacefoundation.org/knowledge-center/school-leadership/key-research/documents/how-leadership-influences-student-learning.pdf

Lerner, J. S., Li, Y., Valdesolo, P., & Kassam, K. (2014). Emotion and decision making. *Annual Review of Psychology, 66*(1), 799–823. doi:10.1146/annurev-psych-010213-115043

Lin, S. Y. & Packer, D. J. (2017). Dynamic tuning of evaluations: Implicit racial attitudes are sensitive to incentives for intergroup cooperation. *Social Cognition, 35*, 245–272. https://doi.org/10.1521/soco.2017.35.3.245

Loeb, S., Darling-Hammond, L., & Luczak, J. (2005). How teaching conditions predict teacher turnover in California schools. *Peabody Journal of Education, 80*(3), 44–70.

Markow, D., Macia, L., & Lee, H. (2013). *The MetLife survey of the American teacher: Challenges for school leadership.* New York: Metropolitan Life Insurance Company. Retrieved from http://files.eric.ed.gov/fulltext/ED542202.pdf

Maslach, C., Jackson, S. E., & Leiter, M. P. (1997). Maslach burnout inventory. In C. P. Zalaquett & R. J. Wood (Eds.), *Evaluating stress: A book of resources* (pp. 191–218). Lanham, MD: Scarecrow Education.

McLaughlin, M. W., & Talbert, J. E. (2001). *Professional communities and the work of high school teaching.* Chicago: University of Chicago Press.

Merrill, R. M., & Sloan, A. (2014). Effectiveness of a health promotion program among employees in a western United States school district. *Journal of Occupational and Environmental Medicine, 56*, 639–644.

New Teacher Center. (2017). *Teaching, empowering, leading and learning (TELL).* Retrieved from https://newteachercenter.org/approach/teaching-empowering-leading-and-learning-tell/

New Teacher Center. (n.d.). *About the North Carolina teacher working conditions survey.* Retrieved from https://ncteachingconditions.org/about

Osher, D., Cantor, P., Berg, J., Steyer, L., & Rose, T. (2017). *Science of learning and development: A synthesis.* Retrieved from https://assets.aspeninstitute.org/content/uploads/2017/09/pre-reading-Science-of-Learning-and-Development-Synthesis.pdf

Osher, D., Kidron, Y., Brackett, M., Dymnicki, A., Jones, J., & Weissberg, R. (2016). Advancing the science and practice of social and emotional learning: Looking back and moving forward. *Review of Research in Education, 40*, 644–681

Osher, D., Sprague, J., Weissberg, R. P., Axelrod, J., Keenan, S., Kendziora, K., & Zins, J. E. (2007). A comprehensive approach to promoting social, emotional, and academic growth in contemporary schools. In A. Thomas & J. Grimes (Eds.), *Best practices in school psychology* (5th ed., Vol. 5, pp. 1263–1278). Bethesda, MD: National Association of School Psychologists.

Pianta, R. C., La Paro, K., & Hamre, B. K. (2008). *Classroom Assessment Scoring System (CLASS) manual: K–3.* Baltimore: Paul H. Brookes.

Rigby, J. G., Woulfin, S. L., & Marz, V. (2016). Understanding how structure and agency influence education policy implementation and organizational change. *American Journal of Education, 122*, 295–302.

Roeser, R. W. (2016). Processes of teaching, learning, and transfer in mindfulness-based interventions (MBIs) for teachers: A contemplative educational perspective. In K. Schonert-Reichl & R. Roeser (Eds.), *The handbook of mindfulness in education: Emerging theory, research, and programs* (pp. 133–148). New York: Springer-Verlag.

Roeser, R. W., Schonert-Reichl, K., Jha, A., Cullen, M., Wallace, L., Wilensky, R., . . . Harrison, J. (2013). Mindfulness training and reductions in teacher stress and burnout: Results from two randomized, waitlist-control field trials. *Journal of Educational Psychology, 105*, 787–804. doi:10.1037/a0032093

Roeser, R. W., Skinner, E., Beers, J., & Jennings, P. A. (2012). Mindfulness training and teachers' professional development: An emerging area of research and practice. *Child Development Perspectives, 6*, 167–173. doi:10.1111/j.1750-8606.2012.00238.x

Ronfeldt, M., Loeb, S., & Wyckoff, J. (2013). How teacher turnover harms student achievement. *American Educational Research Journal, 50*, 4–36.

Schonert-Reichl, K. A., Kitil, M. J., & Hanson-Peterson, J. (2017). *To reach the students, teach the teachers: A national scan of teacher preparation and social and emotional learning. A report prepared for the Collaborative for Academic, Social, and Emotional Learning (CASEL)*. Vancouver, BC: University of British Columbia.

Sharma, M. & Rush, S. E. (2014). Mindfulness-based stress reduction as a stress management intervention for healthy individuals: A systematic review. *Journal of Evidence-Based Complementary & Alternative Medicine, 19*, 271–286. doi:10.1177/2156587214543143

Shulman, L. S. (2004). *The wisdom of practice: Essays on teaching, learning, and learning to teach*. San Francisco: Jossey-Bass.

Skinner, E., & Beers, J. (2016). Mindfulness and teachers' coping in the classroom: A developmental model of teacher stress, coping, and everyday resilience. In K. A. Schonert-Reichl & R. W. Roeser (Eds.), *Mindfulness in behavioral health. Handbook of mindfulness in education: Integrating theory and research into practice* (pp. 99–118). New York, NY: Springer-Verlag Publishing.

Sutcher, L., Darling-Hammond, L., & Carver-Thomas, D. (2016). *A coming crisis in teaching? Teacher supply, demand, and shortages in the U.S.* Palo Alto, CA: Learning Policy Institute.

Tang, Y. Y., Hölzel, B. K., & Posner, M. I. (2015). The neuroscience of mindfulness meditation. *Nature Reviews Neuroscience, 16*, 213–225. doi:10.1038/nrn3916.

Tyson, O., Roberts, C. M., & Kane, R. (2009). Can implementation of a resilience program for primary school children enhance the mental health of teachers? *Australian Journal of Guidance & Counselling, 19*, 116–130.

Yoder, N. (2014). *Self-assessing social and emotional instruction and competencies: A tool for educators*. Washington, DC: Center on Great Teachers and Leaders. Retrieved from http://www.gtlcenter.org/sites/default/files/SelfAssessmentSEL.pdf

Yoder, N. (2015). *Social and emotional skills for life and career: Policy levers that focus on the whole child*. Washington, DC: Center on Great Teachers and Leaders. Retrieved from https://gtlcenter.org/sites/default/files/SEL_Policy_Levers.pdf

Yoder, N., & Dusenbury, L. (2017). A process for developing and articulating learning goals or competencies for social and emotional learning. Chicago: American Institutes for Research and Collaborative for Academic, Social, and Emotional Learning.

Yu, R. (2016). Stress potentiates decision biases: A stress induced deliberation-to-intuition (SIDI) model. *Neurobiology of stress, 3*, 83–95. http://dx.doi.org/10.1016/j.ynstr.2015.12.006

Zhai, F., Raver, C. C., & Li-Grining, C. (2011). Classroom-based interventions and teachers' perceived job stressors and confidence: Evidence from a randomized trial in Head Start settings. *Early childhood research quarterly, 26*, 442–452.

CHAPTER TEN

School Safety, Wellness, and Learning

Conditions for Learning, Barriers to Learning, and School Improvement

Jonathan Cohen, Eric Gordon, and Kimberly Kendziora

Educational philosophers have thought about the aims of education in a range of ways from national prosperity to managerial efficiency to individual happiness (Dunne & Hogan, 2004; Marples, 1999; Noddings, 2004. Families tend to answer this question in a more consistent manner. Over the past 49 years, family members have reported in Phi Delta Kappa/Gallup polls that the single most important purpose of public schooling is to "prepare people to become responsible citizens" (Phi Delta Kappan, 2017; Rose & Gallup, 2000). In the most recent poll, results showed that Americans overwhelmingly want schools to do more than educate students in academic subjects—they also want schools to help position students for their working lives after school through direct career preparation and the development of students' interpersonal skills (Phi Delta Kappan, 2017). That said, Americans do still value traditional academic preparation, especially opportunities for advanced academic studies.

A growing body of empirical research from education, risk prevention, and health-mental health promotion complements this public perception that social-emotional and civic competencies or what is sometimes referred to as wellness or positive psychology provide the very foundation for learning, healthy relationships, and the capacity to work and participate effectively in a democracy (Brown, Corrigan, & Higgins-D'Alessandro, 2012; Cohen, 2006; Gilman, Huebner, & Furlong, 2009; Weissberg, Durlak, Domitrovich, & Gullotta, 2015). For example, a meta-analysis of 213 studies of social and emotional programming delivered classroom-wide or school-wide found overall positive effects on social and emotional skills, attitudes, and prosocial behaviors. Further, based on 35 studies that measured academic performance, there were significant and positive effects on grades (Hedge's $g = 0.27$) and test scores (Hedge's $g = 0.33$; Durlak, Weissberg, Dymnicki, Taylor, & Schellinger, 2011). A review by the National Research Council found that developing social and emotional skills is associated with increased engagement in learning and reduced behaviors that interfere with learning (Pellegrino & Hilton, 2012). In addition, although valuing social responsibility tends to significantly decline from ages 9 to 16, then level off in later adolescence (Wray-Lake, Syvertsen, & Flanagan, 2016), later civic engagement can be strengthened by experiences of democratic homeroom and classroom practices, equitable school climate, and through focused interventions and service experiences (Ballard, Cohen, & Littenberg-Tobias, 2016; Jagers, Lozada, Rivas-Drake, & Guillaume, 2017; Kim & Morgül, 2017; Lin, 2015). In short, evidence shows that experiences in school can produce the kinds of social and interpersonal outcomes that are most desired by Americans.

In this chapter, we focus on the central importance of promoting student wellness and the social, emotional, and civic competences that provide an essential foundation for positive life outcomes. We begin with an overview of the foundations for school safety and wellness, and discuss how schools meet students' needs and can promote prosocial competencies. "Prosocial" education refers to a range of educational traditions that are focused on promoting the skills, knowledge, and dispositions that provide the foundation for learning, healthy relationships, and the ability to work and participate in a democracy, including character education, social emotional learning, and school climate reform (Brown, Corrigan, & Higgins-D'Alessandro, 2012; Cohen, 2017; Kidron & Osher, 2012). We describe implementation road maps for prosocial improvement in schools. Finally, we will describe the Cleveland Metropolitan School District's journey working to introduce and set in motion instructional and systemic improvement processes that are designed to support student learning and wellness.

Foundations for Learning and Healthy Development

Underlying everything that happens in schools—and simply everything that happens involving people—is that we are fundamentally biopsychosocial beings. Students, teachers, administrators, bus drivers all bring a set of biological and psychosocial capacities, tendencies, and needs along with them wherever they go. The physical characteristics we present—big or small, physically attractive or not, and the array of biologically based strengths and weaknesses—play a powerful role in shaping how we are treated, even though we have quite limited control over them. Some individuals bring their fear, anger, or sadness with them, or tendency to react emotionally or intellectually to events, which shapes how they interpret and react to what goes on in their environments. Finally, these elements interact in a social context with all the tendencies that others bring to an encounter (Osher, Cantor, Berg, Strayer, & Rose, 2018; Pellegrino, 2018). A student, unable to read a teacher's notes due to uncorrected vision problems, may disengage from instruction. A teacher, upset about a comment that a colleague made, may be more critical of her students. A principal, energetic and dedicated, may give teachers support in behavior management and lesson planning that helps everyone's day go a little bit more smoothly.

Meeting Student Needs in School

As a field, educators and researchers are still very much in the process of learning about the relative importance of given individual needs and competencies as well as the factors that shape development and learning. With respect to needs, the well-known theory of needs developed by Maslow (1943, 1962) has become a standard in both business and education for understanding motivation for success. Maslow's model is most often presented as a pyramid, with the most basic needs at the bottom. His rationale was that a human in a state of extreme deprivation will be most driven to meet physiological needs for food, water, sleep, and warmth. Indeed, students who attend school hungry, tired, or cold are likely to have difficulty focusing on their work and succeeding academically. This basic set of functions is the basis of the National School Lunch Program, which was established in 1946 and feeds more than 30 million children each year (U.S. Department of Agriculture, 2017).

A second tier of needs identified by Maslow relates to safety and security—a central concept in this volume. Maslow wrote, "Practically everything looks less important than safety, (even sometimes the physiological needs which being satisfied, are now underestimated). A man, in this state, if it is extreme enough and chronic enough, may be characterized as living almost for safety alone" (1943, p. 376).

The application of safety needs to the school context can be dramatic. Schools need to be a place where all children can experience security and trust, and freedom from bullying or prejudice. Nationally representative surveys have shown that 58% of children have been exposed to violence in the past year (physical assault, sexual victimization, maltreatment, property victimization, or witnessing violence; Finkelhor, Turner, Shattuck, Hamby, & Krack, 2015), and schools, on the whole, have been relatively safe havens. Student victimization at school has been dropping steadily since the 1990s. In 2016, 749,400 students experienced a violent victimization at school (Musu-Gillette et al., 2018), down from 841,000 in 2015 (Musu-Gillette et al., 2017), 1.4 million in 2005, and 3.8 million in 1995 (Dinkes, Cataldi, Kena, & Baum, 2006). Paradoxically, while schools are among the most physically safe places for children, this is not the case socially and emotionally. Although rates of verbal bullying and cyberbullying are also dropping over time, they remain much higher than the rates of physical threat in schools (Musu-Gillette, et al., 2018). For example, 22% of middle schools report an episode of bullying at least once a week, and 21% of students ages 12–18 reported being bullied at school during the past year. Schools strive to help their students feel not only physically safe, but emotionally and psychologically as well. Students should feel free to ask questions and share ideas without being mocked by other students or reprimanded by the teacher (Faisal, 2016). The student must feel safe in the classroom and the learning environment before progressing to more advanced needs, including learning (Osher et al., 2018; Pellegrino, 2018).

The third level of Maslow's hierarchy references the need for love and belonging. Maslow referenced the need to connect to friends, a romantic partner, family, or children—above all, a place in the group. For students, these needs may be expressed as a need to identify with peers, fit in with a group, and be accepted by adults. For example, a series of studies of student academic motivation among grade 3–5 students in high-poverty schools (McCaslin & Burross, 2008) showed that students understood schools as having essentially separate social and academic domains. The central motivational processes for these students were participation and validation. The drive to belong (vs. be isolated) mediated concerns about academic achievement. Educational strategies such as collaborative learning may support the fulfillment of such needs (Gillies, 2003).

At the fourth level of the hierarchy are esteem needs. These include self-respect, respect of others (reputation, attention, importance, or appreciation), strengths or achievement, and independence and freedom. It is at this level when teachers may strategically use attention and recognition to promote engagement and ultimately responsibility for and pleasure in learning.

Self-actualization is the driving need at the fifth and top level of Maslow's model. He wrote, "discontent and restlessness will soon develop, unless the individual is doing what he is fitted for. A musician must make music, an artist must paint, a poet must write, if he is to be ultimately happy. What a man *can* be, he *must* be" (1943, p. 382). We suggest that what Maslow referred to as "self-actualization" overlaps with what Csikszentmihalyi (2008) has referred to as "flow." Such needs may go beyond what schools can provide, but the broad principles of identifying strengths and developing talents certainly apply to K–12 education. The inclusion of music, arts, and sports in an educational program is not universal but is widespread and can benefit both learning and development (Spier, Leenknecht, & Osher, in press). For example, despite the lack of federal requirements, 90% of states in the United States require arts instruction from primary through upper secondary levels (Education Commission of the States, 2016). In addition, two federal agencies provide support for arts education on a national scale. The U.S. Department of Education provides Arts in Education Model Development and Dissemination grants, which support the creation and scaling of innovations to promote learning the arts in schools (U.S. Department of Education, 2015).

Promoting Student Competencies in School

Going beyond meeting fundamental human needs, there is great value in promoting children's social, emotional, and civic competencies through schooling. Although there is debate about how to best define and classify these competences, we know that they matter for development. For example, a long-term follow-up study found that kindergarten teachers' ratings of children's prosocial skills helped predict adolescent and adult outcomes 13 to 19 years later (Jones, Greenberg, & Crowley, 2015). The researchers found that social and emotional competencies in early childhood were strongly associated with young adult outcomes in education, employment, need for public assistance, mental health, substance abuse, and criminal activity. Jones and colleagues found that a teacher's rating of a kindergartner's social competence was associated with a student's increased likelihood of graduating from college and having a full-time job by the age of 25, and a decreased likelihood of being arrested. This study did not prove that social competence *caused* these outcomes, but combined with other research, it seems to make clear that developing children's skills in these areas increases their chances of success in school, work, and life.

In 2006, economist James Heckman began publishing a series of studies (Heckman & Kautz, 2012; Heckman, Stixrud, & Urz´ua, 2006) showing that "soft skills"—such as personality traits, goals, motivations—and preferences not only predict but also causally produce success in life, and that programs that promote these skills have an important place in an effective portfolio of public policies—particularly given the shift toward a more service-oriented economy and a media-driven culture (Starcher & Allen, 2016). For example, Heckman and Kautz 2012) showed that students who drop out of high school but obtain a GED (a standardized test that serves as an equivalent to a high school diploma) have cognitive skills more like high school graduates, but personality traits more like dropouts. Specifically, GED recipients tend to exit employment, become divorced, and enter jail at rates similar to those of high school dropouts, while high school graduates are much more persistent. Consequently, in the labor market they earn less and have lower hourly wages. Conversely, Heckman and Kautz pointed out, the Perry Preschool Program improved the lives of its participants without increasing their IQ scores, demonstrating why it is problematic to focus curricula exclusively on improving cognitive test scores.

The malleability of social and emotional skills was demonstrated in a meta-analysis of 213 school-based, universal social and emotional learning (SEL) programs involving 270,034 kindergarten through high school students (Durlak, Weissberg, Dymnicki, Taylor, & Schellinger, 2011). This study documented that SEL programs yielded significant positive effects on targeted social-emotional competencies and attitudes about self, others, and school; enhanced students' behavioral adjustment in the form of increased prosocial behaviors and reduced conduct and internalizing problems; and improved academic performance on achievement tests and grades. An update to this work (Taylor, Oberle, Durlak, & Weissberg, 2017) showed that students in school-based SEL interventions continued to demonstrate significant, positive benefits on outcomes collected up to 3.75 years post-intervention, especially when the interventions focused on social and emotional skills (e.g., self-regulation, problem-solving, and relationship skills) rather than attitudes (e.g., self-esteem, disapproval of substance use or violence, liking school). In addition, SEL interventions not only significantly improved skills, positive attitudes, prosocial behavior, and academic performance, but these programs also served as a protective factor against the development of subsequent problems (i.e., conduct problems, emotional distress, and drug use). The benefits of SEL program participation accrued for all racial and socioeconomic demographic groups represented in the analysis.

The importance of social skills for life success persists beyond schooling. The Harvard Grant Study is a longitudinal, prospective initiative begun in 1938 with 268 male Harvard undergraduates. Vaillant (2012) followed the men into their nineties, examining a rich set of data on relationships, politics and religion, coping strategies, alcohol use, and health. A critical finding from this work was that creative problem-solving or coping—teachable skills—are the single most important psychosocial variables that shape life satisfaction and productivity.

An important final note about promoting social and emotional skills in school pertains to the definition and nature of those skills. Recent and profoundly important research and practice efforts underscore the essential importance of SEL, character education, and other overlapping educational traditions that have intentionally sought to integrate prosocial learning and teaching with cognitive/intellectual pedagogy. Programs that pursue this merged approach to learning may describe what they do as character education; positive youth development; or the development of social and emotional learning, interpersonal and intrapersonal competencies, or noncognitive skills. Although the terms are not entirely interchangeable, there is substantial overlap among them (Berg, Osher, Same, Nolan, Benson, & Jacobs, 2017; Cohen, 2017; Kidron & Osher, 2012). Collectively, the capacity to manage emotions, set and achieve positive goals, feel and show empathy, maintain positive relationships, and make sound decisions represent a range of attributes needed to flourish in school, the workplace, and in personal lives (National Academies of Sciences, Engineering, and Medicine, 2017).

Promoting Safety and Wellness: Prosocial School Improvement

There is confusion about how various prosocial concepts, traditions, and "camps" are similar and different (Berg et al., 2017; Brown, Corrigan, & Higgins-D'Alessandro, 2012; Cohen, 2017). Character education, social, emotional, and academic learning (SEL), school climate (and in an overlapping manner, school culture, conditions for learning, supportive learning environments) to name just a few of the perhaps the most known prosocial approaches today. Each grows out of a particular educational tradition (Cohen, 1999, 2001; Osher, Kidron, Brackett, Dymnicki, Jones, & Weissberg, 2016; Weissberg, Durlak, Domitrovich, & Gullotta, 2015). These labels—"SEL" or "school climate"—have different and particular meanings conceptually. SEL, for example, is about learning socially and emotionally. "School climate" is about the quality and character of the school as a whole.

There are also important similarities and relationships among these concepts (e.g., Berg, Osher, Moroney, & Yoder, 2017; Osher & Berg, 2017). All these overlapping prosocial educational traditions are grounded in the goal of promoting the social, emotional, and civic skills, knowledge, and dispositions that provide the foundation for school and life success. And, all these efforts are committed to setting in motion a process of learning and improvement that supports school leaders taking steps to ignite the intrinsic motivation of students, parents/guardians, school personnel, and even community members/leaders to learn and work together to create safer, more supportive, engaging, and healthy climates for learning that promote school and life success. In other words, the school climate and/or SEL-informed improvement process is intentional, strategic, data-driven, and fundamentally collaborative process of understanding current needs, challenges, and improvement goals, delineating given systemic, instructional, and/or relational improvement strategies, and measuring and learning about successes and challenges in an iterative manner.

Over the past decade, there has been a convergence of school improvement goals, strategies, and metrics that are importantly aligned with implementation science (Blase, van Dyke, & Fixsen, 2013; Bryk, Gomez, Grunow, & LeMahieu, 2015; Fullan, 2011). Implementation science is the study of what really supports school leaders setting in motion a continuous process of learning and school improvement. Improvement requires that schools build internal and external capacity to select and execute evidence-based programs to achieve their desired outcomes with quality (Wandersman et al., 2008). This capacity-building process benefits from support and ongoing professional learning.

Prosocial School Improvement in Action

When one is going on a journey, such as a long hike, scenic tour, or a school improvement process, it is helpful to have a road map. As Yogi Berra said, "If you don't know where you are going, you will end up someplace else." Such a tool provides information about where one is going, what to consider taking along, and what milestones one might encounter along the way. Rather than telling school leaders what to do, a road map for school improvement should suggest what to consider and focus on in ways that are research-based.

There are a number of road maps to improving safety and wellness in schools. Character.org (2014) offers a road map based on the 11 Principles of Effective Character Education. This set of schoolwide and instructional goals is one way that school leaders can compare and contrast their efforts with research-based principles. The Collaborative for Academic, Social, and Emotional Learning has a Guide for Schoolwide Social and Emotional Learning (Meyers, Domitrovich, Dissi, Trejo, & Greenberg, 2018; Meyers et al., 2015), which uses a team structure as the nexus of improvement efforts. Looking at improvement more broadly, and building on Deming's (1986) work 30 years ago, Bryk (Bryk, Gomez, Grunow, & LeMahieu, 2015) and many others use the *plan-do-study-act* model. Fixsen and his colleagues suggest using a model that focuses on *exploration*, *installation*, *initial implementation*, and *full implementation* (Blase, van Dyke & Fixsen, 2013). The National Center for Safe Supportive Learning Environments (http://safesupportivelearning.ed.gov) provides an interactive School Climate Improvement Resource Package, which includes among other tools, School Climate Improvement Action Guides, which provide action steps for district leaders, school leaders, instructional staff, noninstructional staff, families, students, and community partners on how to support school climate improvements, tips on what it looks like when it is being done well and what pitfalls to avoid, and questions to ask to engage in the school climate improvement efforts.

The National School Climate Center (NSCC) offers a School Climate Improvement Road Map. This road map supports the National School Climate Council's understanding of an effective school climate improvement process:

an intentional, strategic, collaborative, data-driven, transparent, and democratically informed process that supports students, parents/guardians, school personnel, and even community members learning and working together to create a climate for learning that supports school and life success. The NSCC's road map is shaped by a series of research-based tasks and challenges that characterize and shape an effective process of school improvement.

The five stages (listed in table 10.1) are (1) preparation and planning for the next phase of school improvement; (2) evaluation; (3) understanding the evaluation findings, engagement, and developing an action plan; (4) implementing the action plan; and (5) reevaluation and beginning the cycle anew (Cohen, 2006; Cohen, Espelage, Twemlow, Berkowitz, & Comer, 2015). Each of these five stages are in turn defined by a series of tasks or challenges. For example, three (of the six) tasks and challenges that define the first stage of preparation and planning include (1) forming a representative leadership team for school climate improvement and establishing ground rules collaboratively, (2) building support and fostering "buy-in" for the school climate improvement process, and (3) working to establish "no-fault" framework and promoting a culture of trust. These are overlapping but separate challenges that support the whole school community coming together in a democratically informed manner to understand current needs and strengths and to develop and carry out an action plan for improvement. The underlying assumption here is that it truly does take the "whole village" to raise and support healthy children who will become successful in school and in life.

It is important to note that schools, like people, are never entirely logical or rational. As logical as it may sound to first prepare and then evaluate and/or develop action plans, this is not always what "real life" is like in schools and districts. We suggest that what is most important is that school leaders consider the following foundational goals and processes that support an effective improvement process:

- Igniting the intrinsic motivation of as many students, parents/guardians, school personnel, and even community members as possible to understand and actively support and co-lead the improvement process. There is a growing body of research that underscores the multifaceted benefit of engaging youth in particular but also their parents/guardians and community members/leaders to be actively engaged and co-leading intergenerational school improvement efforts.
- That school leaders are as transparent and clear as possible about what schoolwide, instructional, and/or relational improvement goals and strategies they are implementing. To be optimal learners as well as leaders, classroom, building, and district leaders need to be clear about what sets of understandings (or improvement model) are shaping specific improvement goals and related systemic, pedagogic, and/or relational strategies.

Table 10.1 Stages in the NSCC road map to prosocial school improvement

Stage One: Preparation and Planning

- Forming a representative school climate improvement leadership team
- Building support and fostering a shared vision and buy-in for the school climate improvement process
- Establishing a "no fault" framework and promoting a culture of trust
- Ensuring the team has adequate resources to support the process
- Celebrating successes and building on past efforts
- Developing plans to support professional learning communities and network improvement communities
- Reflecting and learning from Stage One work

Stage Two: Evaluation

- Systematically evaluating the school's strengths, needs, and weaknesses with any number of school climate as well as other potential measurement tools
- Developing plans to share evaluation findings with the school community
- Reflecting and learning from Stage Two work

Stage Three: Understanding the Findings, Engaging, and Developing an Action Plan

- Understanding the evaluation findings
- Digging into the data to understand areas of consensus and discrepancy, and promote learning and engagement
- Prioritizing goals
- Researching best practices and evidence-based instructional and systemic programs and efforts
- Developing an action plan
- Reflecting and learning from Stage Three work

Stage Four: Implementing the Action Plan

- Coordinating evidence-based pedagogic and systemic efforts designed to (a) promote students' social, emotional, and civic as well as intellectual competencies; and (b) improve the school climate by working toward a safe, caring, participatory and responsive school community
- The instructional and/or schoolwide efforts are instituted with fidelity and monitored, and there is an ongoing attempt to learn from successes and challenges
- The adults who teach and learn with students work to further their own social, emotional, and civic learning
- Reflecting and learning from Stage Four work

(continued)

Table 10.1 (continued)

Stage Five: Reevaluation and Development of the Next Phase
• Reevaluating the school's strengths and challenges
• Discovering what has changed and how
• Discovering what has most helped and hindered further the school climate improvement process
• Revising plans to improve the school climate
• Reflecting and learning from Stage Five work

- That school leaders track and record what specific tasks that they have strategically decided to focus on during each of the improvement stages but to also evaluate what they have done and how well they think they have done it to support learning. This is important for several reasons. First, prosocial school and classroom improvement is an ongoing process. School leaders can only focus on so many new initiatives. Having records of what was done (and how well it was done) during given stages creates the foundation for school leaders (whether they are the same leader(s) or new leaders) to systematically learn "what worked?" and "what did not work?" during the initial cycle. In addition, this kind of process assessment creates an essential platform for fidelity assessment or evaluating what was actually done. When evidence-based approaches or other effective innovations are being used in education, fidelity assessments measure the presence and strength of an innovation as it is used in daily practice.

The Cleveland Metropolitan School District

Following these principles, we share the story of one district—the Cleveland Metropolitan School District (CMSD)—that has engaged in a decade-long improvement effort to support safety and wellness. CMSD is one of the highest-need districts in the nation. It has 38,949 students, of whom 65% are African American, 16% are white, 16% are Latino, 3% are multiracial, and 1% are Asian or Pacific Islanders (CMSD, 2018). CMSD invokes a provision of the National Student Lunch Program that waives the requirement to establish household eligibility for free or reduced-price meals if the district provides free meals to all students. Therefore, all of its students are eligible for free breakfast and lunch. Poverty in Cleveland is extreme: it has the second highest level of childhood poverty of any city in the nation, behind only Detroit, Michigan. In CMSD, 22% of students receive special education services, and 9% receive English language learner supports. Districtwide, the average daily student attendance rate is 91%; for teachers, the attendance rate is 92%. Mobility is relatively high: 20% of students did not spend the majority of the school year in the district. The four-year graduation rate is 72% (CMSD, 2018). On Ohio state's district accountability measures, CMSD received a grade of "F" for all indicators except K–3 literacy, for which it earned a "C." Despite the low absolute performance, there is some evidence that the improvement efforts CMSD has undertaken are bearing fruit. The district's graduation rate had increased by nearly 20% in the past six years and is at a record high of 72%, and has exceeded the goal set by the Higher Education Compact of Cleveland in 2010.

Cleveland's Journey

What happens when one of your best schools, as identified by district indicators—growing population, positive attendance, 94% graduation rate—experiences a school shooting? Cleveland's story of focusing on school safety and student wellness began on October 10, 2007, when a 14-year-old boy who had been suspended from school snuck into his school, shot and injured two students and two teachers before taking his own life.

Like many urban school districts, Cleveland responded in some typical ways. Then-CEO Eugene T. W. Sanders ordered the installation of metal detectors and book bag scanners to help assure the districts more than 45,000 students and their families that they would be safe in school. However, Dr. Sanders recognized that hardware was not really the answer. Instead, he claimed the answer was "Humanware." On that day, Dr. Sanders assigned his new Chief Academic Officer the duty of developing a plan to ensure that Cleveland's students could be assured that they were safe and supported so that no child would ever feel so desperate again.

Cleveland began by hiring the American Institutes for Research to conduct a thorough analysis of the district's capacity to ensure physical and emotional safety, promote student wellness, and ensure students had the supports they needed to thrive. That initial study (Osher et al., 2008) found a school system characterized by:

- Reactive, punitive, and inconsistent approaches to discipline at home and in school, which set the stage for behavioral problems
- High levels of long-term poverty, which made adverse childhood experience more likely and increased the likelihood that children would arrive at school with inadequate relationship and self-regulatory skills
- High rates of lead poisoning and lead effect compared to other U.S. cities, further placing students at risk for academic problems and anti-social behavior
- Poor conditions for learning in schools, resulting in students who felt less safe, less supported by teachers, and viewed their fellow students as having

poorer social and emotional competencies than did peers in other similar districts

The study further concluded that Cleveland's students demonstrated relatively high engagement in risky behavior compared to similar peers and that in many schools, students' social, emotional, and mental health needs overran the capacity of the schools' and district's resources, often forcing the faculties of these schools to intervene with and punish "out of control" behaviors rather than on focus on prevention and early intervention.

So how does a district in Cleveland's situation address these nearly overwhelming conditions? Cleveland set out to implement six core strategies recommended by the AIR study (Osher et al., 2008):

1. Employ a three-tiered approach to building conditions and capacities to learn and teach: (1) promotion and prevention, (2) early intervention, and (3) treatment
2. Align promotion and prevention, early intervention, and treatment in a manner that both addresses immediate needs and prevents the onset and decreases the magnitude of problems
3. Avoid single solutions or unaligned multiple solutions for complex but interrelated problems. Instead, support the ability of schools, agencies, and staff to systemically implement proven practices and programs with quality
4. Eliminate ineffective or counterproductive practices and behaviors
5. Build a climate for change and sustain it over multiple years
6. Use data for planning, monitoring, and evaluation

Cleveland began its pursuit of these goals in the spring of 2008 and over the past 10 years has constructed a social-emotional framework, Humanware, in four core areas of the organization:

- Standards, Curriculum, & Instruction
- Formative & Summative Assessments
- Programming & Interventions
- District Systems

Cleveland began this work by creating a Humanware Team tasked with implementing the six Humanware strategies districtwide. The team's first efforts included implementing an evidence-based social-emotional learning curriculum, PATHS (Greenberg, Kusché, Cook, & Quamma, 1995; Kusché & Greenberg, 1994), in grades K–2. At the same time, the district opened planning centers (Osher & Keenan, 2002, Woodruff et al., 1999) in every school building as early intervention centers for students demonstrating poor behaviors or elevated needs. The district also implemented a Rapid Response Team to address student/school crises as they arose. These efforts were designed to begin building an aligned, three-tiered approach to improving capacity to learn. At the same time, the district implemented an annual Conditions for Learning Survey to capture data to support planning and evaluating.

Over the years, Cleveland continued the implementation of PATHS, expanding it to grades 3–5, and developed school-based Student Support Teams for students with needs that could not be addressed in the Planning Center but required a team of professionals working with the student and family to support the student's needs. The district also created a written Scope and Sequence for social-emotional learning districtwide and implemented advisories and class meetings in an effort to engage students and faculty in changing the culture in their schools into a culture of support and empowerment. The district also added new resources to the planning center, including a computer-based, self-paced social and emotional program called Ripple Effects (Koffman, Ray, Albarran, & Vasquez, 2008), and created an online tool to help Student Support Teams track progress for their students.

CMSD has worked collaboratively with its teachers' union to implement improvement efforts. Through collective bargaining, the district was able to formally establish new practices and roles, including the role of managing a planning center. In addition, teachers agreed to changes to the code of conduct to make it less punitive for students. Perhaps the most innovative change has been that teachers and other staff can now receive bonuses for work in schools that examine their data on conditions for learning and improve their safety, support, challenge, and peer social and emotional climate.

Cleveland used the five-stage prosocial improvement process described above. As noted, the district formed the "Humanware" Team that guided their work (Stage One), completed a systemic evaluation by an outside evaluator (Stage Two), reviewed the findings and prioritized six goals (Stage Three), implemented several elements aligned to those goals (Stage Four), and through evaluation of progress implemented new tools in the Planning Centers and for the Student Support teams (Stage Five). However, to be sure, practice is always messier than pure theory.

For example, in the school years of 2010–2011 and 2011–2012, after having completed the training of all grade K–5 teachers in PATHS, the training of 130 Planning Center Instructional Assistants, and training and supporting hundreds of members of school-based Student Support Teams, the CMSD was hit hard by the national recession. Facing a multi-million-dollar budget crisis, the District closed 23 schools, laid off hundreds of employees, and force transferred remaining employees across the district to new schools and positions. This resulted in profound losses in the professional development investment made in the prior two years as new teachers, aides, and support team members took on these roles in place of the previously trained personnel.

Too often, practitioners discard sound theoretical frameworks because they cannot and do not anticipate this kind of significant disruption. Instead, we should think of these frameworks as recursive and flexible as opposed to strictly linear. Over the past nine years of work in this area, Cleveland has followed this process in the implementation of its work but has entered the step or steps that seemed most appropriate at that time (Osher, Poirier, Jarjoura, Haigt, & Mitchell, 2015; Osher, Poirier, Jarjoura, Kendziora, & Brown, 2015; Wright, Lamont, Wandersman, Osher, & Gordon, 2015). For example, Cleveland had an action plan ready for the 2010–2011 school year (Stage 3). However, upon facing massive budget cuts, personnel reductions, and school closures, jumped immediately to Preparation and Planning (Stage 1), scrapping any implementation and evaluation (Stages 4 and 5) of the previous plan. In fact, in 2010–2011, the only work done by the district in social-emotional learning was retraining of educators and the development of the district's written curriculum scope and sequence, both relatively low-cost investments compared to investments made in the prior years, or in the years after recovering from the recession.

Finally, creating the conditions for learning that support school improvement should be thought of as a journey. Although Cleveland has been investing in social-emotional systems and supports for over nine years now, there is still a great deal to be done to meet the needs of every child and each adult in the district. Despite how long a school or district has invested in these supportive strategies, each year brings new children and adults to those schools who are only beginning year one of their experience in a supportive learning environment (Osher, Poirier, Jarjoura, Haigt, et al., 2015; Osher, Poirier, Jarjoura, Kendziora et al., 2015; Wright et al., 2015).

Conclusion

Schools can play the critical role of protective factors in the lives of students by meeting their essential developmental needs and by helping to promote skills and talents that will support their lifelong success. Cleveland has shown that even in the most challenging contexts, progress is possible. Sources of support exist for other districts as well. Three resources particularly relevant to the promotion of safety and wellness are highlighted here.

One resource for school leaders who wish to work on prosocial school improvement is the National Center on Safe and Supportive Learning Environments (NCSSLE; https://safesupportivelearning.ed.gov/). This Center is funded by the U.S. Department of Education and provides support to schools in three main domains:

- Training and support to state administrators, including grantees funded under the federal Promoting Student Resilience or Project Prevent grant programs as well as other school and district administrators, institutions of higher education, teachers, support staff at schools, communities and families, and students
- Seeking to improve schools' conditions for learning through measurement and program implementation, so that all students have the opportunity to realize academic success in safe and supportive environments
- Promoting and supporting the U.S. Department of Education's free School Climate Surveys (EDSCLS)

The Collaborative for Academic, Social, and Emotional Learning (CASEL; http://www.casel.org) works to help make evidence-based social and emotional learning (SEL) an integral part of education from preschool through high school. Among its strategies to achieve this are:

- The district resource center (drc.casel.org), which documents and shares practical lessons from the field through partner districts to document outcomes and develop models and resources for schools and districts nationwide, and which currently houses more than 500 tools, resources, and guidance documents to support systemic implementation of SEL
- The SEL in Action section of CASEL's web site (https://casel.org/in-action/) offers additional resources aimed at schools, classrooms, and families
- Support for the development of state SEL student learning and implementation guidelines through the efforts of the Collaborating States Initiative

The National School Climate Center (NSCC; https://www.schoolclimate.org/) is a nonprofit that works to measure and improve the climate for learning in schools. NSCC learns and works with educators by providing expertise to K–12 schools, districts, and states in the following areas:

- School climate measurement
- Professional development
- Comprehensive school climate improvement support
- Leadership development
- Policy consultation

As more schools and districts work to improve SEL, school climate, and student wellness, the more the field learns and the more practice can be improved and refined for the good of all students.

References

Ballard, P. J., Cohen, A. K., & Littenberg-Tobias, J. (2016). Action civics for promoting civic development: Main effects of program participation and differences by project characteristics. *American Journal of Community Psychology, 58*(3–4), 377–390. doi:10.1002/ajcp.12103

Berg, J., Osher, D., Moroney, D., & Yoder, N. (2017). *The intersection of school climate and social and emotional development.* Washington, DC: American Institutes for Research.

Berg, J., Osher, D., Same, M., Nolan, E., Benson, D., & Jacobs, N. (2017). *Identifying, defining, and measuring social and emotional competencies.* Washington, DC: American Institutes for Research.

Blase, K., van Dyke, M., & Fixsen, D. (2013). *Implementation drivers: Assessing best practices.* Adapted with permission by The State Implementation & Scaling-up of Evidence-based Practices Center (SISEP). Based on the work of The National Implementation Research Network (NIRN) Frank Porter Graham Child Development Institute, University of North Carolina Chapel Hill. Retrieved from http://implementation.fpg.unc.edu/resources/implementation-drivers-assessing-best-practices

Bronfenbrenner, U. (1979). *The ecology of human development: Experiments by nature and design.* Cambridge, MA: Harvard University Press.

Brown, P. M., Corrigan, M. W., & Higgins-D'Alessandro, A. (Eds.). (2012). *The handbook of prosocial education.* Lanham, MD: Rowman & Littlefield.

Bryk, A. S., Gomez, L. M., Grunow, A. & LeMahieu, P. G. (2015). *Learning to improve: How America's schools can get better at getting better.* Cambridge, MA: Harvard Educational Press.

Character.org. (2014). *11 principles of effective character education.* Washington, DC: Author. Retrieved from http://www.character.org/uploads/PDFs/ElevenPrinciples_new2010.pdf

CMSD. (2018). Facts: *Our students.* Retrieved from http://clevelandmetroschools.org/domain/24

Cohen, J. (1999). Social and emotional learning past and present: A psych educational dialogue. In J. Cohen (Ed.), *Educating minds and hearts: Social emotional learning and the passage into adolescence* (pp. 3–23). New York: Teachers College Press and the Association for Supervision and Curriculum Development.

Cohen, J. (2001). Social emotional education: Core principles and practices. In J. Cohen (Ed.), *Caring classrooms/intelligent schools: The social emotional education of young children* (pp. 3–29). New York: Teachers College Press.

Cohen, J. (2006). Social, emotional, ethical, and academic education: Creating a climate for learning, participation in democracy and well-being. *Harvard Educational Review, 76*(2), 201–237.

Cohen, J. (2007). Interdisciplinary psychoanalysis and the education of children: Psychoanalytic and educational partnerships. In R. A. King, P. B.

Neubauer, S. L. Abrams, & A. S. Dowling (Eds.), *Psychoanalytic study of the child* (Vol. 62, pp. 180–207). New Haven, CT: Yale University Press.

Cohen, J. (2012). Measuring and improving school climate: A pro-social strategy that recognizes, educates and supports the whole child and the whole school community. In P. M. Brown, M. W. Corrigian, & A. Higgins-D'Alessandro (Eds.), *The handbook of prosocial education*. New York: Rowman & Littlefield.

Cohen, J. (2017, September 20). School climate, social emotional learning, and other prosocial "camps": Similarities and a difference. *Teachers College Record*. Retrieved from http://www.tcrecord.org. ID Number: 22165.

Cohen, J., Espelage, D., Twemlow, S. W., Berkowitz, M. W., & Comer, J. P. (2015). Rethinking effective bully and violence prevention effects: Promoting healthy school climates, positive youth development, and preventing bully-victim-bystander behavior. *International Journal of Violence and Schools, 15*, 2–40.

Csikszentmihalyi, M. (2008). *Flow: The psychology of optimal experience*. New York: Harper Perennial Modern Classics.

Deming, W. E. (1986). *Out of the crisis*. Cambridge, MA: MIT Center for Advanced Engineering Study.

Dinkes, R., Cataldi, E. F., Kena, G., & Baum, K. (2006). *Indicators of school crime and safety: 2006* (NCES 2007-003/NCJ 214262). Washington, DC: U.S. Government Printing Office. Retrieved from https://nces.ed.gov/pubs 2007/2007003a.pdf

Dunne, J., & Hogan, P. (Eds.). (2004). *Education and practice: Upholding the integrity of teaching and learning*. Milton, Australia: Blackwell.

Durlak, J. A., Weissberg, R. P., Dymnicki, A. B., Taylor, R. D., & Schellinger, K. B. (2011). The impact of enhancing students' social and emotional learning: A meta-analysis of school-based universal interventions. *Child Development, 82*(1), 105–132. doi:10.1111/j.1467-8624.2010.01564.x

Education Commission of the States. (2016). *State of the states 2016: Arts education state policy summary*. Washington, DC: Author. Retrieved from http://www.ecs.org/ec-content/uploads/2016-State-of-the-States-of-Art.pdf

Faisal, Z. (2016, February). Maslow's hierarchy of needs for learners. The E-Learning Network blog post. Retrieved from https://resources.eln.io/maslows-hierarchy-needs-learners/

Finkelhor, D., Turner, H., Shattuck, A., Hamby, S., & Krack, K. (2015, September). *Children's exposure to violence, crime, and abuse: An update*. Washington, DC: U.S. Department of Justice, Office of Justice Programs, Office of Juvenile Justice and Delinquency Prevention. Retrieved from https://www.ojjdp.gov/pubs/248547.pdf

Fullan, M. (2011). *Choosing the wrong drivers for whole system reform*. Centre for Strategic Education Seminar Series Paper No. 204, May. Retrieved from http://www.michaelfullan.ca/home_articles/SeminarPaper204.pdf

Gillies, R. M. (2003). Structuring cooperative group work in classrooms. *International Journal of Educational Research, 39*, 35–49. doi:10.1016/S0883-0355(03)00072-7

Gilman, R., Huebner, S. H., & Furlong, M. (2009). *Handbook of positive psychology in schools* (1st ed.). New York & London, Routledge.

Greenberg, M. T., Kusché, C. A., Cook, E. T., & Quamma, J. P. (1995). Promoting emotional competence in school-aged deaf children: The effects of the PATHS curriculum. *Development and Psychopathology, 7*, 117–136.

Heckman, J. J., & Kautz, T. D. (2012, June). *Hard evidence on soft skills* (Working Paper 18121). Cambridge, MA: National Bureau of Economic Research. Retrieved from http://www.nber.org/papers/w18121

Heckman, J. J., Stixrud, J., & Urz´ua, S. (2006). The effects of cognitive and noncognitive abilities on labor market outcomes and social behavior. *Journal of Labor Economics, 24*(3), 411–482.

Jagers, R. J., Lozada, F. T., Rivas-Drake, D., & Guillaume, C. (2017). Classroom and school predictors of civic engagement among black and Latino middle school youth. *Child Development, 88*(4), 1125–1138. doi:10.1111/cdev.12871

Jefferson, T. (1903). Thomas Jefferson to William C. Jarvis. In A. A. Lipscomb & A. E. Bergh (Eds.), *The writings of Thomas Jefferson* (Vol. 15, p. 278) Washington, DC: Thomas Jefferson Memorial Association, 1903. Original letter dated September 20, 1820.

Jones, D. E., Greenberg, M., & Crowley, M. (2015). Early social-emotional functioning and public health: The relationship between kindergarten social competence and future wellness. *American Journal of Public Health, 105*, 2283–2290.

Kidron, Y., & Osher, D. (2012). The history and direction of research about prosocial education. In P. M. Brown, A. Higgins-D'Alessandro, & M. Corrigan (Eds.), *Handbook of prosocial education* (pp. 51–70). Lanham, MD: Rowman and Littlefield.

Kim, J., & Morgül, K. (2017). Long-term consequences of youth volunteering: Voluntary versus involuntary service. *Social Science Research, 67*, 160–175. doi:10.1016/j.ssresearch.2017.05.002

Koffman, S., Ray, A., Albarran, N. M., & Vasquez, M. (2008). *Impact of computer-based, psycho-social training on depression among youth at risk for gang involvement and other forms of delinquency* (Unpublished manuscript).

Kusché, C. A., & Greenberg, M. T. (1994). *The PATHS curriculum*. Seattle: Developmental Research and Programs.

Lin, A. (2015). Citizenship education in American schools and its role in developing civic engagement: A review of the research. *Educational Review, 67*(1), 35–63. doi:10.1080/00131911.2013.813440

Marples, R. (1999). *Aims of education*. New York: Routledge.

Maslow, A. H. (1943). A theory of human motivation. *Psychological Review, 50*(4), 370–396. doi:10.1037/h0054346

Maslow, A. H. (1962). *Toward a psychology of being.* Princeton, NJ: D Van Nostrand. doi:10.1037/10793-000

McCaslin, M., & Burross, H. L. (2008). Student motivational dynamics. *Teachers College Record, 110*(11), 2452–2463.

Meyers, D. C., Domitrovich, C. E., Dissi, R., Trejo, J., & Greenberg, M. T. (2018). Supporting systemic social and emotional learning with a schoolwide implementation model. Manuscript under review.

Meyers, D. C., Gil, L., Cross, R., Keister, S., Domitrovich, C. E., & Weissberg, R. P. (2015). *CASEL guide for schoolwide social and emotional learning.* Chicago: Collaborative for Academic, Social, and Emotional Learning.

Musu-Gillette, L., Zhang, A., Wang, K., Zhang, J., Kemp, J., Diliberti, M., & Oudekerk, B. A. (2018). *Indicators of school crime and safety: 2017* (NCES 2018-036/NCJ 251413). Washington, DC: National Center for Education Statistics, U.S. Department of Education, and Bureau of Justice Statistics, Office of Justice Programs, U.S. Department of Justice. Retrieved from https://nces.ed.gov/pubs2018/2018036.pdf

Musu-Gillette, L., Zhang, A., Wang, K., Zhang, J., & Oudekerk, B. A. (2017). *Indicators of school crime and safety: 2016* (NCES 2017-064/NCJ 250650). Washington, DC: National Center for Education Statistics, U.S. Department of Education, and Bureau of Justice Statistics, Office of Justice Programs, U.S. Department of Justice. Retrieved from https://nces.ed.gov/pubs2017/2017064.pdf

Nash, P. (1968). *Models of man: Explorations in western educational tradition.* Malabar, FL: Krieger.

National Academies of Sciences, Engineering, and Medicine. (2017). *Approaches to the development of character: Proceedings of a workshop.* Washington, DC: National Academies Press. doi:10.17226/24684

Noddings, N. (2004). *Happiness and education.* Cambridge, UK: Cambridge University Press.

Osher, D., & Berg, J. (2017). *School climate and social and emotional learning: The integration of two approaches.* University Park, PA: Edna Bennet Pierce Prevention Research Center, Pennsylvania State University.

Osher, D., Cantor, P., Berg, J., Strayer, L., & Rose, T. (2018). Drivers of human development: How relationships and context shape learning and development. *Applied Developmental Science.* Advance online publication. doi:10.1080/10888691.2017.1398650

Osher, D., & Keenan, S. (2002). *Instituting school-based links with mental health and social service agencies.* Safe and secure: Guides to creating safer schools. Portland, OR: Northwest Regional Education Laboratory. Retrieved from https://www.ncjrs.gov/pdffiles1/ojjdp/book6.pdf

Osher, D., Kidron, Y., Brackett, M., Dymnicki, A., Jones, S., & Weissberg, R. P. (2016). Advancing the science and practice of social and emotional learning: Looking back and moving forward. *Review of Research in Education, 40*, 644–681.

Osher, D., Poirier, J. M., Dwyer, K. P., Hicks, R., Brown, L. J., Lampron, S., & Rodriguez, C. (2008, August). *Cleveland Metropolitan School District human ware audit: Findings and recommendations.* Washington, DC: American Institutes for Research. Retrieved from https://files.eric.ed.gov/fulltext/ED502432.pdf

Osher, D., Poirier, J. M., Jarjoura, G. R., Haigt, M. S., & Mitchell, D. (2015). *Follow-up assessment of conditions for learning in the Cleveland Metropolitan School District.* Washington, DC: American Institutes for Research.

Osher, D., Poirier, J., Jarjoura, R., Kendziora, K., & Brown, R. (2015). Avoid simple solutions and quick fixes: Lessons learned from a comprehensive district approach to improving conditions for learning. In D. Losen (Ed.), *Closing the school discipline gap: Research for policymakers* (pp. 192–206). New York: Teachers College Press.

Pellegrino, J. (2018). Sciences of learning and development: Some thoughts from the learning sciences. *Applied Developmental Science.* Advance online publication. doi:10.1080/10888691.2017.1421427

Pellegrino, J. W., & Hilton, M. L. (Eds.) (2012). *Education for life and work: Developing transferable knowledge and skills in the 21st century.* Washington, DC: National Academies Press.

Phi Delta Kappan. (2017, September). *The 49th annual PDK poll of the public's attitudes toward the public schools.* Arlington, VA: Author. Retrieved from http://pdkpoll.org/assets/downloads/PDKnational_poll_2017.pdf

Rose, L. C., & Gallup, A. M. (2000). The 32nd Annual Phi Delta Kappa/Gallup Poll of the Public's attitudes toward the public schools. *Phi Delta Kappan, September,* 41–57.

Spier, E., Leenknecht, F., & Osher, D. (2018). Many layers, many dimensions: Building a new science of holistic education. In M. Binder, S. Crowell, J. Miller, K. Nigh, & B. Novack (Eds.), *International handbook on holistic education.* New York: Routledge. Pages 287–294.

Starcher, D., & Allen, S. L. (2016). A global human potential movement and a rebirth of humanistic psychology. *The Humanistic Psychologist, 44*(3), 227–241. doi:10.1037/hum0000032

Taylor, R. D., Oberle, E., Durlak, J. A., & Weissberg, R. P. (2017). Promoting positive youth development through school-based social and emotional learning interventions: A meta-analysis of follow-up effects. *Child Development, 88*(4), 1156–1171. doi:10.1111/cdev.12864

Torney-Purta, J., & Vermeer S. (2004). *Developing citizenship competencies from kindergarten through grade 12: A background paper for policymakers and educators.* Denver: Education Commission of the States.

U.S. Department of Agriculture. (2017). *The National School Lunch Program.* Washington, DC: Author. Retrieved from https://fns-prod.azureedge.net/sites/default/files/cn/NSLPFactSheet.pdf

U.S. Department of Education. (2015). *Arts in education—Model development and dissemination grants program.* Washington, DC: Author. Retrieved from https://www2.ed.gov/programs/artsedmodel/index.html

Vaillant, G. E. (2012). *Triumphs of experience: The men of the Harvard Grant Study.* Cambridge, MA: Harvard University Press. doi:10.4159/harvard.9780674067424

Wandersman, A., Duffy, J. L., Flaspohler, P., Noonan, R., Lubell, K., Stillman, L., . . . Saul, J. (2008). Bridging the gap between prevention research and practice: The Interactive Systems Framework for Dissemination and Implementation. *American Journal of Community Psychology, 41*(3–4), 171–181. doi:10.1007/s10464-008-9174-z

Weissberg, R. P., Durlak, J. A., Domitrovich, C. E., & Gullotta, T. P. (2015). Social and emotional learning: Past, present, and future. In J. A. Durlak, C. E. Domitrovich, R. P. Weissberg, & T. P. Gullotta (Eds.), *Handbook of social and emotional learning: Research and practice* (pp. 3–19). New York: Guilford.

Woodruff, D. W., Osher, D., Hoffman, C. C., Gruner, A., King, M., Snow, S., & McIntire, J. C. (1999). *The role of education in a system of care: Effectively serving children with emotional or behavioral disorders.* Washington, DC: Center for Effective Collaboration and Practice, American Institutes for Research.

Wray-Lake, L., Syvertsen, A. K., & Flanagan, C. A. (2016). Developmental change in social responsibility during adolescence: An ecological perspective. *Developmental Psychology, 52*(1), 130–142. doi:10.1037/dev0000067

Wright A., Lamont, A., Wandersman, A., Osher, D., & Gordon, E. (2015). Accountability and social emotional learning programs: The Getting to Outcomes® approach. In J. Durlak, T. Gulotta, & R. Weissberg (Eds.), *The handbook of social and emotional learning* (pp. 500–515). New York: Guilford.

CHAPTER ELEVEN

Conditions for Learning and Academic Performance

Elisabeth Davis, Adam M. Voight, Matthew Linick, Michelle N. Pierre-Farid, and Kimberly Kendziora

Research suggests that there are strong relationships between and among social-emotional competence, behavior, school climate and safety, physical and mental health, and academic success (Cheema & Kitsantas, 2014; Hopson, Schiller, & Lawson, 2014; Osher, Kendziora, Spier, & Garibaldi, 2013; Osher, Kidron, Brackett, Dymnicki, Jones, & Weissberg, 2016; Park, 2005; Thapa, Cohen, Guffey, & Higgins-D'Alessandro, 2013). Aspects of school climate that are most closely related to attendance and learning include perceptions of emotional and physical safety, emotional support and connectedness, academic challenge and support, and peer social and emotional competence (Garibaldi, Ruddy, Osher, & Kendziora, 2015; Osher & Kendziora, 2010).

Although these conditions are important for all students, this relationship is especially relevant for students who experience the adversities associated with poverty (Osher, Kidron, DeCandia, Kendziora, & Weissberg, 2015; Osher, Sidana, & Kelly, 2008) and microaggressions (Huynh, 2012) and has implications for equity in education (Lee & Bryk, 1989; Voight, Hanson, O'Malley, & Adekanye, 2015). Students cannot attend to learning and are less receptive to instruction when stressed by bullying, gang activity, harsh punishment, and other factors that contribute to a negative school climate (Osher, Sidana, & Kelly, 2008; Osher & Kendziora, 2010).

In addition, a negative school climate can lead to disengagement and academic difficulties (Berg & Aber, 2015), and a lack of student engagement and connection can have a negative effect on academic achievement, behavior, and student health (Blum & Libbey, 2004). School climate has been shown to predict rates of absenteeism, suspension, and truancy (Bradshaw, Waasdorp, Debnam, & Johnson, 2014), which can influence longer term outcomes such as whether a student is on track for graduation (Allensworth & Easton, 2007; Osher, Sidana, & Kelly, 2008) and postsecondary success (Stephan, Davis, Lindsay, & Miller, 2015).

In this chapter, the authors briefly describe earlier work on conditions for learning, then focus more fully on the application of this work in a district context. The authors explain their work in and with the Cleveland Metropolitan School District (CMSD) and share results relating to how conditions for learning generally and safety specifically are associated with indicators of academic performance. Finally, the chapter closes with a description of the work CMSD does to address and leverage this connection between conditions for learning and student academic outcomes.

The Conditions for Learning

In July 2005, Chicago Public Schools (CPS) were engaged in district reform efforts that identified student connection as a potential lever for meaningful improvement. Researchers at the American Institutes for Research (AIR) had expertise in safe and supportive schools and school climate, so CPS asked AIR to demonstrate that conditions for learning could be assessed and to identify three or four indicators for CPS' high school scorecards that reflected the conditions for learning in a school, such as school climate or student engagement. The indicators had to be (1) practical to measure, (2) scientifically valid, (3) easy to communicate to diverse audiences, and (4) actionable by school personnel.

In August 2005, AIR convened a meeting of national experts in Chicago specifically to address this charge. The group worked with CPS district staff and came to a strong, clear consensus on the most important factors that schools should address if they wanted to improve student attendance, achievement, graduation, and postsecondary success, as well as actionable indicators of these factors. The indicators identified by the meeting participants as most critical, grouped broadly as the *conditions for learning*, are (1) students are safe, (2) students are challenged, (3) students are supported, and (4) students are socially and emotionally skilled. Each of these indicators has extensive research to support its importance for schools and its link to students' academic success, graduation, and postsecondary success. For each indicator, meeting participants defined what was covered, identified some

Table 11.1 Conditions for learning constructs

Students are safe	Students are challenged
• Physically safe	• High expectations
• Emotionally and socially safe	• Strong personal motivation
• Treated fairly and equitably	• School is connected to life goals
• Avoid risky behaviors	• Rigorous academic opportunities
Students are socially capable	**Students are supported**
• Emotionally intelligent and culturally competent	• Meaningful connection to adults
• Responsible and persistent	• Strong bonds to school
• Cooperative team players	• Positive peer relationships
• Contribute to school and community	• Effective and available support

available measures, and described ways that schools could use these measures to improve the conditions for learning. Table 11.1 shows a summary of the conceptual foundation for conditions for learning.

To create a survey to measure these constructs, AIR and its partners at the Collaborative for Academic, Social, and Emotional Learning (CASEL) conducted a series of 22 structured focus groups with students, parents, and teachers to inform the survey with the authentic input of stakeholders. Survey developers combined expert consensus, stakeholder input, and a review of school climate research and instruments to construct a pilot survey, which was tested in 24 high schools with almost 1,700 students. The operational survey was administered in the spring of 2006 to all high schools. In the 2006–2007 school year, a version for middle grade students was developed, tested, and administered districtwide. Details of the development of this instrument may be found in Osher and Kendziora (2010).

Early Associations between Conditions for Learning and Academic Performance

Using data from 136,989 Chicago students in grades 6–12 who took the conditions for learning survey in 2007, Kendziora, Osher, and Chinen (2009) examined the degree of association between student-reported conditions for learning and student achievement. The team had access to the following types of achievement data for students:

- ACT plan tests, given in grades 9 and 10, measured skills and abilities in English, Math, Reading, and Science

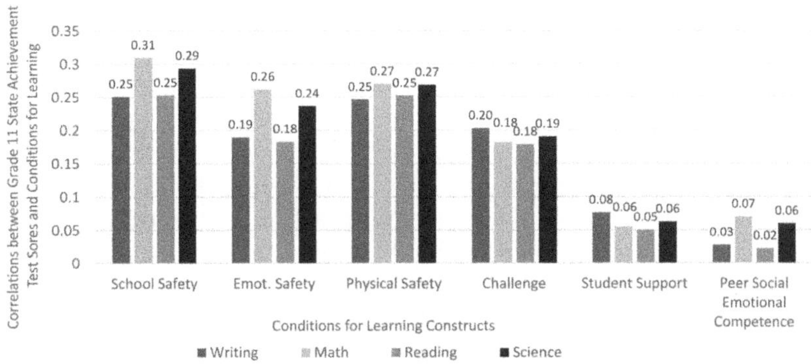

Figure 11.1 Magnitude of correlations between conditions for learning scale scores and State Achievement Test scores for grade 11 students

- State achievement test scores for grade 11 students for Reading, Mathematics, and Science
- Grade point average
- "On track" status, which was computed for ninth grade students as a tool to predict dropout risk, indicated whether a student had earned at least five full-year course credits and no more than one semester F in a core course in their first year of high school.

Overall, results showed that all four conditions for learning constructs were significantly related to student achievement (see figure 11.1). Safety had the strongest association with achievement test scores, and challenge was most strongly related to GPA. Support was the only scale associated with class size (a proxy measure of personalization), and social emotional skills were associated with persistence in school. Grade 9 students who were "on track" to graduate scored higher than "off track" students on the school safety, challenge, and support scales; there was no difference between the two groups for the peer social and emotional competence scale.

The Cleveland Context

After their district experienced a fatal school shooting in 2007, leaders from CMSD recognized the need to address school violence by promoting positive progress, rather than pursuing punitive measures (Osher, Poirier, Dwyer, Hicks, Brown, Lampron, & Rodriguez, 2008). CMSD has made improving conditions for learning in the district a major priority for over a decade with such initiatives as the formation of Humanware, the district office overseeing social and emotional learning (SEL) and school climate initiatives in district schools, the administration of the conditions for learning survey to grades 2–12 multiple times per year to monitor and track student perceptions of school climate, the implementation and evaluation of a universal SEL program in elementary grades (Promoting Alternative THinking Strategies [PATHS]; Faria, Kendziora, Brown, O'Brien, & Osher, 2013), and a researcher-practitioner partnership focused in part on examining the relationship between school climate and student outcomes.

CMSD provides an ideal test case for examining the relationship between school climate and academic performance, particularly for schools that serve large numbers of students who experience the effects of chronic poverty, such as community and media violence, drugs and alcohol, trauma, and loss. This is true for two reasons: (1) Cleveland has high levels of poverty, and (2) the district has good data on school performance as well as on the effects of interventions to improve conditions for learning.

Poverty

Cleveland's poverty rate for young children was 52.5% in 2016, according to the Census' American Community Survey data (Exner, 2017), and has increased markedly over the 10 years since the 2008 recession. CMSD invokes a provision of the National Student Lunch Program that waives the requirement to establish household eligibility for free or reduced-price meals if the district provides free meals to all students. Therefore, all CMSD students are eligible for free breakfast and lunch. In addition, Cleveland has among the highest rates of children with lead poisoning in the nation, and in the St. Clair-Superior area, half of children tested had elevated lead levels (Pell & Schneyer, 2016). Lead exposure is strongly associated with poor academic achievement in elementary and junior high school, even after controlling for potentially confounding variables (Lanphear, Dietrich, Auinger, & Cox, 2000; Zhang et al., 2013).

Good Data

All CMSD schools, like other Ohio schools, have a publicly reported school performance index that is an aggregate of state standardized test scores (Ohio Department of Education, 2017). In addition, since 2008, AIR has administered the conditions for learning survey to assess how conditions change as a product of CMSD's efforts to improve student-teacher relationships, build student social and emotional competence, and provide tiered services to students who are at greater levels of risk and need. The conditions for learning scales assess student perceptions of school climate: physical safety, emotional safety, peer social-emotional competence and norms, student support and connectedness, and academic challenge and support. Academic measures available for CMSD include the following:

- *Measures of Academic Progress* (MAP) are formative assessments generally given three times over the course of a school year. The scaled test scores are independent of grade level and range from 100 to 350; a score of 150 for a second grader and a fifth grader means that both students are working at the same level.
- The *Performance Index* (PI) measures the achievement of every student, not just whether he or she reaches "proficient." Districts and schools receive points for every student's level of achievement. The higher the student's level, the more points the school earns toward its index. This rewards schools and districts that improve the performance of highest- and lowest-performing students.
- *Ohio Graduation Tests* (OGTs) cover five subjects, each of which a student is required to pass before graduating.

School Climate and Student-Level Academic Outcomes

CMSD has collaborated and fostered relationships with AIR since 2008, and its local research partner, the Center for Urban Education (CUE) at Cleveland State University since 2015. AIR and CUE share interests in working with the district and complementary areas of research and expertise and, in 2016, with CMSD formed the Cleveland Alliance for Education Research (CAER). CAER is funded by the U.S. Department of Education's Institute of Education Sciences[1] and aims to help CMSD gain new knowledge about the climate of its schools, specifically how school climate is associated with student education outcomes and how students of different subgroups (e.g., race or ethnicity, English learner status) experience school climate differently. In its first year, CAER focused on the question: *What is the relationship between school-average student survey reports of school climate and school-average standardized test scores, days of attendance, and suspensions; and how might attendance and suspensions mediate the climate-achievement association?*

Safety and Academic Performance

Across all grade levels, CMSD students who view their school as safer had higher math and reading achievement. From one marking period to the next, if a student's perception of safety increased by one point on the conditions for learning survey (e.g., moves from an average of "agree" to "strongly agree"), her or his achievement is expected to increase by about one percentile point on the math and reading MAP tests (see figure 11.2). The data demonstrate that safety matters most for the achievement of students in elementary and middle school, and reading achievement relates more strongly to safety than does mathematics achievement.

If a CMSD student's perception of safety were to move from the lowest to the highest value, her or his achievement would be expected to improve:

- 3.4 percentile points in math and 5.0 in reading in grades 2–4
- 3.4 in math and 3.8 in reading in grades 5–8
- 2.5 in math and 2.9 in reading in grades 9–12

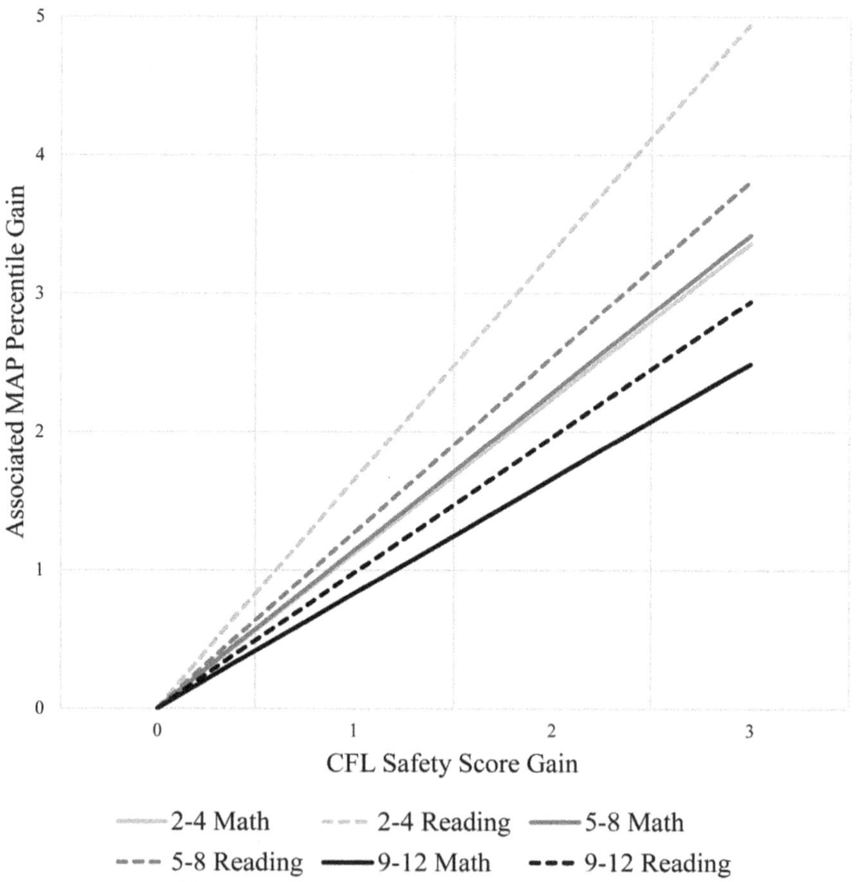

Figure 11.2 Associated gain in a CMSD student's MAP percentile score for gains in CFL safety scores, by grade range and subject

In short, improving students' feelings of safety at school may bring with it an increase in their academic achievement.

AIR originally examined the CMSD's conditions for learning data in 2008 (Osher, Poirier, Dwyer, Hicks, Brown, Lampron, & Rodriguez, 2008) and 2013 (Jarjoura & Osher, 2013) and found relationships between conditions of learning and academic performance. These analyses found that schools' PI, which is based on standardized tests, was highly associated with student perceptions of conditions for learning. Using data from the 2012–2013 school year, analyses found the following:

- For grades 2–4, conditions for learning scale categories explained 63.3% of the variance in the school PI (see figure 11.3). When attendance was added to the analysis, the combination of attendance and the four conditions for learning scales explained 74.8% of the variance. Based on variance decomposition of the component variables, analyses found that emotional and physical safety were especially relevant (and statistically significant).
- For grades 5–8, conditions for learning scales explained 59.3% of the variance in the school PI (see figure 11.4). When attendance was added to the analysis, the combination of attendance and the four scales explained 67.1% of the variance. Again, statistical results showed that emotional safety had a particularly strong association to school performance relevant for students in middle grades.

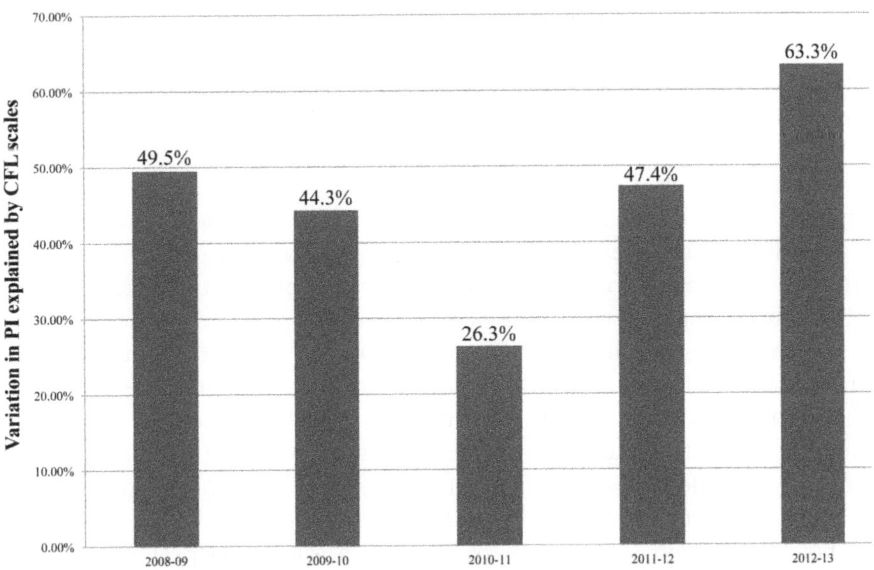

Figure 11.3 Percent of variation in 2008–2009 through 2012–2013 Performance Index (PI) explained by CFL scales, grades 2–4

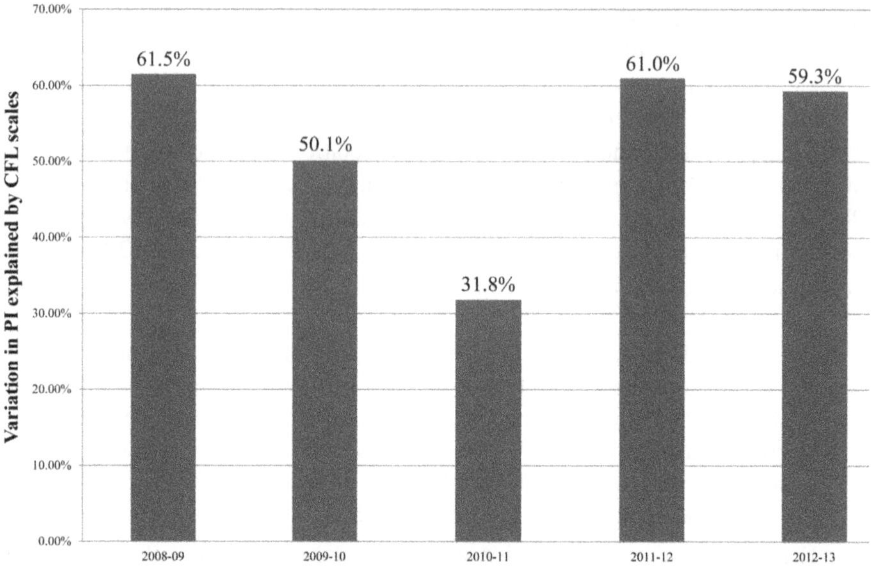

Figure 11.4 Percent of variation in 2008–2009 through 2012–2013 Performance Index (PI) explained by CFL scales, grades 5–8

- For grades 9–12, conditions for learning scale categories explained 79.3% of the variance in the school PI. With attendance included in the model, the combination of attendance and the four conditions for learning scores explained 83.9% of the variance in school performance (figure 11.5).

These analyses were replicated across each of five academic years and produced similar findings (Osher, Poirier, Jarjoura, Haight, & Mitchell, 2014).

More recently, CAER conducted an analysis to examine the relationship between scores on the safety subscale of the conditions for learning survey and school-level contextual characteristics including schools' academic PI. Controlling for changes in schools' demographics and enrollment over time, the analysis showed that improvements in a school's safety scores were significantly associated with improvements in a school's academic PI. Every school year, the typical CMSD school's average safety score goes up or down about a tenth of a point. A CMSD school enrolling students in grades K–8 that improves its safety by this "normal" amount from one year to the next would expect its PI to improve 0.6 points. However, if the same school improved its safety score a "large" amount (e.g., three-tenths of a point), its PI would be expected to go up 1.8 points (see figure 11.6).

For CMSD high schools, the link between safety and performance was even stronger. A CMSD high school that improved its safety by a "normal" amount from one year to the next could expect its PI to improve 2.4 points.

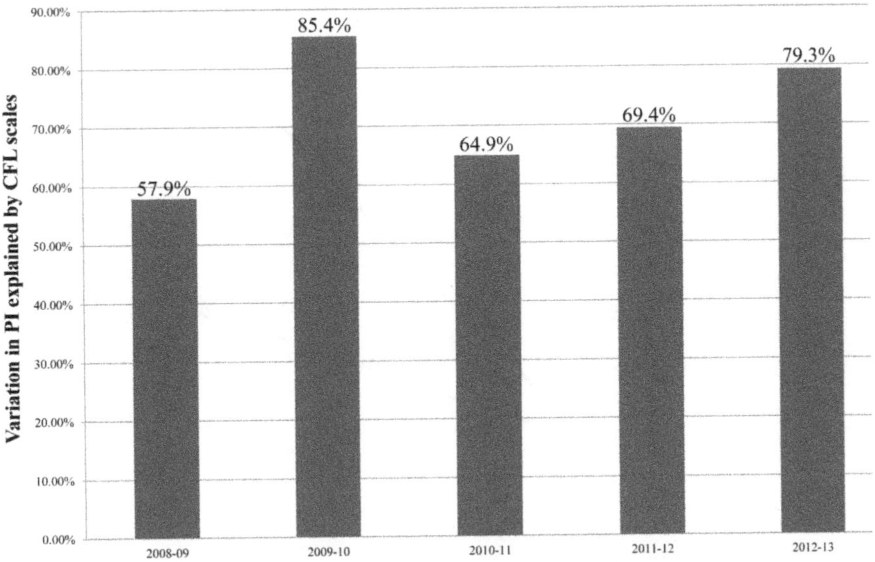

Figure 11.5 Percent of variation in 2008–2009 through 2012–2013 Performance Index (PI) explained by CFL scales, grades 9–12

If the same school improved its safety score a "large" amount (again, around 0.3 points), its PI would be expected to go up 6.7 points.

These strong statistical relationships have practical implications for CMSD high schools. The Ohio Department of Education publishes the yearly Ohio School Report Cards for schools in the state and assigns letter grades to schools on six measures of school success (achievement, growth, closing subgroup gaps, K–3 literacy, graduation rate, and college and career readiness; http://reportcard.education.ohio.gov). Such an improvement in PI from the 2015–2016 to the 2016–2017 school years would have moved four CMSD high schools from an F to a D grade on PI, one high school from a D to a C, and three high schools from a C to a B.

Excellence in Conditions for Learning and Academic Context

After each conditions for learning survey administration in the district, each school is provided with a report detailing their scores in terms of the percentage of students whose conditions for learning scores on each scale fall into one of three categories: excellent, adequate, or needs improvement (see figure 11.7). School-level scores overall are compared with the district average, and scores are disaggregated by student subgroup for groups larger than 10 in the areas of race and ethnicity, gender, students with disabilities, English language learner students, and grade level. Schools in the district have

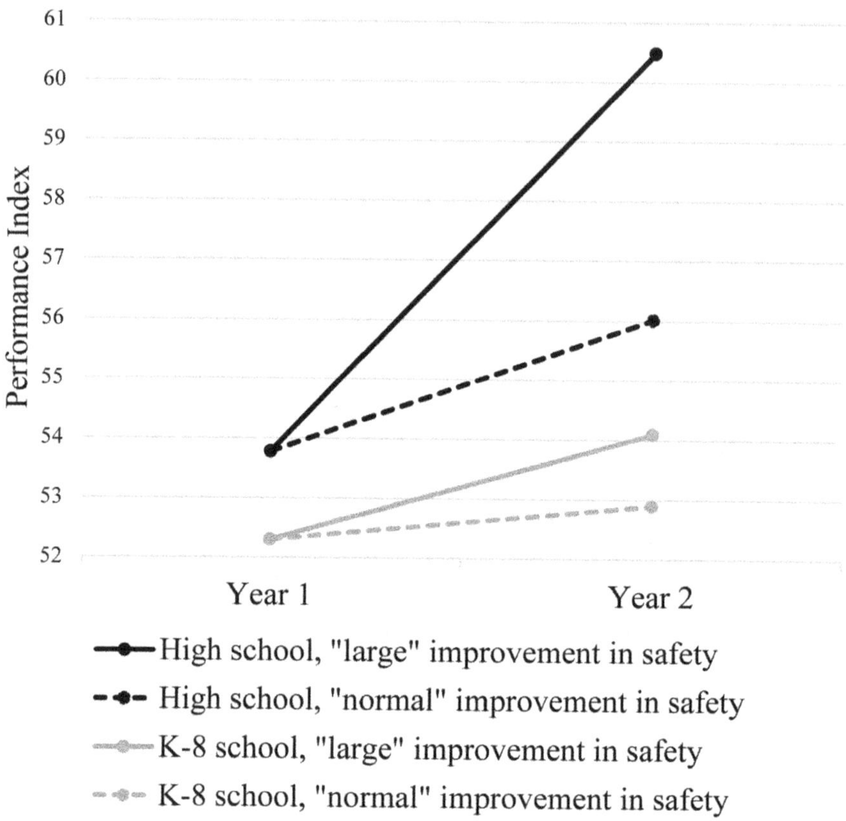

Figure 11.6 Change in an average CMSD K–8 and high school's Performance Index (PI) from one year to the next associated with "normal" and "large" improvements in safety (Note: A "large" improvement in safety is a 0.3-point improvement in the average CFL safety score; a "normal" improvement is a 0.1-point improvement)

generally used the combination of "adequate" and "excellent" as a barometer for how favorably their students are viewing the conditions for learning in their school.

In 2015, the district began to explore the possibility of focusing on scores in the "excellent" range and encouraging schools to focus on increasing the percentage of students whose scores fall into this top category.

As a first step toward earning buy-in among principals, AIR conducted a preliminary, descriptive analysis for principals with the goal of highlighting the relationship between the percentage of students in schools whose conditions for learning scores fall in the "excellent" range and student academic performance, attendance, and behavioral outcomes (Osher & Davis, 2016). This study divided 71 elementary schools, 73 middle schools, and 32 high

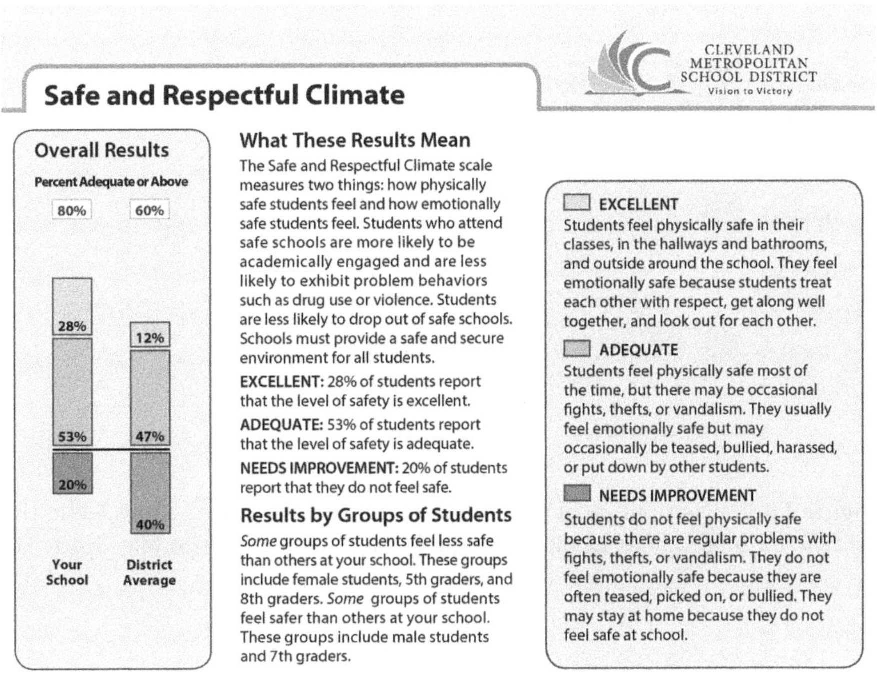

CLEVELAND METROPOLITAN SCHOOL DISTRICT
Vision to Victory

Safe and Respectful Climate

Overall Results

Percent Adequate or Above

80% 60%

28% 12%

53% 47%

20% 40%

Your School | District Average

What These Results Mean

The Safe and Respectful Climate scale measures two things: how physically safe students feel and how emotionally safe students feel. Students who attend safe schools are more likely to be academically engaged and are less likely to exhibit problem behaviors such as drug use or violence. Students are less likely to drop out of safe schools. Schools must provide a safe and secure environment for all students.

EXCELLENT: 28% of students report that the level of safety is excellent.

ADEQUATE: 53% of students report that the level of safety is adequate.

NEEDS IMPROVEMENT: 20% of students report that they do not feel safe.

Results by Groups of Students

Some groups of students feel less safe than others at your school. These groups include female students, 5th graders, and 8th graders. *Some* groups of students feel safer than others at your school. These groups include male students and 7th graders.

EXCELLENT
Students feel physically safe in their classes, in the hallways and bathrooms, and outside around the school. They feel emotionally safe because students treat each other with respect, get along well together, and look out for each other.

ADEQUATE
Students feel physically safe most of the time, but there may be occasional fights, thefts, or vandalism. They usually feel emotionally safe but may occasionally be teased, bullied, harassed, or put down by other students.

NEEDS IMPROVEMENT
Students do not feel physically safe because there are regular problems with fights, thefts, or vandalism. They do not feel emotionally safe because they are often teased, picked on, or bullied. They may stay at home because they do not feel safe at school.

Figure 11.7 Sample page from Conditions for Learning Score Report (Copyright © American Institutes for Research. Used by permission.)

schools into quintiles based on the percentage of students rating their schools as "excellent" in the conditions for learning scales of safety and peer social-emotional competence using data from the May 2015 survey administration. These distributions were analyzed separately for grades 2–4, grades 5–8, and grades 9–12 (each of these grade spans takes a different version of the conditions for learning survey). There were 6 to 7 high schools in each group, and 14 to 15 middle and elementary schools in each group. The distribution of schools in figure 11.8 shows that most schools had low percentages of students whose safety and SEL scores fell in the "excellent" range. Middle and high schools in quintiles 1–4 all had scores in the "excellent" range that fell below 40%, and elementary schools in quintiles 1–4 had scores in the "excellent" range that fell below 60%.

The researchers then calculated suspension rates, attendance rates, and student academic performance for the 2014–2015 school year for each quintile. The percentage of students whose scores fell into the "excellent" range on safety showed a clear pattern of association with MAP mathematics and reading scores. The quintile of schools with 80–100% of their students perceiving their school to be "excellent" in safety scored higher in both math and reading on MAP tests in May 2015 (see figure 11.9).

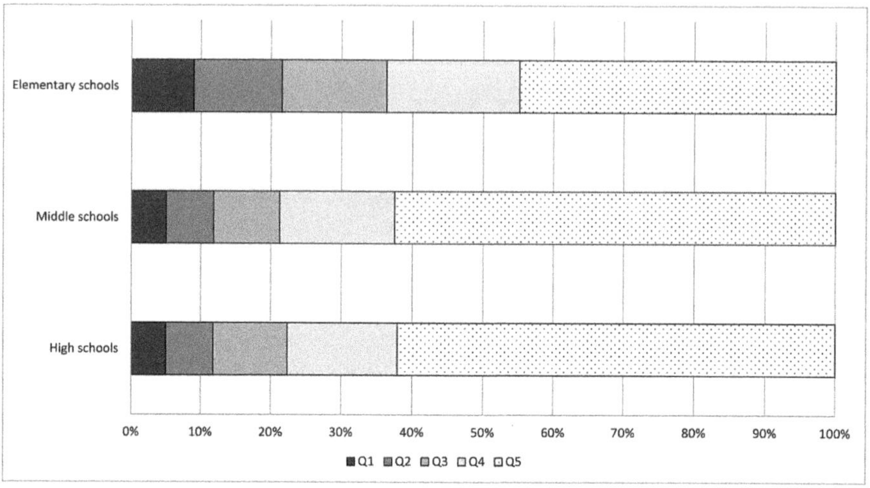

Figure 11.8 Distribution of the percentage of students whose scores fall in the "excellent" range among elementary, middle, and high schools in May 2015

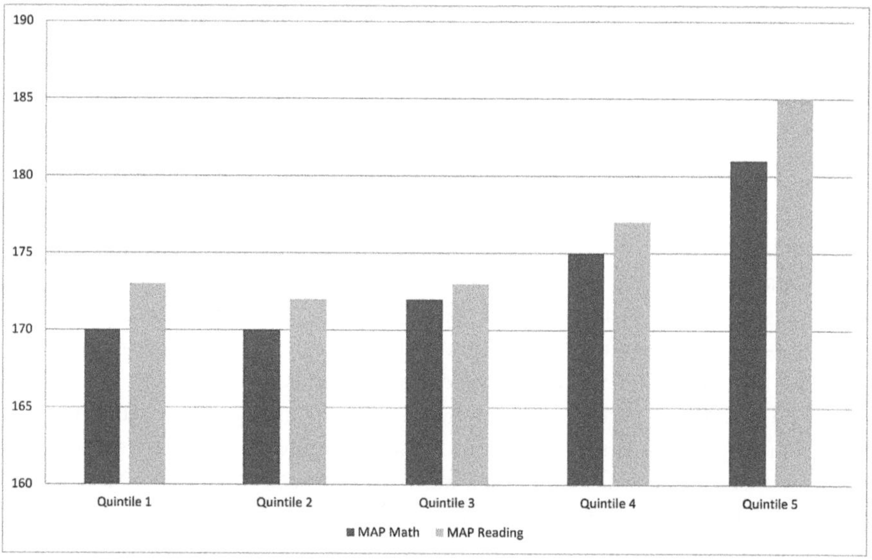

Figure 11.9 MAP mathematics and reading scores by middle school quintile group for excellence in the safety subscale on the CFL

The percentage of high school students whose scores fell into the "excellent" range on safety showed a clear pattern of association with Ohio Graduation Test (OGT) mathematics and reading scores. The quintile of schools with 80–100% of their students perceiving their school to be "excellent" in safety scored higher in both math and reading on the OGT in May 2015

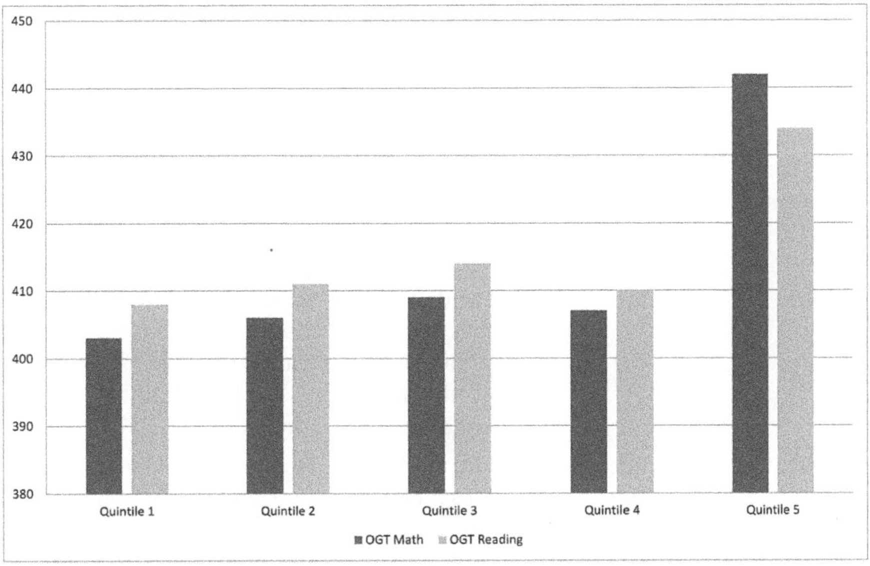

Figure 11.10 OGT mathematics and reading scores by high school quintile group for excellence in the safety subscale on the CFL

(see figure 11.10). The results of both of these analyses emphasize the finding that when students feel both physically and emotionally safe at school and experience a positive peer climate, then that school is likely to have stronger academic performance and graduation rates.

Data in Action: How Cleveland Metropolitan School District Addresses Conditions for Learning

According to CMSD's chief academic officer, Dr. Michelle Pierre-Farid, the district is deeply aware and mindful of the strong connection between conditions for learning and academic performance, particularly the role of safety. CMSD focuses on two dimensions of safety: physical safety, or freedom from harm or dangerous environments, and psychological safety, which refers to feeling comfortable interacting with peers and adults and asking for help when needed. There are multiple ways the district has worked to improve safety since the tragedy in 2007, and consistent with CMSD's strong focus on social and emotional development, most strategies are based on strengthening relationships. Table 11.2 presents a description of the key strategies in place.

CMSD supports these programs through a system of monthly professional development for the key leaders who support the initiatives. These sessions help ensure that the programs are being implemented with fidelity. In

Table 11.2 CMSD strategies for addressing conditions for learning

Strategy	Grade Levels	Description
Promoting Alternative THinking Strategies (PATHS)	Pre-kindergarten–grade 5	The PATHS curriculum is an evidence-based classroom curriculum designed to facilitate the social and emotional development of children PK–5. PATHS provides skill-building for both students and teachers, and promotes use of prosocial skills throughout the day. The program includes techniques to give students feedback and recognize performance. It can be integrated into academic subjects and has a family engagement component.
Second Step	Grades 6–8	Second Step curriculum is an evidence-based classroom curriculum that provides instruction in social and emotional learning with units on skills for learning, empathy, emotion management, friendship skills, and problem-solving. Second Step uses four key strategies to reinforce skill development: brain builder games (to build executive function), weekly theme activities, reinforcing activities, and home links.
Winning Against Violent Environments (WAVE) Peer Mediation Program	All grades	Students participate in conflict management and become agents of change by taking skills, such as effective decision-making, communication, and problem-solving, into the classroom and the community. With adult guidance, young people use these skills in their daily lives and provide assistance to others as conflict managers and mediators.
Not on Our Watch (NOW) Bullying Prevention Program	All grades	Every school in CMSD has a NOW team, which leads a student-centered anti-bullying program. The goal of the bullying prevention is to decrease prevalence of bullying and promote a safe, warm environment. NOW promotes social skill building, self-control, critical thinking, decision-making, and the acceptance of differences using social and emotional learning tools.

(continued)

Table 11.2 (continued)

Strategy	Grade Levels	Description
Planning Centers	All grades	Planning Centers are physical spaces within a school building where students can go to learn problem-solving and develop appropriate behavior. Planning Center Instructional Aides (PCIAs) staff the center and help students improve their conduct, develop their self-esteem, and encourage them to achieve and behave positively. Students can self-refer or be referred by school staff. The Planning Center is the last stop before a student is removed from the building and the first stop when a student returns from being suspended or involuntarily transferred from a school.

addition, CMSD works with the city of Cleveland to create Safe Routes to school to help improve schools' safety scores.

Beyond these specific programs, CMSD also works to create a respectful climate and culture, beginning with adults in the system. CMSD encourages all district and school leaders to engage in three signature practices whenever they have a professional learning event or other meeting with staff. These are: (1) a warm welcoming, (2) an energetic, engaging activity, such as collaborative problem solving, and (3) an optimistic closure. CMSD created a booklet with these practices and promotes it to help staff not only understand the value of personal connections but also to create them. Experience with these strategies so far has shown that opening with celebrations in particular has created positive energy. This year, at principals' roundtable meetings, the district leaders opened each meeting with a different team-building activity. At first, principals complained about this but have warmed to it over the course of the year. For example, in advance of one monthly meeting, every principal who had a birthday that month was asked to share their favorite song. The district team played a clip from the song and asked the other principals to guess whose favorite song that was. The point is that taking an extra moment to get to know each other, celebrate each other, and experience some fun in the day helps to create a more positive atmosphere and change the hearts and minds of the staff.

Conclusion

The analyses reported in this chapter echo a strong finding in the field—that conditions for learning in a school, and especially school safety, are strongly associated with academic performance. These findings are consistent with statewide research in Alaska (Spier, Cai, Kendziora, & Osher, 2007; Windham, Kendziora, Brown, Osher, & Song, 2009) that showed that not only were student-reported measures of school climate associated with school-level achievement but also that positive change in climate was related to significant gains in student scores on statewide achievement tests. Using data from California, O'Malley and Hanson (2012) also documented that school climate was strongly related to state academic PI scores, and as school academic performance increased, so did climate indices showing that schools were safer, more supportive, and more engaging. Specifically, school academic performance was higher among students in California high schools that (1) cultivated more positive student perceptions of adult relationships, opportunities for meaningful participation (e.g., contribute to the school), school safety, and school connectedness; and (2) had students who reported fewer experiences of harassment, bullying, physical violence, and substance use at school and had lower truancy rates.

The puzzle that arises given this strong association is that schools in the United States have been getting much safer over the past two decades, but academic achievement has not improved to a commensurate degree. The National Center for Education Statistics (NCES) monitors school safety with representative surveys each year; these data have shown that student victimization at school has been dropping steadily since the 1990s. In 2016, 749,400 students experienced a violent victimization at school (Musu-Gillette et al., 2018), down from 841,000 in 2015 (Musu-Gillette et al., 2017), 1.4 million in 2005, and 3.8 million in 1995 (Dinkes, Cataldi, Kena, & Baum, 2006). Although these data are not aligned with safety data at a school level, one would hope that an improvement in physical safety would be accompanied by improvements in academic performance.

Emotional, psychological, and identity safety, which are not measured in the NCES surveys, may help solve the puzzle. As other chapters in this handbook indicate, safety also includes psychological, emotional, and identity safety. Emotional safety provides an example. Although rates of verbal bullying and cyber bullying have also dropped over time, they remain much higher than the rates of physical threat in schools (Musu-Gillette et al., 2018). For example, 22% of middle schools reported an episode of bullying at least once a week, and 21% of students aged 12–18 reported being bullied at school during the past year. Districts such as CMSD are improving both their safety and achievement scores over time through efforts that include extensive social and emotional supports and attention to emotional safety. It is possible that such efforts may make the difference in district and school improvements over time (Osher, Cantor, Berg, Strayer, & Rose, 2018). Closely following the work of CMSD and other districts engaged in similar journeys may reveal this answer over time.

Note

1. CAER focuses on school climate and student outcomes through the Cleveland Alliance for School Climate Research (CASCR).

References

Allensworth, E., & Easton, J. Q. (2007). *What matters for staying on-track and graduating in Chicago public high schools: A close look at course grades, failures, and attendance in the freshman year.* Chicago: Consortium on Chicago School Research.

Berg, J. K., & Aber, J. L. (2015, March 5–7). *The direct and moderating role of school interpersonal climate on children's academic outcomes in the context of whole-school, social-emotional learning programs* [Abstract]. SREE Spring 2015 Conference, Washington, DC.

Blum, R. W., & Libbey, H. P. (2004). Executive summary. *Journal of School Health, 74*(7), 231.

Bradshaw, C. P., Waasdorp, T. E., Debnam, K. J., & Johnson, S. L. (2014). Measuring school climate in high schools: A focus on safety, engagement, and the environment. *Journal of School Health, 84*(9), 593–604.

Center for Health Affairs. (2007). *Summary: Community health needs analysis and assessment.* Cleveland: Center for Community Solutions.

Cheema, J., & Kitsantas, A. (2014). Influences of disciplinary classroom climate on high school student self-efficacy and mathematics achievement: A look at gender and racial-ethnic differences. *International Journal of Science and Mathematics Education, 12*(5), 1261–1279.

Dinkes, R., Cataldi, E. F., Kena, G., & Baum, K. (2006). *Indicators of school crime and safety: 2006* (NCES 2007-003/NCJ 214262). Washington, DC: U.S. Government Printing Office. Retrieved from https://nces.ed.gov/pubs2007/2007003a.pdf

Exner, H. (2017, December 21). *Child poverty: Ranking every Ohio city, county—Census snapshot.* Web post. Retrieved from https://www.cleveland.com/datacentral/index.ssf/2017/12/ranking_every_ohio_city_county_3.html

Faria, A. M., Kendziora, K., Brown, L., O'Brien, B., & Osher, D. (2013). *PATHS implementation and outcome study in the Cleveland Metropolitan School District.* Washington, DC: American Institutions for Research. Retrieved from http://www. air. org/sites/default/files/downloads/report/Evaluation_of_PATHS_in_CMSD_final_report_6_2413_0.pdf

Garibaldi, M., Ruddy, S., Osher, D., & Kendziora, K. (2015). Assessment of climate and conditions for learning. In J. Durlak, T. Gulotta, & R. Weissberg (Eds.), *Handbook of social emotional learning* (pp. 348–359). New York: Guilford Press.

Hopson, L. M., Schiller, K. S., & Lawson, H. A. (2014). Exploring linkages between school climate, behavioral norms, social supports, and academic success. *Social Work Research, 38*(4), 197–209.

Huynh, V. W. (2012). Ethnic microaggressions and the depressive and somatic symptoms of Latino and Asian American adolescents. *Journal of Youth Adolescence, 41*(7), 831–846.

Jarjoura, R., & Osher, D. (2013). *School climate, conditions for learning, and academic performance in high poverty schools.* Washington, DC: American Institutes for Research.

Kendziora, K., Osher, D., & Chinen, M. (2009, April). *School safety, achievement, and conditions for learning.* Paper presented at the Annual Meeting of the American Educational Research Association, San Diego, CA.

Lanphear, B. P., Dietrich, K., Auinger, P., & Cox, C. (2000). Cognitive deficits associated with blood lead concentrations <10 microg/dL in US children and adolescents. *Public Health Reports, 115*(6), 521–529.

Lee, V. E., & Bryk, A. S. (1989). A multilevel model of the social distribution of high school achievement. *Sociology of Education, 62*(3), 172–192.

Musu-Gillette, L., Zhang, A., Wang, K., Zhang, J., Kemp, J., Diliberti, M., & Oudekerk, B. A. (2018). *Indicators of school crime and safety: 2017* (NCES 2018-036/NCJ 251413). Washington, DC: National Center for Education Statistics, U.S. Department of Education, and Bureau of Justice Statistics, Office of Justice Programs, U.S. Department of Justice. Retrieved from https://nces.ed.gov/pubs2018/2018036.pdf

Musu-Gillette, L., Zhang, A., Wang, K., Zhang, J., & Oudekerk, B. A. (2017). *Indicators of school crime and safety: 2016* (NCES 2017-064/NCJ 250650). Washington, DC: National Center for Education Statistics, U.S. Department of Education, and Bureau of Justice Statistics, Office of Justice Programs, U.S. Department of Justice. Retrieved from https://nces.ed.gov/pubs2017/2017064.pdf

Ohio Department of Education. (2017). *Technical documentation—2016–2017 performance index score.* Retrieved from https://education.ohio.gov/getattachment/Topics/Data/Report-Card-Resources/Achievement-Measure/Technical-Documentation-PI-Score.pdf.aspx

O'Malley, M. D., & Hanson, T. (2012). *School climate and academic performance across California high Schools.* S3 Factsheet#3. Los Alamitos: WestED. Retrieved from http://surveydata.wested.org/resources/S3factsheet3_API_20120716.pdf

Osher, D., Cantor, P., Berg, J., Strayer, L., & Rose, T. (2018). Drivers of human development: How relationships and context shape learning and development. *Applied Developmental Science.* Advance online publication. doi: 10.1080/10888691.2017.1398650

Osher, D., & Davis, E. (2016, April). *Why conditions for learning matter and how to use the conditions for learning survey to improve attendance, CFL, and academic performance.* Invited presentation at the Cleveland Metropolitan School District CAO Roundtable, Cleveland, OH.

Osher, D., & Kendziora, K. (2010). Building conditions for learning and healthy adolescent development: Strategic approaches. In B. Doll, W. Pfohl, & J. Yoon (Eds.), *Handbook of youth prevention science* (pp. 121–140). New York: Routledge.

Osher, D., Kendziora, K., Spier, E., & Garibaldi, M. L. (2013). School influences on child and youth development. In Z. Sloboda & H. Petras (Eds.), *Advances in prevention science*, vol. 1, *Defining prevention science* (pp. 151–169). New York: Springer.

Osher, D., Kidron, Y., Brackett, M., Dymnicki, A., Jones, S., & Weissberg, R. P. (2016). Advancing the science and practice of social emotional learning: Looking back and moving forward. *Review of Educational Research Centennial Issue, 40*, 644–681.

Osher, D., Kidron, Y., DeCandia, C. J., Kendziora, K., & Weissberg, R. (2015). Interventions to promote safe and supportive school climate. In K. Wenzel & G. Ramani (Eds.), *Social influences on social-emotional, motivation, and cognitive outcomes in school contexts* (pp. 384–404). New York: Taylor Francis.

Osher, D., Poirier, J. M., Dwyer, K. P., Hicks, R., Brown, L. J., Lampron, S., & Rodriguez, C. (2008, August). *Cleveland Metropolitan School District human ware audit: Findings and recommendations.* Washington, DC: American Institutes for Research. Retrieved from https://files.eric.ed.gov/fulltext/ED502432.pdf

Osher, D., Poirier, J. M., Jarjoura, G. R., Haight, K., & Mitchell, D. (2014). *Follow-up assessment of conditions for learning in the Cleveland Metropolitan School District: Final report.* Washington, DC: American Institutes for Research.

Osher, D., Sidana, A., & Kelly, P. (2008). *Improving conditions for learning for youth who are neglected or delinquent.* Washington, DC: National Evaluation and Technical Assistance Center for the Education of Children and Youth who are Delinquent, Neglected, or at Risk.

Park, S.-Y. (2005). Student engagement and classroom variables in improving mathematics achievement. *Asia Pacific Education Review, 6*(1), 87–97.

Pell, M. B., & Schneyer, J. (2016, December 19). Off the charts: The thousands of U.S. locales where lead poisoning is worse than in Flint. Reuters. Retrieved from https://www.reuters.com/investigates/special-report/usa-lead-testing/

Spier, E., Cai, C., Kendziora, K., & Osher, D. (2007). *School climate, connectedness, and student achievement.* Juneau, AK: Association of Alaska School Boards.

Stephan, J. L., Davis, E., Lindsay, J., & Miller, S. (2015). *Who will succeed and who will struggle? Predicting early college success with Indiana's Student Information System* (REL 2015–078). Washington, DC: U.S. Department of Education, Institute of Education Sciences, National Center for Education

Evaluation and Regional Assistance, Regional Educational Laboratory Midwest. Retrieved from https://ies.ed.gov/ncee/edlabs/regions/midwest/pdf/REL_2015078.pdf

Thapa, A., Cohen, J., Guffey, S., & Higgins-D'Alessandro, A. (2013). A review of school climate research. *Review of Educational Research, 83*(3), 357–385.

Voight, A., Hanson, T., O'Malley, M., & Adekanye, L. (2015). The racial school climate gap: Within-school disparities in students' experiences of safety, support, and connectedness. *American Journal of Community Psychology, 56*(3–4), 252–267.

Windham, A., Kendziora, K., Brown, L., Osher, D., & Song, M. (2009). *Academic achievement and school climate in Anchorage and other Alaska schools: 2006 to 2009.* Washington, DC: American Institutes for Research.

Zhang, N., Baker, H. W., Tufts, M., Raymond, R. E., Salihu, H., & Elliott, M. R. (2013). Early childhood lead exposure and academic achievement: Evidence from Detroit Public Schools, 2008–2010. *American Journal of Public Health, 103*(3), e72–e77. doi:10.2105/AJPH.2012.301164

PART 4

Families and Communities as Assets

CHAPTER TWELVE

Families as Assets

Michele P. Brooks and Lisa Lambert

The engagement of families in the education of children is a critical lever that impacts both academic and socio-emotional outcomes of students. Acknowledging families as a major asset to educating and supporting the healthy development of children is critical to shifting outcomes for students and schools. Students thrive in environments that acknowledge and value them as individuals and where they have a sense of safety, not just physically, but equally important is their psychological and emotional safety. The role of educators and support practitioners is to ensure that the schools' environments are places where students thrive and that families are engaged as partners in the healthy development of children. It is also important to understand that one of the most important keys to a child's academic success does not come from the classroom; it comes from the support of the child's family. Families are assets, not only in helping to educate their children and improve schools but also to the many systems in which families, students, and communities interact.

A family supports and provides for their children from birth and helps them survive in the world. Families teach their children their first word, applaud their first step, and shape their values. Children learn about relationships, social norms, self-esteem, worth, and loyalty by being part of their family. Until they go to school, and sometimes even after, family life is where children spend much of their learning time. Families model how to manage emotions, seek out friendships, and how to handle conflict. Children absorb their family's values and strategies for offering and receiving support and building reciprocal relationships. While children bring value to their families, the reverse is also true. Families bring enormous value to their children. When parents are engaged, children are more likely to learn. Studies from the U.S. Department of Education, Harvard University, Johns Hopkins University, and elsewhere highlight the positive effect of family and school partnerships (Epstein & Sheldon, 2002; Fan & Chen, 2001; Mapp & Kuttner, 2014; Wood & Bauman, 2017). Grades and attendance rise, dropout rates and behavioral incidents decrease and graduation rates increase. Family engagement supports students in many ways.

Family engagement begins by seeing families as valuable assets for students, teachers, and schools. It begins by examining core beliefs about families and any assumptions about their desire to be involved or their commitment to their child's education. The chapter begins by defining family engagement and how it interfaces with systems to influence outcomes for children and youth, describing its place in societal institutions in the development of healthy individuals. The chapter also includes a discussion of family engagement in child welfare, juvenile justice, and mental health. Next, we provide a research summary on family engagement, highlighting its impact on children, youth, families, and schools. We then discuss social capital and families, building trusting relationships for meaningful family engagement, and collaboration with culturally and linguistically diverse families. Finally, the chapter concludes with strategies for engaging and communicating with families.

What Is Family Engagement and How Does It Support Systems to Influence Healthy Child Development?

In 2009, the National Working Group for Family, School, and Community Engagement issued a white paper that defined effective family engagement as a process that "cuts across and reinforces learning in the multiple settings where children learn—at home, in prekindergarten programs, in school, in after school programs, in faith-based institutions, and in the community" (National Family, School, and Community Engagement Working Group, 2009). This definition presents a broad definition that encompasses the many supports and various entry points for the work of education support practitioners and is aligned with Urie Bronfenbrenner's Ecology of Human Development, which theoretically grounds a whole child approach to learning and well-being. Bronfenbrenner's (1979) theory at its core provides a rationale for the engagement of families in their children's education and a framework for understanding the role of support practitioners and societal institutions in the development of healthy individuals. The theory is represented by a set of concentric circles that organizes *five levels of external influence* on the development of a child. With the child/individual at the center, the five levels represent the direct interactions, indirect influences, and events that impact child development: microsystem, mesosystem, exosystem, macrosystem, and chronosystem.

The microsystem represents the most significant interactions and influences that directly impact healthy development of children; the family, which is the most intimate influence, school, neighborhood or community, and religious institutions.

The mesosystem represents the interactions between the *influences in the microsystem* (family, school, neighborhood/community, religious institutions) and the extent that they are positively aligned with supporting the well-being of the child. The quality of the interactions, the level of nurturing, and support directly impacts how children view themselves in relationship to others and the world around them. This has direct implications for the engagement of families and the geographical, linguistic, and cultural communities to which they belong. While much of the current focus around family engagement practice has been on building the capacity of school leaders and classroom educators to effectively engage families, there are a number of support practitioners and service providers whose work is significantly impacted by their ability effectively engage with families. The entities and organizations, such as extended family organizations (e.g., parent workplace, social services, school districts) that indirectly impact the life of the child characterize the context in which interactions occur (exosystem) and operate within a set of social and cultural norms and beliefs (macrosystem) that permeate at all five levels affecting interactions, access, and outcomes for the child. The underlying relationships and perceptions have an impact on not only the health and well-being of children, it also influences the norms and interactions within the communities where the children and their families live.

More school districts and schools are shifting their approach to educating children and youth to a more student-centered environment by applying strategies that are grounded in the development of the whole child (Lewallen, Hunt, Potts-Datema, Zaza, & Giles, 2015). Family engagement through the lens of Bronfrenbrenner's theory provides not only for a clear rationale for understanding the implications for effective student and family engagement practice and but also guidance for implementation. According to this theory, the interactions or relationships between families and school (mesosystem) have a direct effect on the outcomes for children. These interactions and relationships do not exist in a vacuum; they are rooted in the broader context of institutions, politics, economics, and culture of the society. In that context, the policies and structures that are imposed (exosystem) have an impact on how the adults operate in this environment along with the beliefs, values, and norms that shape the context of this space (macrosystem), which is typically viewed through the lens of dominant culture.

The dilemma here is that there is a racial and cultural divide between a vast majority of practitioners and service providers and the children and families they serve. The emerging majority of students and families, especially in urban areas, are not of the dominant culture, they are racially, ethnically, linguistically, and socially diverse. This shifting demographic challenges educators and support practitioners to re-examine their approach to educating and supporting the well-being of children and youth by challenging negative perceptions and biases both implicit and explicit, and deepening cultural awareness and understanding. It is in this re-examination that families become a major asset, not only to gain deeper understanding of the individual child and how they are impacted by the events in and across their lives (chronosystem) but also to recognize and acknowledge the cultural values and nuances embrace by their families and communities.

Family Engagement in Child Welfare, Juvenile Justice, and Mental Health

Some youth are justice-involved or have child welfare involvement. Their families may have retained custody or they may not; this depends on statutes and policies in each state, which can vary widely. But when juvenile justice or child welfare is involved with a child or family, there are often other mandates about treatment, school attendance, or curfews. The youth and family have external requirements, set in place by the state agency, which may or may not address their underlying needs. For instance, some youth will be required to go to therapy, attend anger management classes, have random drug testing, and go to supervised visitation. Families may be required to attend parenting classes, family therapy, go to court often while working and caring for other children. Yet, the family may perceive their most important needs to be help navigating services, understanding their child's educational challenges, or simply respite care and find these needs remain unmet. Most families in these circumstances feel overwhelmed, frustrated, and inadequate.

When children are involved in mental health treatment, there are similar concerns, though loss of custody is less of a worry. However, mental health treatment for children varies widely across the country and the options are dictated by the type of insurance the child has. Many children and youth have health insurance as part of a family plan through their parent's employer and their treatment options are often limited. Parents may spend many months trying to access a pediatric mental health provider. Families report that is often difficult to obtain a diagnosis that fully describes their child's behaviors and symptoms, making it tough for them to ask for the services they think will help.

Engaging families in child welfare is moving in this century from expecting compliance to seeking collaboration (Littell & Tajima, 2000). Compliance consists of keeping appointments, completing tasks, and cooperating with caseworkers. Families who participate in treatment planning and goal-setting, and receive services that match their needs are more likely to participate and collaborate with caseworkers and others involved with their family. Child welfare has also begun adopting strategies from the mental health system, such as high-fidelity wraparound, in home therapy and family peer support, which have been the gold standard in mental health treatment.

When a youth goes before a court, their family enters a system they often know little about. Justice-involved youth may have attorneys, probation officers, and a case plan they are expected to follow. Many families report they have been unable to access needed care for their child, especially if there is a mental health concern. While data shows that youth have better outcomes if their families are involved, both families and the juvenile justice system have limited ideas of how to make that occur (Hair, 2005; McWey, Acock & Porter, 2010; Ryan et al., 2010). Several states leading the way with programs for justice-involved youth, including Pennsylvania, Arizona, Massachusetts, and Washington, have developed guides for families or piloted programs to engage families. The Juvenile Justice Detention Alternatives Initiative,[1] funded nationally by the Annie E. Casey Foundation, is promoting family engagement as a key factor in successfully diverting youth to community success. Families are viewed as assets that can substantially improve outcomes.

Research Summary on Family Engagement

Family engagement improves attendance, student attitudes toward school, behavior at school, and academic performance. There is growing evidence that family and school connection make a difference in student success. Parent engagement in schools is defined by the Centers for Disease Control as parents and school staff working together to support and improve the learning, development, and health of children and adolescents (Centers for Disease Control and Prevention, 2012; Guilamo-Ramos et al., 2011). The responsibility for engagement must be shared by both families and schools. The role of schools is to ensure that outreach to parents is done in meaningful ways and parents, in turn, provide active support for their children's and adolescent's learning and overall development. Several studies show that active family engagement in schools leads to improved educational outcomes and health behaviors for their children. Researchers have delineated a direct relationship between parent engagement and educational outcomes, which include improved school attendance (Epstein & Sheldon, 2002) as well as higher grades and test scores (Fan & Chen, 2001). Students are also less likely to become involved in substance use, violence, and other problem behaviors when their school environment is supportive and caring and their parents feel involved and connected to their school (Maman, Campbell, Sweat, & Gielen, 2000).

A study of 700 African American preschoolers in Washington, DC, showed that children whose parents had high involvement ratings, compared to other children with low or median ratings, had higher grades and scores (Marcon, 1999). Teacher reports of parent involvement were correlated to student grades and skill ratings. This finding proved true across family income levels and backgrounds.

This study classified four types of parent involvement as either active (volunteering and visiting the classroom) or passive (getting information from the teacher at conferences or home visits). Active types of involvement produced a stronger impact than the more passive types. Higher levels of parent involvement also appeared to have greater effect than lower levels and were tied to higher marks on both teacher ratings and report cards among the preschoolers.

A parent's sense of efficacy influences the degree of their involvement with school and this is especially true for parents of middle and high school students. Efficacy is defined as the ability to produce desired or intended results. With this in mind, Lee Shumow and Richard Lomax (2002) created a national study of 900 families with children aged 10–17, that examined parents' feelings of accomplishment in guiding their children. They noted that parents have a high sense of efficacy when they believe:

- they can help their children succeed in school, and be happy and safe
- they can counteract negative influences and keep their children away from troublemakers, illegal drugs or alcohol
- they can have a positive impact by improving the quality of school and making their neighborhood a better place.

When parents' sense of efficacy was high, they monitored their children more closely and were significantly more involved at school. The researchers also found that efficacy was related to student outcomes. Using parent reports of their children's grades, academic level (high, medium, or low), and behavior at school combined with student reports of well-being, they reported that a high feeling of efficacy for parents correlated with their children doing better in school. Children also felt happy, safe, and stable.

In another study, Karen Mapp (2002) investigated both how and why parents who experience economic hardship are involved in their child's education. This study looked at various factors affecting parent involvement. One of the most important findings showed that school factors that impact and improve relationships with families can strengthen the involvement of parents. When school staffs build trust and sustain caring relationships with parents, recognizing them as partners in their child's educational development, parents increase their participation and are more motivated to be involved in their child's educational success.

Social Capital and Families

Families often create social networks that support their day-to-day existence in a larger system that has isolated and marginalized them because their circumstances and norms are deemed outside of those of the dominant culture. When educators and practitioners understand the value of these networks and the important role they play in the cultural context of families, they are able to effectively leverage the networks to support the well-being of the child. This requires an understanding of the concept of social capital and the willingness to connect with families in ways that value and respect them and their communities as assets.

The term "social capital" has landed back in our consciousness through two theories. James Coleman and Pierre Bourdieu describe social capital as the solid value of building relationships, which help families access resources such as childcare, transportation, and food. Research has shown that families, regardless of their socioeconomic, linguistic, or ethnic background, have informal networks that represent their social capital or their ability to tap into resources and information (Coleman, 1988), navigate systems, and engage in collective actions. As professionals, we tend to view nondominant cultures through a deficit lens and often miss the opportunities to tap into the social networks these families possess. Social capital will present differently for groups of parents depending on their access and influence.

For example, the social capital exercised by a white middle-class parent may provide the school with financial resources to benefit struggling students; whereas, an immigrant Somali parent may exercise her social capital to connect community elders to support staff in ways that bridge cultural gaps, deepen understanding, and generate more culturally appropriate supports for struggling students and connections with families. Both examples, demonstrate how parents leverage the resources available within their networks toward the same end—supporting struggling students. Activating families to connect and support in these ways requires building relationships of trust and creating a sense of community and shared responsibility around the education and well-being of children and youth.

Robert Putnam also writes about social capital in his 2000 book, *Bowling Alone: The Collapse and Revival of American Community*. Putnam argues that America's sense of community has been undermined by a population shift to the suburbs, longer commuting and work hours, as well as less time spent on social activities and more time spent alone watching television. Putnam defines social capital as networks (friendships and extended family), norms such as interacting (waving) with your neighbor, and trust that lead to cooperation, civic involvement, and positive outcomes for society.

Both Coleman and Putnam consider trust to be a key ingredient in social capital and reciprocal relationships a direct benefit. For example, parents who connect with teachers become more self-confident about how to help their child and better informed about school expectations for their child's academic progress. Teachers also learn about parents' expectations for their child's school life. The relationship and sharing of expectations are reciprocal.

Relationships that contain a high degree of trust and reciprocity build sustainable communities. Putnam posits that social capital can build bridges across divides in society as well as bringing like-minded or like-ethnic groups together (Putnam, 2000). Children live in families and families live in communities. Each has its own culture, while schools often have a unique culture of their own. Families with social capital can build the bridges between all three. Both family and community involvement can foster partnerships among schools, family, and community groups.

Even when communities have high rates of poverty, crime, and housing instability, communities have come together to effectively tackle problems. For example, In Flint, Michigan, a group of grassroots leaders, including many parents, worked for solutions to their water crisis. In 2014, local and state officials decided to change the city's main water source to the Flint River. Almost immediately, residents of Flynn, a majority African American city with 40% of its residents living in poverty, began complaining of health problems. Testing revealed contaminants in the water, including high lead levels and many children showed elevated lead levels. Grassroots leaders, including families, partnered with researchers, journalists, churches, the Michigan Education Association, and lawyers to raise awareness and accountability. Their advocacy created change including state funding for nine new nurses in Flint schools, more nutritious food to combat lead absorption, and early identification.

The stronger and more expansive a family's social networks or capital, the greater the impact will be on the quality of life, health, access to opportunities, and attainment of personal, professional, and financial goals. For many immigrant and low-income families, the social networks are focused on the basic needs for survival within societal structures that perpetuate the marginalization of their nondominant communities (Rupasingha & Goetz, 2007).

Building Trusting Relationships for Meaningful Family Engagement

Meaningful engagement of families requires establishing strong relationships of trust that shift the dynamic between home and school to a more reciprocal and beneficial partnership. For that to occur, educators and practitioners must engage in a process of shifting from a deficit view of families to a more asset-based approach. This will require an examination of their beliefs, assumptions, and biases (both implicit and explicit), and other factors that hinder the authentic, meaningful engagement of families. Partnering with families in ways that honor their contributions builds the capacity of school-based practitioners to more effectively engage a culturally and linguistically diverse student body.

Building relationships with families begins with listening to their stories, to their hopes and dreams, and to their motivations for becoming engaged. It is critical that we apply what we hear from parents to adjust or recreate our models of engagement; this is especially true for families from linguistic minorities or disenfranchised communities. Relationships of trust create opportunities to build both practitioner capacity for engagement and parent capacity to become more deeply engaged.

In 2010, the U.S. Department of Education released the Dual Capacity-Building Framework for School Family Partnerships (Mapp & Kuttner, 2014), which serves as a basis for establishing systemic structures and effective family engagement practice. The framework promotes a capacity-building approach that simultaneously is applied to both educators/practitioners and parents. This framework is grounded in the premise that building the capacity of both families and practitioners to effectively partner, there will be a positive impact on the development, achievement, and well-being of children and youth.

True and robust family engagement goes far beyond attending parent-teacher conferences, school events, or open houses. Teachers, school administrators, and other school staff can select strategies that work for their school and community, tailoring them for the greatest success. It takes creative thinking, persistence, and commitment. Studies on effective strategies to connect schools, families, and communities tell us one thing: when the focus is on building respectful and trusting relationships among school staff, families, and communities, they are effective in creating and sustaining family connections with schools (Epstein & Sheldon, 2002; Mapp & Kuttner, 2014; Wood & Bauman, 2017). Yet, despite this research, parents and schools have much to do—and to learn—in order to implement these strategies and develop true, trusting relationships. Relationships matter, when parents and community members are seen as assets to the process of creating student success, the responsibility for a child's educational development becomes a collaborative enterprise (Bryk & Schneider, 2002).

Partnerships require trust on both sides, and we know that trust benefits students. In one study of 400 schools, students who attended schools that prioritized relationship-building between families and teachers had significant gains compared to students who attended schools that didn't (Bryk & Schneider, 2002). The study also found that relational trust among teachers, parents, and school leaders was key to building effective educational communities. Making the jump from identifying families who are easy to engage to seeing all families as important assets is critical. Never assume that a family doesn't care about their children and instead use a strengths-based perspective, adopting a no-fault policy. Always proceed on the assumption that all families can help improve their child's school performance and influence other key outcomes. While middle-class families tend to be more involved at school, all families, regardless of income, education, or cultural background, are involved in their children's learning and want them to do well.

Family engagement means the participation of families in regular, two-way, and meaningful communication involving student learning and other school activities. This ensures that parents are full partners in their child's education—they play an integral role in their child's education, are actively encouraged to be involved, and are included, as appropriate, in decision-making and on advisory committees to assist their child's education (No Child Left Behind, section 1902, definitions). Unfortunately, many policy makers, educators, and parents still view student learning as the sole responsibility of schools. As educators' responsibilities increase, they realize that they cannot do it alone.

Families, too, may be reluctant to work with educators or increase their involvement. Some parents will point to their own demanding schedules, saying they cannot add anything more than traditional parent-teacher meetings. Others confess that they are uncomfortable communicating with school staff because of language or cultural differences or their own personal experiences as a student. Still others feel frustrated by their lack of knowledge of how to help their child, participate in different ways, or overcome school policies or bureaucratic hurdles they encounter. Nearly all are balancing the needs of more than one child.

Collaboration with Culturally and Linguistically Diverse Families

As the population of our schools and communities become more diverse, the challenge for educators and support practitioners is bridging the cultural and linguistic gaps between families and schools. Too often, educators and nonacademic practitioners operate in isolation, negating the impact and influence that family and community culture have on the healthy development and well-being of children and youth.

One-fifth of U.S. schoolchildren now come from immigrant families, and this number is projected to grow. According to the U.S. Census Bureau, more than half of the nation's children are expected to be part of a "minority race or ethnic group" around 2020. This puts Americans under the age of 18 at the edge of a trend that the overall population will follow by 2044 (Chappell, 2015). Families who come from diverse cultures bring enormous strengths and value to schools. Their starting point for school-family communication may vary and schools may need to suspend their assumptions about family structure, resources, traditions, or cultural practices and approach communication with curiosity and respect. Immigrant families may have a vague or inaccurate idea of school expectations and supports. They may be unfamiliar with education terms and verbal shorthand or jargon used by educators.

Genuine communication and respect for traditions and family structure is an excellent beginning. Some culturally diverse families may feel initial mistrust or suspicion of authority, including some school staff. They may have strong ideas about school discipline and justice that negatively impact their willingness to engage. Families need to be genuinely welcomed and supported to move beyond these perceptions so that practitioners can build the trust needed to solicit their ideas and feedback.

For linguistically diverse families, communication should be in the family's home language as often as possible. For in person meetings, it is very important that students are not used as the interpreter between their parents/caregivers and support practitioners, instead official interpreters need to be used. Consider training bilingual parents to be interpreters, making sure this does not violate privacy rules that the school has agreed on. Speak with the parents, not the interpreter, taking time to answer questions. Parent-teacher meetings can be adjusted to welcome extended family becoming family-teacher meetings, making it clear that the family decides who is there to collaborate in supporting the student. Let the family inform the school if they have a preference on who receives information and makes decisions.

Strategies for Engaging and Communicating with Families

Families bring a wealth of information and insight about their child. They know their social, medical, mental health, and academic history. They have expertise about their strengths and needs. They bring insight on how both their family culture and their ethnic culture affect their child. They often understand what motivates their child and what worries them.

Establishing communication with a student's family may take some time and creative persistence, and it is essential to develop and adopt a set of effective strategies. Some of these strategies can include:

- *Creating a parent-friendly environment.* In Broken Arrow, Oklahoma, teachers send postcards to families before the first day of school, host ice cream socials, and invite parents to an assembly showcasing a different class every Friday morning (see http://www.educationworld.com/a_admin/admin/admin149.shtml).
- *Multiple avenues of communication.* Ensuring multiple methods and avenues for two-way communication with families is key. The days of sending

information home in a backpack are nearly over and many parents prefer email or other electronic communication about school programs, policies, activities, and responses to events. School blogs, emails, coffees, surveys, texts, and phone calls from teachers all offer opportunities for families to ask for clarification, give their feedback, and express their satisfaction or concern.

- *At home parent-teacher visits* increase communication and strengthens relationships. The Parent-Teacher Home Visit Project[2] was created in Sacramento and is designed to establish trust and respect. This program is established on the principle that the student's home provides the most opportunity for learning and sharing. All visits are voluntary, scheduled in advance, performed by trained educators, and intended to foster collaboration. The focus of the visits is relationship-building; educators focus on getting to know the student and the family and the family members share their experiences and aspirations for their child.
- *Provide social networking activities and family support.* Planning networking and social activities is best done in partnership with families. Some communities prefer informal networking opportunities, such as pot lucks or celebrations, while others find meetings with speakers on parent concerns more appealing. Setting up opportunities for families to support each other and network can reduce stress and worry and increase engagement. Building parent social networks can help build the confidence of family members to engage (Wood & Bauman, 2017).
- *Parent volunteering.* Two Indiana mothers began a national parent volunteer program called Three for Me,[3] where parents are asked to donate just three hours of their time over the school year. Parents are given a pledge card and list of volunteer opportunities. In their first year, volunteer hours doubled. The program has expanded to 8,100 schools and 4.5 million parents.

Cultural differences also often impact the ability of families to engage, in some cultures, eye contact is considered polite while in others this is not true. Handshakes or touching may be considered appropriate greetings among some families from diverse cultures, while in others it is inappropriate. There is no substitute for educating and preparing yourself before a meeting—asking respectful questions ahead of time so that you understand the culture of families is a helpful strategy.

Communication built on misinformation, assumptions, or stereotypes can create distance between schools, families, and students. The following strategies will foster communication built on respect:

- Assume good intentions and that families want the best for their children
- Recognize and respect differences in family structures and roles

- Invite parents and family members to share what they know about the child's interests, hopes, and struggles
- Invite parents and family members to share their family cultures and traditions
- Bring a sense of self-awareness and cultural humility to all interactions
- View linguistic, cultural, and family diversity as strengths.

In addition, to setting a tone of respect and inclusivity, strong communication with families also offers teachers an opportunity to invite family involvement and share curricular goals, materials, and resources. There are many ways to learn from families:

- Ask families about ways they encourage their children and how they share their cultural traditions
- Invite families to tell their education stories—What were their schools like? What people or experiences helped them to learn?
- Ask about their expectations for their child's education.

Single parents, grandparents raising grandchildren, parents working multiple jobs, and foster parents often have additional challenges. They may have little free time that overlaps with school hours, difficulties with transportation, and childcare for their other children or problems scheduling multiple or follow-up meetings. It is important to view these barriers as problems to be solved, not excuses for a lack of involvement. When families receive help in dissolving obstacles to involvement, they become more positive about partnering with schools. Ultimately, it is a win-win for students, families, and schools.

Conclusion

The engagement of families in education not only provides a rich opportunity for educators and practitioners that taps into the most influential relationship in the lives of children. It also serves as a vehicle for expanding the social networks of families and enhancing their ability to access resources and information and to leverage relationships in the realm of education. In spite of the decades of research that supports the engagement of families as a key lever for improving student outcomes, schools are challenged to build effective partnerships with families.

> . . . with important exceptions, many of those efforts struggle to engage families meaningfully, much less as full partners. This gap leaves one of

> the most powerful influences in the lives of children and youth on the sidelines. Part of the challenge is that too many institutions and professionals have largely given up on families, believing that the challenges families face and the problems they sometimes create are beyond their reach and responsibility. As a result, sometimes those institutions ignore families. Other times they set up systems and supports that compensate for the failures they perceive in families. And even when schools and programs do engage families, they typically focus on asking parents to support the work of the school or program through activities such as serving on committees, helping with homework, fundraising, and volunteering to lead programs (Syvertsen, 2015, p. 1).

All families bring value to their children and their children's lives. For the child, their family can articulate their history, strengths, and needs and can provide them with advocacy to improve their situation and navigate toward the future. For the family, their involvement underscores their value and increases their knowledge and influence. For everyone else involved with the child's education and other services, families provide the bridge between family life, culture, and community. Initially, schools may see families as partners to increase student success, but their value goes beyond that. Families can be instrumental in creating a culture of respect, thoughtful two-way communication, and shared decision-making.

While families want the best for their children, many have different approaches. Just as schools in this century are responding to the needs of more diverse students, new technologies and changing communities, and outreach and engagement of families will grow and change as well. A strong belief that families bring knowledge, experiences, passion, and value that cannot be found elsewhere creates the foundation for a partnership that serves children and schools.

Notes

1. http://www.aecf.org/work/juvenile-justice/jdai/
2. http://www.pthvp.org/.
3. http://www.educationworld.com/a_admin/admin/admin437.shtml.

References

Bolívar, J. M., & Chrispeels, J. H. (2011). Enhancing parent leadership through building social and intellectual capital. *American Educational Research Journal, 48*(1), 4–38. Retrieved from http://journals.sagepub.com/doi/abs/10.3102/0002831210366466

Bourdieu, P., & Coleman, J. S. (1991). *Social theory for a changing society*. Boulder, CO: Westview Press.

Bronfenbrenner, U. (1979). *The ecology of human development: Experiments by nature and design*. Cambridge, MA: Harvard University Press.

Bryk, A. S., & Schneider, B. (2002). *Trust in schools: A core resource for improvement*. New York: Russell Sage Foundation.

Centers for Disease Control and Prevention. (2012). *Parent engagement: Strategies for involving parents in school health*. Atlanta: U.S. Department of Health and Human Services.

Chappell, Bill. (2015, March 4). For U.S. children, minorities will be the majority by 2020, Census says. NPR. Retrieved from https://www.npr.org/sections/thetwo-way/2015/03/04/390672196/for-u-s-children-minorities-will-be-the-majority-by-2020-census-says

Coleman, J. (1988). Social capital in the creation of human capital. *American Journal of Sociology, 94*, S95–S120. Retrieved from http://www.jstor.org/stable/2780243

Epstein, J., & Sheldon, S. (2002). Present and accounted for: Improving student attendance through family and community involvement. *Journal of Educational Research, 95*(5), 308–318.

Fan, X., & Chen, M. (2001). Parental involvement and students' academic achievement: A meta-analysis. *Educational Psychology Review, 13*(1), 1–22.

Guilamo-Ramos, V., Jaccard, J., Dittus, P., Bouris, A., Gonzalez, B., Casillas, E., & Banspach, S. (2011). A comparative study of interventions for delaying the initiation of sexual intercourse among Latino and black youth. *Perspectives on Sexual and Reproductive Health, 43*(4), 247–254.

Hair, H. J. (2005). Outcomes for children and adolescents after residential treatment: A review of research from 1993 to 2003. *Journal of Child and Family Studies, 14*, 551–575. doi:10.1007/s10826-005-7188-9

Hoover-Dempsey, K. V., & Jones, K. P. (1997). Parental role construction and parental involvement in children's education. ERIC Number: ED411054. Retrieved from https://eric.ed.gov/?id=ed411054

Lewallen, T. C., Hunt, H., Potts-Datema, W., Zaza, S., & Giles, W. (2015). The whole school, whole community, whole child model: A new approach for improving educational attainment and healthy development for students. *Journal of School Health, 85*(11), 729–739. doi:10.1111/josh.12310

Littell, J. H., & Tajima, E. A. (2000). A multilevel model of client participation in intensive family preservation services. *Social Service Review, 74*, 405–443.

Maman, S., Campbell, J., Sweat, M. D., & Gielen, A. C. (2000). The intersections of HIV and violence: Directions for future research and interventions. *Social Science and Medicine, 50*(4), 459–478.

Mapp, K. L. (2002). *Having their say: Parents describe how and why they are involved in their children's education*. Paper presented at the annual meeting of the American Educational Research Association, New Orleans.

Mapp, K. L., & Kuttner, P. (2014). Partners in education: A dual capacity-building framework for family-school partnerships. Austin, TX: Southwest Educational Development Laboratory.

Marcon, R. A. (1999, January 1). Positive relationships between parent school involvement and public school inner-city preschoolers' development and academic performance. *School Psychology Review, 28*(3), 395–412.

McWey, L. M., Acock, A., & Porter, B. (2010). The impact of continued contact with biological parents upon the mental health of children in foster care. *Child Youth Services Review, 32*(10), 1338–1345.

National Family, School, and Community Engagement Working Group. (2009). Recommendations for federal policy. Retrieved from https://c.ymcdn.com/sites/nafsce.site-ym.com/resource/resmgr/Policy/FI_FamilyEngagementRecsForFe.pdf

No Child Left Behind Act of 2001, P.L. 107-110, 20 U.S.C. § 6319 (2002).

Pekel, K., Roehlkepartain, E. C., Syvertsen, A. K., & Scales, P. C. (2015). *Don't forget the families: The missing piece in America's efforts to help all children succeed (summary of key findings).* Minneapolis, MN: Search Institute. Retrieved from https://www.search-institute.org/our-research/youth-development-research/families/

Putnam, R. D. (2000). *Bowling alone: The collapse and revival of American community.* New York: Simon & Schuster.

Rupasingha, A., & Goetz, S. J. (2007). Social and political forces as determinants of poverty: A spatial analysis. *Journal of Socio-economics, 36*(4), 650–671. Retrieved from http://aese.psu.edu/nercrd/economic-development/for-researchers/poverty-issues/social-and-politica-forces-as-determinants-of-poverty-a-spatial-analysis

Ryan, C., Russell S.T., Huebner D., Diaz R., Sanchez J.(2010). Family acceptance in adolescence and the health of LGBT young adults. *Journal of Child and Adolescent Psychiatric Nursing*, 23, 4 (pp. 205–213).

Shumow, L., & Lomax, R. (2002). Parental efficacy: Predictor of parenting behavior and adolescent outcomes. *Parenting: Science and Practice, 2*, 127–150.

Sincero, S. M. (n.d.). Ecological systems theory. Explorable. Retrieved from https://explorable.com/ecological-systems-theory

Wood, L., & Bauman, E. (2017). *How family, school, and community engagement can improve student achievement and influence school reform.* Quincy, MA: Nellie Mae Education Foundation.

CHAPTER THIRTEEN

Community Assets and Challenges

Karen B. Francis and Catherine Cushinberry

Inherently, communities should be dynamic spaces that bring people together and provide opportunities for security, overall health, and well-being. This chapter will discuss the dynamics of assets and challenges defined as risk and protective factors within a community that promote or can hinder the welfare of individuals. Through the lens of a public health framework, the chapter seeks to define what a comprehensive community approach to addressing the health and well-being of children, youth, and families should embody. Additionally, this chapter attempts to focus on providing innovative strategies on how community assets can be leveraged by providing examples of efforts undertaken in real communities. The importance of investments to promulgate protective factors will also be discussed as a strategy to address challenges and to create safe, supportive, and sustainable communities for children, youth, and families.

Community, More Than Just Geography

A community is often defined in terms of geography, highlighting settings, places, and spaces such as neighborhoods, schools, and workplaces in which social relationships occur (Centers for Disease Control and Prevention [CDC], n.d.). These settings exhibit characteristics that can impact the health and overall well-being of children, youth, and families. Going beyond just geographic delineations, the definition of community includes aspects such as population size and diversity, culture, socioeconomic levels, availability of resources that include access to and availability of services, employment opportunities, social supports, and social connections between and among its members (Community Tool Box, n.d.).

Both implicitly and explicitly in the concept of community is culture. Culture embodies the traditions, practices, values, morals, and habits that are embraced by groups of people and that provide structure and organization to the lives of people. Within any community, the convergence of diverse cultures comes alive and influences the very fabric of the community. Consequently, community can also be defined as "a group of people with diverse characteristics who are linked by social ties, share common perspectives, and engage in joint action in geographical locations or settings" (MacQueen et al., 2001, p. 1929). Rosenzweig and colleagues posit that "varying conceptualizations of community are important to families in different ways" (2008). This idea leads to the understanding that community is defined in terms of "people's lives" (Bookman, 2004). Therefore, community can be defined as "the connective tissue that makes [peoples'] work and family lives possible. . . . the invisible framework that connects families to the people and institutions that provide care, services, and supports" (Bookman, 2004).

Unraveling the complexities for defining the concept of community dictates both theoretical and practical perspectives. The theoretical perspective allows for a discussion about the necessary components that define these settings (people, place, space, relationships, and structures). The framework offered through *ecological systems theory* concretizes what this means. Ecological systems theory explains how the interactions of individuals with the systems and environment in which they live, work, and play have influence on their lives (CDC, n.d.). These systems include social organizations, social networks, social capital, formal volunteering and informal helping, sense of community, and community satisfaction (Rosenzweig, Brennan, Huffstutter, & Bradley, 2008). The degree to which these aspects are beneficial and meaningful for individuals helps to form one's sense of community and connectedness. More specifically, within any environment, there are multiple systems (i.e., institutional, social, cultural, political, and economic) that individuals encounter and that influence behavior, reaction, and interaction to different degrees. For example, children who have been exposed to repeated violence experience trauma that has an impact of their overall health and well-being. Others (e.g., individuals who have experienced discrimination or inequity as they access social services) may not be trusting of social service systems based on their experiences. Figure 13.1 depicts the social-ecological model that defines the interrelationship between the individual and the community.

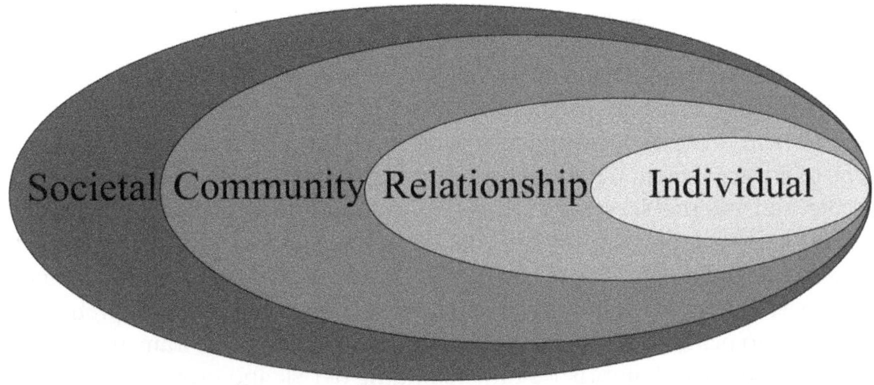

Figure 13.1 Social-ecological model. "The Center for Disease Control (CDC) uses a four-level social-ecological model to better understand violence and the effect of potential prevention strategies. This model considers the complex interplay between individual, relationship, community, and societal factors. It allows us to understand the range of factors that put people at risk for violence or protect them from experiencing or perpetrating violence. The overlapping rings in the model illustrate how factors at one level influence factors at another level" (https://www.cdc.gov/violenceprevention/overview/social-ecologicalmodel.html)

The practical perspective to understanding community speaks more to how the characteristics of the aspects mentioned above hinder or assist the promulgation of risk and protective factors and how they collectively manifest and impact health and well-being. For example, viewing the importance of community engagement and understanding the cultural and linguistic nuances that manifest within a particular community can be a useful tool in identifying needs, and informing the delivery of services and supports to facilitate positive outcomes.

Very much at the heart of the discussion about safe and supportive communities is the concept of *social capital*. Social capital referring to the social networks, reciprocity, trust, cooperation, connection, active participation, and sharing that can and should take place for a community and its' members to thrive. Putnam in his book *Bowling Alone*, posits that "our stock of social capital—the very fabric of our connections with each other, has plummeted, impoverishing our lives and communities" (http://bowlingalone.com/). As our existence becomes more technologically driven, and work/life demands impact family structure and connectedness, communities become increasingly fragmented. These circumstances will therefore challenge communities and their members to develop strategies that will facilitate, build, and leverage social capital to mitigate risk factors and promote protective factors for children, youth, and families in communities across the country.

The Public Health Approach

At the core of discussion about how to facilitate a comprehensive approach to addressing risk and protective factors within communities that impact overall health and well-being is the issue of equity. The adoption of an equity lens to ensure that all members within a community are able to access appropriate and affordable services that are culturally acceptable. Further, this equity lens includes approaches that are data informed and data driven to ensure accountability for positive outcomes across all dimensions of diversity that exist within a community. In discussing the concept of a comprehensive approach to health, well-being, and equity, the public health framework offers a viable approach that satisfies understanding of risk and protective factors at the individual and community level and dictates a multi-sectorial approach.

The public health approach can best be described as a way to impact health and well-being (Miles, Espiritu, Horen, Sebian, & Waetizig, 2010). This approach places community members and the community itself at the center of focus. The public health approach is population focused with program and service delivery at the individual level. Components of the public health approach include (1) a population focus, (2) emphasizes promotion and prevention, (3) addresses determinants of health, and (4) is process oriented (ibid.). The following section provides a discussion of the public health framework and its integration into addressing community assets and challenges to facilitate well-being. See figure 13.2 for the Public Health Approach to Violence Prevention

The Association of State and Territorial Health Officials offers a perspective on a public health approach that outlines a process for effectively addressing health and well-being with an equity lens. The following four-step process is offered:

1. Foster a public health workforce that mirrors the diversity of the population it serves and the differences across multiple generations.
2. Collect public health data that include the social determinants of health—income, housing, education, stigma, social context, health care, and the built environment—and compare those data with the census data.
3. Implement interventions aimed at ensuring the public health workforce reflects the growing population of racial/ethnic minorities and diverse generations within those populations.
4. Strengthen the public health leadership, conduct robust data collections, and take action to address inequities across the social determinants of health.

Source: http://www.astho.org/StatePublicHealth/A-Public-Health-Approach-to-Achieving-Health-Equity/4-3-17/

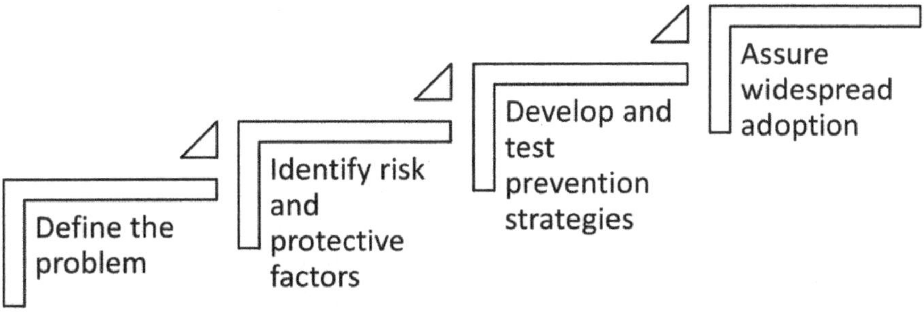

Figure 13.2 The public health model (https://www.cdc.gov/violenceprevention/overview/publichealthapproach.html)

The concept of community racial, ethnic, and cultural diversity, as well as the changing demographic trends, will be discussed later in the chapter. Additionally, we also discuss community risk and protective factors and innovations to address risk factors and build on protective factors at the community level that embody the concepts discussed above.

The Changing Demographics of Communities

Communities across America are culturally, racially, and ethnically diverse and exist across a variety of geographical settings (rural, urban, suburban, and tribal). This diversity is ever growing. In fact, "Americans are more racially and ethnically diverse than in the past, and the U.S. is projected to be even more diverse in the coming decades" (Cohn & Caumont, 2016, http://www.pewresearch.org/fact-tank/2016/03/31/10-demographic-trends-that-are-shaping-the-u-s-and-the-world/). Some of these communities are rich in resources and amenities, while others teeter on the edge of economic decline. The availability, access, affordability, acceptability, and appropriateness of resources, supports, and services can define the overall well-being of all members of these communities.

Frey (2016) stated that demographic trends in the United States indicated that most children would be from racial minorities. Moreover, projections suggest that shifts in demographics will change the racial and ethnic makeup of the population and increase the minority population from 32% in 2005 to 51% in 2050 (Passel et al., 2008). These demographic changes in the population composition have implications for the delivery of education and services to meet the needs of an increasingly diverse student population. As the educational system works to address the needs of its growingly diverse student population, new approaches that foster open and authentic dialogue about achieving cultural and linguistic competence to facilitate academic achievement and positive educational outcomes for all students need to be available and intentionally implemented. The same holds true for other service systems and schools within communities working with children, youth, and their families. Furthermore, school and other social services agencies and organizations need to build administrative, structural, and staff capacity to infuse cultural and linguistic competence (CLC) into policy and practices to ensure that services are provided to leverage strengths and achieve positive outcomes. Specifically, we refer to positive outcomes related to academic achievement, overall health, and well-being. Strategies to facilitate capacity-building for CLC must first be championed and supported by leadership in community service agencies and schools. These strategies also include staff training (i.e., to include the principles and practices of CLC, unconscious bias, and decision-making), implementation of policies and practices that promote the practical application of CLC, development and implementation of standards to guide CLC integration, implementation of strategies to address, for example, disparities in discipline practices, and the availability of resources (financial and structural) to support these efforts. So, what does a culturally and linguistically competent organization with culturally competent staff look like you ask? Consider this approach offered by Cross and colleagues—cultural competence is "a set of congruent behaviors, attitudes and policies that come together as a system, agency or among professionals and enable that system, agency or those professionals to work effectively in cross-cultural situations" (Cross, Bazron, et al., 1989, p. 13). Linguistic competence encompasses "the capacity of an organization and its personnel to communicate effectively, and convey information in a manner that is easily understood by diverse audiences including persons of limited English proficiency, those who have low literacy skills or are not literate, and individuals with disabilities" (Goode & Jones, 2006, p. 2).

Understanding Risk and Protective Factors

Community Risk Factors

There are risk factors in communities that hinder students' abilities to thrive academically. Risk factors are anything that increases the chance that someone will suffer harm; whereas, protective factors are things that decrease the chance of harm to someone (Substance Abuse and Mental Health Services Administration [SAMHSA], 2015). The safety of students can be positively impacted by protective factors in the community that moderate the impact of risk factors or reduce the chance that they will occur (Rutter, 1985). The ability of a community to assist in keeping students safe lies not only in the availability and access to resources but also in community members' understanding of how to potentially offset risk factors and increase the likelihood of children being safe and having the ability to thrive.

Poverty is a community structural characteristic that is important to understanding youth risk (Bursik & Grasmick, 1993; Shaw & McKay, 1942). Neighborhood poverty exists when the community populous is below the poverty level and has high rates of unemployment and residents who receive public assistance. For example, in 2017, the poverty level for a family of four was determined to be $24,000 (http://familiesusa.org/product/federal-poverty-guidelines). These communities where the community populous lives below the poverty line tend to be characterized by residential instability, low community participation (Tolan, Gorman-Smith, & Henry, 2003) and high rates of school dropouts (Eller, 1996). Youth who live in communities where there is neighborhood poverty are at risk for social-emotional and behavior problems (Dupéré, Lacourse, Willms, Leventhal, & Tremblay, 2008), antisocial behavior and school dropout (Brady, Gorman-Smith, Henry, & Tolan, 2008), and poor grades (Hopson & Lee, 2011).

Students who live in communities where there is neighborhood poverty and in urban settings are exposed to more violence than students who do not live in those communities (Buka, Stichick, Birdthistle, & Earls, 2001; Stein, Jaycox, Kataoka, Rhodes, & Vestal, 2003). When students witness ongoing criminal behavior, these factors may increase the risk of students feeling unsafe and lacking the support within their communities to thrive. A sobering fact for many black families is that concerns for safety are also connected to racial bias toward young, black people of color, especially black males. Black parents and caregivers must warn their children against the challenges within their neighborhood and face the reality that they must have the "talk" with their black boys about how to conduct themselves when stopped by the police and how to avoid the unintended consequences of potential harm just by virtue of their skin color. Or consider the experiences of immigrant and refugee families who live in constant fear of being targeted for acts of violence just by virtue of the fact that they may speak a different language, dress differently, or have varying cultural and religious beliefs.

The two examples provided above, exemplify the concept of social norms and impact of the beliefs systems, attitudes, and behaviors of individuals. Social norms can have positive impact in that they "motivate individuals and groups to adopt social norms that result in positive health and wellbeing" (CDC, n.d.). Consequently, social norms can be negatively impacted by neighborhood poverty (Sampson, Morenoff, & Gannon-Rowley, 2002). In communities with high drug use, one social norm may be the perception that adults in the community believe it is acceptable to use drugs and other illegal substances. These social norms can be reinforced by the enforcement of laws within the community related to drugs and illegal substances. If students perceive that laws and enforcement of laws do not discourage drug and substance use, then this could perpetuate the perception that this behavior is acceptable. Another example of the negative impact of social norms is demonstrated through the following—A first grade teacher uses corporal punishment (i.e., physical punishment like spanking) to discipline her students. Her teachers used corporal punishment when she was in school, and she knows other teachers who use it in their classrooms. She doesn't think that corporal punishment is wrong (CDC, n.d.).

Social organization of a neighborhood may also be risk factor. It includes the perceived social support and cohesion among neighbors, sense of belonging, and participation in organizations, both formal and informal. Studies show that lower levels of social organization in neighborhoods are associated with antisocial and maladaptive youth development (Leventhal & Brooks-Gunn, 2000; Duncan, Connell, & Klebanov, 1997). When communities lack a sense of oneness, there can be an absence of social responsibility, which thereby creates a fragmented community. Youth may feel disconnected from a sense of ownership or responsibility to their neighbors or community.

Community Protective Factors

Communities have within them the potential to provide resources to overcome potential risk factors. When communities provide students with opportunities for and reward prosocial involvement this may reduce students' involvement in antisocial or maladaptive behaviors (Kim, Gilman, Hill, & Hawkins, 2016) and increase their feelings of connectedness to their community (Zeldin & Topitzes, 2002). The impact of student connectedness to the community can impact their academic achievement. The concept of connectedness refers to "a belief held by students that the adults and peers in their school care about their learning as well as about them as individuals" (CDC, n.d.). In a study examining factors that influence students' decision to continue on to postsecondary education after high school, researchers found that connectedness to school positively impacted students desire to continue their education (Donlan, Prescott, & Zaff, 2016). They also found that those students still needed additional resources to help them overcome the obstacles.

Asset-based community mapping is a useful tool for helping communities identify their local strengths and assets rather than focusing on local needs (Mathie & Cunningham, 2003). It provides a systematic approach to identifying and cataloging the resources and strengths that contribute to the overall health and well-being of a community. It can be used as a first step when communities are working toward regeneration as in the case of making determinations about available resources when starting a local program. Asset mapping is also used to help inform programmatic decision-making and to engage, mobilize, and empower community members. Table 13.1

Table 13.1 Community asset maps

- You want to start a new local program and need information about available resources. For example, you are interested in teen mothers finishing their education. You could draw a community asset map that identifies school drop-out prevention, tutoring, and education counseling programs for young teen mothers. This helps you see what already exists, or if support services are lacking. You may find it is necessary to develop a program to help young mothers finish their education.
- You are making program decisions. An asset map can help you identify community assets and concerns. The map results help determine new directions for your program or identify new programs that need to be developed. For example, an asset map of food banks and nutrition resources for low-income families in your neighborhood may reveal that there is a lack of programs, or that existing programs are located in areas that are not accessible to families in your service area.
- You want to mobilize and empower the community. If you involve different community members in constructing the asset map, the process itself can be an organizing tool. For example, mapping local public services and identifying the dollars spent per community member can mobilize residents to lobby city or county council members to improve local public services.

Source: http://healthpolicy.ucla.edu/programs/health-data/trainings/Documents/tw_cba20.pdf. © 2003 The Regents of the University of California. Used by permission.

offers examples from the UCLA Center for Health Policy Research that exemplify the utility of the asset-mapping process.

The process of community mapping includes community leaders leading efforts toward an assessment of resources that the community can internally build upon, whether they are people, program, services, or supports within the community. It is the opposite of deficiency-based programs that focus on bringing external resources into the community rather than building on the existing strengths of the community.

There is evidence that students who participate in community-based organizations are less likely to be delinquent or engage in substance use (Gottfedson, Gertenblith, Soulè, Womer, & Lu, 2004). To be clear, reference to community-based organization and student participation is directed at after-school programs offered within the community. Albeit important to discuss the benefits of student volunteer service and involvement in community-based programs that build good citizenship and provide opportunities for engagement in meaningful community service, we focus here on after-school programming as a service delivery point.

Student engagement in activities after school hours are critical for development, helping to build efficacy and social skills and foster positive relationships with adults and peers (Larson, 2000). This also builds the case for the need to ensure availability of quality after-school programs in communities (https://youth.gov/youth-topics/afterschool-programs). According to Shernoff and Vandell (2008), "A recent meta-analysis reviewing evaluations of 73 afterschool programs (Dulak & Weissberg, 2007) found that afterschool programs enhance the personal and social development of youth." This is particularly so where programs had a strong emphasis on social skills and character development. What we know is that the gap between the end of school, what the Afterschool Alliance refers to as "America after 3 pm" (http://www.afterschoolalliance.org/AA3_Key_Findings.pdf), and the time that parents and guardians get home presents a risk factor for some children and youth as they are left unsupervised. After-school programming offers a mitigation.

Innovations and Strategies to Address Risk Factors and Building on Protective Factors at the Community Level

Earlier in the chapter, we discussed the Social Ecological Model that defines the interrelationship between the individual, the community, and society as a whole. We also discussed that within any environment (community) there are multiple systems (i.e., institutional, social, cultural, political, and economic) that individuals encounter and that influence behavior, reaction, and interaction to different degrees. Here we expand further on that to discuss the connectedness of systems at the community level with each other. If there is a change in one part of the system, the entire system is impacted. Communities are one part of a child's system. Other parts would include the child, the family, schools, and society. We need look no further than the opioid epidemic and its devastating impact on children, youth, and families in rural, urban, and suburban communities. This epidemic has created an urgency on the part of community leaders, community members, policy makers, law enforcement, schools, social service agencies, and providers to address this issue as a comprehensive wraparound approach if there is to be success in stemming the rising toll on human life and community well-being.

This notion of interrelated parts is the crux of wraparound services that are showing promise in communities across the country as ways to address the holistic needs of families and children. There are strategies that have proven to be successful in communities across the nation. When examining the effectiveness of strategies and the transferability of them to different communities, it is important to understand the culture of each community and the available resources specific to each community. Strategies that work in one community may not be prudent or effective in another. Strategies may also require informed adaptation to meet community-specific needs.

Examples of four comprehensive community-based strategies that show promise or evidence of effectiveness are the Communities that Care (CTC) Model, Wraparound Milwaukee, Children Come First Initiative, and the Comprehensive Community Mental Health Services for Children and Their Families Program (Children's Mental Health Initiative; CMHI).

Communities that Care (CTC) that has been deemed a promising program by SAMHSA. The program is a prevention system that connects community resources in an effort to address adolescent health and behavior problems (SAMHSA, 2015) and has been implemented in varying communities across the country. The goal is to use tested, empirical interventions to reduce risk factors while encouraging protective factors in the community. The program was developed with benchmarks and milestones to help track progress and fidelity of program implementation. There are five stages that include: (1) Community Readiness Assessment; (2) community training event to introduce CTC to community leaders; (3) CTC board members complete an assessment of the levels and types of youth problem behaviors and hone in on risk and protective factors specific to the community; (4) community action plan is developed; and (5) action plan is implemented based on what was chosen in the prior stage. Studies of the program across 24 communities that followed students over a period of 9 years showed that at grade 7, students in CTC were less likely to initiate delinquent behavior. In grades 8 and 9, there were lowered incidences of delinquent behavior, alcohol, cigarette, and smokeless tobacco use.

Wraparound Milwaukee, founded in 1995, is an internationally recognized model that provides care for children with serious emotional, behavioral, and mental health needs as well as their families (Wisconsin Council on Children and Families, 2016). It is based on a strengths model that focuses on building on the assets of families by providing services that are catered to the unique needs of each family. The wraparound services include one family-one plan of care; cost-effective community-based alternatives to residential treatment placements, juvenile correctional placement as appropriate, and psychiatric hospitalization; increased parent choice and family independence; and care for children in the context of their family and community (Wraparound Milwaukee, 2017). Results from a two-year longitudinal study shows that the rates of recidivism appeared to remain stable over time. Moreover, the longer youth remained in the program, the rate of recidivism decreased.

Another program in Wisconsin that has garnered attention using the wraparound approach is the **Children Come First Initiative** in Dane County. It provides wraparound services for children ages 0–19 with diagnosed mental health concerns (The Children Come First Program, 2018). The focus of the services is to help youth avoid out-of-home placement. The initiative provides individual support, engaged planning that includes the family, professionals, and caring adults as a support team for the youth, along with advocacy services all based in cultural sensitivity.

Since 1993, SAMHSA has funded grants and cooperative agreements through the **Comprehensive Community Mental Health Services for Children and Their Families Program, Children's Mental Health Initiative (CMHI)**, to states, counties, territories, and federally recognized Native American tribes and Alaska Native communities to establish and support the wide scale expansion of systems of care. These communities have established partnerships with child-serving agencies to provide a comprehensive array of coordinated evidence-based services to children and youth, and their families. The goal is to help improve the functioning of children and youth in school, at home, and in the community. This coordination promotes greater access to mental health services, as children and youth are able to enter the system of care through multiple entry points. Data show that among children and youth served by system of care grantees initially funded in 2009–2010, 27% were referred by mental health agencies, 14% by caregivers, 13% by schools, 13% by child welfare agencies, and 9% by the juvenile justice system. This indicates that systems are working together to provide access to mental health services and supports for families (adaptation and language used from source—SAMHSA, 2016).

Conclusion

As we have described in this chapter, communities are dynamic "ecosystems" (a network of interrelated systems), where there is the convergence of diversity, culture, social norms, systems, and structures. Collectively, and quite frankly inevitably, this creates both risk and protection for communities and its members. In many communities, risk factors are amplified by the effects of pervasive discrimination, historical trauma, violence, poverty, and often a lack of capacity to address issues of cultural competence. Coupled with the often fragmented and siloed approaches to providing services and supports, many communities struggle to achieve positive outcomes. Efforts to harness the assets or protective factors of communities that can serve as the necessary armor to address risk factors and challenges must include a comprehensive approach as described in the chapter.

References

Anderson, S., Leventhal, T., & Dupéré, V. (2014). Exposure to neighborhood affluence and poverty in childhood and adolescence and academic achievement and behavior. *Applied Developmental Science, 18*, 123–138.

Blueprints for Healthy Youth Development. (2016). *Blueprints.* Retrieved from http://www.blueprintsprograms.com/factsheet/communities-that-care

Bookman, A. (2004). *Starting in our own backyards: How working families can build community and survive the new economy.* New York: Routledge.

Boyle, M. H., Georgiades, K., Racine, Y., & Mustard, C. (2007). Neighborhood and family influences on educational attainment: Results from the Ontario Child Health Study Follow-up 2001. *Child Development, 78*, 169–189.

Brady, S. S., Gorman-Smith, D., Henry, D. B., & Tolan, P. H. (2008). Adaptive coping reduces the impact of community violence exposure on violent behavior among African American and Latino male adolescents. *Journal of Abnormal Child Psychology, 36*, 105–115.

Buka, S., Stichick, T., Birdthistle, I., & Earls, F. (2001). Youth exposure to violence: Prevalence, risks and consequences. *American Journal of Orthopsychiatry, 71*, 298–310.

Bursik, R. J., & Grasmick, H. (1993). *Neighborhoods and crime: The dimensions of effective community control.* New York: Lexington.

Centers for Disease Control and Prevention [CDC], n.d. *The social-ecological model: A framework for prevention.* Retrieved from: https://www.cdc.gov/violenceprevention/overview/social-ecologicalmodel.html

The Children Come First Program. (2018, April). *Rise.* Retrieved from http://risewisconsin.org/programs/children-come-first/

Cohn, D., & Caumont, A. (2016, March 31). *10 demographic trends that are shaping the U.S. and the world.* Washington, DC: PEW Research Center. Retrieved from http://www.pewresearch.org/fact-tank/2016/03/31/10-demographic-trends-that-are-shaping-the-u-s-and-the-world/

Community Tool Box, n.d. Section 2. *Understanding and describing the community.* Retrieved from https://ctb.ku.edu/en/table-of-contents/assessment/assessing-community-needs-and-resources/describe-the-community/main

Cross, T., Bazron, B., Dennis, K., & Isaacs, M. (1989). *Towards a culturally competent system of care*, Volume 1. Washington, DC: CASSP Technical Assistance Center, Center for Child Health and Mental Health Policy, Georgetown University Child Development Center.

Dean, H. (2017). *A public health approach to achieving health equity.* Retrieved from: http://www.astho.org/StatePublicHealth/A-Public-Health-Approach-to-Achieving-Health-Equity/4-3-17/

Donlan, A. E., Prescott, J. E., & Zaff, J. F. (2016). Differential predictors of academic achievement: Individual and familial factor interactions with community poverty. *Journal of Children and Poverty, 22*, 113–132.

Duncan, G. J., Connell, J. P., & Klebanov, P. K. (1997). Conceptual methodological issues in estimating causal effects of neighborhoods and family conditions on individual development. In J. Brooks-Gunn, G. Duncan, & J. L. Aber (Eds.), *Neighborhood poverty: Context and consequences for children* (pp. 219–250). New York: Sage Press.

Dupéré, V., Lacourse, É., Willms, J. D., Leventhal, T., & Tremblay, R. E. (2008). Neighborhood poverty and early transition to sexual activity in young adolescents: A developmental ecological approach. *Child Development, 79*, 1463–1476.

Durlak, J. A., & Weissberg, R. P. (2007). *The impact of after-school programs that promote personal and social skills.* Chicago, IL: Collaborative for Academic, Social, and Emotional Learning.

Eller, T. J. (1996). *Dynamics of economic wellbeing: Poverty, 1992–1993. Who stays poor? Who doesn't?* Washington, DC: U.S. Government Printing Office.

Frey, W. H. (2016). The "diversity explosion" is America's twenty first baby boom. In E. Lewis & N. Cantor (Eds.), *Our compelling interests: The value of diversity for democracy and prosperous society* (pp. 16–36). Princeton, NJ: Princeton University Press.

Gottfedson, D. C., Gertenblith, S. A., Soulè, D. A., Womer, S. C., & Lu, S. (2004). Do after school programs reduce delinquency? *Prevention Science, 5*, 253–266.

Holliday, M. R., Cimetta, A., Yaden, D., Marx, R. W., & Cutshaw, C. A. (2014). Protective factors for school readiness among children in poverty. *Journal of Education for Students Placed at Risk, 19*, 125–147.

Hopson, L. M., & Lee, E. (2011). Mitigating the effect of family poverty on academic and behavioral outcomes: The role of school climate in middle school. *Children & Youth Services Review, 33*, 2221–2229.

Kim, B. K. E., Gilman, A. B., Hill, K. G., & Hawkins, J. D. (2016). Examining protective factors against violence among high-risk youth: Findings from the Seattle Social Development Project. *Journal of Criminal Justice, 45*, 19–25.

Larson, R. W. (2000). Toward a psychology of positive youth development. *American Psychologist, 55*, 170–183. Retrieved from https://www.researchgate.net/publication/228994496_Youth_Engagement_in_After-School_Programs_A_Perspective_from_Experience_Sampling

Leventhal, T., & Brooks-Gunn, J. (2000). The neighborhood they live in: The effects of neighborhood residence upon child and adolescent outcomes. *Psychological Bulletin, 12*, 313–344.

MacQueen, K. M., McLellan, E., Metzger, D. S., Kegeles, S., Strauss, R. P., Scotti, R., & Trotter, R. T. (2001). What is community? An evidence-based definition for participatory public health. *American Journal of Public Health, 91*(12), 1929–1938.

Mathie, A., & Cunningham, G. (2003). From clients to citizens: Asset-based community development as a strategy for community-driven development. *Development in Practice, 13*, 474–486.

Miles, J., Espiritu, R. C., Horen, N., Sebian, J., & Waetzig, E. (2010). *A public health approach to children's mental health: A conceptual framework: Expanded executive summary.* Washington, DC: Georgetown University Center for Child and Human Development, National Technical Assistance Center for Children's Mental Health.

Overstreet, S., & Mazza, J. (2003). An ecological-transactional understanding of community violence: Theoretical perspectives. *School Psychology Quarterly, 18*, 66–87.

Passel, Jeffrey S. and D'Vera Cohn. (2008). *Trends in unauthorized immigration: Undocumented inflow now trails legal inflow.* Washington, DC: Pew Research Center, October.

Putnam, R. D. (2007). *Bowling alone: The collapse and revival of American community.* New York: Simon & Schuster.

Rosenzweig, J. M., Brennan, E. M., Huffstutter, K., & Bradley, J. R. (2008). Child care and employed parents of children with emotional or behavioral disorders. *Journal of Emotional and Behavioral Disorders, 16*, 78–89.

Rutter, M. (1985). Resilience in the face of adversity: Protective factors and resistance to psychiatric disorder. *British Journal of Psychiatry, 147*, 598–611.

Sampson, R. J., Morenoff, J. D., & Gannon-Rowley, T. (2002). Assessing "neighborhood effects": Social processes and new directions in research. *Annual Review of Sociology, 28*, 443–478.

Sastry, N., & Pebley, A. R. (2010). Family and neighborhood sources of socioeconomic inequality in children's achievement. *Demography, 47*, 777–800.

Shaw, C. R., & McKay, H. D. (1942). *Juvenile delinquency and urban areas.* Chicago: University of Chicago Press.

Shernoff, D. J., & Vandell, D. (2008). *Youth engagement in afterschool programs: A perspective from experience sampling.* Paper presented at the Annual Meeting of the American Educational Research Association, New York, NY, March 26. Retrieved from https://www.researchgate.net/publication/228994496_Youth_Engagement in After-School_Programs_A_Perspective_from_Experience_Sampling

Stein, B. D., Jaycox, L., Kataoka, S. H., Rhodes, H., & Vestal, K. D. (2003). Prevalence of child and adolescent exposure to community violence. *Clinical Child and Family Psychology Review, 6*, 247–264.

Substance Abuse and Mental Health Services Administration (SAMHSA). (2015). Risk and protective factors. SAMHSA. Retrieved from https://www.samhsa.gov/capt/practicing-effective-prevention/prevention-behavioral-health/risk-protective-factors

Substance Abuse and Mental Health Services Administration (SAMHSA). (2016). *SAMHSA: Increasing access to behavioral health services and supports through systems of care* (HHS Publication No. SMA-16-4965). Washington, DC. Retrieved from http://www.samhsa.gov/sites/default/files/programs_campaigns/childrens_mental_health/awareness-day-2016-short-report.pdf

Tolan, P. H., Gorman-Smith, D., & Henry, D. B. (2003). The developmental ecology of urban males' youth violence. *Developmental Psychology, 39*, 274–291.

Von Bertanlaffy, L. (1968). *General system theory.* New York: George Brazzilier.

Whipple, S. S., Evans, G. W., Barry, R. L., & Maxwell, L. E. (2010). An ecological perspective on cumulative school and neighborhood risk factors related to achievement. *Journal of Applied Developmental Psychology, 31*, 422–427.

Wisconsin Council on Children and Families. (2016, May). Wraparound's recipe for success. *Wisconsin Council on Children and Families.* Retrieved from http://www.wccf.org/assets/wraparound-brief-may-2016-2.0.pdf

Wraparound Milwaukee. (2017). Retrieved from http://wraparoundmke.com/

Xue, Y., Leventhal, T., Brooks-Gunn, J., & Earls, F. J. (2005). Neighborhood residence and mental health problems of 5- to 11-year olds. *Archives of General Psychiatry, 62*, 554–563.

Zeldin, S., & Topitzes, D. (2002). Neighborhood experiences, community connection, and positive beliefs about adolescents amounts urban adults and youth. *Journal of Community Psychology, 30*, 647–669.

CHAPTER FOURTEEN

Family Matters

Exploring the Role of Family Socialization and Parenting Practices in Promoting the Social and Emotional Learning of Children and Youth[*]

Robert J. Jagers, Brittney Williams, and David Osher

Children and youth of color and those from under-resourced backgrounds continue to be placed at elevated risk for under-realizing their fullest potential. This is reflected in and results from inequities in the areas of health, education, and economics. These inequities are rooted in nagging poverty, which can be exacerbated by persistent racial, ethnic, class, and gender discrimination. While it is tempting to focus on life challenges, deficits, and shortcomings, we find great utility in viewing children, youth, and adults in terms of their demonstrated and unrealized potential for optimal human development. Settings, both proximal and distal, can be thought of in terms of the degree to which they can and do support such development and families can be viewed not just in terms of the needs but in terms of their

[*] Portions of this chapter are adapted with permission from R. J. Jagers, F. N. Mustafaa, & B. Noel, "Cultural integrity and African American empowerment: Insights and practical implications for community psychology," in M. A. Bond, I. Serrano-García, C. B. Keys, & M. Shinn (Eds.), *APA handbook of community psychology: Methods for community research and action for diverse groups and issues* (pp. 459–474). Washington, DC: American Psychological Association, 2017.

ecological resources such as their social networks, cultural beliefs, and cultural assets (Lee, 2009). Our inclination then is to identify existing social and emotional abilities and strengths and leverage those assets to co-create greater access to necessary and desired resources and opportunities so that young people and adults, especially those from historically marginalized groups, can fully explore, define, and cultivate meaningful individual and collective development and well-being.

Social-emotional learning (SEL) is the process through which children, youth, and adults gain the intrapersonal and interpersonal knowledge, skills, attitudes, and behaviors that allow for constructive interactions. There is clear evidence of that high-quality implementation of well-designed school-based SEL programs and approaches can contribute to the healthy development of children and youth. Such programs have been found to reduce or prevent the onset of problem and health-compromising attitudes and behaviors (e.g., aggression, violence, unsafe sex, and substance use), to promote desirable developmental competencies (e.g., empathy, perspective-taking, constructive social problem-solving, and academic achievement) (Durlak et al., 2011). Kendziora and Osher (2015) argue that SEL can be done at scale and its impacts can be sustained over time (Taylor et al., 2017). The SEL field has grown substantially over the past two decades and is garnering significant attention for demonstrated capacity to improve social, emotional, and academic outcomes (Osher et al., 2016). This growth has included exploring different strategies to ensure programs will be efficacious. One of these strategies has been to add a family or parent component to reinforce the skills taught at school and promote the same skills at home.

As part of the increased interest in SEL, questions are being raised about issues of equity and the appropriateness of SEL frameworks, programs, and assessments to address the developmental imperatives of children and youth of color (e.g., Jagers, Rivas-Drake, & Borowski, in press; Osher et al., 2016). We have begun to elaborate on the ways in which issues of equity inform core competencies and classroom practices. This chapter affords an opportunity to begin to flesh out how families might contribute to the systemic SEL models, and not just as skill reinforcers. This can contribute to developing a program of action research to refine SEL theory and practice. Although the issues raised are relevant and, in some aspects, unique for all cultural groups, we will focus on black and Latino families.

Framing the Issues

Consistent with recent work on the science of learning and development (Osher, Cantor, Berg, Steyer, & Rose, 2017, 2018), we recognize that while families can face substantial adversities, they can and do provide a context for constructive adult and adult-child relationships and thereby promote health developmental of their children and youth. As such, our framing in this chapter is asset-focused, based on the knowledge that most families have positive goals and aspirations for adults and children as well as strategies and practices that can be employed to pursue and achieve such goals and aspirations. This chapter explores the ways in which families can and do contribute to social, emotional, and academic development, both in terms of family socialization processes.

Guiding Frameworks

The CASEL framework for systemic SEL is foundational to our thinking about SEL in the family context. In essence, it is an ecological model that articulates a set of core competencies that develop in classroom, school, family, and community contexts (see figure 14.1).

Additionally, we find utility in the Phenomenological Variant of Ecological Systems Theory (PVEST; Spencer & Swanson, 2013), which provides a lens to understand youth development in the context of inequity. The PVEST model consists of five basic components that form a dynamic theoretical system and are applicable to any period of the life course; however, the nature of protective factors and risks are specific to identity development. While a full treatment of PVEST is beyond the current scope, we point to several elements that help to guide the current chapter. Not only does this framing align with the position of Rivas-Drake and colleagues (this volume) around the critical role of identity as an important social and emotional competence for diverse youth, it also helps us position families as a proximal socializing institution that can help to foster healthy development despite the myriad distal and local risk factors youth may be confronted with (Osher, Cantor, Berg, Steyer, & Rose, 2018).

Finally, this chapter is also informed by Empowerment Theory (Zimmerman, 2000). Empowerment is understood to be a multilevel concept, comprising individual, organizational, and community levels. Each empowerment level includes processes (empowering) and outcomes (empowered); and, depending on the setting, the levels can be interdependent. Psychological empowerment describes empowerment at the individual level and has intrapersonal, interactional, and behavioral components. Organizational empowerment refers to organizational efforts to generate psychological empowerment among members and the capacity for goal attainment. Community empowerment includes efforts to deter community threats, improve quality of life, and facilitate citizen participation in the political, social, and economic life of the community (Zimmerman, 2000). It can, under the right conditions, foster as well as build upon collective resilience (Cadell, Karabanow, & Sanchez, 2001; Ebersöhn, 2012).

The healthy development of individual family members strengthens the family unit, which in turn helps foster psychological empowerment and

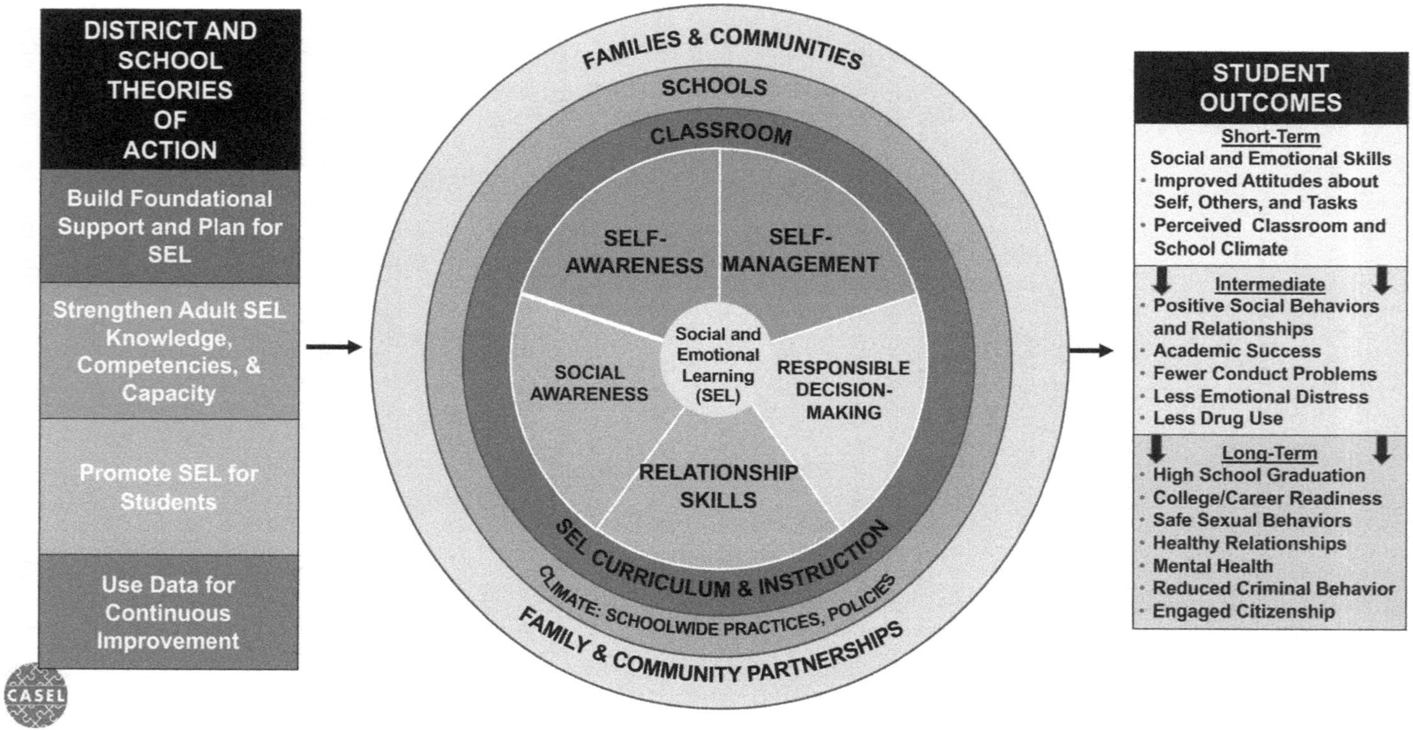

Figure 14.1 A framework for systemic SEL in educational settings (Weissberg et al., 2015)

collective empowerment at the family and community level. Authentic empowerment must be rooted in a group's cultural assets and resources. Psychology tends to focus on subjective culture, which shapes social norms, beliefs, values, and behaviors, such as gender and familial roles, communication patterns, affective styles, in-group/out-group relations, and values regarding the nature of personal control, individualism, collectivism, spirituality, and religiosity (Triandis et al., 1980). Cultural integrity provides a self-affirming, proactive frame through which to articulate and pursue desirable intrapersonal, interpersonal, and institutional processes and outcomes. At the same time, we recognize that culture, race, and class intersect, but should not be conflated. This view allows us to understand cultural similarities and differences that can be found within and across racial and ethnic groups.

Family Stressors and Supports in Social, Political, and Economic Contexts

Families are affected by macro-level factors that include public policy, the distribution of economic and public social resources, and opportunities (Jutte, Miller, & Erickson, 2015; Osher et al., 2018). Importantly, a recent report on the racial wealth gap sheds light on the ways in which institutionalized and interpersonal racial discrimination continues to stifle individual and collective wealth accumulation and its intergenerational transfer for African Americans (Darity et al., 2018). This scenario affects important factors that include parental stress levels, bandwith, and access to financial resources and social capital that bear on the healthy development and functioning of adults and children. For example, housing features, such as insufficient space or privacy and environmental toxins, as well as housing insecurity, provide examples of resource-related factors that can affect the quality of social, emotional, and cognitive development (Bassuk et al., 1997; Diette & Ribar, 2015; Kipke, Simon, Montgomery, Unger, & Iversen, 1997; Matthews & Gallo, 2011; Wigle et al., 2007, 2008). Crowded homes can limit parental responsiveness and speech (Evans, 2004), and housing insecurity can contribute to student mobility and homelessness that have impacts on self-regulation (e.g., Herbers, Reynolds, & Chen, 2013; Masten & Tellegen, 2012; Osher et al., 2018) as well as school mobility that affects attainment. Although family structure per se does not impact development directly, it can indirectly (Bornstein, 2015; Osher et al., 2018). Single parenting provides an example. Single parents typically have less time to spend with their children because they often juggle competing demands for their time (Carlson & Corcoran, 2004; Cenegy & Brewer, 2013; Grusec & Davidov, 2010).

For these reasons and others, the notion of what constitutes a family has changed. Family structure has become more fluid and heterogeneous in the last half century. In 2014, 26% of children younger than age 18 lived with a single parent—up from 9% in 1960 (Pew Research Center, 2015). In 2010, 7% of children lived in households headed by a grandparent (U.S. Census Bureau, 2010) and 17% of these children living with grandparents were being raised in homes with no biological or adoptive parent present. Parents may be monoracial or interracial, may be same-sex or different-sex, and may be adoptive, biological, or a mixture of both (Powell, Hamilton, Manago, & Cheng, 2016). Parents also vary in terms of age and culture. Children's residences also vary; some children live in foster care or custodial care as a result of caregiver maltreatment and abuse, adjudication or conviction, disability or incapacity, incarceration, or death (Osher et al., 2017).

Family configurations vary, and people in many roles can provide parent-like support. Regardless of family structure, family members can fulfill common functions—they can provide bonding, safety, and connection while providing social and cultural capital. Families across all structures and groups can play this role, and families across socioeconomic and cultural spectra succeed in this role in some cases and are less successful in others. However, macro factors that affect access to resources make it harder for some families to realize these functions (Osher & Chasin, 2016).

Be that as it may, successful parenting is not due to family structure, but rather the family's resources, social supports, emotional climate, and stability, and the quality of caregiver-child interactions and relationships—the prerequisites for successful family functioning that provide bonding, connection, and safety necessary for healthy development (Grusec & Davidov, 2010; Patterson & Hastings, 2007). Further, family, tribal, and social networks, which can be key assets, are often underutilized or disincentivized in social policy. For example, many single parents successfully leverage support from their families and social networks (Gerstel, 2011; Perry-Jenkins, Newkirk, & Ghunney, 2013). Effective ecological approaches to intervention, that are also family-driven and culturally responsive, illustrate ways that schools and agencies can include extended family networks and to other social networks (Henggeler & Sheidow, 2012). For example, high-fidelity wraparound leverages the role of grandparents, siblings, other kin, and friends in supporting healthy family functioning and child development in order to provide immediate as well as sustainable social supports (Bruns, Pullmann, Sather, Brinson, & Ramey, 2015; Kendziora, Bruns, Osher, Pacchiano, & Mejia, 2001; Suter & Bruns, 2009). Peer family networks can also be important, and when high-quality interventions are implemented well they can contribute to the development of social capital (Coleman, 1988a, 1988b; Runyan et al., 1998), which can help address school challenges, even amongst Latino families (Larson & Rumberger, 1995; López Turley, Gamooran, McCarty, & Fish, 2017).

How Family-School-Community Partnerships Can Contribute to Systemic Social and Emotional Learning

The benefits of family-school-community partnerships are addressed in other chapters in this volume (see, for example, Hill et al., volume 1, chapter 20). Some compelling work has been generated on how family-school-community partnerships contribute to systemic SEL (Garbacz, Swanger-Gagné, & Sheridan, 2015). Less attention has been given to the ways in which family processes might be relevant to SEL. In the sections that follow, we begin to sketch out some of these protective and promotive factors. We first turn attention to family socialization and parenting before offering a few examples of the ways that families can be engaged in universal SEL initiatives.

Family as a Developmental Context for Social and Emotional Development

Families play an integral role in the social, emotional, and academic development of children and youth. With regards to social and emotional competence development, parents value the development of these life skills and view the home as the first place SEL occurs (Albright & Weissberg, 2009; Learning Heroes, 2018). The family context can function as a safe and open environment where children and youth can be themselves, learn, and practice social and emotional norms, cues, and skills. Substantial evidence has supported that family protective factors, such as quality parent or adult-child relationships, communication of prosocial behavior, positive discipline methods and monitoring, and values and expectations influence adolescent youth prosocial behaviors (Ary, Duncan, Duncan, & Hops, 1999; Center for Substance Abuse Prevention, 2000; Kumpfer & Alvarado, 1998).

Parents form the first emotional relationships with their children as early as infancy through attachment, which is reinforced by neurohormonal processes (Kochanska, 2001; Cantor, Osher, Berg, Strayer, & Rose, 2018). It is the quality of this relationship that creates the landscape for children's emotional and social development. As children mature and become more cognitively developed, parents engage in various behaviors to help them learn social and emotional norms. Warm, supportive, and responsive parenting has been considered the ideal parental characteristics that promote social and emotional growth as well as cognitive development (Landry, Smith, Swank, Assel, & Vellet, 2001). Parents implicitly and explicitly support their child's emotional competence (Katz, Maliken, & Stettler, 2012). For example, Eisenberg, Cumberland, and Spinrad (1998) identified three modes of parental emotional socialization: (1) reactions to emotions, (2) discussion of emotions, and (3) expression of emotion. Studies have examined these three modes extensively over the past 30 years. Parent modeling and expressivity

(Denham, Zoller, & Couchoud, 1994), explicit discourse or discussions about emotions (Baker, Fenning, & Crnic, 2011; Dunn, Bretherton, & Munn, 1987; Kopp, 1992), as well as parental emotional support of child emotional expression (Denham, Bassett, & Wyatt, 2007; Fabes, Poulin, Eisenberg, & Madden-Derdich, 2002), have all been cited as behaviors that contribute to the emotional socialization processes parents utilize that impact children's emotional developmental outcomes (i.e., emotional knowledge, understanding, and regulation).

Although researchers have examined the positive impact parents have on child emotional competence, these studies have largely focused on mothers from white, middle-class families. This is problematic for, as Marc Bornstein observes, specific individuals of specific genders, ages, ethnicities, and cultures differentially emphasize different experiences. For example, Japanese mothers expect early mastery of emotional maturity, self-control, and social courtesy, whereas European American mothers expect early mastery of verbal competence and self-expression (Bornstein, 2015). Fortunately, research that now includes racial and ethnic minorities and fathers is being brought forth to paint a more inclusive picture regarding emotional socialization in families (see Bowie et al., 2011; Cunningham, Kliewer, & Garner, 2009; Labella, 2018; Nelson, O'Brien, Calkins, & Leerkes, 2012; Nelson et al., 2013).

The parenting practices literature is also relevant. Much of this work is rooted in Baumrind's initial work, which highlighted parental warmth and parental control (1967, 1971, 1991). Parental warmth has been referred to as the parents' level of acceptance and responsiveness to their child's behaviors (Kopko, 2007). Parental control is considered the level at which parents manage the behavior of their child with rules or demands (Kopko, 2007). These two dimensions initially yielded three parenting styles or typologies that varied by warmth and control: *authoritative*, *authoritarian*, and *permissive*. The authoritative style or typology is characterized as a reasonable level of control, while exhibiting high levels of warmth and responsiveness (Baumrind, 1972). Research has often identified authoritative style or typology as yielding positive child outcomes (i.e., less externalizing and internalizing behaviors, strong academic achievement, and competency) (Baumrind, 1983; Steinberg, Lamborn, Dornbusch, & Darling, 1992). Due to the positive child outcomes associated with this style or typology, it is often presented as the "ideal" parenting style. However, studies that have promoted the authoritative style as the ideal may lack ecological validity as studies were based largely on white, middle-income families and may neither address other cultural or structural contexts (along with unique individual factors) that are important to understanding the specificity of effects (Borstein, 2015).

The authoritarian parenting style or typology has often been used to characterize African American parenting practices (Baumrind, 1972; Darling & Steinberg, 1993). Authoritarian parenting is described as being low in warmth and high in control (Baumrind, 1971). Parents of this style or typology expect their children to obey their demands and rules without in-depth discussion or explanation (Tamis-LeMonda et al., 2008). With respect to Latino parenting styles, literature based on Baumrind's framework is rather inconclusive. Studies have reported that Latino parenting practices are more aligned with authoritarian parenting (Hill, Bush, & Roosa, 2003). On the other hand, studies have also found that Mexican and Mexican American parents used authoritative practices (Calzada, Huang, Anicama, Fernandez, & Brotman, 2012; Varela et al., 2004). Calzada and colleagues (2012) examined a sample of Mexican and Dominican immigrant mothers, finding that they used more authoritative parenting practices (i.e., having conversations with children, providing choices, and explaining consequences). Critical functions and resources like monitoring of children and clear communication lead to resilience among Latino youth from both immigrant families and families that have been in America for generations (Cardoso & Thompson, 2010; Reyes & Elias, 2011).

It is also important to note that high parental control in the presence of affection and warmth can yield positive outcomes among African American children; however, it is associated with negative outcomes for their European American counterparts (Brody, Flor, & Gibson, 1999; Darling & Steinberg, 1993; McLoyd & Smith, 2002; Spieker, Larson, Lewis, Keller, and Gilchrist, 1999). To explain these differential outcomes, Kelley, Powers, and Wimbush (1992) offer that some African American children perceive parental control behaviors (e.g., parents requiring children to complete house chores) as loving, caring, and an investment in their future.

Issues of intersectionality are important, as are the unique factors that contribute to the particular interaction between a parent and child. Studies must proceed with caution when characterizing ethnic groups (e.g., Latino families). Researchers have acknowledged the influence that acculturation, when an individual's native cultural practices have adjusted to fit the majority, dominant culture (Fuller & García-Coll, 2010), has on parenting behaviors for Latino families that have been in America for generations and those that have recently immigrated. For example, as parents acculturate, their expectations for their children's behavior and their own parenting behavior changes (Calzada et al., 2012). Although ethnic minority groups may represent a particular set of cultural behaviors and values, those groups should not be approached as monolithic. They have varying levels of connection to their native culture and the majority culture.

For instance, the notion of involved vigilant parenting emerged from work with rural African American families. Involved vigilant parenting has been shown to buffer children and youth against adverse neighborhood effects, and thereby reducing problem behaviors and promoting a range of positive youth outcomes (Brody, 2016). Involved-vigilant parenting refers to a combination of parental responsiveness to their children's developmental needs and active monitoring and boundary-setting. Parental responsiveness includes displays of parental warmth and the use of inductive reasoning to help children understand and reflect on family routines, parental rules, and consequences for infractions. Parental vigilance denotes efforts to foresee and protect children from individual, interpersonal, or environmental risks. Young people receiving such parenting have greater sense of autonomy, self-regulation, assertiveness, psychological adjustment, and social and academic competence (Brody, 2016; Hurd & Sellers, 2013).

There may be some benefit to construing parenting as adaptive. Latin American immigrant parents often are required to engage in the interplay between societal, parental, and child factors that contribute to the resiliency of their children (Perreira, Chapman, & Stein, 2006). Many immigrant families have to overcome language barriers and may struggle with living in new sociocultural contexts. Adaptive parenting has been found in Mexican immigrant and Mexican American families, like many African American families, where families are living in high-risk settings parent employ strict monitoring (Cruz-Santiago & Ramírez, 2011). Latino families also balance strict monitoring, control, and warmth to build close bonds between parent and child.

Parental Ethnic and Racial Socialization

Given that issues of identity are foundational to the healthy development of children and youth, family contributions to SEL should also be considered when framing parental ethnic and racial socialization within the context of child and youth development. Parental racial socialization refers to the ways in which parents communicate to their children about being members of their racial group and has been referred to as an example of "group ways" that racially and culturally distinct groups employ to help guide the social and emotional development of their young people (Flanagan, Alfonso, & Mascolo, 2011). Such socialization helps youth execute normative development of forming their identity. In general, positive identity achievement in youth increases their likelihood of engaging in prosocial behaviors while decreasing their likelihood of engaging risky behaviors (Meeus, Iedema, Helsen, & Vollenberg, 1999). In particular, positive ethnic and racial identity development has been linked to positive psychological and health outcomes in African American (Loyd & Williams, 2017) and Latino (Reyes & Elias, 2011) youth.

The primary forms of racial socialization parents report giving and youth report receiving are:

- *Cultural socialization*, which is the emphasis of racial and cultural pride and the promotion of activities that offer youth knowledge on the cultural history of their racial group

- *Egalitarianism*, the transmission of messages that focus on individual characteristics as opposed to ones that acknowledge group differences
- *Preparation for bias*, the discussion of existing racial inequalities and providing youth with coping mechanisms on how to cope with discrimination
- *Silence about race*, the omission of messages about race
- *Self-worth messages*, the focus on a child's individual importance
- *Negative messages*, conveying negative qualities of a racial group
- *Promotion of mistrust*, the promotion of distrust of interracial interactions.

Parents who taught their children to be proud of their racial heritage instilled in adolescents the belief that being black is a positive, and that personal and collective identities are derived from a shared history of struggle and uplift. Such messages promote psychological adjustment in school (Butler-Barnes, Richardson, Chavous, & Zhu, 2018) and helps youth develop ideas about the need for prosocial behavior and involvement in civic matters (Lozada, Jagers, Smith, Bañales, & Hope, 2017). Similarly, among Latino youth, the transmission of cultural values (e.g., familism) has been positively related to prosocial behavioral tendencies, including in dire situations (e.g., "I tend to help people who are in a real crisis or need") (e.g., Calderón-Tena, Knight, & Carlo, 2011).

More importantly, Dunbar and colleagues (2017) offer an integrative model of parental emotional and racial and ethnic socialization. For example, despite the value placed on emotional expressiveness with the African American community, parents need to help their children develop adaptive coping strategies for racial bias. This includes explicit instruction regarding the need to suppress emotions in interracial interactions with authority figures. Given the prevalence and deleterious effects of microaggressions and discrimination experiences in school and community settings, this seems like a fertile line of inquiry.

Participatory Approaches to Engaging Families in SEL Programs

There are relatively few universal SEL-focused family programs (Garbacz et al., 2015); however, there has been considerable work on family-focused prevention programs (see Van Ryzin, Roseth, Fosco, Lee, & Chen, 2016). Notions of cultural relevance, cultural competence, cultural responsiveness, cultural sensitivity, cultural tailoring, and cultural appropriateness are advanced as strategies to improve engagement, uptake, and outcomes of prevention and promotion programs serving members of culturally distinct groups (Kreuter, Lukwago, Bucholtz, Clark, & Sanders-Thompson, 2003; Kumpfer, Magalhães, Xie, & Kanse, 2016). Kreuter and colleagues (2003) specify a number of cultural integration strategies that program developers, implementers, and researchers can employ. These include *linguistic* and *peripheral strategies* that reflect the use symbol systems such as dominant language forms and preferred colors, images, fonts, pictures, or images to appeal to participants. A *sociocultural strategy* integrates the dominant cultural norms, values, beliefs, and behaviors of the group into program activities and materials. An *evidential strategy* provides data on a relevant problem, while a *constituent-involving strategy* seeks to benefit from the experience and knowledge of the group's members in the development, delivery, and evaluation of the intervention.

Consistent with our interest in empowerment and with Winn and Richards-Shuster (chapter 16, volume 2), the literature reveals the significant promise of constituent-involving strategies to improve the content, delivery, engagement, and outcomes of prevention and promotion programs. Such approaches improve program quality and results by increasing the voice and choice of diverse adult stakeholders as aspects of the effort. As Winn and Richards-Schuster point out, programs can vary with regard to the amount of influence or power that researchers and constituents actually exercise in their partnership.

There are a number of parenting programs that were derived through community-based participatory research. Several such programs seek to leverage parenting practices to influence youth outcomes positively. These include controlled trials of programs for nonresidential fathers and their preadolescent sons (Caldwell et al., 2010, 2014), rural African American families (Brody et al., 2006; Murry et al., 2011) and urban Native American families (Kulis, Ayers, & Baker, 2015). These efforts yield evidence of significant risk prevention or reduction effects that are mediated by parenting factors highlighted earlier.

For example, the Fathers and Sons Program is a family-centered, culturally relevant, and gender-specific intervention designed to improve the relationship between nonresident African American fathers and their preadolescent sons as a means to prevent or reduce substance use and violent behavior of fathers and sons and to prevent early sexual initiation among sons (Caldwell et al., 2010). The program was developed through a community-based participatory research approach through which community partners formed a steering committee that guided development, implementation, and evaluation of the 15-session program. Fathers and Sons uses small group sessions and features 24 hours of specific content in the areas of African American cultural connections and history, effective parent-child communication, parental monitoring and role-modeling, social support networks and prevention of violence, unsafe sex, and substance use behaviors. Homework and community activities are used to reinforce content of the structured sessions.

Results indicated a high level of engagement such that the average attendance was 12.2 out of 15 sessions for fathers and 12.5 out of 15 sessions for sons. Among intervention fathers, there were increases in reported parental monitoring, communication about risk behaviors, race-related socialization, satisfaction with parenting skills, and intention for future communications with sons. Sons in the intervention condition reported greater monitoring and communication about sex by their fathers. A subsequent study demonstrated indirect effects of the intervention such that reductions in sons' violent or aggressive behavior and intention for future violent behavior occurred through improvements in fathers' risk communications (Caldwell et al., 2014).

Also, the Strong African American Families Program (SAAF) is an example of a robust family-centered prevention program, specifically designed for African American families, that has demonstrated positive effects for early adolescents and families (Brody et al., 2006). Parent-child dyads in SAAF take part in seven consecutive weekly sessions, with separate parent and child skill-building curricula along with family curriculum. The majority of youth are in the 6th grade, or approximately 11 years old. Each individual training session (for parents and children) is then followed by a joint session during which the families practice the skills that were taught in their respective sessions. Parents and youth receive a total of 14 hours of prevention training. Caregivers are taught communicative and involved-vigilant parenting strategies, while youth focused on the importance of supportive family relationships and agreement of household expectations, peer pressure, positive racial identity, and resistance efficacy strategies. In this quasi-experimental design, parents were found to have increases in regulated, communicative parenting and a decrease in high-risk behavior initiation among youth (Brody et al., 2006). Behavior changes were assessed three months after the final program session, with researchers finding communicative parenting mediated the significance of the programming on youths' perceptions of changes in parenting processes, which was then associated with a difference in youth's alcohol use and sexual activity.

The Caregiver Discussion Guide developed by CASEL practitioners (Salazar, n.d.) offers co-constructed content to support caregiver efforts to be informed partners in school-based SEL initiatives. The eight discussion sessions take place among parents and other concerned community members to illuminate the ways in which caregivers might be actively engaged in systemic SEL. Early indications from an initial pilot study with community organizations serving Latino families, are that caregivers find the discussion series informative and catalytic. For example, several caregivers sought to use their new insights to fill slots and become active participants on school-based SEL parent advisory committees. The discussion series has been taken up by an African American parent group in a nearby school community.

Fuentes (2012) describes a three-year study of Parents of Children of African Ancestry (POCAA) in which family member exercised considerable autonomy. POCAA is a grassroots community organization that formed to address the disproportionate underachievement of black students in the local public schools. After reviewing school district data on academic performance of 9th graders, the group devised an intensive two-semester intervention that including four newly hired teachers to construct a small learning community.

Core courses were augmented by weekly motivational assemblies and courses on study skills and stress management. After 10 weeks, the vast majority of participating students were passing their classes and attending school regularly. Nearly all the students were still on track when they entered the 10th grade. The program served as a catalyst for parent and community organizing in support of student school achievement and prompted the school district to form a district-wide equity task force made up of multiracial coalitions.

Shen and colleagues (2017) review a number of studies of the influences and impacts of parent co-researchers in health research. The 10 studies included both international and U.S. samples and were primarily focused on basic and applied studies of healthy lifestyles. The studies yielded variations in the ways in which parents were engaged in the research process. Caregivers were often involved in developing research questions and priorities, study designs, data collection tools, data management and analysis, write-ups of findings, and the development of interventions. They seldom took part in project conceptualization or grant writing, however.

Engaging parents as co-researchers has been found to result in more ecologically valid, meaningful, impactful, and sustainable health interventions. Parent co-researchers increased their health knowledge, research skills, and sense of empowerment. While Shen and colleagues' findings align with desired empowerment and equity goals, some challenges were noted. Extra resources were required to develop and manage researcher-co-researcher relationships. Researchers and parent co-researchers had different motivations for doing the work and power imbalances among co-researchers and between researchers and co-researchers raised concerns about training and cautions about tokenism.

This review has important lessons for us as we begin a partnership with a collaborating school district that will feature parents as evaluators of implementation and impacts of classroom and school-level SEL.

Conclusion

SEL has tremendous potential to improve developmental outcomes for children and youth from diverse backgrounds. In order to realize that potential, the field must evolve strategies, frameworks, programs, approaches, and assessments that remove barriers and create equitable learning environments and equitable outcomes for each and every student. This chapter provides an opportunity for us to begin to outline some of the implications for advancing this work in the area of family SEL.

Families are essential partners in systemic SEL, but fairly few universal SEL programs include and leverage their potential contributions. We see general parenting practices and emotional and racial socialization as key factors that our work should attend to. There appear to be underexamined variations in emotional socialization that are informed both by cultural preference and the press to cope with racial discrimination. The intersection of emotional and racial socialization messages merits particular attention, given the nature and regularity of the institutional and interpersonal violence (physical and psychological) being visited on people of color currently.

In addition, we need to understand and include other family members in this effort. For example, although parents play a key role in emotional socialization within a family context, siblings also impact how children develop emotionally (Cicirelli, 1982; Osher et al., 2018). Sibling relationships are important and often span across a lifetime (Noller, 2005). The relationships and interactions among siblings can create intense emotional interactions that can be both loving and hostile (Kennedy & Kramer, 2008). Similar to parental characteristics, warm and supportive sibling relationships are associated with age-appropriate emotional regulation (Kennedy & Kramer, 2008) and prosocial behaviors (Pike, Coldwell, & Dunn, 2005). Conversely, if sibling relationships are aggressive, nonsupportive, and conflictual, the outcomes are negative (i.e., externalizing, problem, and antisocial behaviors) (Aguilar, O'Brien, August, Aoun, & Hektner, 2001). Sibling relationships also may fill voids when the parent-child relationship is uninvolved or unsupportive (Dunn, 2015). Positive interactions with siblings often foster emotional expressivity, awareness, and understanding, which in turn foster positive social interactions with others outside of the home.

Further, family support for children and youth often stretches outside the boundaries of the immediate family members for ethnic and racial minority groups. African American extended family and kinship networks are pivotal to the emotional development and psychological well-being of African American children and youth (Boyd-Franklin, 2003). In a study with African American mothers, McLoyd (1990, 1998) reported emotional and practical support from partners, extended family members, and friends may increase consistent and involved parenting behaviors. Having support buffered mothers against depression and helped foster positive parent-child relations, which led to more nurturing and consistent maternal behaviors and less use of punitive strategies (e.g., scolding and ridiculing) (McLoyd, 1990; Weinraub & Wolf, 1983). Similarly, *familismo*, in the Latino community is a term often used to describe cultural characteristics (i.e., loyalty, respect, solidarity, and interdependence), that applies to blood relatives as well as extended kin networks (Falicov, 2005; Padilla & Villalobos, 2007). Extended family and kinship support is essential in sustaining positive development for ethnic and racial minority youth in general, as it provides supplemental or additional, and at times primary, support to youth when parents are not able. Although many agents in and outside of the home play an important role in children's socialization processes, parents, in particular, are considered the main socializing agents for their children (Maccoby, 1992), providing the most direct socialization practices to foster these skills.

Doing this work requires cultural humility (Danso, 2018; Tervalon & Murray-Garcia, 1998), cultural reciprocity (Kalyanpur & Harry, 2012), and cultural responsiveness (Osher et al., 2018) on the part of researchers whose perspectives and stakes may not be the same as those of families. Family agency and voice is important, and this will require culturally competent family-driven approaches (Osher, Wood, & Osher, in press; Osher et al., 2011). We see benefit in using participatory methods to engage families actively and meaningfully in the development, implementation, and evaluation of SEL initiatives, especially components that focus on family processes or partnership with schools or community organizations. This approach has been used successfully in the health sciences (e.g., Osher, Van Kammen, & Zaro, 2001), but we did not find much of any use of this method with family or community stakeholders in the area of SEL. There is a substantial upside to viewing caregivers as collaborators, especially with regard to evaluation, where they can contribute to the validity and reliability of findings. However, doing this well (e.g., authentic partnering) will require the necessary human and material resources that will include support for both families and professionals.

References

Aguilar, B., O'Brien, K. M., August, G. J., Aoun, S. L., & Hektner, J. M. (2001). Relationship quality of aggressive children and their siblings: A multiinformant, multimeasure investigation. *Journal of Abnormal Child Psychology, 29*, 479–489. doi:10.1023/A:1012273024211

Albright, M. I., & Weissberg, R. P. (2009). School-family partnerships to promote social and emotional learning. In S. L. Christenson & A. L. Reschley (Eds.), *The handbook of school-family partnerships* (pp. 246–265). New York: Routledge/Taylor and Francis Group.

Ary, D. V., Duncan, T. E., Duncan, S. C., & Hops, H. (1999). Adolescent problem behavior: The influence of parents and peers. *Behavior Research and Therapy, 37*, 217–230.

Baker, J. K., Fenning, R. M., & Crnic, K. A. (2011). Emotion socialization by mothers and fathers: Coherence among behaviors and associations with parent attitudes and children's social competence. *Social Development, 20*, 412–430.

Bassuk, E. L., Buckner, J. C., Weinreb, L. F., Browne, A., Bassuk, S. S., Dawson, R., & Perloff, J. N. (1997). Homelessness in female-headed families: Childhood and adult risk and protective factors. *American Journal of Public Health, 87*, 241–248.

Baumrind, D. (1967). Effects of authoritative parental control on child behavior. *Child Development, 37*, 887–907.

Baumrind, D. (1971). Current patterns of parental authority. *Developmental Psychology, 4*, 1–103.

Baumrind, D. (1972). An exploratory study of socialization effects on black children: Some black-white comparisons. *Child Development, 43*, 261–267.

Baumrind, D. (1983). Rejoinder to Lewis's reinterpretation of parental firm control effects: Are authoritative families really harmonious? *Psychological Bulletin, 94*, 132–142.

Baumrind, D. (1991). The influence of parenting style on adolescent competence and substance use. *Journal of Early Adolescence, 11*, 56–95.

Bornstein, M. H. (2015). Children's parents. In R. M. Lerner (Editor-in-Chief) & M. H. Bornstein & T. Leventhal (Vol. Eds.), *Handbook of child psychology and developmental science: Vol. 4. Ecological settings and processes in developmental systems* (7th ed., pp. 55–132). Hoboken, NJ: Wiley.

Bowie, B. H., Carrère, S., Cooke, C., Valdivia, G., McAllister, B., & Doohan, E. (2011). The role of culture in parents' socialization of children's emotional development. *Western Journal of Nursing Research, 35*, 514–533.

Boyd-Franklin, N. (2003). *Black families in therapy: Understanding the African American experience.* New York: Guilford.

Brody, G. H. (2016). Family-centered prevention for rural African Americans: The Strong African American Families Program (SAAF), the Strong African American Families-Teen Program (SAAF-T) and the Adults in the Making Program (AIM). In M. J. Van Ryzin, K. L. Kumpfer, G. M. Fosco, & M. T. Greenberg (Eds.), *Family-based prevention programs for children and adolescents: Theory, research, and large-scale dissemination* (pp. 282–307). New York, NY: Psychology Press.

Brody, G. H., Chen, Y., Murry, V. M., Ge, X., Simons, R. L., Gibbons, F. X., . . . Cutrona, C. E. (2006). Perceived discrimination and the adjustment of African American youths: A five-year longitudinal analysis with contextual moderation effects. *Child Development, 77*, 1170–1189. doi:10.1111/j.1467-8624.2006.00927.x

Brody, G. H., Flor, D. L., & Gibson, N. M. (1999). Linking maternal efficacy beliefs, developmental goals, parenting practices, and child competence in rural single-parent African American families. *Child Development, 70*(5), 1197–1208.

Bruns, E. J., Pullmann, M. D., Sather, A., Brinson, R. D., & Ramey, M. (2015). Effectiveness of wraparound vs. case management for children and adolescents: Results of a randomized study. *Administration and Policy in Mental Health, 42*, 309–322. doi:10.1007/s10488-014-0571-3

Butler-Barnes, S. T., Richardson, B. L, Chavous, T. M., & Zhu, J. (2018). The importance of racial socialization: School-based racial discrimination and racial identity among African American adolescent boys and girls. *Journal of Research on Adolescence.* doi: 10.1111/jora.12383

Cadell, S., Karabanow, J., & Sanchez, M. (2001). Community, empowerment, and resilience: Paths to wellness. *Canadian Journal of Community Mental Health, 20*, 21–35.

Calderón-Tena, C. O., Knight, G. P., & Carlo, G. (2011). The socialization of prosocial behavioral tendencies among Mexican American adolescents: The role of familism values. *Cultural Diversity and Ethnic Minority Psychology, 17*, 98–106.

Caldwell, C. H., Antonakos, C., Assari, S., Kruger, D., De Loney, D. H., & Njai, R. (2014). Pathways to prevention: Improving nonresidential African American fathers' parenting skills and behaviors to reduce sons' aggression. *Child Development, 85*, 308–325.

Caldwell, C. H., Rafferty, J., Reischl, T., De Loney, E. H., & Brooks, C. L. (2010). Enhancing parenting skills among nonresident African American fathers as a strategy for preventing youth risky behaviors. *American Journal of Community Psychology, 45*, 17–35.

Calzada, E. J., Huang, K. Y., Anicama, C., Fernandez, Y., & Brotman, L. M. (2012). Test of a cultural framework of parenting with Latino families of young children. *Cultural Diversity & Ethnic Minority Psychology, 18*, 285–296. doi:10.1037/a0028694

Cantor, P., Osher, D., Berg, J., Strayer, L., & Rose, T. (2018). Malleability, plasticity, and individuality: How children learn and develop in context. *Applied Developmental Science*. doi:10.1080/10888691.2017.1398649.

Cardoso, J. B., & Thompson, S. J. (2010). Common themes of resilience among Latino immigrant families: A systematic review of the literature. *Families in Society: The Journal of Contemporary Social Services, 91*, 1–9.

Carlson, M. J., & Corcoran, M. E. (2004). Family structure and children's behavioral and cognitive outcomes. *Journal of Marriage and Family, 63*, 779–792.

Cenegy, L. F., & Brewer, M. (2013). Family matters: Links between family structure and early child health. *Journal of Applied Research on Children: Informing Policy for Children at Risk, 4*(1), article 6. Retrieved from http://digitalcommons.library.tmc.edu/cgi/viewcontent.cgi?article=1117&context=childrenatrisk

Center for Substance Abuse Prevention. (2000). *The national cross-site evaluation of high risk youth programs: Final report*. Rockville, MD: Center for Substance Abuse Prevention, Substance Abuse and Mental Health Services Administration.

Cicirelli, V. G. (1982). Sibling influence throughout the lifespan. In M. E. Lamb & B. Sutton-Smith (Eds.), *Sibling relationships: Their nature and significance across the lifespan* (pp. 267–284). Hillsdale, NJ: Erlbaum.

Coleman, J. S. (1988a). "Social capital" and schools. *The Education Digest, 53*, 6–9.

Coleman, J. S. (1988b). Social capital in the creation of human capital. *American Journal of Sociology, 94*, S95–S120.

Cruz-Santiago, M., & Ramírez, G. J. (2011). "Hay Que Ponerse en los Zapatos del Joven": Adaptive parenting of adolescent children among Mexican-American parents residing in a dangerous neighborhood. *Family Process, 50*, 92–114. doi:10.1111/j.1545-5300.2010.01348.x

Cunningham, J. N., Kliewer, W., & Garner, P. W. (2009). Emotional socialization, child emotion understanding and regulation, and adjustment in urban African American families: Differential associations across child gender. *Development and Psychopathology, 21*, 261–283.

Danso, R. (2018). Cultural competence and cultural humility: A critical reflection on key cultural diversity concepts. *Journal of Social Work, 18*(4), 410–430. doi: 10.1177/1468017316654341

Darity, W., Jr., Hamilton, D., Paul, M., Aja, A., Price, A., Moore, A., & Chiopris, C. (2018). *What we get wrong about closing the racial wealth gap*. Retrieved from https://socialequity.duke.edu/sites/socialequity.duke.edu/files/site-images/FINAL%20COMPLETE%20REPORT_.pdf

Darling, N., & Steinberg, L. (1993). Parenting style as context: An integrative model. *Psychological Bulletin, 113*, 487–496. doi:10.1037/0033-2909.113.3.487

Denham, S. A., Bassett, H. H., & Wyatt, T. (2007). The socialization of emotional competence. In J. E. Grusec & P. D. Hastings (Eds.), *Handbook of socialization: Theory and research* (pp. 614–637). New York: Guilford.

Denham, S. A., Zoller, D., & Couchoud, E. A. (1994). Socialization of preschoolers' emotion understanding. *Developmental Psychology, 30*, 928–936.

Diette, T. M., & Ribar, D. C. (2015). *A longitudinal analysis of violence and housing insecurity* (SSRN Scholarly Paper No. ID 2678794). Rochester, NY: Social Science Research Network. Retrieved from https://papers.ssrn.com/abstract=2678794

Dunbar, A. S., Leerkes, E. M., Coard, S. I., Supple, A. J., & Calkins, S. (2017). An integrative conceptual model of parental racial/ethnic and emotion socialization and links to children's social-emotional development among African American families. *Child Development Perspectives, 11*, 16–22. doi:10.1111/cdep.12218

Dunn, J. (2015). Siblings. In J. E. Grusec & P. D. Hastings (Eds.), *Handbook of socialization: Theory and research* (pp. 182–201). New York: Guilford Press.

Dunn, J., Bretherton, I., & Munn, P. (1987). Conversations about feelings between mothers and their young children. *Developmental Psychology, 23*, 132–139.

Durlak, J. A., Weissberg, R. P., Dymnicki, A. B., Taylor, R. D., & Schellinger, K. B. (2011). The impact of enhancing students' social and emotional learning: A meta-analysis of school-based universal interventions. *Child Development, 82*(1), 405–432.

Ebersöhn, L. (2012). Adding 'flock' to 'fight and flight': A honeycomb of resilience where supply of relationships meets demand for support. *Journal of Psychology in Africa, 22*, 29–42.

Eisenberg, N., Cumberland, A., & Spinrad, T. L. (1998). Parental socialization of emotion. *Psychological Inquiry, 9*, 241–273.

Evans, G. W. (2004). The environment of childhood poverty. *American Psychologist, 59*, 77–92.

Fabes, R. A., Poulin, R. E., Eisenberg, N., & Madden-Derdich, D. A. (2002). The Coping with Children's Negative Emotions Scale (CCNES): Psychometric properties and relations with children's emotional competence. *Marriage & Family Review, 34*, 285–310.

Falicov, C. J. (2005). Emotional transnationalism and family identities. *Family Process, 44*, 399–406. doi:10.1111/j.1545-5300.2005.00068.x

Flanagan, D. P., Alfonso, V. C., & Mascolo, J. T. (2011). Essentials of cross-battery assessment. In D. P. Flangan, S. O. Ortiz, & V. C. Alfonso (Eds.), *Essentials of cross-battery assessment* (Vol. 84, pp. 233–298). Hoboken, NJ: Wiley.

Fuentes, E. H. (2012). On the rebound: Critical race praxis and grassroots community organizing for school change. *Urban Review: Issues and Ideas in Public Education, 44*, 628–648.

Fuller, B., & García-Coll, C. (2010). Learning from Latinos: Contexts, families, and child development in motion. *Developmental Psychology, 46*, 559–565.

Garbacz, S. A., Swanger-Gagné, M. S., & Sheridan, S. M. (2015). The role of school-family partnership programs for promoting student social and emotional learning. In J. Durlak, T. Gullotta, C. Domitrovich, P. Goren, & R. Weissberg (Eds.), *The handbook of social and emotional learning: Research to practice* (pp. 244–259). New York: Guilford Press.

Gerstel, N. (2011). Rethinking families and community: The color, class, and centrality of extended kin ties. *Sociological Forum, 26*, 1–20. doi:10.1111/j.1573-7861.2010.01222.x

Grusec, J. E., & Davidov, M. (2010). Integrating different perspectives on socialization theory and research: A domain-specific approach. *Child Development, 81*, 687–709.

Henggeler, S. W., & Sheidow, A. J. (2012). Empirically supported family-based treatments for conduct disorder and delinquency in adolescents. *Journal of Marital and Family Therapy, 38*, 30–58. doi:10.1111/j.1752-0606.2011.00244.x

Herbers, J. E., Reynolds, A. J., & Chen, C. C. (2013). School mobility and developmental outcomes in young adulthood. *Development and Psychopathology, 25*, 501–515.

Hill, N., Bush, K., & Roosa, M. (2003). Parenting and family socialization strategies and children's mental health: Low-Income Mexican-American and Euro-American mothers and children. *Child Development, 74*, 189–204.

Hurd, N. M., & Sellers, R. M. (2013). Black adolescents' relationships with natural mentors: Associations with academic engagement via social and emotional development. *Cultural Diversity and Ethnic Minority Psychology, 19*, 76–85.

Jagers, R. J. (2016). Framing social and emotional learning among African-American youth: Toward an integrity-based approach. *Human Development, 59*, 1–3.

Jagers, R. J., Mustafaa, F., & Noel, B. (2016). Cultural integrity and African American empowerment. In M. A. Bond, C. B. Keys, & I. Serrano-García (Eds.), *Handbook of community psychology* (pp. 459–474). Washington, DC: American Psychological Association.

Jagers, R. J., Rivas-Drake, D., & Borowski, T. (2018, November). Equity and social-emotional learning: A cultural analysis. CASEL Assessment Work Group Brief series. Retrieved from https://measuringsel.casel.org/wp-content/uploads/2018/11/Frameworks-Equity.pdf

Jutte, D. P., Miller, J. L., & Erickson, D. J. (2015). Neighborhood adversity, child health, and the role for community development. *Pediatrics, 135*(Supplement 2), S48–S57.

Kalyanpur, M., & Harry, B. (2012). *Cultural reciprocity in special education*. Baltimore: Brookes.

Katz, L. F., Maliken, A. C., & Stettler, N. M. (2012). Parental meta-emotion philosophy: A review of research and theoretical framework. *Child Development Perspectives, 6*, 417–422. doi:10.1111/j.1750-8606.2012.00244.x

Kelley, M. L., Power, T. G., & Wimbush, D. D. (1992). Determinants of disciplinary practices in low-income black mothers. *Child Development*, *63*(3), 573–582.

Kendziora, K., & Osher, D. (2016). Promoting children's and adolescents' social and emotional development: District adaptations of a theory of action. *Journal of Clinical Child and Adolescent Psychology*, *45*, 797–811. doi:10.1080/15374416.2016.1197834

Kendziora, K., Osher, D., & Chinen, M. (2008). Student connection research: Final narrative report to the Spencer Foundation. Washington, DC: American Institutes for Research.

Kendziora, K. T., Bruns, E., Osher, D., Pacchiano, D., & Mejia, B. (2001). *Wraparound: Stories from the field*. Washington, DC: Center for Effective Collaboration and Practice, American Institutes for Research.

Kennedy, D. E., & Kramer, L. (2008). Improving emotional regulation and sibling relationship quality: The more fun with sisters and brothers program. *Family Relations, 57*, 567–578.

Kipke, M. D., Simon, T. R., Montgomery, S. B., Unger, J. B., & Iversen, E. F. (1997). Homeless youth and their exposure to and involvement in violence while living on the streets. *Journal of Adolescent Health, 20*, 360–336.

Kochanska, G. (2001). Emotional development in children with different attachment histories: The first three years. *Child Development, 72*, 474–490.

Kopko, A. (2007). Parenting styles and adolescents. Retrieved from http://citeseerx.ist.psu.edu/viewdoc/download?doi=10.1.1.419.6786&rep=rep1&type=pdf

Kopp, C. B. (1992). Emotional distress and control in young children. *New Directions for Child and Adolescent Development, 1992*, 41–56. doi:10.1002/cd.23219925505

Kreuter, M. W., Lukwago, S. N., Bucholtz, D. C., Clark, E. M., & Sanders-Thompson, V. (2003). Achieving cultural appropriateness in health promotion programs: Targeted and tailored approaches. *Health Education & Behavior, 30*, 133–146.

Kulis, S., Ayers, S. L., & Baker, T. (2015). Parenting in 2 worlds: Pilot results from a culturally adapted parenting program for urban American Indians. *Journal of Primary Prevention, 36*, 65–70.

Kumpfer, K. L., & Alvarado, R. (1998). *Effective family strengthening interventions.* Washington, DC: US Department of Justice, Office of Justice Programs, Office of Juvenile Justice and Delinquency Prevention.

Kumpfer, K. L., Magalhães, C., Xie, J., & Kanse, S. (2016). Cultural and gender adaptations of evidence-based family interventions. In M. J. Van Ryzin, K. L. Kumpfer, G. M. Fosco, & M. T. Greenberg (Eds.), *Family-based prevention programs for children and adolescents: Theory, research, and large-scale dissemination* (pp. 256–281). New York, NY: Psychology Press.

Labella, M. H. (2018). The sociocultural context of emotion socialization in African American families. *Clinical Psychology, 59,* 1–15.

Landry, S. H., Smith, K. E., Swank, P. R., Assel, M. A., & Vellet, S. (2001). Does early responsive parenting have a special importance for children's development or is consistency across early childhood necessary? *Developmental Psychology, 37,* 387–403.

Larson, K., & Rumberger, R. (1995). Doubling school success in highest-risk Latino youth: Results from a middle school intervention study. In R. F. Macías & R. G. Garcia-Ramos (Eds.), *Changing schools for changing families: An anthology of research on language minorities, schools, and society* (pp. 157–180). Santa Barbara, CA: University of California Linguistic Minority Research Institute.

Learning Heroes. (2018). *Developing life skills in children: A road map for communicating with parents.* Retrieved from https://r50gh2ss1ic2mww8s3uvjvq1-wpengine.netdna-ssl.com/wp-content/uploads/2018/05/DLS-Report-2018-for-distribution-single-pages.pdf

Lee, C. D. (2009). From DuBois to Obama: The education of peoples of African descent in the United States in the 21st century. *Journal of Negro Education, 78,* 367–385.

López Turley, R. N., Gamoran, A., McCarty, A. T., & Fish, R. (2017). Reducing children's behavior problems through social capital: A causal assessment. *Social Science Research, 61,* 206–217.

Loyd, A. B., & Williams, B. V. (2017). The potential for youth programs to promote African American youth's development of ethnic and racial identity. *Child Development Perspectives, 11,* 29–38. doi:10.1111/cdep.12204

Lozada, F. T., Jagers, R. J., Smith, C. D., Bañales, J., & Hope, E. C. (2017). Prosocial behaviors of black adolescent boys: An application of a sociopolitical development theory. *Journal of Black Psychology, 43*(5), 493–516.

Maccoby, E. E. (1992). The role of parents in the socialization of children: A historical overview. *Developmental Psychology, 28*(6), 1006–1017.

Masten, A. S., & Tellegen, A. (2012). Resilience in developmental psychopathology: Contributions of the project competence longitudinal study. *Development and Psychopathology, 24,* 345–361.

Matthews, K. A., & Gallo, L. C. (2011). Psychological perspectives on pathways linking socioeconomic status and physical health. *Annual Review of Psychology, 62,* 501–530.

McLoyd, V. C. (1990). The impact of economic hardship on black families and children: Psychological distress, parenting, and socioeconomic development. *Child Development, 61*, 311–346.

McLoyd, V. C. (1998). Socioeconomic disadvantage and child development. *American Psychologist, 53*, 185–204.

McLoyd, V. C., & Smith, J. (2002). Physical discipline and behavior problems in African American, European American, and Hispanic children: Emotional support as a moderator. *Journal of Marriage and Family, 64*(1), 40–53.

Meeus, W., Iedema, J., Helsen, M., & Vollenberg, W. (1999). Patterns of adolescent identity development: Review of the literature and longitudinal analysis. *Developmental Review, 19*, 419–461. doi:10.1006/drev.1999.0483

Murry, V. M., Heflinger, C. A., Suiter, S. V., & Brody, G. H. (2011). Examining perceptions about mental health care and help-seeking among rural African American families of adolescents. *Journal of Youth and Adolescence, 40*, 1118–1131.

Nelson, J. A., Leerkes, E. M., Perry, N. B., O'Brien, M., Calkins, S. D., & Marcovitch, S. (2013). European-American and African-American mothers' emotion socialization practices relate differently to their children's academic and social-emotional competence. *Social Development, 22*, 485–498.

Nelson, J. A., O'Brien, M., Calkins, S. D., Leerkes, E. M., Marcovitch, S., & Blankson, A. N. (2012). Maternal expressive style and children's emotional development. *Infant and Child Development, 21*, 267–286.

Noller, P. (2005). Sibling relationships in adolescence: Learning and growing together. *Personal Relationships, 12*, 1–22. doi:10.1111/j.1350-4126.2005.00099.x

Osher, D., Cantor, P., Berg, J., Rose, T., & Steyer, L. (2017). *The science of learning and development*. Washington, DC: American Institutes for Research, Turnaround for Children, The Opportunity Institute, The Learning Policy Institutes, Education Counsel. Retrieved from https://www.air.org/sites/default/files/downloads/report/Intersection-School-Climate-and-Social-and-Emotional-Development-February-2017.pdf

Osher, D., Cantor, P., Berg, J., Steyer, L., & Rose, T. (2018). Drivers of human development: How relationships and context shape learning and development. *Applied Developmental Science*. doi:10.1080/10888691.2017.1398650

Osher, D., & Chasin, E. (2016). Bringing together schools and the community: The case of Say Yes to Education. In J. F. Zaff, E. Pufall Jones, A. E. Donlan, & S. A. Anderson (Eds.), *Optimizing child and youth development through comprehensive community initiatives* (pp. 72–104). New York: Psychology Press.

Osher, T., Garay, L., Jennings, B., Jimerson, D., Markus, S., & Martinez, K. (2011). Closing the gap: Cultural perspective on family-driven care. Retrieved from http://www.yftipa.org/files/file/ClosingTheGap_FamilyDrivenCare.pdf

Osher, D., Kidron, Y., Brackett, M., Dymnicki, A., Jones, S., & Weissberg, R. P. (2016). Advancing the science and practice of social and emotional learning: Looking back and moving forward. *Review of Research in Education, 40*(1), 644–681. doi:10.3102/0091732X16673595

Osher, T., Van Kammen, W., & Zaro, S. M. (2001). Family participation in evaluating systems of care. *Journal of Emotional and Behavioral Disorders, 9*(1), 63–70.

Padilla, Y. C., & Villalobos, G. (2007). Cultural responses to health among Mexican American women and their families. *Family & Community Health, 30*, S24–S33.

Patterson, C. J., & Hastings, P. D. (2007). Socialization in the context of family diversity. In J. E. Grusec & P. D. Hastings (Eds.), *Handbook of socialization: Theory and research* (pp. 433–460). New York: Guilford.

Perreira, K. M., Chapman, M. V., & Stein, G. L. (2006). Becoming an American parent: Overcoming challenges and finding strength in a new immigrant Latino community. *Journal of Family Issues, 27*, 1383–1414.

Perry-Jenkins, M., Newkirk, K., & Ghunney, A. K. (2013). Family work through time and space: An ecological perspective. *Journal of Family Theory & Review, 5*, 105–123. doi:10.1111/jftr.12011

Pew Research Center. (2015). *Parenting in America: Outlook, worries, aspirations are strongly linked to financial situation*. Washington, DC: Author. Retrieved from http://www.pewsocialtrends.org/2015/12/17/parenting-in-america/

Pike, A., Coldwell, J., & Dunn, J. F. (2005). Sibling relationships in early/middle childhood: Links with individual adjustment. *Journal of Family Psychology, 19*, 523–532. doi:10.1037/0893-3200.19.4.523

Powell, B., Hamilton, L., Manago, B., & Cheng, S. (2016). Implications of changing family forms for children. *Annual Review of Sociology, 42*, 301–322.

Reyes, J. R., & Elias, M. J. (2011). Fostering social-emotional resilience among Latino youth. *Psychology in Schools, 48*, 723–737.

Runyan, D. K., Hunter, W. M., Socolar, R. S., Amaya-Jackson, L., Browne, D. H., English, D., . . . Mathew, R. M. (1998). Children who prosper in unfavorable environments: The relationship to social capital. *Pediatrics, 101*, 12–18.

Salazar, J. (n.d.). *Caregiver discussion guide*. Chicago: CASEL.

Shen, S., Doyle-Thomas, K. A. R., Beesley, L., Karmali, A., Williams, L., Tanel, N. T., & McPherson, A. C. (2017). How and why we should engage parents as co-researchers in health research? A scoping review of current practices. *Health Expectations, 20*, 543–554.

Spencer, M. B., & Swanson, D. P. (2013). Opportunities and challenged to the development of healthy children and youth living in diverse communities. *Development and Psychology, 25*, 1551–1566.

Spieker, S. J., Larson, N. C., Lewis, S. M., Keller, T. E., & Gilchrist, L. (1999). Developmental trajectories of disruptive behavior problems in preschool children of adolescent mothers. *Child Development, 70*(2), 443–458.

Steinberg, L., Lamborn, S. D., Dornbusch, S. M., & Darling, N. (1992). Impact of parenting practices on adolescent achievement: Authoritative parenting, school involvement, and encouragement to succeed. *Child Development, 63*, 1266–1281.

Suter, J. C., & Bruns, E. J. (2009). Effectiveness of the wraparound process for children with emotional and behavioral disorders: A meta-analysis. *Clinical Child and Family Psychology Review, 12*, 336–351. doi:10.1007/s10567-009-0059-y

Tamis-LeMonda, C. S., Way, N., Hughes, D., Yoshikawa, H., Kalman, R. K., & Niwa, E. Y. (2008). Parents' goals for children: The dynamic coexistence of individualism and collectivism in cultures and individuals. *Social Development, 17*, 183–209.

Taylor, R. D., Oberle, E., Durlak, J. A., & Weissberg, R. P. (2017). Promoting positive youth development through school-based social and emotional learning interventions: A meta-analysis of follow-up effects. *Child Development, 88*(4), 1156-1171.

Tervalon, M., & Murray-Garcia, J. (1998). Cultural humility versus cultural competence: A critical distinction in defining physician training outcomes in multicultural education. *Journal of Health Care for the Poor and Underserved, 9*, 117–125.

Triandis, H., Lambert, W., Berry, J., Lonner, W., Heron, A., Brislin, R., & Draguns, J. (Eds.). (1980). *Handbook of cross-cultural psychology* (Vols. 1–6). Boston: Allyn & Bacon.

U.S. Census Bureau. (2010). American Community Survey, 2010, 1-year estimates: Grandparent characteristics. (Table S1001). Retrieved from https://www.census.gov/programs-surveys/acs/technical-documentation/table-and-geography-changes/2010/1-year.html

Van Ryzin, M. J., Roseth, C. J., Fosco, G. M., Lee, Y. K., & Chen, I. C. (2016). A component-centered meta-analysis of family-based prevention programs for adolescent substance use. *Clinical Psychology Review, 45*, 72–80.

Varela, R. E., Vernberg, E. M., Sanchez-Sosa, J. J., Riveros, A., Mitchell, M., & Mashunkashey, J. (2004). Parenting style of Mexican, Mexican American, and Caucasian-Non-Hispanic families: Social context and cultural influences. *Journal of Family Psychology, 18*, 651–657.

Weinraub, M., & Wolf, B. M. (1983). Effects of stress and social supports on mother-child interactions in single-and two-parent families. *Child Development, 54*, 1297–1311.

Wigle, D. T., Arbuckle, T. E., Turner, M. C., Bérubé, A., Yang, Q., Liu, S., & Krewski, D. (2008). Epidemiologic evidence of relationships between reproductive and child health outcomes and environmental chemical contaminants. *Journal of Toxicology and Environmental Health, Part B, 11*(5–6), 373–517.

Wigle, D. T., Arbuckle, T. E., Walker, M., Wade, M. G., Liu, S., & Krewski, D. (2007). Environmental hazards: Evidence for effects on child health. *Journal of Toxicology and Environmental Health, Part B, 10*(1–2), 3–39.

Zimmerman, M. A. (2000). Empowerment theory. In J. Rappaport & E. Seidman (Eds.), *Handbook of community psychology* (pp. 43–63). Boston: Springer.

CHAPTER FIFTEEN

Creating Authentic Partnerships with Families

Lisa Rubenstein and Gary M. Blau

Here we explore the evolution of attitudes about family engagement. Upon completion of the chapter, readers will have a better understanding of how health and education professionals' perceptions of families as well as the families' perception of their own roles within the behavioral health and education systems has changed over the years. The National Federation of Families for Children's Mental Health defines a family as "the group of individuals who support a child emotionally, physically, and financially." A family includes individuals of various ages who may be biologically related, related by marriage, or not related at all (Osher, Osher, & Blau, 2008).

The role of family member has evolved from passive observer to active participant in the decision-making process about his/her/their own child's care within a range of child-serving systems including juvenile justice, child welfare, public health, and education. The information presented in this chapter can help you more effectively partner with families to improve the quality and cultural competence of your work with children, youth, and young adults. An excellent example of the transformation of providers' attitudes and behaviors toward family involvement can be found in the field of children's mental health, particularly in the work addressing the needs of children, youth, and young adults with serious mental health conditions. While children with serious mental disorders are often served by a number of different child-serving systems, this chapter will focus on the mental health and education systems. We will begin with a description of behavioral health providers' historical attitudes toward family involvement in the delivery of mental health services. The family movement, which developed in response to providers' attitudes, will be chronicled. The changing attitudes of educators and opportunities for collaboration with families within the education system will be reviewed. The importance of family engagement in both mental health and education systems will be illustrated through data revealing improved outcomes for children, youth, and young adults when families participate actively in their care and education. Finally, examples of effective partnership between families, behavioral health, and education systems will be presented.

Historical Attitudes Related to Family Involvement

Mental health providers' perceptions about the families' impact on the emotional well-being of their children has changed dramatically over the last 80 years. Because the providers historically often held negative attitudes toward the families, they were not inclined to include the families in their child's care. Families were not seen as having any particular expertise in supporting and guiding their child's mental health treatment. Families were actually often viewed as the cause of their child's mental disorder.

Beginning in 1931, American psychiatrists began to attribute their patients' diagnosis of schizophrenia to the behavior of the mother of the child with mental illness, coining the phrase "schizophrenogenic mother" (Hartwell, 1996). Harry Stack Sullivan (1931, in Hartwell, 1996, p. 276) blamed the patient's early relationships for the subsequent development of schizophrenia. David Levy (1931, pp. 886–889, in Hartwell, 1996, p. 277) argued that mothers were the cause of their child's schizophrenia because the mothers were overprotective of the child and also because the mother resented the fact that as a woman, she felt she could not realize her own ambitions due to societal constraints (Hartwell, 1996). Frieda Fromm-Reichmann, Director of Psychotherapy at the Chestnut Lodge, wrote in 1940: "The schizophrenic is painfully disturbed and resentful of other people, due to the severe early warp and rejection he encountered in important people of his infancy and childhood as a rule, mainly in a schizophrenogenic mother" (Fromm-Reichmann, 1948, p. 265).

The argument that mothers were to blame for their child's mental illness continued to be popular in the United States in the 1950s. Scientists at the National Institute of Mental Health (NIMH) including Lyman Wynne, Chief of the Family Study Section of NIMH, argued that young adults developed schizophrenia when they tried to develop a separate identity from their mothers who were perceived as attempting to control all of the members of the family (Wynne, Ryckoff, Day, & Hirsch, 1958, in Hartwell, 1996, p. 286). Scientists also blamed fathers as well for their child's mental illness. In the 1960s, Lyman Wynne attributed the "overall dysfunctional interactions within the child's family" to be the cause of a child's schizophrenia (Wynne, 1978, p. 180, in Hartwell, 1996, p. 286).

As a result of these theories, not only were families excluded from decision-making about care for their children, they could actually lose custody of them. Providers argued that a child could only make progress if he/she/they were taken away from the family's negative influence. These attitudes also contributed to overall prejudice and discrimination on the part of providers toward families in all areas of behavioral health care. Family input was not sought or valued in discussions about family caregiving issues or in planning of overall service delivery or mental health policy development.

The belief that families actually caused mental illness was popular in the United States until as recently as the 1970s. At that time, families began to actively reject these ideas. Family members started to organize together and advocate for family involvement. At the same time, there was growing research demonstrating that biological, environmental, and other factors contributed to mental disorders such as schizophrenia.

History of the Family Movement

Arguably, the national family movement changed attitudes and perceptions about the role of families both in the care of their child and in the delivery of mental health services and supports. The changes are reflected in the shifting language describing the role of families. As the movement began, the emphasis was on *family involvement* in services that providers developed and implemented. This changed to *family-friendly*, *family engagement*, and *family centric* approaches, and today, the language has evolved to *family-driven*, where families are seen as key partners in service delivery. Why did these terms change? Why is the emphasis now on ensuring that families are equal partners with providers in decisions related to the care of their children? How did families become involved in systems reform efforts? A brief review of the history of the family movement can address these questions.

During the 1970s, in response to providers' attitudes toward families, families of children with mental health challenges began to informally meet together in order to address specific behavioral health needs in their communities (Osher, Osher, & Blau, 2008, p. 44). These individual efforts multiplied and some groups began to meet together, eventually paving the way for national efforts to be launched.

In 1979, the first national organization devoted to consumers and families, the National Alliance of Mental Illness (NAMI) was founded. NAMI's mission was to advocate for the needs of people with mental disorders of all ages. Today, NAMI includes 50 state chapters and 900 affiliates and provides education, support, and advocacy services (http://www.nami.org/). In the early years, the organization focused primarily on addressing the needs of adults with mental illness, and family leaders identified the need to advocate specifically on behalf of children, youth, young adults, and their families.

The timeline, figure 15.1, identifies major milestones in the development of the family movement (Osher, Osher, & Blau, 2008; Walker, 2016).

In 1982, Jane Knitzer published *Unclaimed Children: The Failure of Public Responsibility to Children and Adolescents in Need of Mental Health Services* (Knitzer & Olson, 1982). This report highlighted the fragmentation of services and the need to transform the mental health delivery system. This report served as a catalyst for creating the public and political will needed for members of Congress to pass legislation to improve children's mental health services.

In 1984, Congress funded the National Institute of Mental Health (NIMH)'s Child and Adolescent Service System Program (CASSP). In the CASSP program, although services were still driven by providers, there was an emphasis on "child centered and family focused" services. The CASSP Program, in collaboration with the National Institute on Disability and Rehabilitation Research (NIDRR), also created the Research and Training Center on Family Support and Children's Mental Health at Portland State University, pioneering research on family involvement in mental health care (Walker, 2016).

In 1986, with CASSP funding, Portland State University hosted five regional Families as Allies conferences to facilitate collaboration between families and professionals. This was the first national forum for family advocates to meet together (Osher, Osher, & Blau, 2008).

Families identified the need to independently run family advocacy organizations that could represent families with children with mental disorders. Prior to 1988, family-run organizations had to rely on volunteers and lacked a sustainable funding stream, however. In 1988, the federal government began to support statewide family networks through the CASSP program (Osher, Osher, & Blau, 2008).

In December 1988, Portland State University and NIDRR funded the Next Steps Conference to develop a national blueprint for action addressing children's mental health (Walker, 2016).

In 1989, the first national family organization, originally called the Federation of Families for Children's Mental Health (the Federation) was founded. The Federation emphasized the importance of *family involvement* and educated providers and communities about how to include families in making decisions for their child's care. The Federation advocated to stop "blaming and shaming" families for their children's mental health problems and to make a

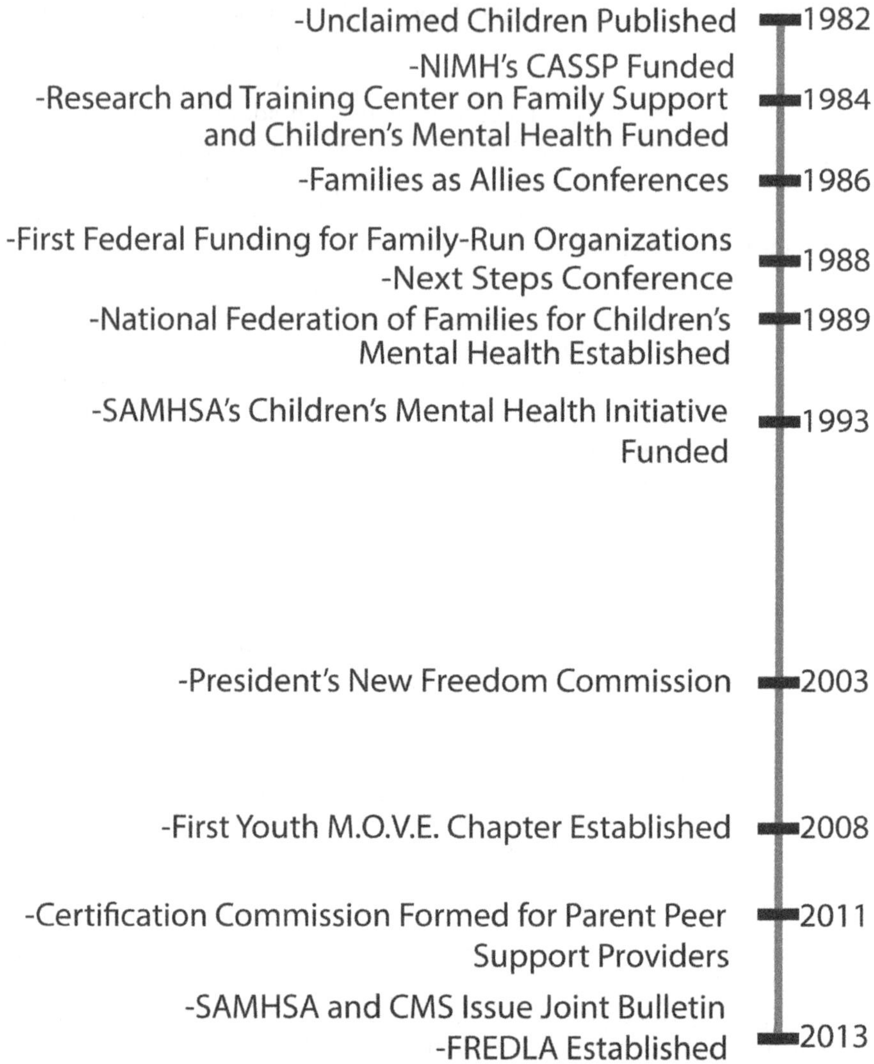

Thank you to Jane Walker, FREDLA and Johanna Bergen, Youth M.O.V.E. for assistance in developing this timeline.

Figure 15.1 Timeline of the family movement in children's mental health

commitment to partnering with families (Osher, 2005). The National Federation of Families for Children's Mental Health, as it is called today, provides education, support, training, technical assistance, and advocacy through a national network of state chapters (http://www.ffcmh.org/).

In 1992, Congress passed legislation establishing the Comprehensive Community Mental Health Services for Children and Their Families Program, also known as the Children's Mental Health Initiative (CMHI). SAMHSA developed the first funding announcement in 1993. CMHI emphasized the "system of care" approach, which was a "comprehensive spectrum of mental health and other necessary services which are organized into a coordinated network to meet the multiple and changing needs of children and adolescents with severe emotional disturbances and their families" (Stroul & Friedman, 1986, p. 3). One of the original principles of system of care was family involvement. The first request for application required grantees to demonstrate a "commitment to family participation and systems development and care of their children and adolescents-evidence of parent participation in local system development efforts to date; development of parent support opportunities at state and local levels; development of statewide family organizations and evidence of parent participation in the development of the application" (Department of Health and Human Services, 1993).

In 2003, President George W. Bush established the President's New Freedom Commission in order to develop a set of recommendations to transform the U.S. mental health service delivery system. Goal 2 of the Achieving the Promise document produced by the members of the New Freedom Commission placed an emphasis for the first time on "consumer and family driven care." The Commissioners insisted that families "must stand at the *center* of the system of care" (The President's New Freedom Commission on Mental Health, 2003, p. 35).

In 2004 and 2005, SAMHSA's Center for Mental Health Services and the National Federation of Families for Children's Mental Health began a national effort to define the term *family-driven.* They gathered feedback from families across the country and drafted a working definition (Osher, 2005). We will review the most recent working definition of *family-driven* care in the next section.

In 2010, the system of care principles were updated. The principle, which addressed family involvement, was expanded to encompass the spirit of family-driven care. The updated principle read "ensure that families, other caregivers, and youth are full partners in all aspects of the planning and delivery of their own services and in the policies and procedures that govern care for all children and youth in their community, state, territory, tribe, and nation" (Stroul, Blau, & Friedman, 2010, p. 6).

By the end of the 20th century, family members were able to play a variety of roles within the behavioral health system. These roles included decision-makers (for their family's care), systems navigators (helping other families to find their way through multiple child-serving systems to get the care and resources their children needed), parent support providers (offering support for the parents and caregivers themselves), leaders for community and state family-run organizations, and advocates for systems change. Through CMHI, systems of care staff were expected to reimburse family members for their work within the system of care. However, apart from short-term federal funding, there were no sustainable funding streams to ensure family leaders and family organizations could continue their work on a long-term basis.

There have been three major steps forward recently to "professionalize" the work that families do in behavioral health systems. These steps have elevated family members in the workforce and have helped to provide sustainable funding for family organizations.

In 2011, a certification commission was formed to develop a certification process for Parent Support Providers, who help families navigate the child-serving systems. According to the National Federation of Families for Children's Mental Health:

> Parent Support Providers (CPSP™) can articulate their experience of parenting a child or teen experiencing emotional, developmental, behavioral, substance use, or mental health concerns, have received specialized training in helping other parents to understand children's wellness and receive regular consultation from a parent/peer supervisor. In turn, they teach, coach, and mentor other parents/caregivers to be effective advocates for their own children (youth and emerging adults) and equal partners with professionals in the delivery of services and policy development. (http://www.ffcmh.org/certification)

In 2013, SAMHSA and the Center for Medicare and Medicaid Services (CMS) released a joint Informational Bulletin identifying peer-to-peer support as an evidence-based and cost-effective service and recommending that states include peer-to-peer support services as a Medicaid benefit (CMCS & SAMHSA, 2013). In states that have a peer-to-peer benefit, family organizations began to contract with behavioral health programs and insurance companies to generate income to help sustain their services.

Also, in 2013, the Family-Run Executive Director Leadership Association (FREDLA) was founded. Created by 16 family-run organizations, FREDLA "serves as the national representative and advocate for family-run organizations and their executive directors, and supports effective stewardship of family-run organizations" (http://www.fredla.org/about-fredla). The organization provides technical assistance to leaders in state and local family-run organizations. This is critical because, while family leaders may be excellent advocates, they must also be knowledgeable about the day-to-day activities of running an organization. Leaders must have skills in managing the budget, addressing personnel issues, ensuring contract deliverables are completed, and communicating effectively with the board of directors.

The evolution of one family organization, Uplift in Cheyenne, Wyoming, is an excellent example of how family organizations have gradually expanded their roles to become major players in the behavioral health system. The Executive Director of Uplift, Michelle Heinen, explains:

> UPLIFT was founded by a group of parents coming out of a parent support group that had been started by Wyoming's lead community mental health center. So initially, the family organization was seen as a place where parents could share mutual support and receive information about behavioral health disorders and available services. Behavioral health providers and educators began to refer families to UPLIFT as a means of connecting parents to a community support system. As UPLIFT grew, they became skilled advocates within the educational system, sharing support and information with parents to assist in receiving the most appropriate educational services for their student. The family organization also began to take on the role of community partner, bringing the family voice to multiple initiatives, projects, and system change efforts.

With the introduction of high-fidelity wraparound[1] into Wyoming, UPLIFT began to train for and fill the role of service provider within wraparound teams. (Heinen, 2016).

Throughout the history of family organizations, families have always encouraged youth and young adults to advocate for their own care as well as to improve child-serving systems. The CMHI supported youth voice within systems of care by requiring grantees to integrate youth into all aspects of system of care and reimburse the youth for the time they participated.

In 2006, with support from SAMHSA, a group of youth and young adults who had lived experience in multiple child-serving systems launched the first national organization for and managed by youth and young adults with mental health challenges. The organization was called Youth M.O.V.E. (Youth Motivating Others through Voices of Experience). The first chapter was established in 2008. Today, the organization has successfully become a 501(c)(3) and has more than 86 chapters across the country. Youth M.O.V.E. provides peer support, training for youth and professionals, technical assistance, and advocacy (http://youthmovenational.org).

Family-Driven Care

In the last section, it was noted that in 2005, the first definition of family-driven care was created. The definition of family-driven care was always considered to be a working definition, meant to change as the family movement evolved. The most recent draft definition, as of 2016, reads as follows:

Working Definition of Family-Driven Care

Family-driven means families have the primary role in decisions regarding their children as well as the policies and procedures governing the well-being of all children in their community, state, tribe, territory and nation. This includes, but is not limited to:

- Identifying their strengths, challenges, desired outcomes/goals, and the steps needed to achieve those outcomes/goals;
- Designing, implementing, monitoring, and evaluating services, supports, programs, and systems;
- Choosing supports, services, and providers who are culturally and linguistically responsive and aware;
- Partnering in decision-making at all levels.

Guiding Values to Achieve Family-Driven Practice

Families and youth, providers, administrators, and policymakers accept and support willingly and enthusiastically shared decision-making and responsibility for outcomes, as evidenced by:

1. Families and youth share and have access to accurate, understandable, and complete information necessary to set goals and to make informed decisions.
2. Families define their family composition and family decision-makers, whether biological, adoptive, foster, sibling, or surrogate family voice advocating on their behalf.
3. Families and family-run organizations engage in peer support to reduce isolation, achieve short- and long-term family goals, and strengthen family capacity and voice.
4. Families and family-run organizations provide direction for policy decisions that impact funding, supports, and services, including the right of families and youth to have meaningful voice at the individual and policy level.
5. Providers, agencies, and systems take the initiative to change policy and practice from provider-driven to family-driven.
6. Providers, agencies, and systems embrace family-driven practice, by allocating staff, training, support, and resources to adequately fund and sustain family-driven services for children, youth, and families, and the work of family and youth run organizations.

7. Community attitude change efforts focus on removing barriers and eliminating bias and discrimination.
8. Communities value and celebrate the diverse cultures of children, youth, and families and work to eliminate disparities.
9. Communities recognize that culture is an ever-changing dynamic and are responsive to the cultural and linguistic needs of all children, youth, and families. (National Federation of Families for Children's Mental Health, 2016).

A key concept included in the definition of family-driven care is the importance of valuing the diverse cultures of families. Each family has its unique culture as well as being part of a larger cultural group. What do we mean by culture? Family culture includes a family's values and beliefs, language, customs, rituals, and shared history (Osher et al., 2011). In family-driven care, it is the responsibility of the providers to recognize and learn about the culture of the family they are working with and at the same time be aware of their own cultural traditions, views, and possible prejudices, which might impact how they perceive the family. The provider should honor the culture of the family by helping the family members to identify and build on the strengths of their culture. For example, in many cultures, relatives and other supportive members of the community are considered to be family members. All of these people can be essential in helping a family through the recovery process. It is also critical that providers recognize the unique challenges that each family may have experienced. Families who have immigrated to the United States may have experienced trauma both in their country of origin and as immigrants, in this country. African Americans, families of Holocaust survivors, indigenous people from around the world, and many others have experienced historical trauma, which can result in historical unresolved grief (Osher et al., 2011). Historical trauma and unresolved grief, as described by Dr. Maria Yellow Horse Braveheart in her work on native cultures, can be defined as the "cumulative emotional and psychological wounding, over the lifespan and across generations stemming from massive group trauma experiences" (Braveheart & DeBruyn, 1998). Providers need to understand how historical trauma may impact families and their potential lack of trust in institutions such as schools and behavioral health agencies. By recognizing and attending to these issues, providers and families can more effectively and honestly partner together (Osher et al., 2011).

How does family-driven care look different than provider-driven care? Table 15.1 illustrates the differences.

Implementing an authentic family-driven approach is difficult. As Cliff Davis (2016, pp. 1–2) of the Human Services Collaborative argues,

Table 15.1 Paradigm shift in service delivery systems for children and youth with emotional disturbance

	Provider-driven	Family-driven
Source of solutions	Professionals and agencies	Child, family, and their support team
Relationship	Child and family viewed as a dependent client expected to carry out instructions	Partner/collaborator in decision-making, service provision, and accountability
Orientation	Isolating and "fixing" a problem viewed as residing in the child or family	Ecological approach enabling the child and family to do better in the community
Assessment	Deficit-oriented	Strengths-based
Expectations	Low to modest	High
Planning	Agency resource-based	Individualized for each child and family
Access to services	Limited by agency's menus, funding streams, and staffing schedules	Comprehensive and provided when and where the child and family require
Outcomes	Based on agency function and symptom relief	Based on quality of life and desires of child and family

Source: Trina W. Osher, M.A. and David M. Osher, Ph.D. "The paradigm shift to true collaboration with families," *Journal of Child and Family Studies, 11*(1), March 2002, 47–60. Used by permission.

family-driven care can only be realized if system leaders, families, and youth have an "unreserved systemic commitment to [this] principle." There is a need to create a culture (involving everyone from policy makers to the direct service providers) that is totally committed to an equal partnership between the systems, the family, and the youth.

Family Involvement in the Education System

During the 20th century, many educators did not acknowledge that families had a significant role to play in their children's education. This was especially true in terms of views about families in low-income communities and communities of color (Weiss, Bouffard, Bridgelall, & Gordon, 2009, p. 6). Much like in the behavioral health field, families were often seen as the source of children's problems, not as experts who could participate in creating solutions. Because of this, education policy through the years tended to only create "random acts of family involvement" (Gil Kressley, 2008) rather than a comprehensive approach to integrate family members as equal partners in the educational system and decision-makers in terms of development and implementation of education policy.

In 1975, Congress passed the Education of the Handicapped Act, retitled in reauthorizations as the Individuals with Disability Education Act (IDEA). The statute outlined rights and responsibilities for parents of special education students including the right to participate in advisory councils. Funding was authorized to provide technical assistance to help families participate in their child's education and advocate for their rights (Osher & Blau, 2008, p. 45).

In 1994, the Department of Education released the National Agenda to Improve Outcomes for Children and Youth with Serious Emotional Disturbance. This document included a target on collaborating with families (U.S. Department of Education, 1994).

In 2001, No Child Left Behind (NCLB) Act was passed by Congress. The legislation strengthened a system of resource centers to provide family members with information and training to increase parental involvement in the schools (Osher, Osher, & Blau, 2008, p. 46). These Parental Information Resource Centers, or PIRCs, first funded in 1995, ensured that each state had at least one PIRC and that the PIRCs played a statewide role in coordinating and fostering successful and effective parental involvement policies, programs, and activities to improve student academic achievement and strengthen partnerships between parents, schools, and communities (Blair, 2008). The PIRC program is no longer funded. However, more recently, language for the Statewide Family Engagement Centers was included in ESSA and the Statewide Family Engagement Center program was recently funded by the Omnibus Appropriations Act of 2018. These centers will carry out family engagement programs and provide technical assistance to states, districts, and schools.

Currently, federal policies are beginning to take a more family-driven approach. On August 1, 2016, the U.S. Department of Health and Human Services and the U.S. Department of Education released a joint letter announcing a new policy supporting family engagement in early learning. This policy statement provides recommendations to early childhood systems and programs on family engagement. It states:

> Family engagement refers to the systematic inclusion of families in activities and programs that promote children's development, learning, and wellness, including in the planning, development, and evaluation of such activities, programs, and systems. For family engagement to be integrated throughout early childhood systems and programs, providers and schools

> must engage families as essential partners when providing services that promote children's learning and development, nurture positive relationships between families and staff, and support families. (U.S. Department of Education and U.S. Department of Health and Human Services, 2016, p. 1)

The Centers for Disease Control and Prevention (CDC) define family engagement in schools as:

> a shared responsibility in which schools and other community agencies and organizations are committed to reaching out to engage parents in meaningful ways, and parents are committed to actively supporting their children's and adolescents' learning and development. . . . School efforts to promote parent engagement can be part of a coordinated school health framework. A coordinated school health framework engages families and is based on community needs, resources, and standards. (Centers for Disease Control and Prevention, 2012, p. 7)

In 2013, Karen Mapp and Paul Kuttner (2013) authored a publication by SEDL funded by the U.S. Department of Education describing a model for creating truly effective partnerships between families and education systems. The Dual Capacity Building Framework for Family-School Partnerships outlines a process for educators and families to develop their knowledge and skills about how to collaborate together while building mutual trust and respect. Adult learning methods are used stressing interactive activities and opportunities to learn from each other in order to effectively support student learning. Multiple roles for families are identified through this process including acting as decision-makers on the array of educational options to be provided in their schools, as collaborators with school staff and other community members for school reform and as activists for improved educational opportunities both for their own children as well as children throughout their community (Mapp & Kuttner, 2013, p. 7).

Cliff Davis conducted a study of best practices in parent engagement and leadership development for the New Hampshire Department of Education in 2016. In reviewing best practice models for family engagement, Davis identified 11 elements the models have in common (Davis, 2016, p. 17; see table 15.2).

Mary Steady, Administrator of the Office of Student Wellness at the New Hampshire Department of Education describes the process of bringing together family and youth leaders to develop a framework for family engagement based upon the lessons learned listed above.

> [The process] really represents a shift in power. [By partnering with families,] it is not so heavily oriented with "professionals." It [allows us to have

Table 15.2 Elements of best practice models

1. **Family engagement is framed strongly within the context of system missions and major goals.** Impact of the family engagement efforts need to be seen as critical to fulfillment of the overall mission of the school system.
2. **Engagement approaches are built upon multidisciplinary partnerships and shared responsibilities.** Expertise from a range of disciplines is needed.
3. **The creation and support of effective family engagement programming is developmental.** Efforts should begin with a systems needs assessment identifying exactly where family engagement efforts are currently and then strategies should be developed building upon the current status.
4. **Implementation of effective family engagement strategies evolve through comprehensive planning and implementation processes.** An ongoing comprehensive strategic planning process is necessary to ensure authentic family engagement, not just a series of individual stand-alone activities.
5. **Collaborative partnership stand at the heart of planning, implementation, and monitoring.** It should be clear to the community that all successes and challenges are the result of a truly collaborative partnership.
6. **Public systems, including education and service sectors, hold responsibility to lead the planning, implementation, and monitoring processes.** The educational system must demonstrate leadership by creating opportunities for family members to participate in a meaningful way.
7. **Family engagement strategies are driven by the ultimate outcomes to be attained, with the primary focus on child learning and well-being.** Strategies should always be designed with the desired outcomes for children and families in mind.
8. **All planning and implementation activities will define expectations and where possible, indicators/standards for the outcome sought by those activities.** All strategic planning strategies must be linked to family engagement outcomes and progress toward those outcomes should be monitored throughout the implementation process.
9. **Two-way communication between systems and parent/families is an essential tool of effective implementation of family engagement systems.** It is the responsibility of the school system to create opportunities for communication in all interactions between the education system and the family members.
10. **Effective family engagement strategies will focus equally on the development of competencies on both sides of the partnership.** Staff must learn how to effectively interact with families and families must gain skills in advocating for themselves and for their children.

(continued)

Table 15.2 (continued)

11. **Family engagement partnerships are, at the core, deeply personal and unique, individual relationships.** Education partners must understand that regardless of how family members may express their concerns, their needs and opinions must be valued.

Source: Davis, 2016, p. 17.

a] more robust look at the work. There are trust issues but it is natural to go through struggles when breaking down silos. We need to have an open dialogue and remember that we cannot give up on our vision for children and families. We are in it together. (Steady, 2016)

The Importance of a Family-Driven Approach

The literature demonstrates that family engagement is a key factor in children's healthy development and their ability to succeed in the classroom (DHHS & DE, 2016; Comer & Haynes, 1991). Going beyond engagement, to adapting a family-driven approach in the behavioral health and education systems provides an opportunity for caregivers to contribute their unique expertise and skills in partnership with providers and educators.

Families and caregivers are key members of the behavioral health treatment team for their child, youth, or young adult. Families and caregivers can support their children to enhance their resilience and make progress toward recovery. David Osher, Trina Osher, and Gary Blau (2008, pp. 49–52) argue that when parents can partner with providers to design, implement, and monitor the treatment strategies for their child or youth, they are often able to improve the effectiveness of their child's treatment. Because parents can promote the healthy development of their children, they can sometimes prevent problems from developing or getting worse. Caregivers can help design culturally and linguistically appropriate treatment approaches tailored to the needs of their specific family. They have the opportunity to observe their children throughout the day and so can monitor how the strategies are implemented and provide feedback to providers on ways to continuously improve treatment (Merton, 1957).

Families and caregivers also have unique experience and skills that can help them support other families. Parents and other caregivers with "lived experience" (meaning that they have children with behavioral health challenges and have advocated in child-serving systems for those children), are uniquely qualified to work in the behavioral health setting. Peer parent support providers can be trained to strategically share their own stories in order to make an authentic connection with families currently going through challenging journeys with their children and child-serving systems. Through the sharing of personal stories, peer parent support providers can develop strong ongoing relationships with the parents or caregivers who may enter services distrustful of the behavioral health system due to past personal experience or experiences of others in their community (Donnelly, Crider, & Miles, 2016). Mental health providers and educators should help peer parent providers to identify and support opportunities for training and certification. They should also create employment opportunities within the educational and behavioral health systems for the critical work of the peer parent support providers. Other members of the educational and behavioral health systems must be trained to learn how to work effectively with the peer parent providers. Another critical role for peer parent support providers is to serve as cultural brokers, bridging between families from underserved communities and their providers. The Federal Health Care Innovations Exchange found that because peer support providers can have this special skill, peer support has the potential to improve care and decrease disparities for underserved communities (Agency for Healthcare Research and Quality, 2012).

A number of studies demonstrate the importance of families as partners with the educational system (Comer & Haynes, 1991; Henderson & Mapp, 2002). Anne Henderson synthesized research from 51 studies exploring the effect of parent involvement on student learning. The subsequent report, "A New Wave of Evidence," found that students whose parents were involved in their education regardless of income or ethnic background are more likely to: "attend school regularly, earn higher grades and test scores; be promoted; graduate and go on to post-secondary education" (Henderson & Mapp, 2002, p. 7).

The level of family involvement makes a difference. Rebecca Marcon (1999) studied African American preschoolers in Washington, DC. She found that parents with high involvement in their child's education tended to have children with higher grades and test scores than parents with a low level of involvement (Marcon, 1999).

When schools make a concerted effort to outreach to families, students do better. Joyce Epstein and her colleagues studied 80 Baltimore elementary schools that received technical assistance to develop six different types of family-school partnerships. Students in the schools with higher-rated partnership programs made significant gains on math and writing tests. Their attendance rates were also higher (Epstein, Clark, Salinas, & Sanders, 1997).

Positive partnerships between families and school staff have resulted in higher quality schools. Charles Payne and Marianne Kaba (2001) describe a study by the Consortium in Chicago School Research that compared the 30 most highly rated schools in Chicago with the 30 lowest rated schools. The study revealed that the quality of the staff to parent relationships, along with the staff-to-staff relationships, could predict the quality of the school (Payne & Kaba, 2001, p. 43).

Families from a wide range of communities have been successful in organizing and improving schools according to staff of the Caring across Communities Project. The program, funded by the Robert Wood Johnson Foundation, includes 15 different projects focused on reducing behavioral health problems among students in low-income immigrant and refugee families. A Latina mother who joined informal parenting workshops in Spanish as part of the Duke University Caring across Communities Project now mentors other Latina mothers (Kugler & Price, 2009, p. 4). Local groups have been able to upgrade school facilities, access new resources and programs to improve teaching and curriculum, improve school leadership and staffing, implement higher quality learning programs for students, and access new funding for after-school programs and family supports (Henderson & Mapp, 2002, p. 149). For example, Mothers on the Move (MOM) is a group of parents in New York City. Originally, they participated in a family literacy program. After identifying many inequities between their school and a school in a higher income area, they created an independent organization. As a result of their advocacy, a new superintendent was hired for the district. With the new superintendent, additional staff were assigned to the schools, facilities were improved, and reading scores improved in over one-third of the district schools (Henderson & Mapp, 2002, p. 150).

Family members and caregivers of lesbian, gay, bisexual, transgender, questioning, and two spirit (LGBTQ2S) youth who are experiencing behavioral health challenges are often excluded from partnerships with schools. Caitlin Ryan and the Family Acceptance Project have examined the importance of families and caregivers to their LGBT children's health and well-being. Traditionally, providers saw their own role as protecting LGBT youth from harm. Because it was widely assumed that families would reject their children if the children came out to their families, the providers and educators felt it was their duty to protect the children from their family members. Ryan has found, however, that family acceptance is a critical protective factor that promotes the health and mental health of the children, youth, and young adults (Ryan, 2014, p. 333). Family members of LGBT youth have developed a powerful voice. Parents, Families and Friends of Lesbians and Gays (PFLAG) is the major family-driven organization supporting all LGBTQ youth and their families. It is the nation's largest family and ally organization including 400 chapters. Members focus on creating safe school environments including addressing school bullying, providing support to families, and advocating for policy and systems change (https//www.pflag.org/our story).

Creating Authentic Partnerships with Families

How do educators and behavioral health providers outreach effectively to families and family organizations? It is necessary to listen to the voices of the family members. A family leader says:

> Personally, as a former educator, it has been good for me to be on both sides of the table. I left the field of education because the school system in which I worked was not effectively meeting my son with behavioral challenges' needs. I wholeheartedly believe that most educators want to partner with parents—they simply do not know how to do so effectively. There is nothing more rewarding than getting a call from a school asking us to reach out to a family because they know our advocacy and support will help not only the family, but also the school system working for the child. In a similar vein, most families are doing the best they can to facilitate their child's success at school. They just sometimes lack the skills to do so most effectively. (Heinen, 2016)

The first step for educators wishing to partner with families is to create a welcoming environment for family members. School personnel must take time and effort to create trusting and respectful relationships with the families. School staff, as discussed in an earlier section, need to be both culturally respectful and culturally responsive by learning about the culture of the family and taking the lead in communicating in ways that are comfortable for the family. They should ask the family members what they need in order to partner effectively. For example, family members often need support in order to care for their own children with behavioral health challenges. Wagner and colleagues (2006) found the parents of special education students identified parent support services as the most difficult service to access. Other family needs might include childcare, transportation to meetings, and training.

Positive partnerships between families and schools tend to occur more frequently in higher income communities than in communities where the families have lower socioeconomic status. School personnel tend to reach out to families with low incomes more often when the children are having problems rather than when the children are successful, than they do with families of higher incomes (Lareau, 1987). School personnel can make a conscious effort to communicate to a family about their child's strengths.

Immigrant families are another group that have traditionally been left out of the education process altogether despite the fact that they may be very resilient as well as knowledgeable about their children and the experiences that their children have had (Kugler & Price, 2009, p. 3). Grace Valenzuela,

Director of the Caring across Communities Initiative in Portland, Maine, public schools states:

> The stereotype is that these families are drains on our resources, but they have great strengths and we need to tap into them. Immigrant and refugee parents have been able to survive extraordinary experiences in bringing their families here, yet once they are here, we disempower them. We need to give them power to be in charge. (Kugler & Price, 2009, p. 3)

In order to facilitate leadership among immigrant family members, Andrea Sobel and Eileen Gale Kugler (2007) emphasize that educators need to help refugee and immigrant families navigate the U.S. educational system. School personnel also need to recognize the importance of families' culture and respect how the families choose to define family involvement for themselves, which may look very different from traditional parent involvement in the United States. Finally, educators must understand families' primary needs when they first arrive in this country. A parent liaison with the Boston Caring across Communities Project, Naima Agalab, argues that "we need to first provide the help they need with other issues." For the families that she worked with, housing, health, and employment needed to be addressed before they could involve family members in the education process (Kugler and Price, 2009, p. 3).

Partnering effectively with families of LGBTQ youth also requires that educators and providers make the effort to understand the family's specific needs and culture. School personnel need to identify where the families and caregivers are in terms of supporting their youth's sexual preferences or sexual identities and work with them from where they are (Ryan, 2014, p. 339). Educators and providers can offer family members an opportunity to discuss their concerns and hopes. They need to treat the family members with respect and validate their feelings (Ryan & Chen-Haynes, 2013, p. 219). Families need access to information and the opportunity to develop skills while their children are still very young so that they can provide a positive environment as the child grows (Ryan, 2014, p. 339).

Kaitlin Ryan identifies a number of strategies schools can implement to develop positive partnerships with families of LGBT youth. Some of the strategies include: promoting positive parenting by providing family members with the data demonstrating the importance of family acceptance to the health of children, youth, and young adults; emphasizing communication between the families and their children about the child's experiences both positive and negative in the school environment; encouraging and providing opportunities for family participation in LGBT activities such as the school's Gay Straight Alliance, connecting families with local resources, and providing trainings to the families (Ryan and Chen-Hayes, 2013, p. 221).

Conclusion

We have seen that authentic partnership between families, mental health providers, and educators based upon a family-driven approach can help children, youth, and young adults with mental health challenges to receive culturally competent and effective treatment. However, there is still much work to be done. Approximately 20% of children in the United States experience a mental disorder at some time in their lives and 10% have experienced a mental disorder with severe impairment (Merikangas, He, Burnstein, et al., 2010). Approximately half of all lifetime cases of mental disorders begin by age 14 (Kessler, Berglund, Demler, et al., 2005); however, between 50% and 70% of children with mental health needs do not receive services (Merikangas & Bernstein, 2011; Merikangas, He, Brody, et al., 2010).

In 2016, Mario Hernandez, Mary Armstrong, Amy Green, and Melissa Johnson (p. 12) examined the status of state offices for children's mental health across the United States. The children's mental health directors that they interviewed identified limited access to services and lack of workforce capacity as continuing challenges. To improve access to effective, culturally appropriate care, it is critical that providers and educators partner with caregivers and family members and integrate them into the mental health and education workforce.

This integration process will require providers and educators to do their own work differently. They will need to create a flexible workplace to enable family members to be able to support the needs of their own children with mental health challenges while they are working. Their colleagues need to be trained on how best to create opportunities to take full advantage of the skills and knowledge of families from a variety of backgrounds and cultures. In addition, providers and educators need to offer the family leaders ongoing training so that they can effectively contribute to improving the child-serving systems.

At the same time as family leaders are gaining new skills, educators and behavioral health providers need to be trained in the family-driven approach, so that they can partner effectively with families. This training should be provided in undergraduate and graduate schools as well as through in-service programs, to prepare current and future educators and behavioral health practitioners. Perhaps the most effective training can be conducted by family leaders as evidenced by the experience of students learning from Uplift family leaders:

> Over the years, UPLIFT representatives have had the opportunity to share with students at the University of Wyoming in the classroom setting. These opportunities were eye-opening to students as they often shared that they had never thought about the family's perspective when addressing behavioral issues. University students indicated a new understanding and compassion that would greatly shape their future work. Students

> should have opportunities to hear directly from parents and youth about their experience in the behavioral health care system. Instructors should also expose students to research-based, educational materials regarding the importance and efficacy of family-driven care. Students should learn early on that members of the family are the most critical members of a treatment team and should be actively engaged in the process. (Heinen, 2016)

New policies must be put in place on the local, state, tribal, territorial, and federal levels to ensure a family-driven approach is implemented in all child-serving systems. To encourage support of new policies, additional research on family involvement is needed. Researchers should conduct studies investigating the impact of family involvement on academic and behavioral health outcomes, as well as potential cost-savings related to integrating families into the workforce.

Advocates must also promote the implementation of existing policy tools addressing family-driven care. For example, many states have still not included family and youth peer support in their state's Medicaid benefit plan despite the release of the CMCS/SAMHSA informational bulletin in 2013. Once states begin offering peer support as a Medicaid benefit, state personnel will need information and technical assistance to implement the benefit appropriately.

If we are to realize the vision that children, youth, and young adults with mental health conditions can fulfill their potential, we must value and support family members as experts in their children's care and change agents for child-serving systems across the country.

Note

1. According to the National Wraparound Initiative, wraparound is an intensive individualized care planning and management process engaging children, youth, and their families with the goal of achieving positive outcomes.

References

Agency for Healthcare Research and Quality. (2012). *Reducing disparities through peer support*. AHRQ. Retrieved from http://www.innovations.ahrq.gov/issues/2012/07/18/reducing-disparities-through-peer-support

Blair, L. (2008, August). USDE's Parental Information and Resource Center (PIRC) program works to boost parent involvement and achievement. *SEDL Letter, 20*(2). Austin, TX: Southwest Educational Development Laboratory.

Braveheart, M. Y. H., & DeBruyn, L. (1998). The American Indian Holocaust: Healing historical unresolved grief. *American Indian and Alaska Native Mental Health Research, 8*(2), 60–82.

Bryk, A. S., Sebring, P. B., Allensworth, E., & Luppescu, S. (2010). *Organizing schools for improvement: Lessons from Chicago.* Chicago: University of Chicago Press.

Centers for Disease Control and Prevention. (2012). *Parent engagement: Strategies for involving parents and school health.* Atlanta: U.S. Department of Health and Human Services.

Comer, J., & Haynes, N. (1991). Parent involvement in schools: An ecological approach. *Elementary School Journal, 91*(3), 271–277. Special Issue: Educational Partnerships Home-School Community.

Davis, C. (2016). *A study of best practices and parent engagement and leadership development.* Final report to the New Hampshire Department of Education. Washington, DC: Human Services Collaborative.

Donnelly, T., Crider, R., & Miles, P. (2016). *Building skills in parent peer-to-peer support.* Presentation given at Second Annual National Wraparound Implementation Academy, Washington, DC, and Rockville, Maryland.

Epstein, J. L., Clark, L., Salinas, K. C., & Sanders, M. G. (1997). *Scaling up school-family- community connections in Baltimore: Effects on student achievement and attendance.* Paper Presented at the Annual Meeting of the American Educational Research Association, Chicago, Illinois.

Fromm-Reichmann, F. (1948). Notes on the development of treatment of schizophrenia by psychoanalytic psychotherapy. *Psychiatry, 11*, 263–273.

Gil Kressley, K. (2008, August). *Breaking new ground: Seeding proven practices into proven programs.* Paper presented at the 2008 national PIRC conference, Baltimore, Maryland.

Hartwell, C. (1996). The schizophrenogenic mother concept in American psychiatry. *Psychiatry, 59*(3), 274–297.

Heinen, M. (2016, September 7). Executive Director, Uplift Wyoming, online interview.

Henderson, A., & Mapp, K. (2002). *A new wave of evidence: The impact of school, family, and community connections on student achievement.* Austin, TX: National Center for Family and Community Connection with Schools, Southwest Educational Development Laboratory.

Hernandez, M., Armstrong, M., Green, A., & Johnson, M. (2016). National survey of state children's mental health directors: Current status and future directions. *Journal of Behavioral Health Services & Research, 44*(1), 3–24. National Council for Behavioral Health. doi:10.1007/s11414-016-9514-y

Kessler, R. C., Berglund, P., Demler, O., Jin, R., Merikangas, K. R., & Walters, E. E. (2005). Lifetime prevalence and age-of-onset distributions of DSM-IV disorders in the national comorbidity survey replication. *Archives of General Psychiatry, 62*(6), 593–602.

Knitzer, J., &. Olson, L. (1982). *Unclaimed children: The status of children's mental health policy in the United States.* Washington, DC: Children's Defense Fund.

Kugler, E. G., & Acosta Price, O. (2009). *Helping immigrant and refugee students succeed: It's not just what happens in the classroom.* Center for Health and Healthcare in Schools School of Public Health and Health Services, George Washington University. Retrieved from /https://nned.net/docs-general/FINAL_Revised_Kappan_article_11-13-09.pdf., Duchnowski, A., Robbins, V., & Keenan, S. (2008). School-based mental health services in systems of care. In B. Stroul & G. Blau (Eds.), *The system of care handbook* (pp. 545–572). Baltimore: Brooks Publishing.

Lareau, A. (1987). Social class differences in family-school relationships: The importance of cultural capital. *Sociology of Education, 60*, 73–85.

Levy, D. M. (1931). Maternal overprotection and rejection. *Archives of Neurology and Psychiatry, 25*, 886–889.

Mann, C., & Hyde, P. (2013). *Joint CMCS and SAMHSA Informational Bulletin: Coverage of behavioral health services for children, youth, and young adults with significant mental health conditions.* Center for Medicare and Medicaid Services, Center for Medicaid and CHIP Services and Substance Abuse and Mental Health Services Administration.

Mapp, K., & Kuttner, P. J. (2013). *A dual capacity-building framework for family-school partnerships.* Department of Education and SEDL. Austin, Texas.

Marcon, R. A. (1999). Positive relationships between parent school involvement in public school inner-city preschoolers' development and academic performance. *School Psychology Review, 28*(3), 395–412.

Merikangas, K. R., He, J. P., Brody, D., Fisher, P. W., Bourdon, K., Koretz, D. S. (2010). Prevalence and treatment of mental disorders among US children in the 2001–2004 NHANES. *Pediatrics, 125*(1), 75–81.

Merikangas, K. R., He, J. P., Burstein, M., Swanson, S., Avenevoli, S., Cui, L. . . . Swendsen, J. (2010). Lifetime prevalence of mental disorders in U.S. adolescents: Results from the national comorbidity survey replication-adolescent supplement (NCS-A). *Journal of the American Academy of Child & Adolescent Psychiatry, 49*(10), 980–989.

Merikangas, K. R., He, J. P., Burstein, M., Swendson, J., Avenevoli, S., Case, B. . . . Offson, M. (2011). Service utilization for lifetime mental disorders in US adolescents: Results of the national comorbidity survey-adolescent supplement (NCS-A). *Journal of the American Academy of Child & Adolescent Psychiatry, 50*(1), 32–45.

Merton, R. K. (1957). *Social theory and social structure* (rev. and ex. ed.). Glencoe, IL: Free Press.

National Federation of Families for Children's Mental Health. (2016). *Draft working statement on family driven* (Unpublished manuscript).

Osher, T. (2005). *Comparing "family involvement" with "family driven" handout.* Retrieved from http://huffosherconsulting.com/wp-content/uploads/2014/08/Ambassadors-Guide-introduction.pdf

Osher, T., Garay, L., Jennings, B., Jimerson, D., Markus, S., & Martinez, K. (2011). Closing the gap: Cultural perspectives on family-driven care. Report prepared for the Child, Adolescent and Family Branch, Center for Mental Health Services, Substance Abuse and Mental Health Services Administration by the Technical Assistance Partnership for Child and Family Mental Health. Washington, DC.

Osher, T., & Osher, D. (2002, March). The paradigm shift to true collaboration with families. *Journal of Child and Family Studies, 11*(1), 47–60.

Osher, T., Osher, D., & Blau, G. (2008). Families matter. In T. P. Gullotta & G. M. Blau (Eds.), *Family influences on childhood behavior and development: Evidence-based prevention and treatment approaches* (pp. 39–62). New York: Routledge Press.

Payne, C. M., & Kaba, M. 2001. *So much reform, so little change: Building-level obstacles to urban school reform.* Northwestern University, 2.

The President's New Freedom Commission on Mental Health. (2003). *Achieving the promise: Transforming mental health care in America.* Final report. Retrieved from http://govinfo.library.unt.edu/mentalhealthcommission/reports/FinalReport/downloads/FinalReport.pdf

Rider, F. (2014). *Applying Medicaid flexibility to improve state design of benefits to meet significant behavioral health needs of young people.* National Association of State Mental Health Program Directors, Children, Youth and Families Division. Alexandria, Virginia.

Ryan, C. (2014). Generating a revolution in prevention, wellness and care for LGBT children and youth. *Temple Political and Civil Rights Law Review,* 23(2), 331–344.

Ryan, C., & Chen-Hayes, S. (2013). Educating and empowering families of LGBTQ K–12 students. In E. S. Fisher & K. Komosa-Hawkins (Eds.), *Creating school environments to support lesbian, gay, bisexual, transgender, and questioning students and families: A handbook for school professionals* (pp. 208–227). New York: Routledge Press.

Sobel, A., & Kugler, E. G. (2007). Building partnerships with immigrant parents. *Educational Leadership,* 64(6), 62–66.

Steady, M. (2016, September 15). Administrator, Office of Student Wellness at the New Hampshire Department of Education, telephone interview.

Stroul, B., Blau, G. M., & Friedman, R. (2010). *Updating the system of care concept and philosophy.* Washington, DC: Georgetown University Center for Child and Human Development, National Technical Assistance Center for Children's Mental Health.

Stroul, B., & Friedman, R. (1986). *A system of care for children & youth with severe emotional disturbances* (rev. ed.). Washington, DC: Georgetown University Child Development Center, CASSP Technical Assistance Center.

Sullivan, H. S. (1931). Environmental factors in the etiology and course under treatment of schizophrenia. *Medical Journal and Record, 133*, 19–22.

U.S. Department of Education. (1994). *Developing a program agenda for Part E Sections 641–643: Research in the education of individuals with disabilities:*

History of the agenda development process. Washington, DC: Chesapeake Institute.

U.S. Department of Health and Human Services, Substance Abuse and Mental Health Services Administration. (1993). *Guidance for program narrative, RFA No SM 93-02 Grants for Comprehensive Community Mental Health Services for Children and Adolescents with Serious Emotional Disturbances.*

U.S. Department of Health and Human Services and US Department of Education. (2016, May 5). *Policy statement on family engagement from the early years to the early grades.* Retrieved from https://www.acf.hhs.gov/sites/default/files/ecd/16_0152reportclean_logos.pdf

Wagner, M., Friend, M., Bursuck, W., Kutash, K., Duchnowski, A. J., Sumi, W. C., et al. (2006). Educating students with emotional disturbances: A national perspective on programs and services. *Journal of Emotional and Behavioral Disorders, 14*, 12–30.

Walker, J. (2016). Timeline of the Family Movement and children's behavioral health. Handout.

Weiss, H., Bouffard, S., Bridgelall, B., & Gordon, E. (2009). *Reframing family involvement in education: Supporting families to support educational equity.* Equity Matters: Research Review No. 5. New York: Campaign for Educational Equity, Teachers College, Columbia University.

Wynne, L. C., Ryckoff, I. M., Day, J., & Hirsch, S. I. (1958). Pseudo-mutuality in the family relations of schizophrenics. *Psychiatry, 21*, 205–220.

CHAPTER SIXTEEN

Family-Driven Care and Practice

One Size Does Not Fit All

Nancy Feyl Chavkin, Trina Osher, and Lacy Wood

This chapter builds on the earlier discussions in this handbook on family involvement by focusing on family-driven care and practical applications of family-driven principles and research findings. In this chapter, we provide background for family-driven care by sharing our definitions of family and family involvement, the importance of involving families, and a discussion of the wraparound[1] approach to engaging children, youth, and families in crisis. The chapter then presents a summary of research on family-driven and wraparound approaches and illustrates a three-tiered approach that can be used for understanding the different levels of support strategies related to family engagement based on different levels of student and family needs. Selected examples of family-driven practice from a variety of fields using the three-tiered approach follow this discussion. Finally, the chapter concludes with sections on strategies and barriers to involving families and recommendations for family-driven care. The practice examples and this chapter illustrate that one size does not fit all. Family engagement strategies should be contextualized to meet the varying needs of different schools and communities; one family engagement strategy is not likely to fit with all families or for every child, youth, or student. It is important to note that, while chapters in this handbook are written for a wide audience including: (1) students and faculty; (2) educators, counselors, and psychologists; (3) family and community stakeholders; (4) agency administrators and staff; and (5) local and state level officials, this chapter pays particular attention to providing information, strategies, and recommendations reflective of the family stakeholder voice.

What Is a Family?

Osher and Huff (2000) aptly pointed out that the family defines itself and that the various child-serving systems and service providers must work with each child and family in that context. Families can include biological or adoptive parents and their partners, siblings, extended family members, called kinship care-givers, and friends who provide a significant level of support to the child or primary care-giver.

The job of a family is to provide love, guidance, care, support, and otherwise nurture all its members for their entire lives. Families are the ultimate zero reject, zero eject group. Families are structured in a variety of ways. Each family has a culture, language, values, and spirituality of its own and these characteristics can vary within families as well. These, as well as the physical environment in which they live, influence how the family approaches simple tasks of daily living as well as significant challenges, such as raising a child with a mental, emotional, or behavioral disorder. Because families operate in their own ways, and they have different resources available to them, they achieve different degrees of success at meeting everyone's needs.

For example, when a family member is under stress, other family members may take on additional tasks and responsibilities to help meet that individual's needs. When a family is under substantial stress, it may need outside supports. Informal community supports may step in to lend a hand or private and public agencies and systems (such as schools or mental health professionals) may provide services. When outside supports are unavailable, insufficient, or inappropriate, the family can become damaged. In such a condition, the family may be temporarily (or permanently in some cases) unable to nurture some or all its members.

What Is Family Involvement?

Family involvement is about access, voice, and ownership. When families are meaningfully involved with personnel working in the service system, they have access to the decision-making process and play an active role in it. Meetings where important decisions are made should *never* be held without family members present.

However, it is not enough for families to be at the table, family involvement requires that the *family voice* be heard at all levels. On a policy or governing council, this requires that there be several family members present who can represent the various perspectives of the diverse families who will be affected by the decisions being made. Family voice is heard only when the others involved pay attention, respect the contribution, and incorporate what families say into the work being done and decisions being made.

When there is true family involvement, there is also family *ownership*. When families are involved with the service system, they agree with and are committed to the decisions, plans, or actions that concern them. They are not silent or submissive. When families are involved, they collaborate to plan activities to implement treatment plans and inform policy decisions because their input is tailored to truly address their priorities and concerns.

Why Involve Families in Decision-Making?

Working collaboratively with families enhances outcomes for the child, the family, the provider, and the system. For a service plan to have a positive outcome, it must be implemented. The child and family must understand and agree with the service plan and be able to carry out any responsibilities assigned to them. The child's family must believe a program will work and have confidence in their ability to support it before they will participate in it (Hoover-Dempsey et al., 2005). More important, when family members feel that a program or plan supports their family's strengths, needs, values, and culture, they relate positively to what it expects of them, actively engage, and support it. When family members are not involved in developing a service plan, they lack information and understanding necessary to buy-into it or participate consistently.

Another reason for involving families is that their adult members are taxpayers and voters—making them stakeholders in building support for initiatives, systems, and funding. Every agency, program, and provider needs broad support in the community to get the political and financial backing necessary to continue its work and to fund the research to demonstrate its accomplishments and effective practices. Families who are meaningfully involved in developing, implementing, and evaluating a program will truly understand it and actively advocate for it in city councils, state agencies, governor's offices, and legislatures.

The Wraparound Approach to Family-Driven Care

Wraparound is an intensive, individualized care planning and management approach that aims to achieve positive outcomes by providing a structured, creative, and individualized team planning process that, compared to traditional treatment planning, results in plans that are more effective and more relevant to the child and family (National Wraparound Initiative, n.d.).

Wraparound is a distinctive approach to addressing children or youth who experience mental health or behavioral challenges. One of the primary principles of Wraparound is that it places the needs of child or youth and family at the center and uses their unique ideas and perspectives about needs to drive the services in Wraparound (National Wraparound Initiative, n.d.). This youth- and family-centered approach addresses at the onset that one size does not fit all when it comes to the services and supports needed by these families and their children. Families and their children work with a wraparound facilitator to establish a wraparound team. Teams can be made up of family friends, community members, as well as providers of services and supports. This model allows the family to take the lead in identifying and developing goals and individualized services and supports customized to their situation (National Wraparound Initiative, n.d.).

Wraparound assembles multiple agencies to work together to meet the goals of families in crisis or may begin with the specific needs of a child. The agencies meet regularly to discuss individual plans and assess progress. Family members participate fully in the meetings and are given the tools they need to assist. Wraparound streamlines the process so families do not have to go to multiple agencies and work on multiple plans. One of the strengths of the approach is its ability to include natural supports and empower families and communities to improve the well-being of children and adolescents with emotional and behavioral challenges.

Wraparound is a cornerstone of family-driven approaches to care because its first principle is to provide "family voice and choice" (Bruns et al., 2004). Wraparound recognizes and acknowledges that the people who have a long-term, ongoing relationship with a child or youth (their families and caretakers) have a distinctive investment and commitment to the process and its outcomes. The principle of family voice and choice confirms that families should have the largest authority over the services choices because of the increased likelihood for successful outcomes when families and youth are allowed to actively participate and influence the decisions (Bruns et al., 2004). There may be others, such as teachers, therapists, probation officers, or family advocates, on the wraparound team. Team composition is unique to each family depending on their strengths, goals, and needs. Team members should actively seek out and encourage the participation of natural supports such as members from the family's networks of interpersonal and community relationships. For more information about Wraparound, *The Ten Principles of the Wraparound Process* (Bruns et al., 2004) presents a full list of Wraparound principles.

Research Support for Wraparound and Family-Driven Care

Initially, the philosophy of wraparound was expressed through the work of local initiatives and agencies, however, this work was not formally captured in the literature until the 1990s (Bruns & Walker, 2008). Wraparound operates across multiple agencies, rather than within a single agency, as such research on wraparound needs to be done collaboratively, due to the highly complex implementation context (Walker, 2008). This complexity was compounded because "there was little, if any, clear definition or standardization of what the wraparound process actually entailed" (VanDenBerg, 2008) Establishment of the National Wraparound Initiative "led to standardized principles of wraparound and definitions of the steps, or phases and activities, of the process"—providing consistency in the field and thus standardizing components for research (VanDenBerg, 2008).

Achieving high-quality implementation of wraparound can be challenging because of the many agencies and stakeholders involved. However, implementation challenges occur at the practice level, and teams can experience difficulty implementing the wraparound process in a way that reflects the principles of Wraparound (Walker, 2008). Using the wraparound principles as a basis for assessing fidelity is key to achieving outcomes. Fidelity to the Wraparound principles and the guidance for implementing the phases of wraparound should require, "at a minimum, assessing (1) adherence to the principles of wraparound, (2) whether the basic activities of facilitating a wraparound process are occurring, and (3) supports at the organizational and system level" (Bruns, 2008). It is also important to note that to be true to the Wraparound principles, "any fidelity measurement approach should allow for the individualization of the model for families as well as communities" (Bruns, 2008).

The research on wraparound and family-driven care and practice comes from a variety of disciplines. This section provides a short summary of research on family-driven care and wraparound services. The cross-disciplinary research on wraparound highlights the need for targeted strategies based on family context. The studies featured in this section provide snapshots of the research addressing (1) the wraparound process and support needed, (2) family voice and choice in wraparound, (3) wraparound and school-based intervention, (4) wraparound services for residential care and juvenile delinquent youth, and (5) future research and evaluation efforts. These studies illustrate that systems of care and practitioners need differentiated strategies for working with families based on family need.

Wraparound Process and Support

In Coldiron, Bruns, and Quick's (2017) review of 206 wraparound peer-reviewed studies and literature, they found evidence for cost-effectiveness of wraparound services. The bulk of the literature that emerged focused on the definition of the model and advocating for its use. Although there was no clear consensus on the definition, there were many similarities and widespread use of wraparound and family-driven practices. Walter and Petr's (2011) systematic review of the effectiveness of wraparound using a multidimensional evidence-based practice approach cited policy barriers and lack of support of higher level administrators. It was rare for natural, nonprofessional supports to actively participate in the meetings. They recommended including more parent advocates and family partners on the team and more opportunities for youth and families to lead the meetings rather than merely participate.

The results of these studies show that the process of implementing wraparound needs contextually driven approaches—one size is not going to fit all.

Family Voice and Choice

The need to combine family voice with informed choices that are research-based was found by Bruns and colleagues (2014). Their study showed that some programs were effective when they coordinated wraparound approaches with the Managing and Adapting Practice (MAP) system. The MAP system is designed to address a specific issue encountered in modern behavioral health care—improving outcomes and quality of care. MAP achieves these aims through *structured collaboration*, a framework for coordinating individuals and information around key decisions.[2] They suggested there was a strong need to leverage evidence-based treatment with family and child contexts, preferences, and needs. They presented four enhancements:

1. During wraparound planning use, MAP tools to generate a broader array of research-based options that fit the youth and family's needs and preferences.
2. When therapeutic needs are identified, support clinicians to use effective practice elements that connect to the youth and family's strengths and preferences.
3. Train and support parent and youth partners, mentors, behavioral specialists, and other roles to serve as care extenders who can enhance treatment strategies.
4. Monitor progress and practices consistently and use the information to revise plans as needed. (Bruns et al., 2014, pp. 11–12).

Wraparound and School-Based Intervention

Eber, Hyde, and Suter (2011) discussed how wraparound can be an effective part of a schoolwide system of positive supports (SWPBS), particularly in meeting the needs of students who have emotional and behavioral challenges. Wraparound was studied as part of a Response to Intervention (RTI) approach. Although they report issues in collecting consistent and regular data, data on a sample of 125 students gave promising results. For 70 of the 125 who were tracked for six months with three complete sets of outcome data, the perceived risk of school placement failure decreased to only minimal risk, and there were significant behavior and academic outcome gains, including a reduction in discipline referrals and an increase in academic performance.

Wraparound Services for Residential Care and Juvenile Delinquent Youth

Cox, Baker, and Wong (2010) looked at factors predicting positive outcomes in the wraparound process in residential care and found that when the goal was to shorten the time from residential care to home living or to maintaining home placement, youth with lower levels of impairment did best. As in many earlier studies, wraparound results were more favorable for children with moderate impairments. There were more challenges for clients with complex needs. In comparing wraparound services with conventional services for juvenile delinquent youth, Carney and Buttell (2003) found that wraparound youth were less likely to engage in subsequent at-risk behavior. For example, they had fewer unexcused absences and did not get expelled or suspended from school as often as youth receiving conventional services. In addition, there were also fewer reports of assaults with youth receiving wraparound services. The authors suggest that the study reinforces the notion that juvenile offenders must be appropriately matched to services.

Future Research and Evaluation

At the University of Washington (UW), the Wraparound Evaluation and Research Team (WERT) conducts rigorous studies across the nation. The UW WERT is currently working with counties in Washington state and Florida to evaluate wraparound initiatives. They are also conducting implementation and fidelity assessments for initiatives in Indiana and Texas using their Wraparound Structured Assessment and Review (WrapSTAR) process. More information on these efforts can be found on their Web site (https://depts.washington.edu/pbhjp/projects-programs/listing).

This snapshot of research on family-driven care and practice with a particular focus on wraparound care coordination shows it is important to remember that participant needs, attention to context, and tailoring to that context are key to the success of these types of programs.

A Three-Tiered Approach

Using multitiered approaches as an assistance strategy helps to focus and concentrate on supporting the unique needs of families while providing a structure for addressing the reality that *one size does not fit all*. Strategies for family involvement can be organized into categories using a three-tiered approach described in figure 16.1 developed by Osher and Huff (2006).

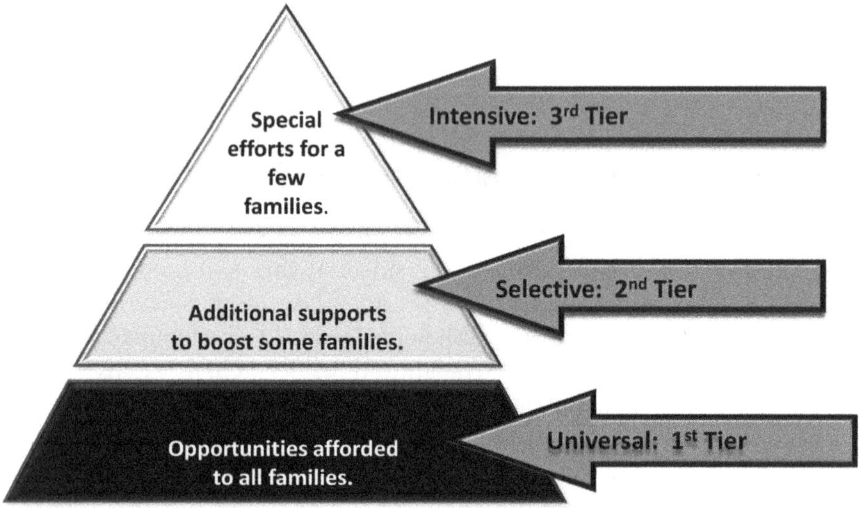

Figure 16.1 3-Tier Model for Differentiating Strategies to Maximize Family Engagement (From Osher, T. & Huff, B. Working With Families of Children in the Juvenile Justice and the Corrections Systems: A Guide for Education Program Leaders, Principals, and Building Administrators. National Evaluation and Technical Assistance Center for the Education of Children and Youth who are Neglected, Delinquent, and At-Risk. Pages 8–9)

Administrators of agencies and programs providing services to children and youth can use this three-tiered approach (or similar framework for differentiated support) to coordinate and customize efforts for involving family members. Because families need varied, differentiated strategies for involvement with staff, similar to students, this chapter describes three levels of support (see figure 16.1) and lists examples of family involvement strategies that fall into each category. This organizing approach identifies and provides contextualized supports that can be used by agencies when developing a plan for family involvement that is compatible with their own setting.

In the first tier of the triangle are *foundational or universal strategies*. These opportunities are made available to all families and are designed primarily to establish a relationship, gain trust, and open communication channels. These Tier 1 supports typically focus on strategies such as:

- Creating a welcoming environment
- Soliciting family input
- Providing an orientation to the program
- Establishing routine mechanisms for ongoing communication
- Sponsoring group social activities

In the second tier of the triangle are *selective* strategies for particular groups of families with needs that may require a boost or extra encouragement to get involved. Providing supports such as transportation, child care, and qualified translators all fall into this tier. Tier 2 strategies focus on:

- Connecting families with each other and supporting the creation of parent networks
- Offering families opportunities for education and training
- Taking advantage of the family's visits to a program or facility in order to meet individually with them

In addition, families who are responding to second tier strategies can be a good source for recruiting family members who desire or are willing to become more involved in advisory groups focusing on the overall program.

Intensive strategies in the third tier of the triangle focus on meeting the individual needs and more substantial challenges that keep a few families from getting involved. Effective approaches are intentionally individualized and may require intensive effort over time. Home visits where staff can get to know families in their space, learn their needs, and provide targeted supports is one example of a third-tier strategy. Another strategy used to support these individualized needs is hiring a "family partner," a trained and experienced parent or family member assigned to reach out to these families. Family partners are able to gain the trust of a hesitant family, build a bridge between the family and the agency or program, and support the family until it feels comfortable interacting directly with program staff. Family partners have also been able to maintain a relationship with the family once their child has graduated from the program or moved to another service.[3]

Examples of Family-Driven Practice

By its nature, family-driven practice needs to be individualized to each family, one size does not fit all. Each family will be different. Family-driven care may also vary by agency setting, age of child, experience of family, cultural norms, policies, and other factors. The overarching *Guiding Principles of Family-Driven Care* emphasize that the approach must be strength-based so that families have access to services and information, voices that are heard, and ownership for decisions. The examples below are from multiple settings and were selected to illustrate a variety of strategies across the three tiers and provide a starting point to understanding the many ways that family-driven practice can work effectively. The list is not comprehensive but provides an opportunity to see some of the many strategies being used across different settings. Examples have been selected so that readers can appreciate the creativity and uniqueness of the varied approaches and recognize the common threads of family-driven care and practice.

A number of the examples come from programs using wraparound (see Kendziora, Bruns, Osher, Pacchiano, & Mejia, 2001). The section that follows presents six examples of family driven approaches.

Family-Run Organizations of Nebraska

The mission of Family Run Organizations of Nebraska, an organization collaborative, is to "constantly advance the systems of care for children's behavioral health." The Family Run Organizations of Nebraska group is an example of a first-tier approach that is focused on ensuring that "all children and families in Nebraska are emotional, behaviorally and mentally strong." The group makes certain that all families benefit from family-driven choices and that diversity is honored. The network includes a variety of organizations including: S. P. E. A. K. O. U. T.! For Children with Disabilities, Family Care, Parent to Parent Network, Families Inspiring Families, and Nebraska Family Support Network. This network views parents and family members as active participants in treatment, policy development, and system reform and is working hard to transform the field so that families become true partners. The unique approach of this network is that it is totally family-run. Families are helping each other. They are sharing what they have learned and helping each other through their own peer-to-peer network. You can learn more about their work from their Web site (https://nefamilies4kids.org).

Brevard County, Florida, C. A. R. E. S. Wraparound

In contrast to traditional child welfare services that remove children at risk from their family and community, Brevard County's Coordination, Advocacy, Resources, Education, and Support (C. A. R. E. S.) focuses on identifying and developing an extensive system of formal and informal supports within the community and connecting them to families. The Alliance for Strong Families and Communities recently released a study finding that 93% of children whose families participated in Brevard County C. A. R. E. S. had no incidents of maltreatment (Schneider-Muñoz, Renteria, Gelwicks, & Fasano, 2015). The program director believes these positive results are linked to early engagement of families and building strong, effective partnerships with high-fidelity wraparound services, which parallels research findings on early intervention with families (Schneider-Muñoz, Renteria, Gelwicks, & Fasano, 2015). The program believes that all families, even the most challenged parents and caretakers, have the potential to make changes. Putting the emphasis on preventative resources and reconfiguring the system of care to provide more formal and informal community services and supports in the family's home rather than outside of it is a third-tier approach. Brevard County C.A.R.E.S. effectively shifted a deficit approach to a family-strengths approach supporting the family and child to be safe and healthy in their home. To read more about the program and these research results, visit their Web page (http://brevardfp.org/).

Wraparound Milwaukee with Juvenile Justice Youth

Wraparound Milwaukee, recipient of a 2009 Innovations in American Government Award, is a program in Milwaukee County, Wisconsin, that serves more than 1,600 families annually and has a daily enrollment of 1,050 youth and their families. The program was founded in 1995 and focuses primarily on youth with serious emotional and mental health needs in the juvenile justice system. As a third-tier program, Wraparound Milwaukee serves approximately 750 children and youth from the juvenile justice system. The program incorporates family- driven and youth-guided care with a strengths-based, highly individualized approach and has a strong community focus. Once selected for the Wraparound Milwaukee Program, a Care Coordinator works with the child and the family. The probation officer or therapist or both are members of the team to ensure cross-system collaboration. Each family has a family advocate, and families have choices about which services they will get and the providers who will deliver them. The program is known for its transparency in sharing information with families. Parents see the billings for services and give their feedback about which are most useful and "worth the money." As a result, providers are responsive to families and families become smarter consumers and stronger advocates. Giving families choices about who is on the team and what services to get is an important part of Wraparound Milwaukee's success. The program has excellent outcome results with a low and stable rate of recidivism. For more information, see the *SAMHSA Brief* (Kamradt & Goldfarb, 2015).

Education CAFE, Texas

The Intercultural Development Research Association (IDRA) has developed an innovative model called Education CAFE (Community Forums for Excellence). The aim of the Education CAFE is to improve schools by transforming traditional parent involvement into a more effective vehicle. The current work is focused on (1) ESSA-mandated early childhood plans; (2) planning for equitable resource distribution; and (3) promoting college success. Three components of this program's success are a focus on being community-based with distributive leadership, partnering with school districts, and conducting education projects that include actionable data. The model includes both first- and second-tier approaches for engaging families who have previously been excluded or underserved.

For a recent and effective advocacy project based on actionable data, family members surveyed 1,600 families about their knowledge of Texas's new graduation requirements. Based on that information, they organized community meetings (*mesa communitarias*) and trainings to share information with families about what courses students should take in high school to gain admission to college. For more information, see IDRA's Web site (http://www.IDRA.org).

Coordinated Systems of Care, Louisiana Office of Behavioral Health

This program includes four nonprofit, private agencies that provide wraparound services via contract with the statewide managed care office. They serve children under the age of 22 who have a mental health, substance abuse, or a co-occurring disorder and are at-risk for an out-of-home placement and usually with involvement in more than one system (child welfare, juvenile justice, mental health, special education). One strategy that stands out in this third-tier approach is that all care coordinators require certification and training. In addition, families and youth are able to access parent/youth support and parent/youth training and resources. Parent/caregiver peer support is encouraged and training is provided. The emphasis on training and support for care coordinators, family members, and peer supporters is a strong feature of this program. The statewide managed care organization (MC) is responsible for tracking and measuring outcomes and a full report is available on their Web site. For more information, see their Web site: Coordinated System of Care, Louisiana Office of Behavioral Health (http://www.ldh.la.gov/index.cfm/subhome/49).

Massachusetts Children's Behavioral Health Initiative

Massachusetts works with 22 private, nonprofit agencies to provide Integrated Care Coordination (ICC) across 32 Community Service Agencies. The program uses a third-tier approach and primarily serves youth who meet defined criteria for serious emotional disturbance (SED). All Care Coordinators must be certified and have experience working with youth who have serious emotional disturbance, and their families. The program values parent/caregiver support and provides training and support in this area. One of the outstanding features of this program is the emphasis on Family Advocates. Family Advocates guide new families all the way through services. They attend meetings, they share resources, they help families ask questions, and they help families decide what is best for their youth and their families.

Outcomes are tracked and results show that inpatient hospitalization has decreased. For more information, see their Web site (http://www.mass.gov/eohhs/consumer/insurance/cbhi/).

The examples above highlight the variety of settings and approach's that can be applied when implementing the principles of Wraparound along with illustrating where strategies fall across the three tiers of the framework described above. This information is intended to provide a starting point for understanding the varied ways that family-driven practice can be contextualized to individual family needs and work effectively.

What Are the Primary Barriers to Family Involvement?

There are four overarching barriers to family involvement that anyone who wishes to collaborate with family-members must understand and overcome. (Osher, 1994).

- *Lack of information* is a major barrier to family involvement. It is certainly true that being a family member makes someone an expert on raising a child with a problem. However, this status does not automatically confer comprehensive knowledge about how all the programs or systems are organized, where the power lies, or what kind of political minefield has to be negotiated to make changes. Information is power. Denying access to information has long been a means of oppression and control. Family members are fully capable of making good program and system decisions when they have the information necessary to understand the alternatives.
- *Inequity* dulls the family voice. Typically, when teams and working groups gather to discuss the system of care, family members are outnumbered by agency representatives and providers who, by virtue of their position and expertise, are usually intimidating to the one or two family members present. For families to have a partner's voice at the table they have to be present in sufficient numbers to be influential. Involving one or two family members in decision-making forums, even if they are outspoken, is tokenism.
- *Isolation* is a major fact of life for families raising a child with a mental health need. This and the stigma associated with mental illness significantly influences how families interact with systems. Families are frequently, and falsely, blamed for being inadequate, not caring about their children, or letting them run wild. Families are shunned by neighbors, and sometimes relatives, who do not want their children to associate with a "problem child." Schools call parents to take their children home when they are exhausted by dealing with their challenging behavior(s). No one knows better than family members how tough it is to be with a child who has a behavior problem or is emotionally out of control. Yet, they fear blame, shame, criticism, and

losing their children to the system when calling for help, especially if they are poor. In addition, the need for confidentiality within child-serving systems can keep families from getting to know others facing similar challenges who could provide emotional and peer support.

- *Dependence* on the system for services and support and basic survival needs is a barrier for families who fear reprisal or negative consequences if they speak honestly about how they are affected by what the system does, what needs to be changed, or how to improve the quality of life of children and families in the community. Families who are involved in the child welfare and protective service systems could risk loss of benefits and perhaps custody of their children if they speak critically. Families of youth in juvenile corrections system fear their children will be punished if, as concerned parents, they question how their child is being treated or ask about the services their child is (or is not) receiving. Some spokespersons for the family movement have experienced reprisals at their workplace for their public advocacy.

Recommendations for Family-Driven Care

As we plan to work with families, it is important to consider that professionals have more time to devote to their collaborative responsibilities and have more resources and information at their disposal than their family partners. Family members' first responsibilities are caring for, protecting, and nurturing children, holding down a job, and maintaining a safe and healthy home. Leaders and workers in the all systems concerned with the well-being of children can easily and inexpensively provide support for their family partners by taking some simple steps (Osher, 1994).

- *Scaffold information carefully.* It is incumbent upon those inside the system to provide orientation to family members who serve on policy councils or advisory groups so they know what is going on and have a chance to think about the issues before they get to the meeting. The challenge is not to overwhelm these family members. For example, sharing all 500 pages of a budget is not necessary; instead, providing a clear explanation of what has been allocated to the children's project under discussion and how it relates to the bigger picture for team discussion honors the time commitment of families. Staff should review key laws or policies with family partners and personally introduce them to agency heads and others who control resources and make other critical decisions. Family partners need to be aware of the individual projects and concerns of various team members so they understand the full context before providing input.
- *Support family partner's efforts.* Professionals who want the benefits of family involvement should provide family members with the support and tools

necessary to do the job well. The amount and type of support needed will depend on the skills and resources of each family member and the specific nature of the project. This could take the form of preparing meeting notes or drafting position statements and committee reports they are working on as well as distributing resources to share with other team members. System personnel and family members should have a conversation about what would be most helpful in each situation and how to best use the skills of individuals on the team.

- *Be respectful of a family member's time.* Their time is valuable and there must be clear evidence to family members that when invited to provide advice and feedback or serve on policy groups, that others are listening to them and their time is well spent on activities focused on the task at hand. It is best for those collaborating with families to ensure they start on time, stick to the agenda, and end promptly. Before engaging families in these collaborations staff should understand the individual situations of family partners and how that may affect participation with the team. Some may be taking unpaid leave from work, paying for a babysitter by the hour, have a long drive, or need to pick up their children at a specific time.
- *Recognize a family's contribution.* Professionals can show family members their efforts are appreciated by including names in a product or report, mentioning their family-run organization in articles about the project, or sending letters of appreciation pointing out how you made use of their work. It may be appropriate to tell employers about how the family partner's participation is helping to make the program or community a better place to live and work. Professionals should remember to directly thank to family members who are collaborating with them.
- *Ease the burden.* Many family members who recognize the importance of participating and would like to get involved have insufficient resources and time with which to make that contribution. Policy developers and program planners need to find ways to ease the burden that is associated with family involvement. Family members pay, directly or indirectly, for the opportunity to collaborate by giving up time with their families, vacation time, or taking leave without pay and paying for others to care for their children, while professionals usually are drawing a salary for being at the same event or working on the same task. The cost to families is a resource allocation issue that must be solved if families are to truly be empowered to take an equal place at the table. Systems must find ways to reimburse (or offset) costs to families for lost wages and travel, provide or pay for child care, serve coffee or lunch, hold meetings close to where families live and at times convenient for them, or include them in meetings via a toll-free conference call. Systems of care should encourage employers to allow families paid leave to make this partnership work.
- *Family partners should not be marginalized.* Facilitate peer support. Advisory boards and teams that include families should recruit a diverse team of

family members for a project or team. Facilitating peer support is a strategy for making family members more comfortable in their role. Arranging for family members to meet and get to know each other before formal meetings and giving them the opportunity to informally caucus from time to time will help ensure everyone is comfortable voicing their unique perspective. Providing resources to develop and sustain family-run advocacy and support networks, such as a local chapter of the Federation of Families for Children's Mental Health. Encouraging family members to reach out to each other can help keep other families in the community informed of the progress being made by the system of care.

- *Be culturally competent and culturally responsive.* It is impossible to be family-driven without being culturally competent. Culture, as defined by a family, is an inherent part of what a family is. How a family defines its own culture is a complex and fluid matter that takes into consideration current contexts (and how they change) as well as family history. A family's culture is its foundation. How the family or its members respond to experiences, the decisions they make, how they feel, what they dream, the way they view others, what risks they are willing or able to take, what they fear most, and so on depends on their cultural perspective. Family voice and choice require taking the time to learn about the family and making decisions in accordance with what has been learned.

Conclusion

Family-driven care means being culturally competent and culturally responsive.[4] Involving family members in making decisions about systems and services is not difficult, but it does require making some changes in how business is conducted. Most important, it requires being respectful, having an open mind, active listening, and a conscious and deliberate willingness to truly share responsibility for making decisions and responsibility for achieving outcomes. These are qualities valued by all the human service professions and should be "natural" behaviors stressed in training human services workers. Recognizing that one size does not fit all and shaping policy and practice accordingly is fundamental to successfully engaging families and critical to insuring all children receive what they need to thrive.

Notes

1. Lowercase "w" has been used when the term "wraparound approach" is used generically, but a capital "W" has been used when referring to the official approach developed by the National Wraparound Institute.

2. https://www.practicewise.com/Community/MAP.
3. Description of three-tiered approach from Osher & Huff (2006).
4. For more information and suggestions on cultural competence and family-driven care, please refer to Osher et al. (2011).

References

Bruns, E. J. (2008). Measuring wraparound fidelity. In *Resource guide to wraparound* (Chapter 5e.1). National Wraparound Initiative. Retrieved from https://nwi.pdx.edu/NWI-book/Chapters/Bruns-5e.1-(measuring-fidelity).pdf

Bruns, E. J., & Walker, J. S. (2008). Ten principles of the wraparound process. In *Resource guide to wraparound* (Chapter 2.1). National Wraparound Initiative. Retrieved from https://nwi.pdx.edu/NWI-book/Chapters/Bruns-2.1-(10-principles-of-wrap).pdf

Bruns, E. J., Walker, J. S., Adams, J., Miles, P., Osher, T. W., Rast, J., et al. (2004). *Ten principles of the wraparound process.* Portland, OR: National Wraparound Initiative, Research and Training Center on Family Support and Children's Mental Health, Portland State University.

Bruns, E. J., Walker, J. S., Bernstein, A. D., Daleiden, E., Pullmann, M. D., & Chorpita, B. F. (2014). Family voice with informed choice: Coordinating Wraparound with research-based treatment for children and adolescents. *Journal of Clinical Child and Adolescent Psychology, 43*(2), 256–269.

Carney, M. M., & Buttell, F. (2003). Reducing juvenile recidivism: Evaluating the Wraparound services model. *Research on Social Work Practice, 13*(5), 551–568. doi:10.1177/1049731503253364

Coldiron, J. S., Bruns, E. J., & Quick, H. (2017). A comprehensive review of Wraparound care coordination research, 1986–2014. *Journal of Child and Family Studies, 26*(5), 1245–1265. doi:10.1007/s10826-016-0639-7

Cox, K., Baker, D., & Wong, M. A. (2010). Wraparound retrospective: Factors predicting positive outcomes. *Journal of Emotional & Behavioral Disorders, 18*(1), 3–13.

Eber, L., Hyde, K., & Suter, J. C. (2011). Integrating Wraparound into a schoolwide system of positive behavior supports. *Journal of Child and Family Studies, 20*(6), 782–790. doi:10.1007/s10826-010-9424-1

Hoover-Dempsey, K. V., Walker, J. M. T., Sandler, H. M., Whetsel, D., Green, C. L., Wilkins, A. S., & Closson, K. E. (2005). Why do parents become involved? Research findings and implications. *Elementary School Journal, 106*(2), 105–130.

Kamradt, B., & Goldfarb, P. (2015). *Demonstrating effectiveness of the wraparound model with juvenile justice youth through measuring and achieving lower recidivism.* Baltimore: Technical Assistance Network for Children's Behavioral Health.

Kendziora, K. T., Bruns, E. J., Osher, D., Pacchiano, D., & Mejia, B. X. (2001). *Wraparound: Stories from field.* Systems of care: Promising practices in children's mental health, 2001 series, Volume 1. Washington, DC: American Institutes for Research, Center for Effective Collaboration and Practice.

Mears, S. L., Yaffe, J., & Harris, N. J. (2009). Evaluation of Wraparound services for severely emotionally disturbed youths. *Research on Social Work Practice, 19*(6), 678–685. doi:10.1177/1049731508329385

National Wraparound Initiative. (n.d.). *Wraparound basics.* National Wraparound Initiative, Regional Research Institute, School of Social Work, Portland State University. Retrieved from https://nwi.pdx.edu/wraparound-basics/

Nordness, P. D. (2005). A comparison of school-based and community-based adherence to Wraparound during family planning meetings. *Education & Treatment of Children, 28*(3), 308–320.

Osher, T. W. (1994). *Getting me on your team: Building partnerships with families.* Presented October 26, 1994, at Issues in Community Mental Health: Focus on families. A symposium sponsored by the Westchester County Department of Community Mental Health.

Osher, T. W., Garay, L., Jennings, B., Jimerson, D., Markus, S., & Martinez, K. (2011). *Closing the gap: Cultural perspectives on family-driven care.* Washington, DC: Technical Assistance Partnership for Systems of Care, American Institutes for Research. Retrieved from http://www.pasocpartnership.org/uploads/SOC_PACKET_closing_gap_osher_final_version_2016_(1).pdf

Osher, T. W., & Huff, B. (2000). Involving families in making decisions about systems of care. *Journal of NAMI California, 2*(1), 14–16. Osher, T. W., & Huff, B. (2006). *Working with families of children in the juvenile justice and the corrections systems: A guide for education program leaders, principals, and building administrators.* Washington, DC: National Evaluation and Technical Assistance Center for the Education of Children and Youth who are Neglected, Delinquent, and At-Risk.

Osher, T. W., & Huff, B. (2006). *Working with families of children in the juvenile justice and corrections systems: A guide for education program leaders, principals, and building administrators.* Washington, DC: National Evaluation and Technical Assistance Center for the Education of Children and Youth Who Are Neglected, Delinquent, or At Risk. Retrieved from https://neglected-delinquent.ed.gov/sites/default/files/docs/Family%20Involvement%20Guide_FINAL.pdf

Schneider-Muñoz, A., Renteria, R., Gelwicks, J., & Fasano, M. (2015). Reducing risk: Families in Wraparound intervention. *Families in Society: The Journal of Contemporary Social Services, 96*(2), 91–98.

VanDenBerg, J. (2008). Reflecting on wraparound: Inspirations, innovations, and future directions. In *Resource Guide to Wraparound* (Chapter 1.4). National Wraparound Initiative. Retrieved from https://nwi.pdx.edu/NWI-book/Chapters/Walker-5a.1-(support-wrap-implement).pdf

Walker, J. S. (2008). Supporting Wraparound implementation: Overview. In *Resource guide to wraparound* (Chapter 5.1). National Wraparound Initiative. Retrieved from https://nwi.pdx.edu/NWI-book/Chapters/Walker-5a.1-(support-wrap-implement).pdf

Walter, U. M., & Petr, C. G. (2011). Best practices in Wraparound: A multidimensional view of the evidence. *Social Work, 56*(1), 73–80.

PART 5

Collaboration

CHAPTER SEVENTEEN

Interdisciplinary and Cross-Stakeholder Collaboration for Better Outcomes

David Osher, Sandra K. Williamson, Kimberly Kendziora, Kelly Wells, and Curtiss Sarikey

Children and youth with emotional, behavioral, or mental health needs often receive or require services from multiple professionals in schools as well as multiple agencies and multiple systems, and schools are the major entry point for these services (Farmer, Burns, Phillips, Angold, & Costello, 2003). Since time and money resources are scarce, children, their families, providers, and communities can benefit from effective coordination, the sharing of ideas and perspectives, and collective empowerment, ownership, and responsibility (Bai Wells & Hillemeier, 2009; Osher, 2002). Families and professionals often call attention to these needs, and their input has been incorporated into federal plans and agendas. Two relevant examples are the National Agenda for Improving Results for Children and Youth with Serious Emotional Disturbance and Pathways for Youth. Parents of children with emotional disturbance and other caregivers talked about the burdens posed by fragmented services, the need to master different professional languages, and professionals' ignoring their input (U.S. Department of Education, 1994). Professionals in 10 cities spoke about how they could provide better services if they had knowledge of and time to collaborate with other agencies (Interagency Working Group on Youth Programs, December 2016).

Coordination and collaboration are not easy as professionals and agencies often function in intradisciplinary silos. Each professional has a knowledge base, mental mind set, and role set that is affected by job demands and professional responsibilities (Merton, 1957b); and each agency has its own mission, mandates, funding streams, service areas, accountability processes, and organizational cultures. Many school-based and school-involved professionals have different training and knowledge, philosophical orientation, terminology, and perspectives (Rappaport et al., 2002; Waxman, Weist, & Benson, 1999). Diverse agencies are staffed by individuals who have been trained, credentialed, and socialized into various disciplines and who continue to receive ongoing professional information from different guilds and intradisciplinary reference groups. Professionals participate in distinct communities of knowledge and practice, which often increase their specialized knowledge and commitment to intradisciplinary service paradigms.

The diverse agencies and staff operate in separate service systems that address particular needs or problems, and although collaboration is still not easy, it is easier within common systems than across them (Rivard & Morrissey, 2003). Agencies and staff work under legislative mandates, which only authorize certain functions, and through bureaucratic and professional orientations that focus on specific problems or indicators. Each of these service systems has its own institutional patterns that are grounded in the history of each services system and nested in the statutory authorizations, budgetary allocations, auditing procedures, and time horizons that are specific to each service system (Woodruff et al., 1999). Some services are usually organized locally (e.g., education), others are organized on a municipal or county basis (e.g., mental health), while still others are organized on a state or regional basis (e.g., child welfare).

The disconnections created by the differences between and among professions, agencies, and service systems contribute to both the duplication and the fragmentation of services. Duplication of effort occurs when different professionals or agencies intentionally or unintentionally provide similar services (Weist et al., 2012). This duplication wastes scarce resources; increases child, family, and staff burden; and may undercut the potency of particular interventions. Fragmentation of services occurs when children and their families require services and supports from multiple professionals or across multiple domains. Since the services provided by different professionals or agencies are specialized and delimited, children and their families can fall between the cracks of mandates, protocols, and catchment areas.

Fragmentation can lead to crisis-oriented interventions that do not address overall social and emotional functions. It also challenges families who often already have limited bandwidth whether due to the challenges of addressing their children's needs and/or due to financial struggles (Mullainathan & Shafir, 2013). Families must negotiate between and among different agencies and disciplines, each of which has its own language, definitions, and procedures. The number of agencies can be daunting to family members who must also maintain jobs and care for other family members. The need to wrap their hands around different service systems, each with its own jargon, acronyms, and procedures, challenges the ability of families to assess options and advocate for their children. Effective cross-system advocacy may require attending numerous meetings and the mastery of multi-vocal discourses as well as the understanding of distinct organizational and professional cultures.

This organizational fragmentation challenges practitioners and policy makers as well. While some practitioners may feel more at ease in the predictability of their roles, professional colleagues, and job descriptions, their work increasingly requires that they interact effectively with consumers and professionals who come from other disciplines or agencies. Policy makers are similarly challenged by the need to improve outcomes while efficiently husbanding money and time, both of which are scarce. Both fragmentation and duplication challenges their ability to get a handle on how to improve complex systems or even whom to hold accountable for the failure to improve outcomes.

Building Collaboration

Conceptualizing Collaboration

Although cooperation, coordination, interagency collaboration, and consumer-driven collaboration are often used interchangeably, they describe different stages in the transformation of the relationships between and among agencies and consumers.

The term "collaboration" can be confused with cooperation and coordination (Frey, Lohmeier, Lee, & Tollefson, 2006). Although the last two terms refer to processes that are essential to effective collaboration, they refer to less transformative approaches to service coordination and delivery. *Cooperation* involves a superficial level of agency interaction, implying that agencies are aware of one another and interact to provide general information, support, or referral. For example, agency staff (e.g., mental health and child welfare workers) may know about each other and in some cases may even make referrals to each other without in any way altering the way they (or their agencies) conduct their business. *Coordination* alters the relationships of independent organizations, staff, or resources. Coordination, for example, involves agency staff working together to plan and schedule activities. *Collaboration* is the most sophisticated and demanding level of interagency and professional relationships. Collaboration involves efforts to unite organizations and people for the purpose of achieving common goals that could not be accomplished by any single individual or organization acting alone. There is a significant difference between "limited cooperative efforts and more intensive collaborative arrangements" (Melville & Blank, 1993, p. 4). "If collaboration is to result in more responsive services for children and families," Charles Bruner observed, "it must do more than redesign organizational flow charts" (1991, p. 5). Collaboration involves four key elements: (1) agreed upon and institutionalized mutuality and common goals, (2) jointly developed structure and shared responsibility, (3) mutual authority and accountability for success, and (4) shared resources and rewards.

Just as collaboration can be distinguished from cooperation and coordination, so too can consumer-driven collaboration be distinguished from interagency collaboration without consumer-driven collaboration. Although interagency collaboration represents a major advance over fragmented interdependent service coordination and delivery, it does not necessarily transform the top-down relationship between agencies and consumers (families, children and youth, and even the community), addressing which can improve both outcomes and collaboration (Morrissey-Kane & Prinz, 1999; Osher & Osher, 2002). This is particularly the case for families of color and other marginalized families who are often stigmatized for who they are (e.g., Harry & Klinger, 2014; Osher, Cartledge, Oswald, Artiles, & Coutinho, 2004). Agency staff, for example, may be socialized into viewing clients (or particular clients) and the community (or particular parts of the community) as problems to be fixed or as the passive receivers of services, and this may be reinforced by organizational culture (Olin et al., 2014). At the same time, families may fear raising issues that would compromise their or their child's access to resources (Wilensky & Lebeaux, 1965). Similarly, professionals may assume that their training and expertise prepares them to determine agendas, diagnose problems, prescribe solutions, and evaluate results or have prejudicial beliefs, mindsets, or attitudes. Collaboration with consumers involves a transformation of attitudes, behaviors, and organizational cultures (Alegria, Atkins, Farmer, Slaton, & Stelk, 2010; Kalyanpur & Harry, 2012; Olin et al., 2014) as well as a reorganization of structures (e.g., the timing of meetings) so that voice is shared and everybody is fully able to partner in developing agendas, analyzing problems, determining solutions, and evaluating results (Osher, Osher, & Blau, 2006; Spencer, Blau, & Mallery, 2010).

A recent study of coordination between school personnel involved with implementing tiered systems of support and those involved in providing mental health literacy training found that these levels of collaboration could be distinguished by examining how staff members described training, planning, communication, and organizational structures (Kendziora, Mack, Jones, & Pate, 2018). Collaboration at a low level was defined as the independent execution of activities, or activities were conducted with limited interaction. Examples included referrals and communication letting the other organizations know about planned activities. Moderate collaboration was defined as shared implementation of activities involving altered relationships of the independent organizations, staff, or resources. That is, rather than independent action or superficial interaction, agency staff actively worked together to plan and conduct activities. Collaboration at a high level was defined as the integration of efforts and activities by organizations and staff to achieve common goals unattainable by a single individual or an organization acting alone. This level of collaboration involved agreed-on common goals, shared responsibility, mutual accountability for success, and shared resources.

Overcoming the Barriers to Collaboration and Building Supportive Structures

Building collaboration requires overcoming challenges that have confronted earlier and more limited efforts at cooperation and coordination between and among existing organizations (Johnson, McLaughlin, & Christensen, 1982) as well as supportive structures and facilitators. Common challenges to collaboration are shown in table 17.1.

Supportive structures at a school level do more than coordinate efforts—they support common perceptions and a collaborative vision. Dwyer and Osher (2000) developed such a model to support mental health and school safety, in a guide that was supported by 23 national professional associations. The model combines a schoolwide team, which can include families and youth as well as other members of the school community, that addresses all schoolwide functions and a student support team that focuses on identifying and implementing interventions designed to address individual student needs. One key to the model is shared personnel between the two teams to realize a common vision and coordinate efforts—a principal, mental health professional, and a teacher. The second key is to have the schoolwide team absorb and coordinate the functions of the existing school team to avoid fragmented planning and facilitate understanding of issues and implementation.

Kendziora and colleagues' (2018) study of coordination among school personnel focusing on school safety and mental health found that a majority of school staff identified communication as the primary factor that supported improved coordination. Communication ranged from regularly scheduled meetings (e.g., quarterly) to more informal discussions that offered the opportunity to discuss successes and challenges, provide updates, and identify ways in which they could support each other. In some cases, school staff created new teams to facilitate ongoing dialogue about their work. Communication was further facilitated by factors such as having a preexisting culture of collaboration, creating an organizational structure that encompassed both safety and mental health, such as a cross-sectional team (i.e., a team

Table 17.1 Challenges to collaboration

Challenge	Explanation
Organizational interests	Competitiveness and parochial interests of agencies and the lack of incentives
Systemic factors	Lack of organizational structures to bring agencies together around mutual interests, the lack of decision-making rules, and the complex nature of the current system
Experiential and training factors	Lack of experience in how to coordinate and implement service delivery and lack of training capacity
Organizational culture	How things are done in a given agency or site (Glisson & James, 2002; Hartnell, Ou, & Kinicki, 2011)
Communications	Awkward interdisciplinary communication, poor communication with constituencies, and the absence of common procedures for information dissemination
Focus	Focusing on systems design and managerial issues rather than on the functional role of the system and the needs of consumers
Time	Lack of time to include and train staff
Readiness	Low levels of motivation (including buy-in) or organizational capacity or individual capacity to collaborate (Osher, 2018; Scaccia et al., 2015)
Funding and licensing mandates	These mandates may limit the ability to collaborate
Definitions	Disagreement on target populations, variability in client eligibility, variability and inconsistency of role definitions and responsibilities across and within agencies
Data and indicators	Lack of centralized information base and common indicators and metrics

that spans several departments), and including community organizations in action planning meetings. Additional factors that enhanced collaboration included having common goals, having stakeholder buy-in, having a champion or an identified leader for coordination efforts, and having a strong professional network.

Supportive structures at an interorganizational level foster coherence and focus through the development of common perceptions and visions. For example, Say Yes to Education supports a collective citywide model through a Community Leadership Council (CLC), an Operating Committee, task forces, and a Scholarship Board. The Council meets quarterly and includes a wide cross-section of local leadership, including representatives of all key public and private agencies, as well as stakeholder groups (e.g., family organizations), the faith community, and the business community. The CLC structure allows for regular, transparent accountability and provides a public forum for addressing policy issues. The Operating Committee meets biweekly and includes the school superintendent, high-ranking representatives from the offices of the mayor and the county executive, philanthropic leaders, higher education leaders, teacher and administrative union leaders, and parent representatives. The Operating Committee monitors the delivery and the quality of services, scales services, and ensures the long-term sustainability of services. The task forces foster community collaboration in specific areas. For example, task forces in Buffalo address community mobilization, student health and wellness, legal services for families, teacher engagement, postsecondary pathways (in partnership with institutions of higher education), services for children from birth to age 8 years, religious community engagement, expanding business partnerships, and engaging community-based organizations (Osher & Chasin, 2016).

Supportive structures at a governmental level can coordinate activities, align information in a way that supports collaboration, provide for cross-training, and provide models of collaboration. The Federal Interagency Work Group on Youth Programs (IWGYP) illustrates how governmental agencies can collaborate as well as support collaboration. Founded in 2008 with 10 mandated federal departments, it now includes 10 additional agencies. IWGYP developed the first Federal Strategic Plan for Collaboration, Pathways for Youth (December 2016), where one of three strategic targets is "collaboration and coordination—Promote coordinated strategies to improve youth outcomes." It has three objectives: (1) align and simplify federal guidance for youth programs; (2) coordinate youth programming and funding support at the federal, state, local, and tribal levels; and (3) coordinate technical assistance efforts to leverage resources. The IWGYP meets monthly to learn about promising programs and initiatives in common and to discuss and plan collaborative activities that realize the agenda. IWGYP has an accessible information website to provide one-stop shopping for youth-serving organizations and others (https://youth.gov), and this website also has a section that showcases federal collaboration.

Resistance to Change

Collaboration involves changes in, between, and among professional bureaucracies—agencies and schools. Professional bureaucracies have evolved over a long period, and, while they may appear dysfunctional to outside observers, they have demonstrated a capacity to withstand the forces of reform (Cuban, 1984; Merton, 1957b). Changing them requires addressing six factors that go beyond adopting the value of collaboration.

The first factor involves legal mandates and the tendency of organizations to control boundaries—turf—to protect themselves in order to maintain resources and a predictable environment in which to operate (Huberman, Levinson, Havelock, & Cox, 1981). The second factor involves the institutionalized practices and routinized behaviors that have evolved over time and which, although they may respond to agency needs, are unresponsive to the needs of consumers and other potential collaborators. Until collaboration becomes the normal way of doing things or until consumers are able to have sustained input into a review of policies, these routines will remain the default position. The third factor involves the incentive systems of organizations—how people are evaluated and rewarded (both formally by the organization and informally by their peers). Organizations and their professional staff rarely reward activities that cross bureaucratic and professional boundaries (Goode, 1973). The fourth factor involves the press of time and cognitive and logistical bandwidth (Mullainathan & Shafir, 2013). Staff and administrators face demanding and often unstable workloads—a situation that often eliminates the willingness of many individuals to take on new roles or to adopt new strategies that might take time to master. Until agencies (including schools) are reorganized to build in time for collaboration, the time taken for collaboration has an opportunity-cost and is an add-on to regular jobs. The fifth factor involves family and organizational cultures that provide distinct ways of viewing things that mediate the way potential collaborators interact and interpret their interactions. The sixth factor involves social networks (Miles, 1978), which support or constrain particular behaviors and provide channels for circulating information. Particular barriers to collaboration include the fact that collaboration must take place between and among culturally diverse stakeholders who often have a history of poor relations and are divided themselves by their current access to privilege, power, and resources (Goldenberg, 1978). These barriers affect the ability of individuals to understand one another, and they make it particularly difficult to change relations of voice and power (McGuire, 1969; Rothman, 1976).

The power of these factors is reinforced by a conceptual fuzziness that equates agency-driven approaches to planning, operationalization, and evaluation with family or consumer-driven approaches to these activities (Osher & Osher, 2001). This conceptual looseness reflects the extent to which the factors that hinder collaboration have become so much a part of day-to-day thinking that they are taken for granted. A successful strategy to promote collaboration must address structures, belief systems, and unconscious knowledge (Clark, 2008) that sustain ordinary routines.

Operationalizing Collaboration

The challenges to collaboration are great—they are deeply embedded in the system that collaboration is trying to reform (Kagan, 1991). This "embeddedness" is rooted in the organizational patterns of long-standing agencies, the routines of long-standing practices, and the day-to-day rituals of day work. Collaboration requires an infrastructure to enable it to take place, a collaborative culture with a shared mission and articulated mission training and support to help people collaborate, resources to support the collaborative efforts, and data collection to reinforce collaboration and measure the impact of services through understandable measures that have credibility across agencies, disciplines, and stakeholders (Bruner, 1991).

If collaborative efforts are not congruent and coherent at multiple levels, it will be hard to build meaningful collaboration, and even harder to sustain it. The need for congruence exists at multiple levels. One level is organizational. Hodges, Nesman, and Hernandez (1999) suggest that collaboration be congruent at legislative, agency, program, and service levels, including schools. If state legislators do not support collaboration, it will be hard for agencies to sustain collaborative efforts. If agencies in these states do not collaborate, it will be hard for programs to collaborate, without undue effort. If programs do not collaborate, they will not provide an appropriate host environment for collaboration in the provision of individual services by line workers who must collaborate across different programs and agencies and with families. Fortunately, many states are supporting some level of coordination. For example, in 2017, 36 states had coordinating bodies (The Forum for Youth Investment, 2017).

A second collaboration level is functional: policy-making, budget allocation, leadership, middle management, progress monitoring, and service delivery. Collaborative policy is necessary to authorize and frame collaborative activities. Budget support is necessary to enable and provide incentives for collaboration and stable funding streams. Leadership can encourage collaboration, "give permission" to collaborate, to model collaborative behaviors, and to problem-solve when the predictable barriers to collaboration are encountered (Dwyer & Osher, 2000). Middle management involvement is necessary because middle managers are in a place to supervise and allocate resources to line staff. Line staff involvement is critical so that the collaboration is realized at the service level. Progress monitoring and quality improvement procedures should employ common indicators that represent the Venn Intersect across organizations (Osher & Chasin, 2016).

A third level is jurisdictional—collaboration needs to be supported at the broadest levels, middle levels, and street levels of implementation. In some cases (e.g., mental health) the relevant distinction is federal, state, and local. In other cases (e.g., education) the relevant distinctions may be state, district, and school. No matter what the relevant jurisdiction is, collaboration can be facilitated or stifled by a lack of higher level support (Bruner, 1991; Hodges, Nesman, & Hernandez, 1999).

A fourth level is personal. Individuals need to be ready to collaborate with each other, and this involves interpersonal relationships and readiness to collaborate (Osher, 2018). Relationships are at the heart of building sustainable collaboration, which involves understanding of different perspectives and the development of relational trust (Bryk & Schneider, 2002). Readiness involves being motivated to collaborate, having the social and emotional skills as well as technical knowledge to collaborate, and being an organizational environment that fosters collaboration. The social and emotional skills include self-awareness and cultural competence. Knowledge includes expertise in their own domain (e.g., teaching) and interprofessional knowledge and respectful understanding of consumer's contexts. Organizational features include supportive norms and processes, the provision of time to cross-train and collaborate, and organizational culture (Williams et al., 2017).

Federal Support for Collaboration

The need for collaboration has been recognized and realized by federal agencies for over 25 years. Two examples are Systems of Care for Children's Mental Health and the Safe Schools/ Healthy Students Program.

Systems of Care

Systems of care are coordinated networks of community-based services and supports organized to meet the challenges of children and youth and their families that emphasize and improve outcomes through coordination and collaboration between agencies and family-driven and youth-guided partnerships between and among agencies, children, and families (Hawley & Weisz, 2003; Miller, Blau, Christopher, & Jordan, 2012; Osher, Penn, & Spencer, 2008; Stroul & Blau, 2008). Between 1993 and 2015, the Federal Center for Mental Health Services (CMHS) funded 300 grants in states, territories, counties, and federally recognized tribal entities to community or county grantees that used federal and matching funding to create or expand systems of care that serve children and youth with serious emotional disturbances and their families. In 2015, CMHS FY 2015, provided grants to support expansion of systems of care and funded an additional 127 grants. These included 50 one-year Expansion Planning grants, as well as 77 four-year system of care Expansion and Sustainability grants to stimulate the wide scale adoption of the system of care approach. These grants aimed at promoting the expansion of system of care services and supports, including infrastructure development and collaboration and partnership between child-serving systems (e.g., child welfare, education, juvenile justice, primary care and substance abuse services and systems, and strategic financial planning), so that the system of care framework can be brought to scale and sustained after grant funding has ended. The preliminary evaluation of these expansion grants found that:

- There were significant improvements in behavioral and emotional symptoms and functioning among children and youth. Total mean symptom scores significantly improved by more than five points from 68.5 at intake to 63.3 at 12 months. The proportion of children and youth with clinical levels of impairment in functioning dropped from 70.6% at intake to 56.4% at 12 months.
- Thoughts of suicide and suicide attempts among children and youth served fell significantly from intake to 12 months as reported by caregivers, children, and youth respondents. Thoughts of suicide dropped from 19.4% to 12.2%, a 37.5% decrease in suicidal ideation. Suicide attempts dropped from 9.1% to 1.7%, an 80.8% decrease in suicidal attempts.
- The proportion of children and youth who attended school regularly, and who received grades of C or better, significantly increased from intake to 12 months. Attendance increased from 70.6% to 83.1%, a 17.6% improvement. The proportion receiving grades of C or better increased from 58.2% to 74.5%, a 28.1% improvement.
- Youth served by CMHI-funded grantees reported a significant decrease of 42.6% (68.8% at intake to 48.2% at 12 months) in unlawful activities (Substance Abuse and Mental Health Services Administration, 2018).

Safe Schools/Healthy Students

Another example of a federally funded grant program that understands the importance of collaboration is the Safe Schools/Healthy Students (SS/HS) initiative. SS/HS was launched in 1999 as a joint effort between the U.S. Departments of Education, Health and Human Services, and Justice in response to rising concerns about youth violence, substance abuse, mental health, and school safety. SS/HS supports universal, selective, and indicated interventions, promotes healthy child development, and supports school-community collaboration. While school districts (local education agencies, or LEAs) are the eligible grantees, the application must involve a collaboration that includes the LEA, local public mental health authority, and local law enforcement agencies, with the recommendations that grantees also include the involvement of family members, students, and juvenile justice officials.

The federal departments modeled collaboration by braiding funding to create what was experienced as one grant that provided students, schools, and communities with enhanced comprehensive educational, mental health, social service, law enforcement, and juvenile justice system services that promote healthy childhood development and prevent violence and alcohol and drug abuse. In actuality, there were three grant programs, but due to braiding of funding and accountability at a federal level, grantees were able to access resources through one application, having one review process, one grant officer, one evaluation, one technical assistance provider, and one annual and final report (Furlong, Paige, & Osher, 2003).

In 2013, the Substance Abuse and Mental Health Services Administration (SAMHSA) funded SS/HS grantees and scaled it from the local level to the state level. To date, more than 13 million students in almost 400 communities from all 50 states have benefited from SS/HS programming. The crux of SS/HS are the partnerships formed at both the state and local level between education, mental health, law enforcement, juvenile justice, and other youth- and family-serving organizations working together to conduct needs assessment, use data to select evidence-based programming, revise policies to continuously meet the needs, and develop a comprehensive plan to prevent youth violence and promote mental health among school-aged youth. This collaborative approach works as data suggested from the initial SS/HS communities found that more than 90% of school staff saw a reduction in violence on school grounds and 80% reduced violence in their communities.

Caregiver Alliance, Wraparound, and the Importance of Readiness to Collaborate

Interagency, interprofessional, and cross-stakeholder collaboration are necessary to eliminate fragmented services and build consumer-caregiver alliance (Family Caregiver Alliance, 2006: Feinstein, Fielding, Udvari-Solner, & Joshi, 2009; Osher, 2002). Fragmentation wastes financial resources, limits access, wastes time, and frustrates participants. Lack of interprofessional and consumer-professional collaboration limits the perspectives of both professionals and consumers. Professionals and consumers only know what they can know through their individual, mental models, or personal tool kits. They are also limited by what sociologists call visibility and observability—how people's lives and organizations are structured so that people can and cannot see certain things due to the organization of their daily and work lives (Merton, 1957b). Coordination and collaboration can save resources and expand access (Substance Abuse and Mental Health Services Administration [SAMHSA], 2018). Coordination and collaboration can also, under the right conditions, lead to the expansion and alignment of perspectives and knowledge, while enhancing the engagement of participants (Feinstein et al., 2009; Osher, Osher, & Blau, 2006).

Effective wraparound teaming exemplifies the promise of collaboration (Kendziora, Bruns, Osher, Pacchiano, & Mejia, 2001). Wraparound is an individualized, team-based care planning and coordination process that integrates professional and natural supports, develops a holistic treatment plan that includes supports for families and siblings, and oversees an individualized strengths based process of goal-setting and progress monitoring (Walker, Bruns, & Penn, 2008). It has been often been employed to realize system of care principles at a youth and family level (Poduska, Kendziora, & Osher, 2012) and has been used in other arenas as well (Blessing, Tierney, Osher, Allegretti-Freeman, & Abrey, 2005). To be most effective it should be family- and youth-driven, culturally competent, strengths-based, employ progress monitoring to assess implementation, and operationalize the principle of zero eject (Kendziora et al., 1999; Osher & Hanley, 2001). Wraparound has been demonstrated to be effective when implemented with fidelity to it principles. For example, a meta-analysis of nine empirical studies found significant effects of wraparound across all five domains examined, including maintenance of youth in community residential placements (Cohen's $d = .44$), mental health outcomes (0.31), overall youth functioning (0.25), school functioning (0.27), and juvenile justice outcomes (0.21) (Suter & Bruns, 2009).

These results are replicable, but as in the case of other efficacious and promising interventions, only when they are implemented with fidelity to key principles and under the right organizational conditions (Bruns, Pullmann, Sather, Brinson, & Ramey, 2015). We can also learn from what happens when wraparound is implemented without readiness and fidelity. An experimental study that compared service experiences and outcomes for youth with serious emotional disorder randomly assigned to care coordination via a defined wraparound process (n = 47) versus more traditional intensive case management (n = 46) found that although the wraparound group received more mean hours of care management and services, there were no group differences in restrictiveness of residential placement, emotional and behavioral symptoms, or functioning. The implementation data suggested:

- Fidelity of wraparound implementation was found to be poor by all measures employed; fidelity during the current study was at the 29th percentile for parent reports and at the 13th percentile per a team observation measure.
- The process did not consistently engage youths and family members in the development of the wraparound team, involve family natural supports, develop crisis plans based on functional assessments, link caregivers to social supports, and involve youths in community activities.
- The team process was implemented inconsistently: statements of mission, goals, or priority needs were not developed; teams were not brainstorming individualized strategies to meet youth and family needs; team members were not following through on tasks; and effective transition plans were not being developed.

- System conditions for wraparound (e.g., role clarity, caseload sizes, availability of flex funds, and availability of training and coaching) also were not rated favorably.
- Key services were not provided—less than one-third of the youth and families, received community-based supports such as mentoring or respite, or in-home services such as behavioral aides; only 2 of 51 families in the wraparound condition were found to have received family support services; and the youth had less access to evidenced-based treatment.
- The organizational culture, climate, and morale were found to be far better for case managers of the university-affiliated mental health organization than those employees of the state mental health system who facilitated wraparound teams (Bruns, Pullmann, Sather, Brinson, & Ramey, 2015).

Wraparound has great potential. Due to its use of natural supports and harnessing of consumer expertise in monitoring and personalization, it is sustainable, cost-efficient, and produces positive results with ethnically and linguistically diverse children and youth (Kendziora et al., 1999). However, wraparound must be more than a label. It requires the readiness on the part of all parties to implement its principles with fidelity while adapting them to the individual strengths and needs of individual children, youth, and their families. Readiness involves motivation to change and take risks, having or developing the personal skills to collaborate, and being in the right organizational conditions to collaborate, which include training, support, and organizational culture (Osher, 2018). Policy and the allocation of resources and support can enable this to happen.

Conclusion

Collaboration, like wraparound, has great potential. This potential can be seen in effective schools and communities that promote safety without the use of exclusion (Quinn, Osher, Hoffman, & Hanley, 1998; Woodruff et al., 1999). When collaboration includes all stakeholders, it harnesses and expands collective expertise, engages end-users to ensure effective planning, implementation, and monitoring, adapts to local contexts, and produces sustainable results. And like wraparound, collaboration requires readiness and the ability to use data for progress monitoring and continuous improvement.

Although different frameworks, paradigms, technical terminology, and practical constraints, impede collaboration, a commitment to a common goal (such as safety) or a common mission (such as student mental health) can foster school-based collaboration (Dwyer, Osher, Maughan, Tuck, & Patrick, 2015; Weist et al., 2012), address challenges, and facilitate collaboration. Training, support, and facilitation can build readiness to collaborate. Participation in collaborative endeavors creates opportunities for (1) learning about other perspectives and how to work together; (2) reinforcement of collaborative successes; (3) shared experiences that build coherence and common perspectives; and (4) the development of relational trust that can enrich collaboration.

References

Alegria, M., Atkins, M., Farmer, E., Slaton, E., & Stelk, W. (2010). One size does not fit all: Taking diversity, culture and context seriously. *Administration and Policy in Mental Health, 37*(1–2), 48–60. doi:10.1007/s10488-010-0283-2

Bai, Y., Wells, R., & Hillemeier, M. M. (2009). Coordination between child welfare agencies and mental health service providers, children's service use, and outcomes. *Child Abuse and Neglect, 33*(6), 372–381. doi: 10.1016/j.chiabu.2008.10.004

Blessing, C., Tierney, M., Osher, D., Allegretti-Freeman, J., & Abrey, B. (2005, December). *Person/family-centered planning processes: Learning from other communities.* Prepared for consensus meeting on Person/Family-Centered Planning, Substance Abuse and Mental Health Services Administration, Rockville, MD.

Bruner, C. (1991). *Thinking collaboratively: Ten questions and answers to help policy makers improve children's services.* Washington, DC: Education and Human Services Consortium, Institute for Educational Leadership.

Bruns, E. J., Pullmann, M. D., Sather, A., Brinson, R. D., & Ramey, M. (2015). Effectiveness of wraparound vs. case management for children and adolescents: Results of a randomized study. *Administration and Policy in Mental Health, 42*(3), 309–322. doi:10.1007/s10488-014-0571-3

Bryk, A. S., & Schneider, B. (2002). *Trust in schools: A core resource for improvement.* New York: Russell Sage Foundation.

Clark, R. E. (2008). Resistance to change: Unconscious knowledge and the challenge of unlearning. In D. C. Berliner & H. Kupermintz (Eds.), *Changing institutions, environments, and people* (pp. 75–94). Mahwah, NJ: Lawrence Erlbaum.

Cuban, L. (1984). Transforming the frog into a prince: Effective schools research, policy, and practice at the district level. *Harvard Educational Review, 54,* 129–151.

Dwyer, K., & Osher, D. (2000). *Safeguarding our children: An action guide.* Washington, DC: U.S. Departments of Education and Justice, American Institutes for Research.

Dwyer, K. P., Osher, D., Maughan, E. D., Tuck, C., & Patrick, K. (2015). Team crisis: School psychologists and nurses working together. *Psychology in the Schools, 52*(7), 702–713.

Family Caregiver Alliance. (2006). *Caregiver assessment: Principles, guidelines and strategies for change.* Report from a National Consensus Development Conference (Vol. I). San Francisco: Author.

Farmer, E. M. Z., Burns, B. J., Phillips, S. D., Angold, A., & Costello, E. J. (2003). Pathways into and through mental health services for children and adolescents. *Psychiatric Services, 54*(1), 60–66.

Feinstein, N. R., Fielding, K., Udvari-Solner, A., & Joshi, S. V. (2009). The supporting alliance in child and adolescent treatment: Enhancing collaboration among therapists, parents, and teachers. *American Journal of Psychotherapy*, *63*(4), 319–344.

The Forum for Youth Investment. (2017). *2017 State policy survey: Child and youth policy coordinating bodies in the U.S.* Takoma Park, MD: Author.

Frey, B. B., Lohmeier, J. H., Lee, S. W., & Tollefson, N. (2006, September). Measuring collaboration among grant partners. *American Journal of Evaluation, 27*(3), 383–392.

Furlong, M., Paige, L. Z., & Osher, D. (2003). The Safe School, Healthy Students Initiative: Lessons learned from implementing healthy youth development programs. *Psychology in the Schools, 40*(5), 447–456.

Glisson, C., & James, L. R. (2002). The cross-level effects of culture and climate in human service teams. *Journal of Organizational Behavior, 23*(6), 767–794.

Goldenberg, I. I. (1978). *Oppression and social intervention.* Chicago: Nelson-Hall.

Goode, W. (1973). *Explorations in social theory.* New York: Oxford University Press.

Harry, B., & Klinger, J. K. (2014). *Why are so many minority students in special education? Understanding race and disability in schools* (2nd ed.). New York: Teachers College Press.

Hartnell, C. A., Ou, A. Y., & Kinicki, A. (2011). Organizational culture and organizational effectiveness: A meta-analytic investigation of the competing values framework's theoretical suppositions. *Journal of Applied Psychology, 96*, 677–694.

Hawley, K. M., & Weisz, J. R. (2003). Child, parent, and therapist (dis)agreement on target problems in outpatient therapy: The therapist's dilemma and its implications. *Journal of Consulting and Clinical Psychology, 71*(1), 62–70.

Hodges, S., Nesman, T., & Hernandez, M. (1999). *Promising practices: Building collaboration in systems of care.* Systems of care: Promising Practices in Children's Mental Health, 1998 Series, Volume 6. Washington, DC: Center for Effective Collaboration and Practice, American Institutes for Research.

Huberman, M., Levinson, J., Havelock, R. G., & Cox, P. L. (1981). Interorganizational arrangements. *Knowledge: Creation, Diffusion, Utilization, 3*(1), 5–22.

Interagency Working Group on Youth Programs. (December 2016). *Pathways for youth: strategic plan for federal collaboration.* Washington, DC: Author. Retrieved from https://youth.gov/sites/default/files/IWGYP-Pathways_for_Youth.pdf

Jewett, J., Conklin, N. F., Hagans, R., & Crohn, L. (1991). *Integration of Education and Human Services Project: Conceptual synthesis and review of community-based integration activity.* Portland, OR: Northwest Regional Educational Laboratory.

Johnson, H. W., McLaughlin, J. A., & Christensen, M. (1982). Interagency collaboration: Driving and restraining forces. *Exceptional Children, 48*(5), 395–399.

Joint Commission on the Mental Health of Children. (1973). *Mental health: From infancy through adolescence*. Report of the Joint Commission on the Mental Health of Children. New York: Harper & Row.

Kagan, S. L. (1991). *United we stand: Collaboration for child care and early education services*. New York: Teachers College Press.

Kalyanpur, M., & Harry, B. (2012). *Cultural reciprocity in special education: Building family-professional relationships* (2nd ed.). Baltimore: Brookes.

Kendziora, K., Mack, A. R., Jones, W., & Pate, W. E. (2018). *Collaboration for safe and healthy schools: Study of coordination between School Climate Transformation Grants and Project AWARE*. Washington, DC: U.S. Department of Education, Office of Planning, Evaluation and Policy Development, Policy and Program Studies Service. Retrieved from https://www2.ed.gov/about/offices/list/opepd/ppss/index.html

Kendziora, K. T., Bruns, E. J., Osher, D., Pacchiano, D., & Mejia, B. X. (2001). *Systems of care: Promising practices in children's mental health, 2001 series, volume 1: Wraparound: Stories from field*. Washington, DC: American Institutes for Research, Center for Effective Collaboration and Practice.

McGuire, W. J. (1969). The nature of attitudes and attitude change. In G. Lindzey & E. Aronson (Eds.), *Handbook of social psychology* (Vol. 3, pp. 136–314). Reading, MA: Addison-Wesley.

Melville, A. I., & Blank, M. J. (1993). *Together we can: A guide for crafting a profamily system of education and human services*. Washington, DC: U.S. Departments of Education and Health and Human Services.

Merton, R. K. (1957a). *Social theory and social structure*. Glencoe, IL: Free Press.

Merton, R. K. (1957b). The role-set: Problems in sociological theory. *British Journal of Sociology, 8*, 106–120.

Miles, M. M. (1978). *On "networking."* New York: Center for Policy Research.

Miller, B. D., Blau, G. M., Christopher, O. T., & Jordan, P. E. (2012, June). Sustaining and expanding systems of care to provide mental health services for children, youth and families across America. *American Journal of Community Psychology, 49*(3–4), 566–579.

Morrissey-Kane, E., & Prinz, R. (1999). Engagement in child and adolescent treatment: The role of parental cognitions. *Clinical Child and Family Review, 2*, 183–198.

Mullainathan, S., & Shafir, E. (2013). *Scarcity: Why having too little means so much*. New York: Times Books.

Olin, S. S., Williams, N., Pollock, M., Armusewicz, K., Kutash, K., Glisson, C., & Hoagwood, K. E. (2014). Quality indicators for family support services and their relationship to organizational social context. *Administration and Policy in Mental Health and Mental Health Services Research, 41*, 43–54.

Osher, D. (2002). Creating comprehensive and collaborative systems. *Journal of Child and Family Studies, 11*(1), 91–101.

Osher, D. (2018). Building readiness and capacity. In Osher, D., Moroney, D., & Williamson, S. (Eds.), *Creating safe, equitable, engaging schools: A comprehensive, evidence-based approach to supporting students*. Cambridge, MA: Harvard Education Press.

Osher, D., Cartledge, G., Oswald, D., Artiles, A. J., & Coutinho, M. (2004). Issues of cultural and linguistic competency and disproportionate representation. In R. Rutherford, M. Quinn, & S. Mather (Eds.), *Handbook of research in behavioral disorders* (pp. 54–77). New York: Guilford.

Osher, D., & Chasin, E. (2016). Bringing together schools and the community: The case of Say Yes to Education. In J. F. Zaff, E. Pufall Jones, A. E. Donlan, & S. A. Anderson (Eds.), *Optimizing child and youth development through comprehensive community initiatives* (pp. 72–104). New York: Psychology Press.

Osher, D., & Hanley, T. V. (1996). Implications of the national agenda to improve results for children and youth with or at risk of serious emotional disturbance. In R. J. Illback & C. M. Nelson (Eds.), *Emerging school-based approaches for children with emotional and behavioral problems: Research and practice in service integration* (pp. 7–36). Binghamton, NY: Haworth Press.

Osher, D., & Hanley, T. V. (2001). Implementing the SED national agenda: Promising programs and policies for children and youth with emotional and behavioral problems. *Education and Treatment of Children, 24*(2), 1–29.

Osher, T., & Osher, D. (2002). The paradigm shift to true collaboration with families. *Journal of Child and Family Studies, 11*(1), 47–60.

Osher, T., Osher, D., & Blau, G. (2006). *Ambassador's guide to family driven practice.* Rockville, MD: Federation of Families for Children's Mental Health.

Osher, T., Penn, M., & Spencer, S. A. (2008). Partnerships with families for family-driven systems of care. In B. A. Stroul & G. M. Blau (Eds.), *The system of care handbook: Transforming mental health services for children, youth, and families* (pp. 249–274). Baltimore: Brookes Publishing.

Poduska, J., Kendziora, K., & Osher, D. (2012). *Coordinated and individualized services within systems of care.* Washington, DC: Center for Effective Collaboration and Practice, American Institutes for Research.

Quinn, M. M., Osher, D., Hoffman, C. C., & Hanley, T. V. (1998). *Safe, drug-free, and effective schools for all students: What works!* Washington, DC: Center for Effective Collaboration and Practice, American Institutes for Research.

Rappaport, N., Osher, D., Dwyer, K., Garrison, E., Hare, I., Ladd, J., & Anderson-Ketchmark, C. (2002). Enhancing collaborations within and across disciplines to advance mental health programs in schools. In M. D. Weist, S. Evans, & N. Tashman (Eds.), *School mental health handbook* (pp. 107–118). New York: Kluwer Academic.

Rivard, J. C., & Morrissey, J. P. (2003, May). Factors associated with interagency coordination in a child mental health service system demonstration. *Administration and Policy in Mental Health, 30*(5), 397–415.

Rothman, J. (1976). Promoting an innovation. In J. Rothman, J., Erlich, & J. G. Teresa (Eds.), *Promoting change in organizations and communities* (pp. 22–57). New York: John Wiley.

Scaccia, J. P., Cook, B. S., Lamont, A., Wandersman, A., Castellow, J., Katz, J., & Beidas, R. S. (2015). A practical implementation science heuristic for organizational readiness: R = MC^2. *Journal of Community Psychology, 43*(4), 484–501.

Schulberg, H. C. (1973). From institutions to human services. In Y. Bakal (Ed.), *Closing correctional institutions* (pp. 39–48). Lexington, MA: Lexington Books.

Spencer, S. A., Blau, G. M., & Mallery, C. J. (2010). Family-driven care in America: More than a good idea. *Journal of the Canadian Academy of Child and Adolescent Psychiatry, 19*(3), 176–181.

Stroul, B. A., & Blau, G. M. (Eds.). (2008). *The system of care handbook: Transforming mental health services for children, youth, and families*. Baltimore: Brookes Publishing.

Substance Abuse and Mental Health Services Administration. (2018). *The Comprehensive Community Mental Health Services for Children with Serious Emotional Disturbances Program: Report to Congress, 2016.* Rockville, MD: Author.

Suter, J. C., & Bruns, E. J. (2009). Effectiveness of the wraparound process for children with emotional and behavioral disorders: A meta-analysis. *Clinical Child and Family Psychology Review, 12*(4), 336–351.

U.S. Department of Education. (1994). *National agenda for achieving better results for children and youth with serious emotional disturbance.* Washington, DC: Author.

Walker, J. S., Bruns, E. J., & Penn, M. (2008). Individualized services in systems of care: The wraparound process. In B. A. Stroul & G. M. Blau (Eds.), *The system of care handbook: Transforming mental health services for children, youth, and families* (pp. 127–153). Baltimore, MD: Paul H Brookes Publishing.

Waxman, R. P., Weist, M. D., & Benson, D. M. (1999). Toward collaboration in the growing education-mental health interface. *Clinical Psychology Review, 19*, 239–253.

Weist, M. D., Mellin, E. A., Chambers, K. L., Lever, N. A., Haber, D., & Blaber, C. (2012). Challenges to collaboration in school mental health and strategies for overcoming them. *Journal of School Health, 82*, 97–105.

Wilensky, H. L., & Lebeaux, C. N. (1965). *Industrial society and social welfare.* Menlo Park, CA: The Free Press.

Williams, N. J., Glisson, C., Hemmelgarn, A., & Green, P. (2017). Mechanisms of change in the ARC organizational strategy: Increasing mental health clinicians' EBP adoption through improved organizational culture and capacity. *Administration and Policy in Mental Health, 44*(2), 269–283. doi:10.1007/s10488-016-0742-5

Woodruff, D. W., Osher, D., Hoffman, C. C., Gruner, A., King, M., Snow, S., & McIntire, J. C. (1999). *The role of education in a system of care: Effectively serving children with emotional or behavioral disorders.* Washington, DC: Center for Effective Collaboration and Practice, American Institutes for Research.

CHAPTER EIGHTEEN

Collaborating to Provide and Align Services for Children and Youth with Intensive Mental Health Needs

JoAnne M. Malloy, Gene Chasin, Kathryn Francoeur, and Eric J. Bruns

More than 1 in 10 youths in the United States experience a serious behavioral health disorder (Williams, Scott, & Aarons, 2018), impairing their ability to function and causing them personal distress (Merikangas et al., 2010; O'Connell, Boat, & Warner, 2009). Youth and young adults with serious emotional or behavioral challenges (EBC, also referred to as serious emotional disturbance, or emotional and behavioral disorders) frequently find it difficult to navigate the significant physical, emotional, social, neurobiological, and developmental changes of adolescence along with the tasks required to transition successfully from school to adult life. Youth and young adults with EBC are not well served by U.S. schools and community agencies, indicated by their dismal outcomes including high rates of substance misuse, arrest and incarceration, unemployment, and early pregnancy and parenting (Cobb et al., 2013; Davis, Banks, Fisher, & Grudzinskas, 2004; Davis & Koroloff, 2006; Huizinga, Loeber, Thornberry, & Cothern, 2000;

Newman et al., 2011). Nearly half (45%) of students with an emotional disturbance drop out of school (Planty et al., 2008).

The challenges faced by youth with EBC are both individual and ecological. While many youth are dealing with personal challenges as they try to function in school, at home, and in their community, they often live in circumstances where the resources to help them are scarce, imposed upon them, or mismatched to their needs. A primary barrier to receipt of effective care is a lack of coordination across helpers. Whereas interventions that have the greatest likelihood of addressing the needs of children, youth, and young adults with EBC require collaboration among helpers to develop an integrated plan of care based on a positive, strengths-based vision and a manageable number of goals and strategies, child serving systems such as child welfare, juvenile justice, behavioral health, and education are governed by vastly different missions, funding streams, and eligibility requirements, compromising likelihood of effective coordination of care. For example, community mental health services are funded by individual patient fees, face-to-face contacts, and do not allow reimbursement for collaborative activities such as consulting with school staff or child protection workers. As a result, youth with serious EBC, who are in greatest need of collective action across helpers and providers, are often the least likely to receive it.

This chapter describes the contexts that are fueling reform to address these problems of practice and highlights two promising approaches, both of which aim to (1) assist the youth to create a positive, strengths-based vision that focuses on their transition to successful adulthood; and (2) build a bridge across the multiple agencies and systems to allow each youth access to the services and supports they will need to be successful. Throughout the chapter, we focus on the importance of cross-agency and cross-sector collaboration between education and community behavioral health, and how it is critical to implementation of both of these approaches.

Converging Values, Principles, and Practices across Behavioral Health, Community, and Schools

Systems of Care

The system of care framework, originally described by Stroul and Friedman (1986), was developed to respond to the problems of a disorder-focused and fragmented service system that leaves many children and youth with emotional or behavioral health challenges and their families without the support they need and want to improve their lives. Systems of care represent a paradigm shift focused on creating cross-agency collaboratives that operationalize the core values of family-driven and youth-guided practice, cultural and linguistic competency, and community-based supports and services (Stroul, Blau, & Friedman, 2010; Stroul, Blau, & Sondheimer, 2008). This type of support requires significant changes in the way traditional services are delivered in mental health, child welfare, juvenile justice, and education (Burchard, Bruns, & Burchard, 2002).

Systems of care seek to create a seamless and coherent continuum of care through authentic partnership and collaboration with youth, families, and other stakeholders at the individual level, the family level, the school and community level, and at the policy level. The goal of creating a more coherent system can only be achieved when partners work together in true collaboration toward a commonly held vision and goals. There is emerging evidence that the system of care approach results in more efficient use of resources across multiple sectors, including education, mental health, substance misuse, justice, child welfare, vocational rehabilitation, and other youth-serving systems and programs (Foster & Conner, 2005; Foster, Kelsch, Kamradt, Sosna, & Yang, 2001; Foster, Qaseem, & Connor, 2004).

Wraparound planning is an individualized planning intervention that operationalizes system of care values and principles at the youth and family level. In wraparound, an expert facilitator works with the youth and family to develop their vision for the future, identify underlying needs to be met to achieve that vision, and strategies (including both formal services and informal supports) to meet each priority need. The aim of family- and youth-driven wraparound is to develop a single plan for each youth and family, regardless of how many service systems are involved. Over the past 30 years of system of care implementation, this notion of family- and youth-driven planning has been shown to be effective in reducing out-of-home placements, behavioral health functioning, and youth participation in the community (Bruns, Suter, Force, & Burchard, 2005; Kamradt, 1996; Suter & Bruns, 2009). There is widespread agreement that youth need to be fully engaged in their care, and that services and supports must include opportunities to develop self-determination skills and experiences, work-based learning opportunities, individualized options for school-to-career transition that include high school completion and post-secondary education (Carter, Lane, Pierson, & Glaeser, 2006; Eisenman, 2007; Wagner & Davis, 2006).

The education system has also identified the need for significant school-based reform to support students with EBC, beginning with the National Agenda to Improve Results for Children and Youth with Serious Emotional Disturbance (U.S. Department of Education, 1994), and continuing with amendments to education and special education laws in 1997 and 2001. The results of these reforms have included the development of research-based practices and inclusive approaches for supporting students at risk of and who exhibit problematic behaviors (Osher & Hanley, 1996), including collaboration with community providers. Schools can play a critical role in a system of care, providing resources and environments through which to build the supports that children and youth with emotional and behavioral challenges and their families need to be more successful (Sebian et al., 2007; Woodruff et al., 1998).

Multitiered systems of support for behavior (MTSS-B), represents a school-based public health model for the organization and delivery of research-based practices for all students, including those with EBC. The MTSS-B framework borrows from the three-tiered multitiered logic used in public health to reduce and prevent disease. Using this framework, MTSS-B implementation includes a *universal* system of evidence-based behavioral practices for all students, a *targeted* system of practices for youth who need additional behavior support, and an *intensive* system of individualized interventions for a relatively small percentage (1%–5%) of students with the greatest behavioral needs. The main idea is to more effectively identify and meet the behavioral needs of students in schools so that all students can learn and be successful.

As part of the transformation to more comprehensive and collaborative models of care, school and mental health providers have developed a vision for school-based mental health that is fully integrated into the educational fabric of each school and based on the multitiered support framework (Barrett, Eber, & Weist, 2013; Bruns et al., 2016; Weist, 1997). This framework includes criteria for screening and identification of student needs, the use of research-based prevention, early intervention, and intensive mental health services provided by community behavioral health providers in collaboration with school staff, families, and youth. All of these models require deep collaboration between families, youth, schools, and community stakeholders.

Collaboration: Aligned Visions and Values

As described above, multi-stakeholder collaboration is necessary to achieve a true comprehensive system of care as well as to achieve positive results for youth with EBC that require multisystem involvement. Yet schools, providers, families, and youth do not commonly engage in authentic collaborative work. Collaborative work needs to be prioritized and requires time, flexibility, resources, awareness, and a common vision among helpers. As Osher indicates, "collaboration involves efforts to unite organizations and people for the purpose of achieving common goals that could not be accomplished by any single individual or organization acting alone" (2002, p. 94).

Authentic collaboration requires an intentional effort to transcend boundaries and barriers at the individual, community, and policy levels, a clearly understood and commonly held vision, and a set of skills that are not common in traditional behavioral health or education work. The obvious barriers to collaboration include organizational, philosophical, outcome, and resource allocation decisions that differ significantly between schools, community-based behavioral health providers, families and youth, and state systems (such as child welfare and juvenile justice). The challenge is how to find the benefits of collaboration for each partner. The result should be more effective and streamlined interventions in collaboration with and for children, youth, and families.

One of the essential features of the MTSS framework in schools is a team-based decision-making structure to identify the needs of students and implement more effective interventions that are matched to the needs of students. In order to be effective, MTSS-B team leaders facilitate the development of positive working relationships, co-constructed vision and goals, create shared understanding and common language, procedures, and policies for sharing information and implementing interventions, and shared progress and outcome measures (Mellin et al., 2010; Weist et al., 2012). While schools have typically not included community-based agencies or families/youth on these decision-making teams, there is growing recognition and a few emerging examples of the need to do so (Barrett, Eber, & Weist, 2013). In a fully developed MTSS-B model, intensive services for the students with the most significant support needs are individualized, and collaborative teaming is critical to design supports and services that are consistently applied across school, home, and community contexts.

To summarize, systems of care, wraparound, and MTSS-B are frameworks that are designed to transform the system's response to children and youth with EBC and their families. These frameworks have several key values and principles in common including an emphasis on youth and family self-determination, identification and mobilization of strengths, and collaboration among systems and helpers. Second, services and supports are geared to help the youth to be successful in community-based settings and included with their peers. This requires building the youth's skills to function in community-based settings while at the same time building the capacity of the community to support the youth in their endeavors. Additionally, service providers demonstrate cultural and linguistic competency, where individual youth receive and access the supports they want and need without respect to their individual cultures, values, and beliefs. Finally, there is an emphasis on research-based practices and interventions, ensuring that youth receive supports that have the greatest likelihood of helping them (Sinclair, Christenson, & Thurlow, 2005; Wagner & Davis, 2006).

Two Examples of Cross-Sector Collaboration

Despite acceptance of the core values and principles of systems of care and PBS, there is a dearth of empirically validated interventions anchored in communities or educational settings that address both the educational development and social support needs of youth with EBC (Sinclair, Christenson, & Thurlow, 2005; Wagner & Davis, 2006). Given what is known about the personal and environmental challenges that youth with EBC must overcome, we need approaches and interventions that focus on the development of self-determination skills, self-efficacy, and an effective network of helpers. What follows is a description of two approaches that are consistent with the values and principles of systems of care and MTSS-B. The first, Say Yes to Education, is a citywide approach to addressing college access and completion by applying a community-wide approach to addressing cumulative school and neighborhood risk factors related to achievement (Whipple, Evans, Barry, & Maxwell, 2010). The second example is an individualized, youth-driven school-to-career intervention for transition-age youth with EBC called Rehabilitation for Empowerment, Natural Supports, Education, and Work (RENEW) implemented in high schools in collaboration with community-based partners.

Say Yes to Education

Say Yes to Education is a comprehensive, coordinated, and sustainable approach to engaging whole cities around the goal of dramatically increasing postsecondary matriculation and completion rates for all young people, especially those from low-income and minority backgrounds. This approach builds a universal platform that includes services for children, including those with intensive mental health needs. Say Yes organizes entire communities around the goals of high school graduation for every public school student, and the preparation and support to attain, afford, and complete a postsecondary education. Say Yes believes that if given the opportunity to maximize their gifts and talents, all children can progress along the pathway to a successful postsecondary education and go on to be actively contributing members of their communities.

At the heart of Say Yes is a powerful incentive for families and communities: the prospect of a college scholarship, whether to an in-state public institution or one of the more than 100 private colleges and universities in the Say Yes Higher Education Compact. Say Yes leverages its scholarship and other incentives in the form of seed capital to bring together every stakeholder in a community—city and county government, the school district, parents, teachers, businesses, unions, philanthropic and faith-based organizations, and colleges and universities—and then provides that coalition with the tools to boost postsecondary participation and success. That partnership, equipped with a powerful data platform, puts in place the academic, social-emotional, and wellness supports necessary to ensure students are ready for postsecondary success.

Say Yes and its partners ensure that students and their families have the resources outside the classroom to clear the path to academic achievement, including tutoring, after-school and summer programs, medical care, counseling, and legal help. Say Yes and its partners use data to ensure that students reach critical benchmarks on the pathway to postsecondary readiness, and to make supports available to them (and their families) to prevent falling behind.

In Buffalo, Say Yes partners work in myriad ways to provide and facilitate programs that help remove barriers preventing students in the Buffalo Public Schools from graduating from high school prepared to succeed in college. The range of programs now available through its collective efforts begins in kindergarten and carries on through a student's collegiate years.

Kindergarten through Grade 12 Programs

Family Support and Social Services

Say Yes Buffalo school-based staff, called Family Support Specialists (FSS), are located at all 55 Buffalo Public Schools. In partnership with Erie County's Department of Social Services, they are responsible for working with students who demonstrate poor attendance or behavior problems to help them get back on track. This can include connecting students and their families to health, mental health, after school and basic needs programs, providing individual and group mentoring for the student and/or family, and assisting families with navigating school processes including registration, enrollment, and parent-teacher conferences. One of the primary goals of this program is to increase student attendance, and to date, internal data showed a four-percentage-point increase in attendance for those students engaged in the program.[1]

Mental Health Services

Mental health clinics are in 52 Buffalo public school buildings to help students address social-emotional issues that may be preventing them from being successful at home or in the classroom, including depression, anger, and anxiety. Services are provided by licensed clinical mental health professionals and are billed to the student's health insurance (e.g., private insurance or Medicaid). In 2016–2017, these mental health clinics served 4,500 students, for an estimated total of 13,250 students served since they were first instituted.[2]

Legal Advice

Free legal advice is available to all Buffalo Public School students and families on noncriminal matters year-round at any one of five school-based legal clinic locations. Clinics are open four days per week during the school year and two days per week during the summer at a school-based location and a sixth location housed within the Buffalo Public School District's Central Registration Office. Advice is provided by attorneys from local law firms and coordinated by Say Yes's partners at the Erie County Bar Association Volunteer Lawyers Project. Since the first clinics opened in January 2015, more than 1,461 people have received help through this service and in 2016–2017, 51 attorneys volunteered their time and expertise.[3]

Summer Camps

The Buffalo Public Schools, City of Buffalo, and Say Yes Buffalo jointly signed a memorandum of understanding that commits those parties to organizing and providing free summer programming to students in kindergarten to grade 6 through 2021. The first session of these "summer camps" was held in summer 2015 in programs hosted by church and community-based organizations throughout the city. The camp day consists of an academic component that incorporates the Mayor's Summer Reading Challenge and reinforces school-year lessons plus an enrichment component that seeks to expand students' exposure to leadership, arts, culture, and other activities. For summer 2016, the programs were expanded from four weeks to six and attracted 2,100 students.[4]

College Preparation

NYGEAR UP (Gaining Early Awareness and Readiness for Undergraduate Programs)

Say Yes Buffalo is proud to be a part of a local partnership funded through this federal initiative designed to increase the number of students who are prepared to succeed in college. Led in Buffalo by the University at Buffalo Graduate School of Education, in 2015, NYGEAR UP staff worked at 10 Buffalo Public Schools to help 570 eighth graders envision and plan their paths to college. Activities included parent workshops, college tours, counseling support, mentoring, tutoring, planning for high school and college, and an academic summer program. In 2016–2017, the program also worked with high school students on college-going pathways.[5]

Say Yes to College Workshop Series

Free workshops are held monthly to help demystify the college and financial aid application processes for high school students by exploring topics such as the college application process, essay writing, standardized tests, scholarships, financial aid, self-advocacy skills, college 101, and making the transition from high school to college. Workshops are led by Say Yes staff and representatives from many of its higher education partners and attracted an average of 40 students per workshop in 2015.[6]

FAFSA Completion Project

This effort, led by the University at Buffalo, provides one-on-one support to students and families as they navigate the financial aid process. Largely responsible for a 61% increase in successful federal financial aid applications by Buffalo public school students during the first year it was available (2013), this program places volunteer financial aid experts at every Buffalo public and charter high school to help families complete the Free Application for Federal Student Aid (FAFSA), New York State Tuition Assistance Program (TAP) application, and the Say Yes Buffalo Scholarship application (Daun-Barnett & Sullivan, 2014).[7]

College Level Supports

College Scholarships

Say Yes Buffalo is best known for is its scholarship program. Funded by the generosity of more than 250 individuals, families, businesses, and foundations, the Say Yes Buffalo Scholarship fund provides college tuition scholarships to all eligible Buffalo public and charter school students at any college or university in the State University of New York (SUNY) and City University of New York (CUNY) system and at nearly 100 private colleges around the country. The scholarship fund currently has $37.8 million committed, including a $10 million commitment from New York State, plus an additional $12 million in planned gifts. The 10-year goal for the total endowment is $30 million. The class of 2013 was the first eligible for the Say Yes Buffalo Scholarship. Since its inception, the program has helped nearly 4,300 students get to college.[8]

Scholar Mentoring Program

In partnership with Compeer of Greater Buffalo, the Say Yes Scholar Mentoring Program launched in January 2015 to match high school seniors and current Say Yes Scholars with volunteer mentors. The program provides guidance and support to scholars, many of whom are the first in their families to go to college, as they make the sometimes difficult transition to college. Matches are made based on similar interests, career aspirations, and preferences of both participants. To date, 81 students have been matched with mentors.[9]

Internship Program

Say Yes teamed up with the Buffalo Niagara Partnership, Western New York Association of College Career Centers, area businesses, and local institutions of higher education to create a paid summer internship program specifically for Say Yes Buffalo Scholars who have completed at least two years of college. Launched in spring 2016, with more than 45 paid internship opportunities, the positions cover a wide range of industries, including not-for-profit, accounting, education, human resources, retail operations, sales management, marketing, customer service, information technology, health care, and more. Internship providers include Wegmans, Buffalo Niagara Medical Campus, and BlueCross BlueShield of Western New York.[10]

Say Yes Ambassadors

This student leadership program is dedicated to the positive promotion of Say Yes Buffalo within the community. Say Yes Ambassadors are all current Say Yes Scholars, who serve as liaisons between the organization and students, families, colleges, donors, and other key stakeholders in the Say Yes Partnership. They participate in Say Yes events throughout the year and help educate the community at large about the mission of Say Yes. Ambassadors also receive professional development training in communication, public speaking, and networking. The inaugural class of 15 ambassadors began their work in January 2016.

Summer Success Academies

Another group of programs that focus on supporting students as they transition to college is the Summer Success Academies. Open to students matriculating to Erie Community College, Buffalo State College, and Medaille College, each program is tailored to address potential barriers to student success prior to the students beginning their first semester of college. As an added incentive, students who participate in the programs have the opportunity to be paid for their work through a partnership with the Mayor's Summer Youth Employment Program. To date more than 400 students have participated in these programs and early internal data shows they are persisting better than their peers.[11]

The provision of these supports has helped to drive positive outcomes in the first four years of operation. Since the launch of Say Yes Buffalo, the postsecondary enrollment rate has increased by 8 percentage points, from 57% in 2012 to 65% in 2016 (National Student Clearinghouse, 2017). High school graduation rates have increased by 15 percentage points, from 49% in 2012 to 64% in 2016, and the number of African American students graduating high school in Buffalo has increased by 17 percentage points (New York State Education Department [NYSED], 2013, 2017).

RENEW

In 1996, staff at the Institute of Disability (IOD) at the University of New Hampshire and the Institute on Emotional Disabilities at Keene State College developed an individualized planning and support intervention focused on assisting transition-age youth and young adults with emotional and behavioral challenges. This model, called Rehabilitation for Empowerment, Natural Supports, Education, and Work (RENEW) is steeped in system of care values and principles, including self-determination, strengths-based, and community-based supports. In 2002, RENEW was included as the primary intensive intervention in New Hampshire's high school dropout prevention initiative (Malloy & Hawkins, 2010). This dropout prevention model used MTSS as the framework for implementing research-based practices at all 3 tiers, including schoolwide behavior expectations for all students, small group interventions for students at risk of failure and disengagement, and RENEW for the students with significant emotional and behavioral challenges and at the greatest risk of dropping out of school. Data from participating high schools found that RENEW was associated with reductions in dropout rates and significant improvement in behavioral health functioning (Malloy, Sundar, Hagner, Pierias, & Viet, 2010). In one case study, school students who received RENEW experienced significant improvement in grade point average and high school completion (Malloy & Francoeur, 2014; Malloy, Bohanon, & Francoeur, 2018). Since 2009, RENEW has also been provided by New Hampshire's community mental health agencies, and it is being implemented in Illinois, Pennsylvania, Wisconsin, North Carolina, Vermont, and Maryland, in collaboration with state and district centers for MTSS implementation.

RENEW Practice Model Elements

RENEW is a fully developed, manualized practice with growing evidence that it leads to improved education and behavioral health outcomes for some of the most disengaged youth (Cheney, Hagner, Malloy, Cormier, & Bernstein, 1998; Hagner, Malloy, Mazzone, & Cormier, 2008; Malloy, Sundar, Hagner, Pierias, & Viet, 2010). The primary goals that drive the RENEW process are high school completion, finding and maintaining employment, participation in postsecondary training or education, and community inclusion. These goals look different for each youth, and yet these are critical elements in a positive transition from adolescence to adult life. For example, completion of high school is critical to adult life vocational success and opens the door to postsecondary education, training, the military, and a larger range of employment opportunities than are available to high school dropouts.

The RENEW theory of change focuses on strategies to build self-determination, social capital, and positive youth development (see figure 18.1), hypothesizing that youth-driven planning and individualized connections with formal and natural supports will result in improved youth functioning and outcomes.

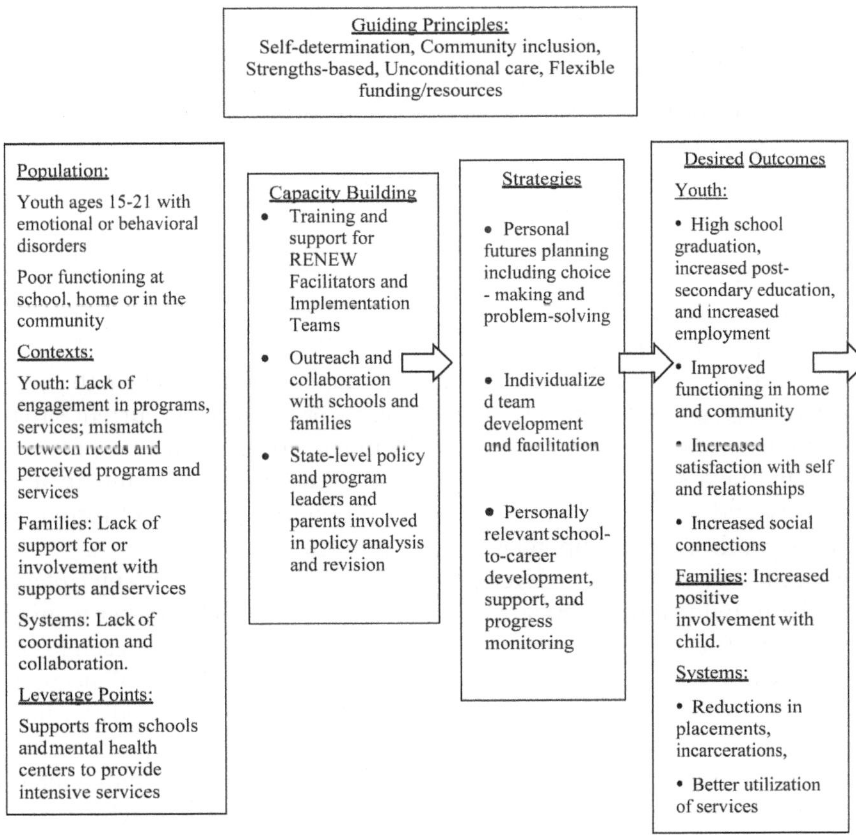

Figure 18.1 RENEW Theory of Change (Malloy, Francoeur, Drake, & Cloutier, 2016)

The RENEW principles of self-determination, unconditional care, strengths-based supports, flexible resources, and use of natural supports are consistent with the core values and principles of systems of care. The primary elements of the RENEW process include: (1) youth-driven planning using the personal futures planning process and graphic facilitation techniques; (2) the development of an individualized team based upon the youth's interests, needs, and identified relationships; (3) implementation of each youth's plan including using resources within the team and other supports to develop, implement, and assess progress toward educational, vocational, and community-based goals and supports based upon the youth's futures plan; and (4) eventual and flexible transition to less intensive supports and resources.

The youth's uniquely constructed team is where individualized collaboration occurs. Team members engage in shared work toward the youth's goals and provide individualized support based on the youth's needs. The focus is on vocational, educational attainment and behavioral health-related activities that are critical to a successful transition from school to career. This emphasis on career development may represent a shift in thinking for mental health providers and, in fact, for some school-based providers who are often focused on symptom reduction. The RENEW process focuses on helping the youth attain incremental successes, which will build competence and motivation to continue to pursue their goals.

There are four phases of the RENEW process consistent with the phases of wraparound. The first phase is Engagement and Initial Plan Development when trained RENEW facilitators guide each youth through the person-centered planning process using graphic facilitation techniques. During these meetings, the facilitator uses flip chart paper to depict the youth's perspective in response to nine prompts about his or her history, current situation, preferences, strengths and accomplishments, people, dreams, barriers, goals, and next steps. Graphic facilitation is used because it results in self-discovery and is an effective tool for recognition of patterns and resources that the youth will draw upon later in the process.

Once the futures plan is developed, the youth and facilitator enter phase two, the Initial Planning Phase, when the youth develops his or her team of supporters. The team is expressly designed to help each youth to reach his or her goals and may change as the youth's goals evolve. The RENEW meetings are highly structured to focus on the youth's future plan and needs for help and support. These RENEW Youth Teams include people who are key to the youth's attainment of the goals, and so the teams often include family members or other caregivers, community providers, mentors, peers, school staff, and vocational experts. The youth and team members agree on what the indicators of success are and what data is used to monitor progress toward the goals.

When the youth and team members agree to the basic goals, they enter the Implementation Phase, when long- and short-term goal attainment and progress monitoring are the focus of each meeting. Finally, when the youth and team members believe that the youth will be able to achieve continued progress without formal team support or the RENEW Facilitator, the team moves in the Transition Phase, where the youth prepares for the next year, including a backup plan and designation of one point person (such as a parent or a mental health counselor) who has the responsibility of monitoring the youth's progress and reconvening the team if needed. This process through all four phases is typically between one and two years and results in the development of sustainable relationships for each youth that did not exist before the RENEW process was initiated.

RENEW Systems Features

Each school or agency that implements RENEW forms a systems-level team that is responsible for implementation of the RENEW practice and for developing connections with community-based resources. Using the principles of effective, mutually reinforcing implementation supports (Fixsen, Naoom, Blase, Friedman, & Wallace, 2005), the RENEW Implementation Team (1) identifies the youth within the school or agency who are eligible for and are most likely to benefit from RENEW; (2) identifies staff who will be RENEW facilitators; (3) monitors RENEW implementation process and outcomes, ensuring fidelity of implementation, using data; and (4) helps facilitators to problem-solve issues such as how to find the time to provide RENEW, policy barriers that impede youth progress, and accessing community resources, such as vocational rehabilitation, mental health, and probation, among others. The IOD has manualized the RENEW Implementation Team practices, tools, and procedures, and provides training and coaching for implementation sites.[12] RENEW Implementation Teams are critical to the high-quality and sustained implementation of the RENEW practice (Mallow & Francoeur, 2017).

The RENEW Implementation Team uses several data tools to guide its work. First, the RENEW Readiness Checklist allows the team to assess the status of its organization's capacity to provide RENEW, with particular attention to staff and community support for implementation. The team is formed using research-informed team development processes, including clear delineation of team member roles, a mission statement, and logistical procedures. Second, the team assesses its own progress toward implementing the major features of RENEW by completing the RENEW Implementation Checklist at least two times a year. Finally, the team assesses student progress and outcomes by using a Youth Progress Tracker, typically reviewed monthly. Given that the teams include community partners, the RENEW Implementation Team is also responsible for executing formal collaborative and data-sharing agreements between entities that will be responsible for participating on youth RENEW teams. Another system feature is the development of qualified internal RENEW coaches who are staff members within the school or agency. Candidates for RENEW Internal Coaches are selected by the Implementation Team and are in a position to provide two to three hours a week of RENEW mentoring and data collection for the facilitators and the Implementation Team.

Collaboration for RENEW Implementation: Exeter High School and Seacoast Mental Health

Using the RENEW Logic Model (figure 18.1), the Institute on Disability has implemented multiple projects in New Hampshire designed to build the capacity of schools and mental health centers to provide RENEW. One of those projects, funded by a state foundation, was the RENEWed Opportunities on the Seacoast, implemented beginning in June 2103 and lasting for three years. This project took place in Exeter High School, a community of approximately 1,690 students in a relatively affluent New Hampshire community. Approximately 10% of the school's population is from low-income households and 6% are from ethnic or racially diverse backgrounds. The RENEWed Opportunities project built a formal collaboration between a community mental health center and the high school to meet the needs of every student who was at risk of failure in school due to an EBC.

The School-Based RENEW Implementation Team

The RENEWed Opportunities project Implementation Team was formed in September 2013 and included representatives from school counseling, special education, teachers, administration, the Seacoast Mental Health Center Director of Children's Services, and one of the agency's RENEW facilitators. The IOD coach provided training and coaching for the RENEW Implementation Team and assisted with the development of Memorandum of Collaboration between the school and the mental health center that outlines how data would be shared and other procedures for working together with youth RENEW participants.

By fall 2013, the team was fully established and trained in the RENEW model and fundamentals of its implementation. The team developed criteria for students who were appropriate candidates for RENEW (such as multiple discipline infractions, class failure rates, multiple absences from school, or staff nomination). The team also worked with the IOD to schedule and support 29 school and 2 mental health center staff to attend a 3-day RENEW

Facilitators' Training. This training increased capacity to provide RENEW to more students and developed relationships to foster collaboration between the mental health agency and the school.

At the same time, the mental health center and school executed a memorandum of understanding and business agreement that outlined their respective responsibilities when providing RENEW to students from the high school, how individual information would be exchanged, and how data could be collected and shared. The team also attended a two-day RENEW Sustainability Planning Retreat to learn how to change and/or improve their school systems to sustain RENEW after the project ends. The school chose to improve their collaboration with Seacoast Mental Health Center, the referral structure for students to receive RENEW, and to develop a better map of their resources in order to efficiently serve youth in RENEW. The Center's Children's Director and RENEW Coach have participated on the RENEW Implementation Team since it was developed in order to coordinate facilitated referrals and share resources and strategies to support youths' RENEW plans. There were two mental health clinicians involved in multiple youth teams in order to help the students reach their goals. Both parties report this collaboration produced improved outcomes and attendance rates for youths in RENEW and indicated that the collaboration helped to make their jobs easier because they had easier access to the information and people they needed to support each youth. Decisions about how the mental health agency and school would collaborate were made together, thus improving buy-in and follow-through.

Collaboration with Peer-to Peer Support

Peer-to peer support is an emerging best practice and an important element of youth-driven services. The project staff worked with the New Hampshire Youth Motivating Others through Voices of Experience (Youth MOVE) chapter to identify and train two youth who had received RENEW services within the previous five years to become peer-to-peer mentors. Youth MOVE is a youth-led national organization devoted to improving services and systems that support positive growth and development by uniting the voices of individuals who have lived experience in various systems including mental health, juvenile justice, education, and child welfare. The youth mentors were responsible for helping youth who were receiving RENEW to understand the process during the orientation phase, to support the youth during future's planning, and to help problem-solve and offer ideas during the action planning and team phases. The RENEW mentors met one-on-one with 7 youth and contributed more than 240 hours of mentoring activities throughout the project. Additionally, the youth peer supporters joined the RENEW Implementation Team to provide their perspectives about how youth could be better supported within the RENEW process. The school and the students found the mentors invaluable and school staff reported increased youth engagement and participation as a result of peer-to-peer support.

Youth Outcomes with RENEW

Beginning in December 2013, the high school's Implementation Team identified 22 youth who were eligible for RENEW. Seventeen agreed to participate. Facilitators met with the youth for an hour or more every week for the remainder of the year to complete their futures plans and to develop individualized support teams. The school tracked the youth's RENEW process and outcome data in the RENEW School Tracker, which captures youth demographic information and outcomes in RENEW over time. The 17 youth who received RENEW included 60% who were eligible for special education services, 64% who lived in single-family homes, 29% who were involved in the juvenile justice system, and 23% who were involved in the child protective system. Outcomes for those youth were generally positive. Individualized Teams were created for 71% of the youth, 53% reached all of their goals, 53% obtained jobs, and 41% obtained internships. There was a 29% reduction in Office Discipline Referrals, and the number of classes taken increased by 11% and the rate of classes passed increased by 13%. Unexcused absences increased by 56%, however, and the team began to problem-solve around why students continued to miss even more school days than they had previously.

Benefits of Collaboration to Partner Organizations

As a result of its work with Exeter High School, the Seacoast Mental Health Center promoted one of its RENEW facilitators to become a RENEW coach, reducing her required "billable hours" in order to allow her to train and supervise RENEW facilitators at the school and mental health agency. In addition to the collaborative work with Exeter High School, Seacoast Mental Health Center expanded its collaboration with three other high schools in its region around serving youth with the RENEW model. When the foundation funding ended, Exeter High School developed a contract with Seacoast Mental Health to continue to provide coaching and training for the RENEW Implementation Team and both school-based and community-based RENEW facilitators.

Summary: How Collaboration Results in the "Win-Win"

Although multi-stakeholder collaboration takes time and is often not a priority, it is a critical and necessary condition if we are to effectively meet the complex needs of youth with emotional and behavioral challenges. Youth with complex needs encounter multiple, disparate systems and providers that use different approaches, operate under different requirements, and have different goals. Families and youth are often left to navigate these systems by themselves, and so they disengage and give up. Further, when they are engaged with a service, families and youth are often not treated as partners, but are instead subjected to rules and contingencies that are driven by the system.

The system of care and MTSS-B frameworks offer guidance for how to organize and align services and support, how to mobilize the strengths of the youth, families, and systems, and how to put youth and families at the center of the decision-making process. Each framework offers tools and guidelines for collaborative work. The efforts of Say YES to Education demonstrate how to align efforts at multiple levels and across sectors toward a common vision to improve the educational and vocation outcomes of the highest-need youth. Say YES to Education demonstrates how a focus on positive youth development and community-wide collaboration to leverage resources across sectors can result in positive educational outcomes for a large group of high-risk youth. The result is that each system and participating organization is more effective in helping the youth.

In a different way, the RENEWed Opportunities project demonstrates how a positive youth development approach and cross-sector collaboration can result in better educational outcomes for transition age youth with significant emotional and behavioral challenges. The project demonstrates how a community mental health provider and school can be more effective and efficient by creating a shared vision, common language, shared expertise, and common outcomes. Both case examples illustrate how a focus on collaboration can leverage existing resources, for the most part, to enhance the quality of care and achieve better outcomes through collaborative work.

There are significant differences between these two approaches as well. While Say YES to Education strategies focus on a population-based, community-wide system for creating pathways to college for youth who are at risk of school failure, RENEW is a highly individualized approach for youth who exhibit significant EBC and who are disengaged from school. Say YES to Education is working at a community-wide level, while RENEW is working at the individual level. What is important to note, however, is the common emphasis between these two examples on high expectations, educational success and career development, and support services focused on a common goal: helping each youth to achieve success and become more self-sufficient. In addition, instead of creating new services, these two projects focused on developing new structures, collaborations, and connections between existing resources and using data to show the partners the value of continued collaboration, proving that it is highly worth the effort to help youth to focus on their strengths and positive, hope-filled futures.

Notes

1. Key partners providing this service include: Buffalo Public Schools, Catholic Charities of Western New York, and Erie County.

2. Key partners providing this service include: Buffalo Public Schools, Erie County, Community Foundation for Greater Buffalo, Baker Victory Services, Lake Shore Behavioral Health, Jewish Family Services, Kaleida Health, Catholic Health, Child & Family Services, Gateway Longview, Catholic Charities, Child & Adolescent Treatment Services, New York State Office of Mental Health, and Mid-Erie Counseling & Treatment Services.

3. Key partners providing this service include: Erie County Bar Association Volunteer Lawyers Project, Barclay Damon LLP, Gibson, McAskill & Crosby LLP, Harris Beach PLLC, Hodgson Russ LLP, Lippes Mathias Wexler Friedman LLP, and Phillips Lytle LLP.

4. Key partners providing this service include: Buffalo Public Schools, City of Buffalo, community-based and religious organizations, and Erie County.

5. Key partners providing this service include: Buffalo Public Schools, University at Buffalo, and Higher Education Services Corporation.

6. Key partners providing this service include: Canisius College, University at Buffalo, and Courier College Prep.

7. Key partners providing this service include: Buffalo Public School District and University at Buffalo.

8. Key partners providing this service include: Say Yes Buffalo Angel Donors and Members of the Say Yes Buffalo Private College Compact.

9. Key partners providing this service include: Compeer of Greater Buffalo, Rich Products, Sandhill Investment Management, First Niagara, and The Buffalo Sabres.

10. Key partners providing this service include: The Buffalo Niagara Partnership, Western New York Association of College Career Centers, University at Buffalo, Buffalo State College, Medaille College, Villa Maria College, Erie Community College, Bryant and Stratton College, Niagara County Community College, First Niagara, Harmac, HSBC, Wegmans, The InVentures Group, BlueCross BlueShield of WNY, National Grid, Darwin Martin House, Goodwill Industries, Superior Group, Deep Wells Ministries, WNY Consortium of Higher Education, Community Foundation for Greater Buffalo, NFTA, and Roswell Park Cancer Institute.

11. Key partners providing this service include: Medaille College, Buffalo State College, Erie Community College, and City of Buffalo.

12. For more information about RENEW Implementation Team tools, see http://iod.unh.edu/projects/rehabilitation-empowerment-natural-supports-education-and-work-renew/renew-implementation.

References

Barrett, S., Eber, L., & Weist, M. (Eds.). (2013). *Advancing education effectiveness: Interconnecting school mental health and school-wide positive behavior support.*

Retrieved from http://www.pbis.org/common/pbisresources/publications/Final-Monograph.pdf

Bruns, E. J., Suter, J. S., Force, M. D., & Burchard, J. D. (2005). Adherence to wraparound principles and association with outcomes. *Journal of Child and Family Studies, 14*, 521–534.

Carr, E. G., Dunlap, G., Horner, R. H., Koegel, R. L., Turnbull, A. B., Sailor, W., . . . Fox, L. (2002). Positive behavior support: Evolution of an applied science. *Journal of Positive Behavior Interventions, 4*(1), 4–16, 20.

Carter, E. W., Lane, K. L., Pierson, M., & Glaeser, B. (2006). Self-determination skills of transition-age youth with emotional disturbances and learning disabilities. *Exceptional Children, 72*, 333–346.

Center for Behavioral Health Statistics and Quality. (2015). *Behavioral health trends in the United States: Results from the 2014 National Survey on Drug Use and Health* (HHS Publication No. SMA 15-4927, NSDUH Series H-50). Retrieved from http://www.samhsa.gov/data/

Cheney, D., Hagner, D., Malloy, J., Cormier, G., & Bernstein, S. (1998). Transition services for youth and young adults with emotional disturbance: Description and initial results of Project RENEW. *Career Development of Exceptional Individuals, 21*, 17–32.

Cobb, R. B., Lipscomb, S., Wolgemuth, J., Schulte, T., Veliquette, A., Alwell, M., . . . Weinberg, A. (2013). *Improving post-high school outcomes for transition-age students with disabilities: An evidence review* (NCEE 2013-4011). Washington, DC: National Center for Education Evaluation and Regional Assistance, Institute of Education Sciences, U.S.

Daun-Barnett, N. J. & Sullivan, M. (2014). *The Buffalo FAFSA completion project: Final report 2013–14*. Buffalo: University at Buffalo.

Davis, M., Banks, S., Fisher, W., & Grudzinskas, A. (2004). Longitudinal patterns of offending during the transition to adulthood in youth from the mental health system. *Journal of Behavioral Health Services and Research, 31*(4), 351–366.

Davis, M., & Koroloff, N. (2006). The great divide: How public mental health policy fails young adults. In W. H. Fisher (Ed.), *Community based mental health services for children and adolescents* (pp. 53–74). Oxford, UK: Elsevier Sciences.

Eisenman, L. (2007). Self-determination interventions: Building a foundation for school completion. *Remedial and Special Education, 28*(1), 2–8.

Fixsen, D., Naoom, S. F., Blase, D. A., Friedman, R. M., & Wallace, F. (2005). *Implementation research: A synthesis of the literature*. Tampa: University of South Florida, Louis de la Parte Florida Mental Health Institute, The National Implementation Research Network.

Foster, E. M., & Conner, T. (2005). Public costs of better mental health services for children and adolescents. *Psychiatric Services, 56*(1), 50–55.

Foster, E. M., Kelsch, C. C., Kamradt, B., Sosna, T., & Yang, Z. (2001). Expenditures and sustainability in systems of care. *Journal of Emotional and Behavioral Disorders, 9*, 53–62, 70.

Foster, E. M., Qaseem, A., & Connor, T. (2004). Can better mental health services reduce the risk of juvenile justice system involvement? *American Journal of Public Health, 94*(5), 859–865.

Hagner, D., Cheney, D., & Malloy, J. (1999). Career-related outcomes of a model transition demonstration for young adults with emotional disturbance. *Rehabilitation Counseling Bulletin, 42*, 228–242.

Hagner, D., Malloy, J., Mazzone, M. W., & Cormier, G. (2008). Youth with disabilities in the criminal justice system: Considerations for transition and rehabilitation planning. *Journal of Emotional and Behavioral Disorders, 16*, 240–247.

Hodges, S., Nesman, T., & Hernandez, M. (1999). *Promising practices: Building collaboration in systems of care.* Systems of Care: Promising Practices in Children's Mental Health, 1998 Series, Volume 6. Retrieved from http://cecp.air.org/promis ingpractices/1998monographs/vol6.pdf

Huizinga, D., Loeber, R., Thornberry, T. P., & Cothern, L. (2000). *Co-occurrence of delinquency and other problem behaviors.* Bulletin. Washington, DC: U.S. Department of Justice, Office of Justice Programs, Office of Juvenile Justice and Delinquency Prevention.

Kamradt, B. (1996). Wraparound Milwaukee: Aiding youth with mental health needs. *Juvenile Justice, 7*(1), 14–23.

Knitzer, J., & Olsen, L. (1982). *Unclaimed children: The failure of public responsibility to children and adolescents in need of mental health services.* Washington, DC: Children's Defense Fund.

Malloy, J., & Francoeur, K. (2014). *PBIS implementation in high schools at all 3 tiers: An examination of the benefits of deep implementation.* Presentation for the 19th Conference on Advancing School Mental Health. Pittsburgh, PA.

Malloy, J., & Francoeur, K. (2017). *Shared work, shared values, shared outcomes: Scale-up of RENEW in New Hampshire. Presentation for the 2017 Annual Global Implementation Conference.* Toronto, Canada.

Malloy, J., Suter, J., & Haber, M. (2014). *RENEW: School and Community based wraparound process for emerging adults.* Presentation for the 27th Annual Children's Mental Health Research and Policy Conference, Tampa.

Malloy, J. M., Bohanon, H., & Francoeur, K. (2018). Positive Behavioral Interventions and Supports in high schools: A case study from New Hampshire. *Journal of Educational and Psychological Consultation.* doi:10.1080/10474412.2017.1385398

Malloy, J. M., & Hawkins, M. O. (Eds.). (2010). *Positive behavioral interventions and supports and dropout prevention.* Monograph, National Dropout Prevention Center. Clemson, SC: Clemson University.

Malloy, J. M., Sundar, V., Hagner, D., Pierias, L., & Viet, T. (2010). The efficacy of the RENEW model: Individualized school-to-career services for youth at risk of school dropout. *Journal of At Risk Issues, 15*(2), 17–25.

Mellin, E. A., Bronstein, L., Anderson-Butcher, D., Amorose, A. J., Ball, A., & Green, J. (2010). Measuring interprofessional team collaboration in expanded school mental health: Model refinement and scale development. *Journal of Interprofessional Care, 24*(5), 514–523.

Merikangas, K. R., He, J. P., Burstein, M., Swanson, S. A., Avenevoli, S., Cui, L., . . . Swendsen, J. (2010). Lifetime prevalence of mental disorders in U.S. adolescents: Results from the National Comorbidity Survey Replication—Adolescent Supplement (NCS-A). *Journal of the American Academy of Child and Adolescent Psychiatry, 49*(10), 980–989. doi:10.1016/j.jaac.2010.05.017

Newman, L., Wagner, M., Knokey, A.-M., Marder, C., Nagle, K., Shaver, D., . . . Schwarting, M. (2011). *The post-high school outcomes of young adults with disabilities up to 8 years after high school* (A report from the National Longitudinal Transition Study-2 (NLTS2); NCSER 2011-3005). Menlo Park, CA: SRI International. Retrieved from https://nlts2.sri.com/reports/2011_09_02/index.html

O'Connell, M. E., Boat, T., & Warner, K. E. (Eds.). (2009). *Preventing mental, emotional, and behavioral disorders among young people: Progress and possibilities*. Washington, DC: National Academies Press. doi:10.17226/12480

Osher, D., & Hanley, T. V. (1996). Implications of the national agenda to improve results for children and youth with or at risk of serious emotional disturbance. In R. J. Illback & C. M. Nelson (Eds.), *Emerging school-based approaches for children with emotional and behavioral problems* (pp. 7–36). Binghamton, NY: Haworth Press.

Osher, D. M. (2002). Creating comprehensive and collaborative systems. *Journal of Child and Family Studies, 11*(1), 91–99.

Planty, M., Hussar, W., Snyder, T., Provasnik, S., Kena, G., Dinkes, R., . . . Kemp, J. (2008). *The condition of education 2008* (NCES 2008-031). Washington, DC: National Center for Educational Statistics.

Sebian, J., Mettrick, J., Weiss, C., Stephan, S., Lever, N., & Weist, M. (2007, June). *Education and system-of-care approaches: Solutions for educators and school mental health professionals*. Baltimore: Center for School Mental Health Analysis and Action, Department of Psychiatry, University of Maryland School of Medicine.

Sinclair, M. F., Christenson, S. L., & Thurlow, M. L. (2005). Promoting school completion of urban secondary youth with emotional or behavioral disabilities. *Exceptional Children, 71*(4), 465–482.

Stroul, B. (2015). Return on investment in systems of care for children with behavioral health challenges: A look at wraparound. *The TA Telescope, 1*(2), 2. Retrieved from http://nwi.pdx.edu/pdf/WrapROI.pdf

Stroul, B., Blau, G., & Friedman, R. (2010). *Updating the system of care concept and philosophy*. Washington, DC: Georgetown University Center for Child and Human Development, National Technical Assistance Center for Children's Mental Health.

Stroul, B., & Friedman, R. (1986). *A system of care for children and youth with severe emotional disturbances*. Washington, DC: Georgetown University

Child Development Center, National Technical Assistance Center for Children's Mental Health.

Stroul, B. A., Blau, G. M., & Sondheimer, D. L. (2008). Systems of care: A strategy to transform children's mental health care. In B. A. Stroul & G. M. Blau (Eds.), *The system of care handbook: Transforming mental health services for children, youth, and families* (pp. 3–23). Baltimore, MD: Paul H Brookes Publishing.

Sugai, G., & Horner, R. H. (1999). Discipline and behavioral support: Preferred processes and practices. *Effective School Practices, 17*(4), 10–22.

Suter, J. C., & Bruns, E. J. (2009). Effectiveness of the wraparound process for children with emotional and behavioral disorders: A meta-analysis. *Clinical Child and Family Psychology Review, 12*, 336–351.

U.S. Department of Education. (1994). *National agenda for achieving better results for children and youth with serious emotional disturbance.* Washington, DC: American Institutes for Research.

Wagner, M., & Davis, M. (2006). How are we preparing students with emotional disturbances for the transition to young adulthood?: Findings from the National Longitudinal Transition Study-2. *Journal of Emotional and Behavioral Disorders, 14*, 86–98.

Wagner, M., Kutash, K., Duchnowski, A. J., Epstein, M. H., & Sumi, W. C. (2005). The children and youth we serve: A national picture of the characteristics of students with emotional disturbances receiving special education. *Journal of Emotional and Behavioral Disorders, 13*(2), 79–96.

Weist, M., Mellin, E. A., Chambers, K. I., Lever, N. A., Haber, D., & Blaber, C. (2012). Challenges to collaboration in school mental health and strategies for overcoming them. *Journal of School Health, 82*(2), 97–105.

Weist, M. D. (1997). Expanded school mental health services: A national movement in progress. In T. H. Ollendick & R. J. Prinz (Eds.), *Advances in clinical child psychology* (vol. 19, pp. 319–352). New York: Plenum Press.

Whipple, S. S., Evans, G. W., Barry, R. L., & Maxwell, L. E. (2010). An ecological perspective on cumulative school and neighborhood risk factors related to achievement. *Journal of Applied Developmental Psychology, 31*(6), 422–427. http://dx.doi.org/10.1016/j.appdev.2010.07.002

Williams, N. J., Scott, L., & Aarons, G. (2018). Prevalence of serious emotional disturbance among U.S. children: A meta-analysis. *Psychiatric Services, 69*(1), 32–40.

Woodruff, D. W., Osher, D., Hoffman, C. C., Gruner, A., King, M. A., Snow, S. T., & McIntire, J. C. (1998). *The role of education in a system of care: Effectively serving children with emotional or behavioral disorders.* Systems of care: Promising practices in children's mental health, 1998 Series, Volume 3. Washington, DC: Center for Effective Collaboration and Practice, American Institutes for Research.

CHAPTER NINETEEN

Making Collaboration Work among Students, Families, and Other Key Stakeholders

Frank Rider, Rebecca Ornelas, Reyhan Reid, Lisa Lambert, and Trina Osher

The traditional African proverb, "It takes a village to raise a child," applies well to American students in the 21st century, too. Each child experiences the "village" around him or her—family and peers, school and community—in unique ways. As such, efforts to prepare each new generation to lead satisfying and productive lives, and make a positive difference as citizens in the world, must include children, their parents, and the village that surrounds them. But what does it take to bring together such diverse perspectives in complementary nurturance of the village young? Collaboration.

Collaboration is the practice of working together toward a common goal. Effective collaboration brings stakeholders—including students and families—together to address identified concerns or goals in the school community, and to make ecological approaches work so that students can thrive and thus enjoy improved outcomes. This chapter reviews the benefits and key components of effective collaboration, with a focus on the three domains of (1) practice, (2) research and evaluation, and (3) systems and policy. We examine how intentional, broad-based collaboration supports student learning while promoting well-being and other desirable outcomes in the classroom and beyond. We identify associated challenges and provide recommendations, techniques, tools, and resources that will help to cultivate and support meaningful student and family contributions.

For many of us, collaboration began when we were preschoolers playing with other children, sharing toys and creating "make believe" worlds together. Later on, some of us shared pursuits in groups (scouts, school projects) or joined teams where collaboration was essential to achieving a desired goal. Skillful coaches of team sports taught many of us something about how to facilitate the development and blending of individual assets and contributions into a coherent and purposeful game plan, in which success depended on each player understanding how to contribute to the pattern of play and victory.

As we tackled increasingly complex objectives in teams, we realized that collaboration allowed us to achieve results that would be unattainable if we worked alone; that engaging and applying the capacities of many different players contributed to a whole that was greater than the sum of its component parts. And we gradually learned what distinguishes positive, worthwhile collaborations from less successful ones.

During the past quarter century, collaboration across multiple disciplines has been encouraged by both visionary and pragmatic agents seeking to design and ensure resources to support broad-based strategies and sophisticated programs and practices to address complex human service challenges. An early example can be found in Congress's 1984 launch of the Child and Adolescent Service System Program (CASSP). Growing out of a set of principles (Stroul & Friedman, 1986), CASSP recognized that children with significant mental health needs tend to be involved in multiple systems—schools, health care, child welfare, juvenile justice, and substance abuse. Family members, providers, advocates, and policy makers knew that each system played a significant role and offered a unique set of resources and expertise; but they did so separately, resulting in service fragmentation, inefficient use of human resources and funds, and poor outcomes for children, youth, and families (Knitzer & Olson, 1982). CASSP was designed to generate holistic, ecological improvement strategies.

As the 1990s were ending, early attempts at collaboration across systems were often being met with skepticism and resistance, as agency administrators were uncomfortable stepping out of their own programs and disciplines to tackle a problem they perceived as being outside their scope of responsibility, training, or expertise. Participation in such efforts was usually seen as an add-on to one's "real job." Collaboration was colloquially described as "an unnatural act by non-consenting adults" (Clevenger, 1997).

Collaboration has evolved forward in ensuing decades to become a fairly common aspiration in contemporary system change initiatives. We now have a variety of collaboration models and frameworks including *Collective Impact*

(Collaboration for Impact, 2018), *Leading by Convening* (Cashman et al., 2014), *Essentials for Childhood* (National Center for Injury Prevention and Control, 2014), and *Communities That Care* (University of Washington, 2018). Unlike our own pretend games as young children, collaborating to address complex issues—such as ensuring that all children are safe and thriving—can be complicated and challenging, given the multiplicity of systems involving people from different generations, cultures, disciplines, and roles, each bringing to the mix their own life experiences, values, languages, and perspectives.

Understanding Whole Systems

Research suggests that complex community issues affect the health and well-being of children and are best addressed by applying a whole system approach that takes the life circumstances of students and their families into consideration (Comer & Haynes, 1991; Gould, 2007). The contextual conditions that nourish or hinder learners' development include biology and physiology; family and interpersonal relationships; socioeconomic, environmental, cultural, and historical factors; and the conditions for learning in and around schools (Cantor, Osher, Berg, Steyer, & Rose, 2018). An extensive range of factors influence our ability to navigate the complex ecology of contemporary life. Developmental systems theories (Griffiths & Tabery, 2013) and the *Whole School, Whole Community, Whole Child* model (ASCD and Centers for Disease Control, 2014) provide holistic frameworks to organize the recent research about how children become learners and develop as individuals.

Improving student outcomes will require a range of expertise that reflects this multifaceted context for learning. The education process must support children and youth so that they *thrive,* feel emotionally secure, have a sense of agency and purpose, are emotionally and physically engaged, and feel cared for and genuinely respected for who they are (Cantor et al., 2018). Thriving students adapt to and learn from the experiences and challenges they encounter in both school, and in life.

Meaningful Student and Family Engagement

Collaborative efforts within human services in the 21st century have evolved to recognize the quintessential place of "lived experience" and *direct* stakeholder participation in the full range of activities required to undertake and accomplish positive systemic change. The best collaboration models understand family and youth partnerships as essential cornerstones of change initiatives intended to improve how well systems address people's needs, support their aims, and track their trajectories. Their participation must be significant, not symbolic. *Meaningful* means that each participant's contribution is respected and valued.

The rise of the family movement in children's mental health (National Federation of Families for Children's Mental Health [NFFCMH], 2017), and the promotion of positive youth development (Catalano, Berglund, Ryan, Lonczak, & Hawkins, 1998) in public health, child welfare, and substance abuse prevention, have provided platforms for their equitable representation and impactful participation in decisions on policy and programs that impact the lives of students and families, and the well-being of their whole communities.

Effective models capitalize on persuasive powers of students and families to secure lasting reshaping of systems' "business as usual." To invite, nurture, and apply their expertise, practitioners, managers, evaluators, researchers, and policy makers must invest time and effort to learn about the strengths, assets, cultural touchstones, and resilience of those students, their families, and the neighborhoods in which they live.

"You cannot be an effective problem-solver from a distance. There are details and nuances to problems that you will miss unless you are close enough to observe those details." With those words Bryan Stevenson, founder and director of the Equal Justice Initiative, explained to the 2016 Carnegie Foundation Summit on Improvement in Education (Stevenson, 2016) the importance of routinely engaging students and families who represent the diversity of their communities in school improvement efforts. Their first-hand experience with services, programs, policies, and systems will enlighten and guide well-intentioned state officials and local providers. Students and families will raise tough questions but also offer creative solutions. Stevenson contends that being "proximate to suffering" (Stevenson, 2014) leads to better processes and results—and also redefines human relationships, building empathy and enriching human connections.

Meaningful student and family engagement in education means that families, schools, and communities work together to intentionally support students in learning and development, using research-based practices in conjunction with community-defined evidence and cultural wisdom in classrooms, at home, and throughout their communities. Students and families, especially when they reflect the diversity of the school's subpopulation(s), are essential partners in planning and decision-making. Families who must deal with long-standing social and political issues in their neighborhoods can provide critical knowledge about their needs and their experiences of what helps and what hurts.

Effective collaborative teams include students and family members who represent the diversity of "lived experience" across their communities. Such teams value their up-close and real-time perspective on programs, services, policies, and systems that are working well, where there are gaps, and what is ineffective. Lived experience means having personally dealt with policy barriers, system challenges, social issues, and the very problems the initiative aims to address and change. It likewise means having direct, first-hand knowledge about what actually works that should be sustained or even expanded. In effect, the voices of students and family members bring clarity of purpose and focus to a collaborative team, and heighten the potential of the collective to achieve lasting system improvements that matter in the lives of children, families, and communities.

State-level efforts exemplify progress in pursuit of meaningful student and family engagement:

- Dianna R. Wentzell established the Commissioner's Roundtable for Family and Community Engagement in Education in Connecticut, whose purpose is to "advise the Commissioner of Education regarding policy and programmatic priorities to improve outcomes for all students and advance the State Board of Education's comprehensive plan for equity and excellence in Connecticut schools." The Roundtable's commitment to partnership is supported by balanced representation of school/district staff, parents, community members, and students. Dr. Wentzell noted, "We must work with parents to develop and implement policies and programs instead of attempting to bring them on board after the fact (Wood & Carson, 2016)."
- In Pennsylvania, complementary state-level initiatives supported by the federal Substance Abuse and Mental Health Services Administration (SAMHSA) have long promoted core guiding values of "family-driven" and "youth-guided" care for students with mental health needs. Pennsylvania established a State Leadership and Management Team (SLMT) to oversee and guide the interrelated System of Care Partnership and Safe Schools, Healthy Students initiatives, and in 2008 structured the SLMT so that 25% of its members are students or youth, 25% are parents and family members, and the remaining 50% are designated system leaders from education, health care, child welfare, courts and juvenile justice, behavioral health, drug and alcohol, and early childhood systems (Pennsylvania Care Partnership, 2018). In 2011, Pennsylvania applied the same representative structure at the county level, promulgating standards for Family-Driven and for Youth-Driven care to which all participating service systems commit themselves, collectively and individually. Dozens of county-level community management teams create opportunities for students to actively participate in improvement activities at the program, school, and community levels. The statewide expectations have spawned numerous creative efforts:
    - High school students from all four school districts in Crawford County, for example, kick off each new school year with a day-long retreat during which they collectively review the local Pennsylvania Annual Youth Survey data, and formulate recommendations and action plans to address the priority needs they identify through that facilitated process.

    - Students and school personnel from all 17 school districts in York County have formed the Youth Mental Health Alliance (National Resource Center for Mental Health Promotion and Youth Violence Prevention, 2017) that earned national recognition by the Center for School Mental Health for its robust student-level activities including annual forums with local political leaders and school and service system managers, regular community-wide mental health awareness, and anti-stigma events (Gonzalez, 2018). The students have adopted the tag line, *#TheSilenceEndsHere.*
- In Illinois, family engagement is considered a core component to be strategically integrated within the state's K–12 education systems (Wood, Myers, Scherr, & Wright, 2015). The governor convened a family engagement task force in 2008, a family engagement action planning series in 2011, and launched the Illinois State Board of Education (ISBE) Family Engagement Committee in 2012. ISBE's family engagement initiative is grounded in a statewide framework calling for four actions: (1) develop a family engagement system, (2) enhance communication, (3) build a welcoming and supportive environment, and (4) include parents in decision making. The task force and committee have framed family engagement as a strategy for educational excellence and equity, and launched a public awareness campaign to share that message broadly. Family engagement in Illinois is also supported through a "P-20 Council," established in 2009, to foster collaboration among state agencies, education institutions, local schools, community groups, employers, taxpayers, and families.
- In Washington State, students have long been actively invited to participate in substantial ways in decision-making directly related to school success and student well-being. In a number of schools, students are involved in selecting textbooks, creating classroom behavior guidelines, and designing new buildings. Members of the Student Engagement Team at the Black Hills High School in Tumwater conducted building-wide surveys and testified before the Education Committee of the state House of Representatives (Fletcher, 2008).
- Nevada established an Office of Parental Involvement and Family Engagement within its State Department of Education in 2012, to promote and actively support engagement and meaningful participation of families at the multiple levels its ecological context requires. The state office shares best family engagement practices with school districts and uses an Advisory Council on Parental Involvement & Family Engagement to create and evaluate statewide policies. Key aspects of Nevada's support for family engagement include personnel licensure requirements for at least three semester hours of learning about parental involvement in education, adoption of related standards for school districts, and appointment of family engagement liaisons to each division within the state department. Key goals include establishing district advisory councils statewide, integrating family

engagement training into on-boarding and professional development expectations, and requiring that District and School Improvement Plans focus efforts on intentional family engagement.

Strong collaboration models are increasingly defining strategies to improve student outcomes in recognition of the many relevant contextual factors. Federal grant programs have advanced our knowledge about how to cultivate family and community engagement in schools; and the major presidential and congressional initiatives that have shaped the nation's K–12 education landscape since 2001 (No Child Left Behind; Every Student Succeeds Act) have helped to shape state- and district-level education policies that are clarifying standards, methods, and expectations for family and community engagement that address student achievement, school performance, and district planning.

Effective engagement of both students and families requires creating a range of opportunities that can best fit their strengths and interests. Figure 19.1 identifies a spectrum of openings to capitalize on the expertise of both students and their families across three specific realms of activity that are quintessential to ensuring that students can learn and thrive in safety: practice, research and evaluation, and system and policy.

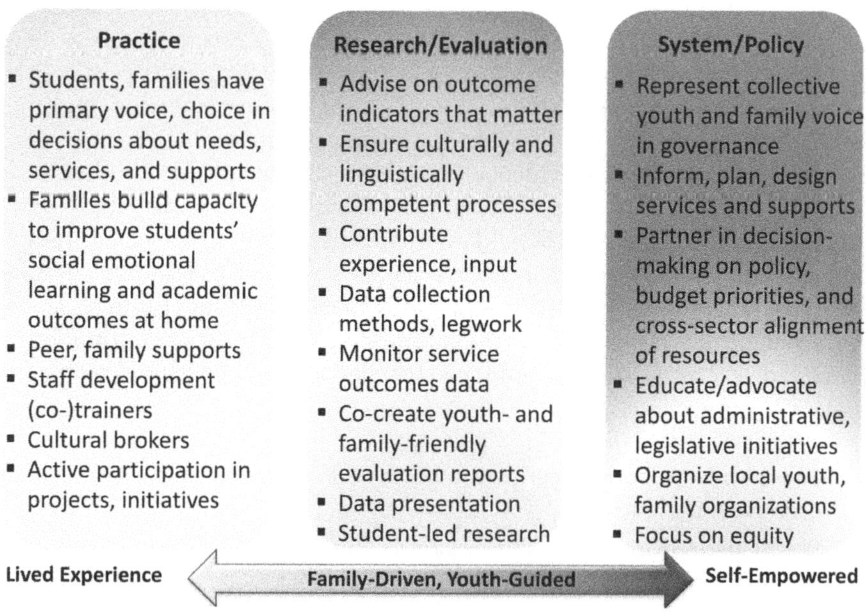

Figure 19.1 Youth and family roles in practice, research, and policy (Rebecca Ornelas)

Practice

In any given school or school district, on any given day, one is likely to encounter a variety of heterogeneous teams working together to apply best practices to student success. Typical collaborations at the practice level might include:

- A student, his or her family, teachers, and community agency personnel planning as a (wraparound, RENEW, or IEP) team to craft objectives and strategies around the student's academic goals and related strengths, circumstances, and needs;
- A team of students, community substance use disorder treatment providers, and school staff reviewing evaluation data collected at prevention trainings that were conducted by students and staff or community sponsors;
- Families, students, staff, and community agencies working on a grant project along with system administrators to address school violence prevention.

Why are such activities becoming more commonplace these days? Supporting the belief that students offer unique and valuable expertise and insight relevant to decision-making is a growing body of evidence that professionals who perceive them as resources also see improvement in the quality of subsequent decisions that are made (see, e.g., Zeldin, 2004). In addition, such benefits become reciprocal, as students themselves can accrue relational, developmental, and educational benefits from participation in collaborative practices, in ways that promote both their own well-being, and that of their school and community (Akiva, Cortina, & Smith, 2014).

Likewise, considerable evidence suggests it is important for families to be engaged with their children's studies. The long-running Harvard Family Research Project (now the Global Family Research Project) collected, vetted, and disseminated empirical research across several decades that cumulatively documented several benefits of family involvement for children's learning, including young children's readiness to enter school, promoting improved academic success, and preparing youth for college. Among the project's findings:

- Family involvement in early childhood years is positively related to children's literacy outcomes.
- Parent participation in K–3 school activities is positively associated with students' high-quality work habits and task orientation.
- Children across the K–12 age range whose parents provide support with homework perform better academically, including lower rates of

delinquency and higher rates of social competence and academic growth among adolescents.

- Youth whose parents are engaged in their college application process are most likely to graduate from high school and attend college.
- Family involvement has been shown to benefit children from diverse ethnic and economic backgrounds. For example, low-income African American children whose families maintained high rates of parent participation in elementary school are more likely to complete high school. Latino youth who are academically high achieving have parents who provide encouragement and emphasize the value of education as a way out of poverty (Kreider, 2006; Knitzer & Olson, 1982).

Blakeslee and Walker (2018) have synthesized the extant "state of the science" regarding how to support meaningful engagement of youth as participants in decision-making processes, and have identified both common challenges ("systemic barriers including tokenism, institutional bureaucracy, lack of high-level buy-in, and the relational challenge of supporting young people who had histories of disempowerment within the system they were advising" [p. 4]); and promising strategies ("high-level administrative commitment, resource allocation, and ongoing stakeholder reflection are required to install and sustain meaningful youth participation" [p. 5]).

It is essential to keep in mind the ecological context for this emerging dimension of stakeholder investment in collaborative partnerships to strengthen school success: individual-level, group-level, program-level, and organization or system-level challenges and strategies to access and apply students' expertise must be explicated, and will complement and reinforce one another. Box 19.1 features new tools designed to support engagement at the individual level. Blakeslee and Walker suggest a three-stage "process of commitment"—awareness of youth participation as a desired outcome, securing and dedication of resources and skills to achieve their participation, and development of operating procedures to guide and sustain their participation. Zeldin, Petrokubi, and McNeil (2008) identify implementation goals and leverage points at each of these three stages of "Planting Seeds," "Walking the Talk," and "How We Do Business."

We know much more, at this point, about what works, and what confounds, parallel efforts to access the expertise of *parents* to improve schools and help students thrive, given the relatively deeper roots of such efforts back to the mid-1970s. In terms of staging, family partnership is now considered essential in model early childhood programs, where critical practices can begin that can then evolve forward across the course of K–12 education. In 2016, the U.S. Department of Health and Human Services (HHS), which oversees Head Start/Early Head Start (HS/EHS), and the U.S. Department of

BOX 19.1 TOOLS SUPPORT ENGAGEMENT OF STUDENTS AND PARENTS

The Research and Training Center for Pathways to Positive Futures offers a suite of tools to stimulate, generate, and reinforce meaningful youth participation in holistic, team-based collaborative futures planning through a curriculum called *Achieve My Plan* (AMP). The Global Family Research Project offers interactive case study tools (https://globalfrp.org/Articles/How-to-Use-Interactive-Family-Cases) to facilitate problem-solving in support of effective family engagement to benefit young students.

Source: Pathways RTC, Achieve My Plan. Portland, OR: Portland State &University. https://www.pathwaysrtc.pdx.edu/p3c-achieve-my-plan.

Education (ED) issued a joint family engagement policy statement and guiding principles urging all early childhood systems and programs to recognize and support families as key partners in providing services that improve children's development, learning, and wellness. Family members work in concert with high-quality early learning programs to prepare young children for future success in school. From their child's initial entry to the program, parents participate in family involvement contracts that address shared commitment and accountability for school readiness. HS/EHS programs with strong family partnership have produced positive outcomes in children's literacy skills, math skills, school readiness, and health (U.S. Department of Health and Human Services, 2013). Key elements of these programs include data-driven improvement processes, intensive professional development, and family training (Acelero Learning, 2018).

When parents from diverse socioeconomic, educational, racial, and ethnic backgrounds are provided with culturally relevant and usable activities, skills-building opportunities, and supports, they develop the capacities needed to support their child's learning at home and school. Although involving culturally and linguistically diverse parents may require more intentional strategies, students thrive when schools acknowledge and engage the important adults in their lives. Recommended strategies to promote home-school partnerships include developing an interactive curriculum for student and family with activities linked to specific knowledge and skill goals; incorporating multicultural books and materials across the curriculum along with in-home activities; providing families with training and resources to help them monitor homework; including families and members of their cultural community in classroom activities; and communicating often with parents about their child's progress, success, and concerns, utilizing trained interpreters when needed (National Education Association, 2007).

Parents considered "hard to reach" will become involved if schools implement strength-based (rather than deficit-driven) approaches to understanding different family cultures, practices, and values (Weiss, Bouffard, Bridglall, & Gordon, 2009). Research indicates that to effectively engage families from very diverse backgrounds schools must focus on building trusting collaborative relationships with families and community members, demonstrate respect and understanding of class and cultural differences, and embrace a philosophy of partnership where power and responsibility are shared (Henderson & Mapp, 2002).

The U.S. Department of Education offers *The Dual Capacity-Building Framework for Family-School Partnerships* that shows how building the capacity of families in the "4 C" areas—capabilities, connections, cognition, and confidence—can help families to negotiate multiple roles, including but also transcending direct practice, and equipping them for opportunities to contribute to program monitoring, decision-making, and policy advocacy as full-fledged partners in collaboration (Mapp & Kuttner, 2013).

Research and Evaluation

An ecological approach requires in-depth data to inform planning and decision-making. Students experience efforts to improve school functioning and academic learning first hand, and their families see the impact on their children. Both are ideally positioned to contribute valuable data and perspectives to research and evaluation components of the collaborative improvement initiative. Their lived experience can provide raw qualitative data that offers an up-close and real-time perspective on what is needed, "a granular level of understanding of what works, for whom, and in what circumstances" (Comer & Haynes, 1991, pp. 271–277) in their community. Students and families can also help to set research agendas and help identify questions that can best be addressed through well-constructed research and evaluation. Such evidence and insight equips collaborative teams to identify priorities that matter to the diverse range of students and families, and to co-create sustainable solutions that will work for them.

Researchers and evaluators initially sought student perspectives by asking them to respond to surveys. Indeed, tens of thousands of students now regularly inform school climate and performance improvement efforts through the national Youth Risk Behavior Survey (YRBS) (Centers for Disease Control & Prevention, 2017) and similar statewide input protocols.[1] A community's collaborative improvement efforts can make use of a variety of user-friendly school climate measurement survey tools for middle and high school students, their parents, teachers, instructional staff, non-instructional staff, and administrators provided at no cost through a web-based platform sponsored by the U.S. Department of Education and hosted by the National

Center on Safe and Supportive Learning Environments (NCSSLE, 2018). Harvard University's Graduate School of Education documents a variety of developmentally appropriate strategies to elicit meaningful student input even among elementary school students (Shafer, 2016).

Of course, survey response is a limited, one-way channel for student input. We recommend their meaningful participation in virtually all research and evaluation functions. *Student-led* research can provide insights that can catalyze and create change in schools, especially when students are empowered to select topics for investigation that are directly relevant to them, such as student engagement, graduation rates, and student leadership. They bring their expertise about such topics in ways that are uniquely impactful. Here are some early examples:

- The U.S. Department of Education's Regional Education Laboratory Network undertook an extensive examination of student views about restructuring public K–12 schools in 1997, including eight case studies, and produced an extensive report (Kushman, 1997) not only of findings but also of methodological insights from direct learning from student informants, including a chapter, "Finding Out What Students Think: One-Day Methods Schools Can Use."
- In 2004, students at North High School in Denver investigated the low graduation and high drop-out rates in their school by surveying 700 students, reviewed pertinent school reform and education research, and generated four sets of detailed solutions that helped fuel changes that improved outcomes (Jovenes Unidos & Padres Unidos, 2004).
- In 2003, Austin (Texas) Voices for Education and Youth (AVEY), a group of students and adults, began gathering student input to highlight their priorities during a school reform process. Fifteen years later they continue this work as a nonprofit organization that has led community engagement efforts for the local school district, the Gates Foundation, and the local E3 Alliance. The *Austin Chronicle* has described this group as "a powerful force for educational change."[2]

Researchers and evaluators who have purposefully recruited youth and family members as partners report a variety of ways they add value to the work:

- identifying measurable outcomes that are useful and relevant to their everyday lives
- shaping data collection methods to facilitate substantial and reliable reporting
- helping skeptical respondents work through reluctance to participate

- fine-tuning interpretation of data to match audience interests
- reporting data to persuasively substantiate recommendations for services, management, and policy changes (Fisher, Manteuffel, & Grossman, 2010).

The Substance Abuse and Mental Health Services Administration's (SAMHSA) Children's Mental Health Initiative has required grantee communities to involve families and youth with lived experience in implementation of their evaluation activities since 2005.[3] A *Framework for Involving Families and Youth in Evaluation* (National Federation of Families for Children's Mental Health, 2006) delineated best practices to accomplish this. Families and youth should be:

- appropriately compensated for their time and experience-based expertise
- provided training in evaluation and receive supportive supervision that guides their development as evaluation team members
- supported to link with and have access to other families and youth who are involved in similar efforts.

Additional lessons about collaborating with youth and families when conducting research are being generated from patient-centered research in health care. A qualitative study comprising 80 patient advisors, researchers, physicians, and nurses recently identified a list of challenges to engaging patients and family members in research, including their initial reluctance to participate, their lack of skills and training, and "problems connecting with the right person at the right time." Significantly, the study participants identified an equally long list of strategies to support patient and family engagement in research, including creating an environment within which they can offer a genuinely valuable and unique contribution, building community among patients, caregivers, and researchers, best practice activities for researchers to facilitate engagement, and tools and training (Harrison, Anderson, Fagan, & Auerbach, 2018).

Researchers and evaluators can motivate students and families to bring their expertise to collaborative partnerships by understanding that they can contribute to the development of an evidence base to identify, and lend credibility to, the most effective practices and programs that fit various academic, socioeconomic, developmental, cultural, and situational contexts. They can then be encouraged to use the resultant evidence in tandem with their primary authority as central actors to support advocacy and public education activities essential to influence the embrace of what really works by policy makers and formal system leaders.

System and Policy

Throughout our country family-run organizations[4] collaborate with local and state providers, administrators of agencies and systems, community organizations, political leaders and others to educate policy makers about how best to establish policies and align resources to ensure all children can thrive. Increasingly, young people, too, are developing uniquely effective voice at the community, state, and national levels:

- Then Arizona Governor Janet Napolitano invited several youth in 2003 to join her Children's Cabinet, to work alongside heads of the state departments of Education, Juvenile Corrections, Health Services, Housing, Courts, Economic Security and Environmental Quality because "(these) people should be working and talking with each other on a daily basis . . . to bust the barriers between them—not by looking at budget line items, but by being child-focused—measuring how prepared a child is to be healthy, go to school, and succeed in life" (Skalsky, 2007).
- Dozens of thoughtful columns[5] have analyzed how organized student voices have uniquely managed to shift intransigent stalemates about gun control and school safety policies in the wake of the mass shooting tragedy at Marjorie Stoneman Douglas High School in Parkland, Florida, on February 14, 2018; mobilizing hundreds of thousands of people in the highly visible *March for Our Lives* protest in over 800 locations (*New York Times*, 2018); and with almost immediately discernible impacts on both federal and state policy (Biette-Timmons & Burnett, 2018).
- A group of U.S. Senators based their joint request for specific administrative policies to the nation's Secretaries of Education, and of Health and Human Services, on their report of the lived experiences of students living in protective placements. "Members of Congress have heard from current and former foster youth that oftentimes their school offered the only safe place for them while they were in foster care."[6]

Additional Keys to Strengthen Collaborative Partnerships Involving Students and Families

Effective collaboration requires that stakeholders share power in new ways. Students, families, practitioners, researchers, and policy makers often do have shared interests, but typically have little experience sharing power with stakeholders who bring very different perspectives to the table. Often, each stakeholder group knows its own perspective well, while having only limited understanding of others' perspectives. Barry Oshry summarized this challenge in his 2007 book, *Seeing Systems*:

> Generally, if we are paying attention, we know what life is like for us in our part of the system. Other parts of the system are, for the most part, invisible to us. We do not know what others are experiencing, what their worlds are like, what issues they are dealing with, what dilemmas they are facing, what stresses they are undergoing. To make matters worse, we sometimes think we know, when in fact we do not. We have our beliefs, myths, and prejudices, which we accept as the truth and which becomes the bases of our actions. This blindness to other parts of the system . . . is a source of considerable misunderstanding, conflict, and diminished system contribution. (Oshry, 2007, p. 1)

As each of us is subject to our own limited perspectives, meaningful collaboration both challenges and also rewards diverse stakeholders—including students and families—because recognizing the differences offered by their perspectives helps all of us see our systems more completely, and therefore enables more effective improvements and solutions.

Collaboration begins with a group of people with diverse backgrounds, ideas, skills, and values coming together to work on a shared goal. Students, families, educators, and administrators who begin with different information and assumptions should recognize that contributions of diverse expertise can generate better results. Professional staff bring their knowledge and education. Families and students bring expertise from personal experience (that they may be initially cautious about sharing). Each may hold worries as well about sharing decision-making power with others who may not hold as much accountability or sharing authority. Good collaborations set ground rules so that everyone can openly discuss issues and share their views without passing judgment, setting the stage to build trusting relationships and create solutions.

Developing a shared vision, shared values, and shared goals across a large group of diverse stakeholders with a wide range of roles and expertise is tantamount to establishing a North Star that can help the group to navigate even confusing and tempestuous challenges. Individuals must be willing to invest in cultivating mutual trust, to invite and respect vastly different perspectives, to be guided by shared leadership, to commit to active listening and open-minded flexibility, and to collectively embrace a willingness to learn together.

Conclusion

To bring about positive results, strategies that can keep students safe and help them to thrive must address multiple levels of socio-ecological factors spanning individual behavior; social, family, school, and community networks; living and working conditions; and broad social, economic, cultural, health, and environmental conditions and policies (Institute of Medicine, 2002). Students, and family members must serve alongside political and system leaders and other community members as equal partners in research, planning, decision-making, implementation, evaluation, continuous improvement, and sustaining and expanding services and programs that work to accomplish these aims.

Collaboration based on mutual respect, trust, and open communication ensures that stakeholders can understand one another's perspectives and appreciate their contributions. Partners must be ready and willing to step out of their comfort zone and be open-minded and open-hearted to new possibilities and innovative solutions informed by youth and family members.

Notes

1. For example, Ohio Youth Environments Survey (http://www.ohyes.ohio.gov/), and Pennsylvania Youth Survey (http://www.pccd.pa.gov/Juvenile-Justice/Pages/Pennsylvania-Youth-Survey-(PAYS).aspx).

2. See Austin Voices for Education and Youth. Retrieved from https://www.austinvoices.org/about-avey/history/.

3. SAMHSA's Safe Schools, Healthy Students framework (https://healthysafechildren.org/sshs-framework) and grant program likewise require "connecting families, schools and communities" as one of five essential elements.

4. Schools that have established robust family participation stress the importance of building a defined structure to organize and sustain family engagement activities, acquire formal endorsement and financial support from system leaders, and employ family leaders to coordinate and mentor families to build such capacity for collaboration.

5. See, for example, "How Parkland students changed the gun debate," *The Atlantic*, February 28, 2018 (https://www.theatlantic.com/politics/archive/2018/02/parkland-students-power/554399/).

6. U.S. Senators Patty Murray, Orrin G. Hatch, Ron Wyden, Charles Grassley, and Al Franken, in May 5, 2016, letter to then Secretary of Health and Human Services Sylvia Burwell and Secretary of Education John B King.

References

Acelero Learning. (2018). Acelero family services approach: The achievement gap—Family strengths and goals and professional development. Retrieved from http://www.acelero.net/approach/

Akiva, T., Cortina, K. S., & Smith, C. (2014). Involving youth in program decision-making: How common and what might it do for youth? *Journal of Youth and Adolescence, 43*(11).

ASCD, Centers for Disease Control and Prevention (CDC). (2014). *Whole school, whole community, whole child: A collaborative approach to learning and health.* Alexandria, VA: ASCD. Retrieved from http://www.ascd.org/programs/learning-and-health/wscc-model.aspx

Biette-Timmons, N., & Burnett, J. (2018, April 8). The Parkland kids' gun reform platform, explained. *The Trace.* Retrieved from https://www.thetrace.org/rounds/the-parkland-kids-gun-reform-platform-explained/

Blakeslee, J., & Walker, J. (2018). *Assessing the meaningful inclusion of youth voice in policy and practice: State of the Science.* Portland, OR: Research and Training Center for Pathways to Positive Futures, Portland State University. Retrieved from https://www.pathwaysrtc.pdx.edu/state-of-the-science-articles-2018-spac

Cantor, P., Osher, D., Berg, J., Steyer, L., & Rose, T. (2018). Malleability, plasticity, and individuality: How children learn and develop in context. *Applied Developmental Science.* doi:10.1080.10888691.2017.1398649

CAP Tulsa Strategic Framework. (2016–2025). Retrieved from https://www.captulsa.org/uploaded_assets/pdf/Strategic-Framework-CAP-Tulsa_2016-2025.pdf

Cashman, J., Linehan, P., Purcell, L., Rosser, M., Schultz, S., & Skalski, S. (2014). *Leading by convening: A blueprint for authentic engagement.* Alexandria, VA: National Association of State Directors of Special Education.

Catalano, R. F., Berglund, M. L., Ryan, J. A. M., Lonczak, H., & Hawkins, J. (1998). Positive youth development in the United States: Research findings on evaluations of positive youth development programs. *Prevention & Treatment, 5*(1). Retrieved from https://aspe.hhs.gov/report/positive-youth-development-united-states-research-findings-evaluations-positive-youth-development-programs

Centers for Disease Control & Prevention. (2017). Youth risk behavior surveillance system overview. CDC. Retrieved from https://www.cdc.gov/healthyyouth/data/yrbs/overview.htm

Clevenger, J. (1997). Collaboration: Why participate in an unnatural act? *Journal of Chemical Education, 74*(8), 894. doi:10.1021/ed074p894

Collaboration for Impact. (2018). Collective impact framework. Retrieved from http://www.collaborationforimpact.com/collective-impact/

Comer, J. P., & Haynes, N. M. (1991). Parent involvement in schools: An ecological approach. *Elementary School Journal, 91*(January), 271–277. doi:10.1086/461654

Fisher, S., Manteuffel, B., & Grossman, L. (2010). *National evaluation orientation training.* National Evaluation of Comprehensive Community Mental Health Services for Children and Their Families Program. Atlanta: ICF Macro.

Fletcher, A. (2008). The architecture of ownership. *Educational Leadership, 66*(3). Retrieved from http://www.ascd.org/publications/educational-leadership/nov08/vol66/num03/The-Architecture-of-Ownership.aspx

Gonzalez, J. (2018, April 3). York County youth hold town hall on mental health. *York Dispatch*. Retrieved from https://www.yorkdispatch.com/story/news/education/2018/04/03/york-county-youth-hold-town-hall-mental-health/470736002/

Gould, R. (2007). *An ecological approach to national education reform*. National Center for Youth Law. Retrieved from https://youthlaw.org/publication/an-ecological-approach-to-national-education-reform/

Griffiths, P. E., & Tabery, J. (2013). Developmental systems theory: What does it explain, and how does it explain it? *Advances in Child Development and Behavior, 44*, 65–94.

Harrison, J., Anderson, W., Fagan, M., Robinson, E., Schnipper, J., Symczak, G., Hanson, C., Carnie, M. B., Banta, J., Chen, S., Duong, J., Wong, C., & Auerbach, A. (2018, August). Patient and Family Advisory Councils (PFACs): Identifying challenges and solutions to support engagement in research. *The Patient, 11*(4), 413–423. doi:10.1007/s40271-018-0298-4

Henderson, A. T., & Mapp, K. L. (2002). *A new wave of evidence: The impact of school, family, and community connections on student achievement*. Austin, TX: Southwest Educational Development Laboratory. Retrieved from http://www.sedl.org/connections/resources/evidence.pdf

Institute of Medicine. (2002). *The future of the public's health in the 21st century*. Institute of Medicine, Committee on Assuring the Health of the Public in the 21st Century. Washington, DC: National Academies Press. Retrieved from https://www.ncbi.nlm.nih.gov/books/NBK221239/

Jovenes Unidos & Padres Unidos. (2004, March). North High School Report: The voices of over 700 students. Denver. Retrieved from https://issuu.com/padresunidos1/docs/north_high_report

Knitzer, J., & Olson, L. (1982). *Unclaimed children: The failure of public responsibility to children and adolescents in need of mental health services*. Washington, DC: Children's Defense Fund.

Kreider, Holly. (2006, July 24). Family involvement: What does the research say? Usable Knowledge—Connecting Research to Practice. Retrieved from https://www.gse.harvard.edu/news/uk/06/07/family-involvement-what-does-research-say

Kushman, James W. (Ed.). (1997). *Look who's talking now: Students' views of learning in restructuring schools*. Portland, OR: Northwest Regional Educational laboratory. Retrieved from https://files.eric.ed.gov/fulltext/ED404752.pdf

Mapp, K. L., & Kuttner, P. (2013). *Partners in education: A dual-capacity framework for family-school partnerships*. Austin, TX: SEDL. Retrieved from https://www2.ed.gov/documents/family-community/partners-education.pdf

National Center for Injury Prevention and Control. (2014, August). *Essentials for childhood framework: Steps to create safe, stable, nurturing relationships and environments*. Atlanta: Centers for Disease Control and Prevention.

National Education Association. (2007). *C.A.R.E.: Strategies for closing the achievement gaps*. Retrieved from http://www.nea.org/assets/docs/mf_CAREbook0804.pdf

National Federation of Families for Children's Mental Health (NFFCMH). (2006). *Integrating families and youth into the national and local evaluation of systems of care communities*. Rockville, MD: Author.

National Federation of Families for Children's Mental Health (NFFCMH). (2017). *Our history*. Retrieved from https://www.ffcmh.org/history

National Resource Center for Mental Health Promotion and Youth Violence Prevention. (2017). Youth Mental Health Alliance—York County Schools. Retrieved from https://healthysafechildren.org/grantee-field-spotlight/pennsylvania-youth-mental-health-alliance-york-county-schools

NCSSLE. (2018, May). ED School Climate Surveys. Retrieved from https://safesupportivelearning.ed.gov/edscls

New York Times. (2018, March 24). March for Our Lives highlights: Students protesting guns say "Enough Is Enough." Retrieved from https://www.nytimes.com/2018/03/24/us/march-for-our-lives.html

Osher, T. W., Osher, D., & Blau, G. (2008). Families matter. In T. Gullotta & G. Blau (Eds.), *Family influences on childhood behavior and development evidence-based prevention and treatment approaches* (pp. 39–61). New York: Routledge.

Oshry, B. (2007). *Seeing systems: Unlocking the mysteries of organizational life*. Oakland, CA: Berrett-Koehler.

Pennsylvania Care Partnership. (2018). State leadership & management team. *Pennsylvania Care Partnership*. Retrieved from http://www.pasocpartnership.org/about-us/state-leadership-management-team/

Shafer, L. (2016, August). Giving students a voice: Five ways to welcome student input and bolster your school's success. Usable knowledge—Connecting research to practice. Retrieved from https://www.gse.harvard.edu/news/uk/16/08/giving-students-voice

Skalsky, y Cindy. (2007, August 9). Napolitano releases report on status of children in Arizona. *Douglas Dispatch*. Retrieved from http://www.douglasdispatch.com/news/napolitano-releases-report-on-status-of-children-in-arizona/ article_6926a1fe-b684-5372-baff-a95d9cc58952.html

Stevenson, B. (2014). *Just mercy: A story of justice and redemption*. New York: Spiegel & Grau.

Stevenson, B. (2016). *Empathy and social justice: The power of proximity in improvement science*. Keynote presentation to Carnegie Foundation Summit on Improvement in Education, San Francisco. Retrieved from https://www.carnegiefoundation.org/blog/empathy-and-social-justice-the-power-of-proximity-in-improvement-science/

Stroul, B., & Friedman, R. (1986). *A system of care for severely emotionally disturbed children & youth*. Washington, DC: Georgetown University CASSP Technical Assistance Center. Retrieved from https://www.ncjrs.gov/pdffiles1/Digitization/125081NCJRS.pdf

University of Washington Center for Communities That Care. (2018). *Communities that care PLUS*. Retrieved from https://www.communitiesthatcare.net/how-ctc-works/; and https://www.communitiesthatcare.net/Prevention%20Strategies%20Guide/introduction.pdf

U.S. Department of Education. (2016, May 5). Joint policy statement on family engagement from the early years to the early grades. Retrieved from https://www2.ed.gov/about/inits/ed/earlylearning/files/policy-statement-on-family-engagement.pdf

U.S. Department of Health and Human Services. (2013). *The parent, family and community engagement framework: Understanding family engagement outcomes* (Research to Practice Series—Family Engagement and School Readiness). Retrieved from https://eclkc.ohs.acf.hhs.gov/sites/default/files/pdf/rtp-school-readiness.pdf

Weiss, H. B., Bouffard, S. M., Bridglall, B. L., & Gordon, E. W. (2009). *Reframing family involvement in education: Supporting families to support educational equity* (Equity Matters: Research Review No. 5). New York: Campaign for Educational Equity, Teachers College, Columbia University.

Wood, L., & Carson, J. (2016). *Promoting equity through family-school partnerships.* Washington, DC: U.S. Department of Education. Retrieved from http://www.ed.gov/family-and-community-engagement/bulletin-board/promoting-equity-through-family-school-partnerships

Wood, L., Myers, V., Scherr, B., & Wright, M. (2015, July). *Laying the groundwork: State frameworks for family engagement.* Presented at the Combined Federal Programs Summer Meeting—All In: Achieving Results Together. Washington, DC.

Zeldin, S. (2004). Youth as agents of adult and community development: Mapping the processes and outcomes of youth engaged in organizational governance. *Applied Developmental Science, 8*(2), 75–90.

Zeldin, S., Petrokubi, J., & McNeil, C. (2008). Youth-adult partnerships in decision-making: Disseminating and implementing an innovative idea into established organizations and communities. *American Journal of Community Psychology, 41*(3–4), 262–277.

CHAPTER TWENTY

School-Family-Community Partnerships

School Safety, Mental Health, and Family Resilience

Tracy Hill, Lisa Baskin Naylor, Denine A. Goolsby, Eric Gordon, and Frank A. Fecser

This chapter examines the challenges to implementing practices that are based on research regarding the importance and benefits of partnerships between schools and families. This chapter also highlights the collective efforts of schools, families, mental health agencies, and communities that have been successful in changing school practice, labor contracts, state requirements, and other policies, supporting rather than constraining the desired shift in practice.

Portfolio of Strategies in a Portfolio District

Cleveland is transitioning from a traditional school district to a new system of district and charter schools using the Portfolio Strategy. Schools being created and transformed in this new system are held to the highest standards of performance. These standards aim to yield dramatic student achievement gains for every child. The Portfolio Strategy is viewed as an extraordinary local effort to modernize Cleveland's large urban school district. This is being accomplished through innovative new school design and ongoing support.

Cleveland's success will be apparent when every neighborhood has a variety of great schools from which families can choose. The Portfolio Strategy will aggressively grow the number of high-performing schools and increase the enrollment of students served by those schools. The goal is for each school to provide a rigorous curriculum, engage families as partners in education, and collaborate with community partners and stakeholders to provide essential supports and services.

This chapter examines challenges to implementing practices that are based on research on the importance and benefits of partnerships between schools and families. It also highlights collective efforts of schools, families, mental health agencies, and communities that have been successful in changing school practice, labor contracts, state requirements, and other policies, supporting rather than constraining the desired shift in practice. These challenges and the efforts to address them will be examined through examples of the collective efforts in the Cleveland Metropolitan School District (CMSD) in Cleveland, Ohio, and its many community partners.

This chapter details districtwide efforts to implement best practices for parent-teacher conferences, including the implementation of student-led conferences and the development and implementation of Academic Parent Teacher Teams. It describes the district's work in building the power of parents as teachers, advocates, leaders, and learners at Parent University. And it examines the use of Family Support Liaisons who provide second- and third-tier support for families with higher identified needs.

The chapter explores how CMSD and the Cleveland Teachers Union (CTU) have impacted positive family engagement through data-driven collaborative labor-management work teams and through collective bargaining efforts that have embedded promotive practices into contract language.

It reviews Cleveland's unique success in changing state law to ensure that parents are intentional and anticipated partners in whole school reform efforts with mandatory requirements for meaningful engagement with their children's teachers and school.

Lastly, the chapter outlines multiple initiatives that have reshaped local policies and practices through wraparound support services in partnership with the United Way of Greater Cleveland and several community-based agencies, along with how the district provides family-based healthcare through a unique partnership with the MetroHealth hospital system.

Throughout the chapter, both local data and national research is highlighted to give greater context to the importance and impact of these models.

Engaging Parents as Partners

Cleveland's Plan for Transforming Schools (*The Cleveland Plan*) was adopted in 2012 with the strong support of Mayor Frank Jackson, CMSD, the CTU, civic leaders, elected officials, charter school operators, businesses, philanthropists, community organizations, religious organizations, parents, and students. Its goal is to ensure that every child in Cleveland attends a high-quality school and that every neighborhood has a multitude of great schools from which families can choose. The plan is built upon growing and expanding the number of excellent schools in Cleveland—district and charter—and holding schools to the highest standards as they work in partnership to create dramatic student achievement gains for every child. *The Cleveland Plan* is supported by House Bill 525 (signed into law in July 2012), which made sweeping changes to state law around district autonomy and flexibility, employment policies and practices, and charter school quality and collaboration. *The Cleveland Plan* includes a stipulation that requires the parents or guardians of students enrolled in the district participate in at least one parent-teacher conference or similar event held at schools during the school year. The intention is to emphasize the importance of family engagement and school-family partnerships to the success of reform efforts outlined in *The Cleveland Plan*. As a result of these family engagement provisions, the district has a laser-like focus on parent-teacher conferences and, using research-based practices to inform families of student progress, provides strategies to assist with learning at home and building awareness of resources available in the community.

CMSD's Office of Family and Community Engagement (FACE) has adopted the U.S. Department of Education's Dual Capacity-Building Framework for Family-School Partnerships to further the work of engaging families in student learning. This framework recommends that school districts work to build the capacity of educators and families to work collaboratively to support student achievement. FACE promotes meaningful districtwide engagement of families and community stakeholders in *The Cleveland Plan* by expanding school capacity to partner with families and community-based organizations.

The FACE office employs eight full-time FACE Coordinators who are assigned to a network support team that serves 10–15 schools. Every school in the district receives Title I Federal Funding and a portion of that funding is dedicated to family engagement. Each school has a Family Engagement Committee comprised of a building administrator, parents/caregivers, teachers, school support staff, and community partners. The FACE Coordinators work with Family Engagement Committees at each school to develop Title I Action Plans that link engagement efforts to the strategic priorities of the Academic Achievement Plan so that family engagement is intentional, authentic, and builds the capacity of families to support their students' academic and social and emotional growth. Research demonstrates that when schools develop strong partnerships with families, student are more likely to attend school regularly, graduate from high school, take more advanced classes, and achieve at higher levels (Bryk, Sebring, Allensworth, Luppescu, & Easton, 2010; Dearing, Kreider, Simpkins, & Weiss, 2006; Henderson & Mapp, 2002).

Families can be engaged in many ways to support their students at home, in the community, and at school. When a district broadens the definition of family engagement to include not only participation in parent-teacher conferences and school events but also how they support learning, social and emotional growth, and physical well-being in the home and community to enhance student experiences, then they can better acknowledge families for work they do outside of school. Dr. Karen Mapp of the Harvard Graduate School of Education has identified the important roles that parents and caregivers play (Mapp & Kuttner, 2013):

- Supporters of their children's learning
- Encouragers of an achievement identity, a positive self-image, and a "can do" spirit
- Monitors of their children's time, behavior, boundaries, and resources
- Models of lifelong learning and enthusiasm for education
- Advocates for improved learning opportunities for their children at their schools
- Decision-makers/choosers of educational options for their child, the school, and community
- Collaborators with school staff and members of the community

According to *The Cleveland Plan*, parents must attend at least one parent-teacher conference at their school during the school year. The district established a parent-teacher conference committee in school year 2013–2014 to create a strategy for how to collect data to achieve this goal and evaluate conference format on parent attendance rates. The parent-teacher conference committee was comprised of district administrators and CTU partners. Together the committee defined what meetings would qualify as a conference and created a mechanism in the student information system that teachers would use to capture parent attendance. In the first year that data was collected, 73.1% of parents attended conferences for their students. The percentage increased in 2014–2015 to 80%, 90.9% in 2015–2016, and 91.6% in 2016–2017. Parents are now attending conferences in record numbers, so the focus of the committee shifted to deepening the conversations during conferences and expanding partnerships with families through the use of evidenced-based models designed to create interactions and conversations that are more intentional and meaningful to families. Two formats for conferences were identified to assist in this endeavor: Academic Parent Teacher Teams (APTT) and student-led conferences.

Academic Parent Teacher Teams

Recently, Dr. Mapp, a Harvard Senior Education Lecturer and a consultant on family engagement to the U.S. Department of Education, said, "If effective cradle-to-career educational partnerships between home and school are to be implemented and sustained with fidelity, engagement initiatives must include a concerted focus on developing adult capacity, whether through pre- and in-service professional development for educators; academies, workshops, seminars, and workplace training for families; or as an integrated part of parent-teacher partnership activities" (Mapp & Kuttner, 2013, pp. 7–9). In 2015–2016, CMSD piloted the APTT model in four pre-kindergarten through 8th grade schools. APTT was expanded to 10 schools for the 2017–2018 school year, with the goal of deepening the partnerships between home and school and engaging parents around the instructional core.

APTT is recognized by the both the U.S. Department of Education and the Harvard Family Research Project as a "best practice in family-school partnerships" (Mapp & Kuttner, 2013, p. 15). The APTT model is a high-impact strategy for family engagement that aligns grade-level learning concepts, student performance data, and family-teacher communication and partnerships. The APTT model provides school leaders and teachers with a developmental and collaborative process for building strong relationships with families focused on student academic growth and achievement. The APTT model was developed by Dr. Maria C. Paredes in 2008, for the Creighton School District in Arizona, in response to a strong need to provide families with the information, data, and tools they needed to know to support academic achievement for their children. APTT has been implemented in 250 schools in 16 states and Washington, DC. The practice was originally designed to help parents who did not complete high school or receive a college education support their children's education.

APTT requires the classroom teacher to invite families to participate in three 75-minute team meetings and one 30-minute individual session. During the APTT meetings, teachers introduce and review grade-level foundational skills, share student performance data, and demonstrate concrete activities that families can do at home to help students master those skills. Parents set 60-day learning goals for the classroom and their child based on their current level of achievement. Parents are also given time to collaborate with each other to share helpful strategies. The APTT strategy provides parents with training and targeted assistance so they can help their children at home with simple strategies that are directly linked to classroom learning and student data.

In May 2017, focus groups were conducted with parents and caregivers who participated in the pilot. They overwhelmingly indicated that they loved seeing their student's data compared to the class, setting smart goals, and receiving activities to practice at home. A parent of a first grader at McKinley School who attended all three APTT meetings testified that she always struggled with helping her daughter at home because she did not know what to focus on. The meetings helped her provide focused activities at home to support her daughter's academic goals.

Teachers learned that implementing the APTT model is both time- and labor-intensive, and it became clear that the central office should provide training, resources, and supports to implement it effectively. Providing resources to support the change in practice is critical. Teachers had a chance to look at sample take-home learning materials during APTT teacher training and prepare their own resources based on the foundational skills they selected. Teachers had to spend an inordinate amount of time searching for and selecting appropriate take-home activities for their parents. To be successful, this initiative requires a unified effort between FACE, the academics office, and teaching partners. Since APTT focuses on academic skills selected by teachers based on their in-depth knowledge of students, the support systems built around the practice by the team must relate to teacher awareness and their emerging skill set when working with parents as adult learners. Training must also address cultural competence and changing the mindset from looking at families' deficits to acknowledging the strengths and skills that parents bring to the table despite the many challenges in their lives.

In order to sustain this practice, the district must ensure that members of the academics and FACE team are trained in the model and afforded the time and resources to provide critical support to teachers so they do not become overwhelmed and disheartened. The district must also evaluate the effectiveness of this practice as it relates to student achievement to demonstrate that APTT is worth the time and energy. The district is also focusing on sustainability and is working with consultants to create a team of in-house experts who will lead the work in the future.

Student-Led Conferences

For years, parent-teacher conferences have been the primary means of parent-teacher communication. Because traditional parent-teacher conferences typically exclude the student from the process, this model does little to facilitate dialogue between parent and child or to recognize the need for students to assume greater responsibility for their academic learning. But now, many schools are using a different approach that puts the student at the center of the conversation and allows them to own their learning in a unique way. The student-led process typically has three phases: preparation, the actual conference, and an evaluation component. To prepare students for the conference, teachers instruct students on how to lead the conference, assist them with collecting and preparing information to be shared with parents, and describe how to explain and interpret any information to be shared. Often times, the teacher will have the student practice or co-facilitate the presentation for younger students. Student-led conferences are being conducted with students in grades K–12.

During student-led conferences, students take the lead by sharing a portfolio of their school work, discussing interests and goals, and reflecting on what they do well and areas of difficulty. Together, they create a plan with their parents on how to achieve their goals and make improvements in their academic and social and emotional learning (SEL). This form of conferencing allows all three people to have shared responsibility for student achievement. Student-led conferences are designed to achieve one or more of the following goals: allow students to accept personal ownership for their learning; teach students the process of self-evaluation and reflection; facilitate the development of students' organizational and oral communication skills and to increase their self-confidence; encourage students, parents, and teachers to engage in open and honest dialogue; and increase parent attendance at conferences. When conference attendance was evaluated in Cleveland schools, it was found that schools which used this format had nearly a 100% attendance rate at conferences compared to schools that used a traditional format. In the 2015–2016 school year, three CMSD schools utilized student-led conferences. In the 2016–2017 school year, after providing professional development to teachers and administrators, 21 schools adopted this format to help them create a stronger partnership between parents, students, and teachers.

The district's goal is that schools will move away from the traditional parent-teacher conferences and utilize APTT or student-led conferences to create more meaningful engagement with parents. In several CMSD schools, both models are being used: APTT is used for K–3 grade classes to align with Ohio's Third Grade Reading Guarantee mandate, and student-led conferences are used grades 4–8.

Parent University

School districts around the country have realized that family engagement is vital to the success of their schools and students. There are many efforts to engage and empower parents by offering workshops, classes, and other opportunities to learn about district initiatives and curricula and to become engaged in decision-making. In Cleveland, the FACE office sponsors multiple opportunities to build parent capacity through its Parent University program. Parent University was created in CMSD after members of the FACE team traveled to similar districts to examine family engagement best practices. In 2010, on a trip to Boston Public Schools (BPS) sponsored by the Institute for Educational Leadership's Family Engagement and Community Engagement National Network of District Leaders, the team visited the BPS Parent University and met with the family engagement team there to learn about their strategies. The CMSD FACE team launched a Parent University program in Cleveland in the fall of 2011 by partnering with community organizations and agencies to provide workshops for parents throughout the school district and community locations. Some of the organizations that have provided workshops include the Cleveland Clinic, Neighborhood Leadership Institute, Esperanza, WVIZ/PBS ideastream, the Literacy Cooperative, and mental health agencies like Applewood and Beech Brook.

CMSD's Parent University has four focus areas that support parents in ways that empower them to be leaders and advocates for student learning and school improvement.

- *Parents as Teachers* provides a clearer understanding of how children grow and learn and the teaching and learning approaches used in CMSD
- *Parents as Advocates* builds capacity to advocate for children, understand the standards and expectations for learning, and support learning at home
- *Parents as Leaders* helps parents build the skills necessary to assume leadership roles in schools and the community
- *Parents as Learners* provides parents with the opportunity to build upon their own skills for personal and professional growth

Parent University consists of a variety of workshops aligned with the four focus areas related to academic support, social and emotional learning, career and college readiness, and health and mental wellness. These workshops are presented at individual schools and districtwide events throughout the school year by content area specialists in the academics and Humanware departments. Many of CMSD's community partners, including mental health agencies, arts institutions, medical institutions, and community service agencies also conduct workshops to help parents learn about the systems of support available in their neighborhoods.

Cleveland's Parent University has evolved over the years to include family college tours to universities and colleges in Ohio, Michigan, and Pennsylvania. FACE collaborates with College Now of Greater Cleveland to organize the tours in the fall and spring. Parent University college bus tours provide an opportunity for families to experience college with their students. During the visits, families meet with admission representatives, take a walking tour of the campus, and speak with current students who are usually CMSD graduates. The trips are open to students in grades 8–12 with the belief that it is never too early to plan for college and postsecondary opportunities.

These trips give families an opportunity to understand their role in their student's postsecondary education, including applying for financial aid through FAFSA, the college admission process, and supports available to students while in college to help them succeed and graduate. For families who have aspirations and expectations for their students to attend college, the tours build their capacity and understanding of how to make their dreams a reality. Many of the parents did not go to college themselves and have never been on a college campus. These tours demystify the college admissions process by providing parents with the unique opportunity of visiting a college campus and envisioning the world of possibilities with their child.

Since its inception, thousands of parents and caregivers have participated in Parent University events to build their capacity and empower them to be a part of the reform efforts outlined in *The Cleveland Plan*. It has also helped the district shift from a culture that sees parents as the problem to one that views them as true partners.

Keeping Students Safe and Helping Them Thrive

On October 10, 2007, a student at CMSD's SuccessTech Academy entered the building with a gun. He shot two teachers and two students before killing himself. The student had been suspended from school and reportedly had been bullied by other students. It was at this time that CMSD Chief Executive Officer Dr. Eugene Sanders and Chief Academic Officer Eric S. Gordon recognized the need to provide additional security in schools. Hardware—metal detectors, wands, X-ray machines, and security officers—was installed in every school.

The design team researched several curricula that focused on social and emotional learning. The evidence-based program Promoting Alternative THinking Strategies (PATHS) was selected for pre-kindergarten through grade 5. The PATHS curriculum provides instruction that deals with student emotions and teaches them how to solve problems intrinsically. The district believed that there needed to be a human approach to problem-solving that children could learn and utilize as they faced the many challenges of life.

Other initiatives were initially implemented in the district. Student Support Teams were created to serve the needs of all students when additional supports were needed in the areas of academics, attendance, and behavior. A Quality Standards process was designed to verify that all external agencies that came into the schools were evidence-based. Planning Centers were developed and replaced the in-school suspension model. The centers serve as a place where individual needs can be met with personalized interventions. These selected curriculums and initiatives were coined Humanware because they addressed the human side. This entailed systematically teaching social and emotional competencies to students that they can routinely use when faced with traumatic or challenging circumstances.

Humanware is an important part of CMSD's strategic plan to address conditions for learning so that all students are academically and socially equipped to succeed. The conditions for learning include a safe, well-managed, respectful, and supportive learning environment. Humanware provides opportunities for all students to acquire social and emotional competencies through evidence-based programs that teach students to recognize strengths and emotions, manage emotions and behaviors to achieve goals, show understanding and empathy toward others, form positive relationships, work in teams, deal effectively with conflict, and make ethical and constructive choices about personal and social issues. Humanware advocates best practices to ensure that all human resources in a child's school, family, and community function together so that students are learning in safe, supportive, and successful schools. Additional information regarding Humanware can be found at http://www.ClevelandMetroSchools.org/Domain/108.

Humanware is a collective effort between district administrators and the CTU. Decisions that are made for the district are made jointly. Many of the Humanware initiatives are a part of the negotiated collective bargaining agreement, which is an agreement between district management and the teachers union. This collaboration codifies the practices in the district, which promises to sustain their existence. The leadership of the Humanware Department is comprised of a partnership between union and district management co-chairs. This partnership is evident in all decisions that are made by the group. This collaboration ensures that all voices are heard, allowing for seamless implementation.

Parents have been provided with several opportunities to become acquainted with the programming and initiatives of Humanware. Every year, the department participates in the Mayor's Back to School Fair which is a joint venture between the Family and Community Engagement (FACE) Department and the mayor's office. The Back to School Fair is one of the district's Parent University events and draws thousands of families. During the event, parents have the opportunity to attend various workshops that teach social and emotional strategies that can be used to build a common language between the school and the home.

Specifically, parents have learned how to recognize the various forms of bullying and the steps to take if their child is being bullied. They have also attended developmental sessions that focused on the PATHS curriculum. During the sessions, parents learn problem-solving strategies that they can reinforce with their children and use themselves. They receive information regarding all Humanware programming that includes resources to support use of the same language and practices at home. These sessions are included in the district Parent University program and offered at individual schools at the request of staff and parent leaders.

Another Humanware initiative is the Student Advisory Committee, a high school initiative that is mandated by *The Cleveland Plan*. The composition of each team is representative of the entire student body. During the quarterly sessions, the students analyze the conditions for learning (CFL) data for their schools and develop actionable items that are to be implemented in their schools. The CFL survey is a student perception instrument that is administered two times to students in grades 2–12. The CFL survey gauges student perceptions in the areas of Safe and Respectful Climate, Student Support, Challenge, and Social and Emotional Learning. The sessions also provide an opportunity to share school pride and brainstorm ideas with students from other schools that are focused on district improvement. The CEO attends each of these sessions and is an active part of planning and facilitating interactive sessions with the students. His presence and involvement solidifies that he is passionate about creating a school environment that reflects the ideas and feedback of students. He is very focused on ensuring that the students' suggestions become actionable in their schools and in the district. Approximately 450 students participate in this high-energy leadership opportunity. The students enjoy having the opportunity to share their ideas, apply social and emotional learning competencies, and develop leadership skills. Student voice is integral to the success of CMSD. When student voice is noticeably collected and used in planning, students demonstrate an increase in connection to their school.

As CMSD strives to meet the varying needs of its school communities, the district provides community service partnerships in every school. Community and mental health providers are screened through a Quality Standards process. This process requires external supporters to provide information about their programming along with evidence that the program has been successful. These evidence-based programs are then admitted to work in Cleveland schools. They are required to provide end-of-year data that solidifies their effectiveness in district schools.

The District has worked in collaboration with Cleveland's MetroHealth hospital system to provide extensive health services in schools. The hospital system opened an in-school clinic at one of the district's pre-kindergarten through grade 8 schools, which serves the families from three neighborhood schools. It also opened a mobile unit at a high school, which provides service to seven other schools in the district. These services assist families by ensuring that medical attention is accessible. This effort was made possible by funding from the Cleveland Foundation, the George Gund Foundation, the Eaton Corporation Charitable Trust, Third Federal Foundation, the Ginn Foundation, the Medical Mutual of Ohio Charitable Fund, the Callahan Foundation, the United Way, and individual donors.

The Humanware department will continue to strive toward excellence in SEL by providing opportunities for parents to become more engaged in the initiatives and programming. The Humanware team will continue to work in collaboration with the FACE department by continuing to provide learning activities for parents that can be utilized at home through the Parent University programs.

Engaging Stakeholders—Community Wraparound Schools

The social, economic, and political problems that prevent progress in many urban areas and school districts have also plagued Cleveland, Ohio. The city of Cleveland is one of Ohio's largest urban centers, as well as one of the nation's poorest big cities, with a little over half of its children living in poverty (U.S. Census Bureau, 2011–2015). Students and their families are impacted by poverty, educational and health disparities, violence, and other issues that create barriers to academic achievement.

In 2013, as part of *The Cleveland Plan*, CMSD invited the community to join the district as partners in promoting student engagement and success. By using a community-based initiative, CMSD and the United Way of Greater Cleveland partnered to implement the Community Wraparound Strategy in 25 schools to provide social services and community resources to students and families who face significant barriers to achieving success in education. Cleveland's Community Wraparound Strategy is founded in the National Community Schools Strategy.

A Community Wraparound School is a public school that is the hub of its neighborhood, uniting families, educators, and community partners to provide all students with top-quality academics, enrichment, health and social services, and opportunities to succeed in school and in life (Coalition for Community Schools). Bringing together community-based partners, families, and educators in a coordinated, child-centered effort to support students' educational success helps to build stronger families and communities (Lubell, 2011). In Cleveland, the focus is on coordinating needed supports such as tutoring and mentoring, as well as mental and physical health services, in order to make a positive impact on attendance, behavior, and ultimately, academic achievement for students.

The 25 schools were chosen because of a number of indicators including, but not limited to, low academic performance, poor CFL based on safety both in and out of school, school climate, and perceptions of students' SEL skills (Calkins, Guenther, Belfiore, & Lash, 2007).

The schools implementing the Community Wraparound Strategy choose a local nonprofit organization as their Lead Agency partner. The United Way of Greater Cleveland awards grants to the Lead Agency that supports the strategy, including the hiring of a school-based Site Coordinator who is housed in the school full-time and whose job is to create, strengthen, and maintain the bridge between school, parents, and the community-based providers in the community and surrounding neighborhoods (Table 20.1). The Community Wraparound Strategy in Cleveland includes the 25 schools and 16 diverse Lead Agencies partners including two higher education institutions, three settlement houses, two community development corporations, two arts organizations, three social service/mental health organizations, and four

Table 20.1 Cleveland community wraparound schools and lead agency partners

Lead Agency	School
The Cleveland Playhouse	Almira PreK–8 , Walton PreK–8 , Adlai E. Stevenson PreK–8, Robert H. Jamison PreK–8, Kenneth W. Clement Boys' Leadership Academy PreK–8
Burton, Bell, Carr Development, Inc.	Anton Grdina PreK–8, George Washington Carver PreK–8
Case Western Reserve University	Michael R. White K–8, Bolton PreK–8
Esperanza	Lincoln West High School, Luis Muñoz Marín PreK–8
Boys and Girls Club of Cleveland	Franklin D. Roosevelt PreK–8, Alfred A. Benesch K–8
University Settlement	Mound PreK–8, Fullerton K–8
Bellaire Puritas Development Corporation	Robinson G. Jones PreK–8
The Centers for Families and Children	Harvey Rice PreK–8
Friendly Inn Settlement	East Tech High School
Eleanor B. Rainey Memorial Institute	Case PreK–8
Cuyahoga Community College	Marion Sterling PreK–8
Beech Brook	Patrick Henry PreK–8
Ohio Guidestone	New Tech Collinwood
Neighborhood Leadership Institute	Glenville High School
West Side Community House	H. Barbara Booker PreK–8
College Now	John Adams High School

community-based organizations. The Lead Agencies and Site Coordinators work with school teams to ensure they are bringing in the right partners doing the right work with the right students.

Key to the success of the Community Wraparound Strategy is the full-time presence of the school-based Site Coordinator. The Community Wraparound Site Coordinators across the district participate in monthly learning circles led by the United Way of Greater Cleveland and CMSD. Because the Site Coordinators are not school district employees, they all participate in professional development called CMSD 101. This session provides strategies that help Coordinators navigate a large, bureaucratic system.

Along with community partners, Lead Agency partners also provide services to students in the Community Wraparound Schools. Funding cuts in arts education have left a gap in arts enrichment for scholars. Arts-related Lead Agencies are able to fill some of those disparities. The Cleveland Playhouse, a Lead Agency for five schools, provides arts programming with a focus on SEL. Cleveland Play House has a Classroom Matinee program that features two plays each season focusing on issues including bullying, poverty, friendship, and the consequences of lying. Plays are accompanied by classroom workshops and family workshops.

Over the past three years, the schools implementing the Community Wraparound Strategy have seen growth in all or some of the CFL indicators: perceptions of safety, feeling supported by adults, academic challenge, and SEL. Schools are seeing 12% to 24% increases in perceptions of safety, 15% to 19% increases in support from adults, 12% to 14% increases in academic challenge, and 14% to 27% increases in indicators of SEL. In addition to improvements in school culture, the Community Wraparound Schools have demonstrated improvements including decreased chronic absenteeism, reduced behavior incidents, and an increase in meaningful family engagement over the last three years. The Wraparound Site Coordinators have worked hard building relationships with CMSD staff in their buildings and at the central office. They meet with the teachers and other school staff to ensure after-school programming aligns to the work students are doing during the day. They work hand in hand with their FACE Coordinators to incorporate day and evening programs for families that are meaningful and linked to learning, and they work closely with CMSD's attendance office to tackle issues of chronic absenteeism. While each CMSD school has a mental health agency in their building, those agencies do not always have the capacity to meet the critical need in schools. The Community Wraparound Site Coordinators will work closely with CMSD's Humanware department to see if an additional agency can be placed in the building or they will work with community and organizational partners to fill those gaps so students' mental health needs are being met.

CMSD schools do not have full-time nurses in every school. In order to address the physical health needs of students, CMSD partnered with the county hospital and other community health partners. The MetroHealth School Based Health Program provides one on site School Based Health Center, and a Mobile Health Unit travels to 12 additional CMSD schools with plans to expand to more schools in the future. CMSD has additional health care partners including two Federally Qualified Health Centers—Neighborhood Family Practice and Care Alliance—that provide health care services to students. For many CMSD students, the only meals they get are the ones provided at school. Because of this, Community Wraparound Site Coordinators have established relationships with the Greater Cleveland

Food Bank where families are provided hot meals in the evening, backpacks of food for the weekend and nine of the Wraparound Schools are sites for food pantries open to the school and general community. "Health related problems play a major role in limiting motivation and ability to learn of urban minority youth, and the interventions to address those problems can improve educational as well as health outcomes," says health and education researcher Charles E. Basch (2010). "Healthier students are better learners" (Executive summary, p. 4).

Cleveland's children require substantial resources that exceed the service capacity of any one educational or service institution. Together, United Way of Greater Cleveland and the Cleveland Metropolitan School District's Community Wraparound Strategy works with community and organizational partners to address those needs through aligned, meaningful, and linked to learning programs and experiences for students and their families.

Parent Partnerships in Day Treatment Centers

Positive Education Program (PEP) was founded in 1971 and serves children with severe emotional challenges and their families in the Greater Cleveland, Ohio, region. PEP operates seven-day treatment centers serving annually over 750 children ages 5 to 22. One of the centers specializes in children with emotional disturbance and cognitive delays, and another serves children with autism and severe communication disorders. All students attending PEP's day treatment centers have individualized education programs (IEPs) and a diagnosis confirming a severe emotional disturbance. They are referred by their public school districts to this alternative placement. PEP also operates a case management program, Connections, annually serving over 750 children ages 3 to 22 who are multi-system involved and at risk for placement. In addition, PEP runs a collection of consultation programs serving pre-school children as well as a consultation program placing PEP consultant-trainers in the public schools. PEP touches the lives of over 2,500 children and families each year.

The guiding philosophy underlying PEP's mission is known as Re-Education of Emotionally Disturbed Children (Re-ED), an ecological approach developed by Nicholas Hobbs in the 1960s (Hobbs, 1982). Re-ED places the family at the center of the work of building social and emotional well-being. At PEP, in each center and at Connections, a Family Support Liaison (FSL) is on staff. The FSL is the parent of a child who has been served by PEP. The families PEP serves have typically encountered problems at agencies, institutions, and schools and often are wary of "professionals" who have not walked a mile in their shoes. PEP's FSLs offer a knowing ear and can address many of the concerns of parents at intake as well as throughout the course of treatment.

Among the responsibilities of the FSL are the following: participate in the intake process, provide in-home training and support, and, modeling under the supervision of a case manager, teach skills like housekeeping, budgeting, smart shopping, nutrition and meal planning, wellness, and healthy hygiene. They also assist in helping the family develop a safety plan to be used when tension develops, and they help parents develop quality family time. They assist the case manager in teaching and modeling effective parenting techniques and behavior management in the home utilizing various agency-approved parenting curricula such as Northern Illinois Council on Alcoholism and Substance Abuse (NICASA) Parent Project, Sanctuary, Life Space Crisis Intervention and Conscious Discipline.

The NICASA Parent Project is an evidence-based curriculum (Kumpfer, 1999). NICASA is nationally recognized for leadership in advocacy, training, and education programming, as well as substance abuse prevention and treatment. The Parent Project curriculum focuses and builds on the strengths of the parent and child, supported by the belief that parents are the most important influence in their child's life. This complements PEP's Re-ED philosophy of an ecological approach to treatment, and supports the belief that parents are the experts on their children as well as the major change agent of their family. The curriculum is comprehensive with seven volumes of material that address the unique needs of PEP's population. For example, there are specific manuals for single parents, grandparents raising grandchildren, and one for the blended family.

About the time of the economic recession of 2009–2011, two important realities emerged that shaped the course of PEP's development. The average age of students being referred to PEP began to rise and their challenges were becoming increasingly more intense. Many, if not most, have experienced traumatic life events or live with toxic stress daily. Also at that time, brain research was clearly demonstrating the importance of trauma-informed care. PEP embarked on a three-year commitment to become certified as a trauma-informed agency through the Sanctuary Institute. The process involved each person in the organization in understanding developmental stress and trauma and its impact on the brain. Among the items in the Sanctuary Institute's tool box is the safety plan: a list of actions one can take personally to self-regulate when stress begins to mount. FSLs help parents develop their individual safety plan and self-care plan. Some parents have developed a family safety plan. The safety and self-care plan development are components of the Sanctuary Institute training materials used by parents, clients, and staff. The safety and self-care plan are revisited periodically throughout the school year with parents.

Facilitating parent groups under the supervision of a clinician is an important function performed by the FSL. These groups offer parents the emotional support needed in facing the daily challenges of raising a child with severe emotional and behavioral disorders, along with parent training and educational information. It is always a challenge to balance the content of the groups. Along with discussing proven strategies to structure and stabilize family life, parents often use the group as a forum to share personal issues and gain support from group members. Over the years, it was found that to sustain a successful group it is necessary to address both of these aspects. Parents complete a needs and interest survey at the beginning of each school year. The content of each group is driven by the results of the needs and interest survey.

In addition to routine responsibilities, Family Support Liaisons perform many other functions. Recently an FSL was asked to discuss some of the non-traditional services she provides for groups of parents as well as for individuals. She described involving parents and families in working with the Kiwanis Club to host a breakfast for veterans. She also facilitates a parent's breakfast to celebrate Mother's Day as well as organizing multi-family outings on weekends. Recently she arranged for 19 families to go to the circus together. She organized transportation and provided a Sunday dinner before the show.

When asked about some of the more personal and private supports she provides for parents, she described a situation in which she was recently involved. She discussed trying to work with a very resistant mother who would frequently show up at the day treatment center angry and at the boundaries of self-control. This parent would threaten and curse at staff and refused to cooperate at every turn no matter how accommodating they tried to be. It was during this time that the woman was convicted of several crimes and served months in the county jail. Her children were placed in the care of their grandmother, a tenuous situation at best. Throughout this time, the FSL was highly supportive. She accompanied the woman to her hearing and frequently looked in on the children making sure their primary needs were met. She visited the mother at the jail and spent time with her when she was released, re-establishing the family. She had formed a trusting relationship, possibly the only one in this woman's life.

The FSL is an important member of the treatment team, but the position comes at a cost. There are administrative barriers that can make it difficult to sustain the position. Currently the position is non-revenue-generating, and there is no avenue by which services provided by the FSL can be billed. Other costs are associated with parent groups, which typically occur in the evening. Barriers to attending parent group must be minimized, so PEP pays staff overtime to provide transportation, meals, and child care. But these are the costs involved in running an ecologically based program, and the FSL is key to making it work.

Conclusion

Effective partnerships seek out meaningful relationships with parents. No partnership, either within or outside of the school system, has greater impact on the educational success of children and youth than the partnership between parents and the school. Effective partnerships consider parent engagement as a top priority and seek ways to provide meaningful and relevant opportunities for parents to fully participate as allies, advocates, and leaders in their children's education and in the partnerships that impact them.

Improving child and youth outcomes won't happen overnight. Effective partnerships build in time for planning, for developing trust, for coming to a shared understanding of a problem, and, most important, for action. Effective partnerships acknowledge the incremental progress they make and celebrate "small wins."

Community partnerships play a vital role in engaging families around the academic and social well-being of their scholars, and supporting a new kind of school district that ensures results and equity for all children. Effective, broadly based partnerships are essential to addressing the educational, youth-support, and development issues involved in redesigning school districts. School districts can play a primary role in developing these partnerships, and different kinds of partnerships may be needed for different starting points. CMSD's commitment is to work closely with the community using a portfolio of strategies to bring about its vision, so that all young people can grow up to become knowledgeable, productive, and caring adults.

References

Basch, C. E. (2010). *Healthier students are better learners: A missing link in school reforms to close achievement gap.* New York: Teachers College, Columbia University.

Bryk, A. S., Sebring, P. B., Allensworth, E., Luppescu, S., & Easton, J. Q. (2010). *Organizing schools for improvement: Lessons from Chicago.* Chicago: University of Chicago Press.

Calkins, A., Guenther, W., Belfiore, G., & Lash, D. (2007). *The Turnaround Challenge: Why America's best opportunity to dramatically improve student achievement lies in our worst-performing schools.* Boston: Mass Insight Education & Research Institute.

Dearing, E., Kreider, H., Simpkins, S., & Weiss, H. B. (2006). Family involvement in school and low-income children's literacy: Longitudinal associations between and within families. *Journal of Educational Psychology, 98,* 653–664.

Henderson, A., & Mapp, K. L. (2002). *A new wave of evidence: The impact of school, family, and community connections on student achievement*. Austin, TX: Southwest Educational Development Laboratory.

Hobbs, N. (1982). *The troubled and troubling child*. San Francisco: Jossey-Bass.

Institute for Educational Leadership. (2017). *Community schools standards*. Washington, DC: Institute for Educational Leadership.

Kumpfer, K. L. (1999). *Strengthening America's families: Exemplary parenting and family strategies for delinquency prevention*. Washington, DC: U.S. Department of Justice, Office of Justice Programs, Office of Juvenile Justice and Delinquency Prevention.

Lubell, E. (2011). *Building community schools: A guide for action*. New York: Children's Aid Society.

Mapp, K. L., & Kuttner, P. J. (2013). *Partners in education: A dual capacity-building framework for family-school partnerships*. Austin, TX: Southwest Education Development Laboratory.

U.S. Census Bureau. (2011–2015). The Center for Community Solutions, City of Cleveland Profile. Retrieved from https://www.communitysolutions.com/resources/community-fact-sheets/cleveland-neighborhoods-and-wards/

About the Editors and Contributors

Editors

Robert J. Jagers, PhD, is the Vice President of Research at the Collaborative for Academic, Social and Emotional Learning (CASEL). He was a faculty member in the Combined Program in Education and Psychology at the University of Michigan, a Co-PI of the Center for the Study of Black Youth in Context (CSBYC) and the founding director of a university-sponsored diversity pipeline program for qualified secondary school students. He now leads CASEL action research efforts to leverage social and emotional learning to promote equitable learning environments and equitable developmental outcomes, especially for students from historically underserved groups.

Kimberly Kendziora, PhD, has worked at the American Institutes for Research for 20 years. In this time, her work has been shaped by her lived experience as a family member of individuals with mental health challenges, her training as a practitioner, and her professional role as a researcher. She is honored to contribute to this project as an editor and author and support the blending of voices in support of better environments and better outcomes for our children.

Matthew J. Mayer, PhD, is an Associate Professor at Rutgers University. His published research includes analyzing national-level data, modeling school violence processes, related school safety issues, cognitive-behavioral interventions, and methodological issues and evidence-based standards in social-behavioral research. Dr. Mayer has led several trans-disciplinary teams in research journal special issues and book projects addressing school safety. He is on the editorial boards of *Behavioral Disorders* and *Journal of School Violence*, and is an associate editor of *School Psychology Quarterly*. He led a Capitol Hill briefing on school safety for American Educational Research Association (AERA) and was on the AERA task force on bullying prevention.

David Osher is Vice President and Institute Fellow at the American Institutes for Research, where he has led many national centers and research and consultation projects that involve school improvement, conditions for learning, social and emotional learning, mental health, student support, cultural competence, family engagement, youth development, collaboration, and implementation science. Osher has worked in every U.S. state and over 20 other countries. He has authored or coauthored over 450 books, monographs, chapters, articles, and reports and 200 peer-reviewed papers and invitational presentations, and served as Academic Dean of a Liberal Arts College and Dean of two Schools of Human Services. Osher received his AB, AM, and PhD from Columbia University.

Lacy Wood, a Principal Technical Assistance Consultant at the American Institutes for Research has been in working in the field of family and community engagement and supportive learning environments for over 18 years. Her work focuses on education policy consulting and building professional development, and technical assistance programs. She has particular expertise in state education policy, family and stakeholder engagement, expanded learning opportunities, school improvement supports, and supporting State Education Agency (SEA) staff to implement federal initiatives. She currently serves as vice-chair of the National Association of Family, School and Community Engagement (NAFSCE) Policy Committee and is a founding board member of the association. Wood also chairs the Family Engagement State Leaders Network, a cadre of SEA family engagement staff across the United States, focused on providing resources and capacity-building supports for SEA family engagement initiatives.

Contributors

Howard S. Adelman, PhD, is professor of psychology and codirector (along with Linda Taylor) of the national Center for Mental Health in Schools at UCLA (which operates under the auspices of the School Mental Health Project). With Dr. Taylor, the two have worked together for over 40 years, with a constant focus on improving how schools and communities address barriers to learning and teaching, reengage disconnected students, and promote healthy development. Over the years, they have led major projects focused on dropout prevention, enhancing the mental health facets of school-based health centers, and developing comprehensive, school-based approaches for students with learning, behavior, and emotional problems. Their work has involved them in schools and communities across the country. Their current focus is on policies, practices, and large-scale systemic transformation. This work includes facilitating the 2015 National Initiative for Transforming Student and Learning Supports.

JuanCarlos Arauz, EdD, is the founding executive director of E3: Education, Excellence & Equity. Arauz has been working in the field of education since 1990. He has mastered the art of addressing the delicate topics of 21st-century education, immigration, and black/brown male youth development. While his research has been in immigration, youth of color in education, his current focus is on measurement and evaluation tools that are culturally responsive built in. He is also involved in collective healing as a community organizer, foster parent, and family partner.

Gary M. Blau, PhD, is a Licensed Clinical Psychologist and Chief of the Child, Adolescent and Family Branch at the federal Substance Abuse and Mental Health Services Administration. In this role, he provides national leadership for children's mental health and for creating "systems of care" across the United States. Dr. Blau has over 70 publications and is the editor of 8 books. He has received numerous awards for his work, including the Rock Star Award, presented by Youth M.O.V.E., for "being a true champion for the youth movement and advocate for youth voice." This award has now been named the "Dr. Gary Blau Award." He also received the HHS Secretary's Award for Meritorious Service for his national leadership in children's mental health.

Marc A. Brackett, PhD, is founding director of the Yale Center for Emotional Intelligence and Professor in the Child Study Center at Yale University. His research focuses on the role of emotional intelligence (EI) in learning, decision making, creativity, relationships, and health, and the impact of EI training on student and educator effectiveness and school climate. He has published 125 scholarly articles and is lead developer of RULER, an evidence-based approach to social and emotional learning that has been adopted by over 2,000 schools across the United States and in other countries.

Catherine P. Bradshaw, PhD, MEd, is a Professor and the Associate Dean for Research and Faculty Development at the Curry School of Education at the University of Virginia. Her primary research interests focus on the development of aggressive behavior and school-based prevention. She collaborates on research projects examining bullying and school climate; the development of aggressive and problem behaviors; effects of exposure to violence, peer victimization, and environmental stress on children; children with emotional and behavioral disorders and autism; and the design, evaluation, and implementation of evidence-based prevention programs in schools. She was previously the Associate Editor for the *Journal of Research on Adolescence* and is currently the editor of *Prevention Science*. She is a coeditor of the *Handbook of School Mental Health* (2014) and the editor of *Handbook on Bullying: A Life Course Perspective* (2017).

Michele P. Brooks is a parent activist, educational advocate, and educator, who currently serves as the principal consultant for Transformative Solutions in Education. Brooks served as the Assistant Superintendent for Family and Student Engagement for the Boston Public Schools from 2008 until 2015, where her implementation of systemic engagement influenced the U.S. Department of Education's Dual Capacity-Building Framework. As a result, in 2013, she was recognized as one of 16 Leaders to Learn From by *Education Week Magazine*. Prior to serving in this role, Brooks was the founding director of the Boston Parent Organizing Network, serving from 1999 until 2005. She has also served as a member of the Boston School Committee from 2004 to 2008.

Eric J. Bruns, PhD, is a clinical psychologist and Professor of Psychiatry and Behavioral Sciences in the University of Washington, School of Medicine. Dr. Bruns's research focuses on implementation and effectiveness of behavioral health services provided in public child-serving systems, most prominently intensive care coordination models and school mental health services. He has served as PI or Co-I on six Institute for Education Sciences (IES)-funded research studies, on topics such as development and testing of an efficient engagement, triage, and brief intervention approaches for school clinicians; efficacy testing of intensive intervention models for high school students with serious mental health needs; and methods for addressing racial disparities in school discipline.

Pamela Cantor, MD, is Turnaround for Children's Founder and Senior Science Advisor. Dr. Cantor practiced child psychiatry for nearly two decades, specializing in trauma; she founded Turnaround after coauthoring a study on the impact of the 9/11 terrorist attacks on New York City schoolchildren. Turnaround helps educators understand the impact of adversity on learning so they can put children on a healthier developmental trajectory, no matter their start in life. Dr. Cantor received an MD from Cornell University Medical College and a BA from Sarah Lawrence College. She is a Visiting Scholar in Education at Harvard University, a member of the Council of Distinguished Scientists for the National Commission on Social, Emotional and Academic Development, and a leader of the Science of Learning and Development Initiative. Her research on the science of learning and development has been published in the journals *Mind, Brain, and Education* and *Applied Development Science*.

Sarah Caverly, PhD, is a principal researcher at the American Institutes for Research. She has been conducting rigorous research for over 15 years. Dr. Caverly has experience in early childhood, social and emotional learning interventions, and early literacy. In addition, she leads projects focused on building the capacity of local and state education agencies related to conducting, planning, and implementing rigorous evaluations, and translating science into practice.

Gene Chasin is the President and Chief Operating Officer of Say Yes to Education. Gene has been working in the field of education for 36 years, serving as a teacher, principal, assistant superintendent, superintendent, CEO of a school improvement organization, and a senior leadership team member at Say Yes. His areas of emphasis are college access and success, provision of academic and nonacademic supports through braiding of local funds, and building networked governance structures and processes that ensure sustainability.

Nancy Feyl Chavkin, PhD, is the author of four books and more than a hundred publications on family/community involvement in education, child welfare, program evaluation, and community partnerships. Dr. Chavkin currently serves as Regents' Professor and University Distinguished Professor Emerita of Social Work at Texas State University. Professor Chavkin has served on the steering committee for the National Center for Family and Community Connections with Schools, as a panel expert for National Household Survey on Early Childhood/Parent Involvement, and as a member of the National Parental Information and Resource Center Local Evaluation Panel.

SooYun Chung is a research assistant at the American Institutes for Research (AIR). Chung has been in working in the field of school-based program research related to students' social and emotional learning, behavior, and health for four years. She holds an Honors Bachelor of Arts in Psychology from Rutgers University.

Jonathan Cohen, PhD, is the copresident of the International Observatory for School Climate and Violence Prevention; Adjunct Professor in Psychology and Education at Teachers College, Columbia University; President Emeritus, National School Climate Center; and a practicing clinical psychologist and psychoanalyst. He has particular expertise in social-emotional learning/character education, school climate, and mental health research, policy, and practice.

Susan Cole, JD, MsEd, is director of the Trauma and Learning Policy Initiative (TLPI), a joint program of Massachusetts Advocates for Children (MAC) and Harvard Law School. She serves as lecturer on law at Harvard Law and as project manager for MAC. TLPI works directly both with families whose traumatized children struggle in the education system and with schools, bringing to the policy level best practices that are needed to create environments that are safe, supportive, and trauma-sensitive.

Catherine Cushinberry, PhD, is a nonprofit executive with City Year Memphis. Dr. Cushinberry has been working in the field of nonprofit for over 20 years. She has expertise in youth development, building community relationships, and research methods. She is involved in leading school-based work to improve the outcomes for students to increase their chances for on-time graduation.

Elisabeth Davis, PhD, is a senior researcher at the American Institutes for Research. Dr. Davis's expertise includes college access and readiness, school climate, and quantitative statistical methodology. She leads applied research studies and technical assistance projects, most recently as the principal investigator of an IES-funded researcher-practitioner partnership examining college and career readiness for English learner students. She now serves as an advisor on this project. Dr. Davis also serves on the executive committee for the Cleveland Alliance for Education Research. She participates as a member of several working groups in the areas of English learner success, the ESSA tiers of evidence, and social-emotional learning, and is a certified What Works Clearinghouse reviewer for group design standards, version 3.

Kevin P. Dwyer, MA, NCSP, is a past president, Distinguished and Life-time Achievement Awardee of the National Association of School Psychologists. He retired from 30 years as a school psychologist in Maryland to serve the profession in supporting public and professional policies using the prevention early and intensive intervention paradigm. In 1998, at the request of the United States Department of Education Secretary Richard Riley, Dwyer led the development of *Early Warning Timely Response: A Guide to Safe Schools* a cornerstone for applied violence prevention science in the schools. In 2000, he received the Tipper Gore "Advocacy Award for Improving the Lives and Mental Health of America's Children" from the National Mental Health Association. He continues to provide consultation on school climate and mental health and systems change.

Maurice J. Elias is Professor, Psychology Department, Rutgers University, Director, Social-Emotional and Character Development Lab (http://www.secdlab.org), and Codirector of the Academy for Social-Emotional Learning in Schools (http://SELinSchools.org), which provides online certificates in SEL Instruction and School Leadership and access to a virtual professional SEL learning community, worldwide. He received the Joseph E. Zins Memorial Senior Scholar Award for SEL from CASEL and the Sanford McDonnell Award for Lifetime Achievement in Character Education.

Frank A. Fecser, PhD, is CEO of Positive Education Program, a children's special education and mental health agency in Cleveland, Ohio. He has been working in the field of emotional disturbance for 40 years. He is also president of the Life Space Crisis Intervention (LSCI) Institute training professionals in working with challenging children and youth in a trauma-informed verbal intervention.

Karen B. Francis, PhD, is a Principal Researcher at the American Institutes for Research. Dr. Francis is a Medical Sociologist and has grounded her work in the principles of cultural competence and a commitment to address disparities across social, health, juvenile justice, and educational service systems. Her expertise span a variety of issues, including, children's behavioral health, gender responsive programming, rural behavioral health, youth violence prevention, safe and supportive learning environments, health disparities, juvenile justice, cultural and linguistic competence, and diversity, equity, and inclusion. She has contributed to national workgroups focused on addressing the needs of LGBTQ youth. She is also involved in research on evidenced-based interventions for Black Women in Mid-life.

Kathryn Francoeur, Med, is a Project Director at the Institute on Disability at the University of New Hampshire (UNH). Francoeur provides training, consultation, and technical assistance to schools and mental health centers in the development and expansion of implementation of schoolwide Positive Behavioral Interventions and Supports and Rehabilitation for Empowerment, Natural Supports, Education, and Work (RENEW), an intensive support intervention to help at risk youth engage in high school completion and post-secondary options. She was a school counselor for 15 years before joining the staff at UNH.

Denine A. Goolsby is the Executive Director of Humanware/SEL at the Cleveland Metropolitan School District. Goolsby has been working in the field of education for 41 years. She has particular expertise in educational administration, elementary and middle level curriculum, student voice implementation, and programs related to students' social and emotional learning, behavior, and health. She is also involved in analyzing conditions for learning data and developing strategies to address the needs in schools.

Eric Gordon is the Chief Executive Officer at the Cleveland Metropolitan School District. Gordon has been working in the field of Education for over 20 years. He has expertise in the implementation of the Common Core State Standards curriculum and in the implementation of Social and Emotional Learning Standards for children. He is also involved and serves as a member of the Executive Committee for the Board of Directors for the "Council of the Great City Schools," a member organization representing 70 large urban districts across the United States. In addition, he serves as secretary-treasurer for the Council's Board of Directors. Gordon, together with Cleveland Mayor Frank G. Jackson and other business, philanthropic, and educational leaders, successfully lobbied Ohio legislators in 2012 to pass *The Cleveland Plan*, a revolutionary package of education reform legislation that was signed into law on July 2, 2012. *The Cleveland Plan* has received national attention for its strong bipartisan support and unprecedented collaborative process that united the people of Cleveland around a collective mission to transform their public-school system.

Tracy Hill has served as the Executive Director of Family and Community Engagement for the Cleveland Metropolitan School District since August 2010. One of her primary responsibilities is working with schools, community partners, and stakeholders to develop programs that are aligned to district goals and build the capacity of parents/caregivers to support their children's academic achievement. She began her education career as a teacher/counselor for students with Severe Behavioral and Cognitive challenges at the Positive Education Program. She is committed to engaging parents and caregivers to support their children's academic, social, and emotional growth, and physical wellbeing, so that they can be successful in an ever-changing world. A member of the Institute of Educational Leadership's District Leaders Network on Family and Community Engagement, she was recognized as one of 16 Leaders to Learn From by *Education Week Magazine* in 2014. Hill has presented nationally about family engagement as a key driver to school improvement.

Sharon Hoover, PhD, is an Associate Professor of Child and Adolescent Psychiatry at the University of Maryland School of Medicine and Codirector of the national Center for School Mental Health (CSMH). She is a leading figure in advancing school mental health (SMH) research, training, policy, and practice at national, state, and local levels. She serves as the Principal Investigator on several federal- and state-funded efforts studying the implementation of effective mental health supports in schools and leads CSMH efforts to establish and disseminate national performance standards for quality and sustainability of comprehensive SMH systems (http://www.theSHAPEsystem.com). Dr. Hoover has trained school and community behavioral health staff and educators in districts across the United States, as well as internationally, including consultation on building trauma-responsive, SMH systems in Canada, China, Northern Ireland, South Korea, and Ukraine, and throughout the Middle East as an advisor and trainer for the World Health Organization (WHO).

Patricia A. Jennings, PhD, is an Associate Professor of Education at the Curry School of Education at the University of Virginia. She is an internationally recognized leader in the fields of social and emotional learning and mindfulness in education with a specific emphasis on teacher stress and how it impacts the social and emotional context of the classroom. Earlier in her career, Dr. Jennings spent over 22 years as a teacher, school director, and teacher educator.

Stephanie M. Jones is a Professor of Education at the Harvard Graduate School of Education. Her research, anchored in prevention science, focuses on the effects of poverty and exposure to violence on children's and youth's social, emotional, and behavioral development. Over the last 10 years, her work has focused on both evaluation research addressing the impact of preschool and elementary focused social-emotional learning interventions on behavioral and academic outcomes and classroom practices; as well as new curriculum development, implementation, and testing. Jones also serves on numerous national advisory boards and expert consultant groups related to social-emotional development and child and family antipoverty policies.

Wehmah Jones, PhD, is a Senior Researcher at the American Institutes for Research. Wehmah has been working in the field of behavior and social science research for 15 years. She has particular expertise in program evaluation and research on school-based programs related to students' social and emotional learning, mental health, and trauma. She is also involved in projects related to the assessment of culture and climate and conditions for learning in schools.

Jennifer Kahn is a Research Manager at the EASEL Lab at the Harvard Graduate School of Education, where she manages a complex social and emotional learning lab with many diverse projects that work to translate research into practice. Kahn has worked in the field of social and emotional learning for the past seven years. Her recent work has focused on understanding and identifying key features of social and emotional learning curricula through an analysis of leading programs. She also recently coauthored a report on the evidence base for SEL with the National Commission on Social, Emotional, and Academic Development.

Lisa Lambert is the Executive Director of Parent/Professional Advocacy League, a family-run organization focused on children's mental health. She has created a statewide peer-to-peer network for family partners and instituted monthly "content" trainings, which are highly successful, as well as using highly effective social media strategies to connect families and share information. She has created numerous guides, including a guide for law enforcement and a handbook for parents of transition age youth. She serves on several state and national committees and speaks widely across her state and nationally. Ms. Lambert authored several studies that collected data from families on topics ranging from privacy and electronic health records to access to services and is the coauthor of several papers focused on the key role of families.

Matthew Linick, PhD, is the Executive Director of Research and Evaluation at the Cleveland Metropolitan School District. Dr. Linick has been in working in the field of education for 14 years. He has particular expertise in program evaluation and research-practice partnerships. He is also involved in various activities related to the research and evaluation practices of the Cleveland Metropolitan School District.

Joseph L. Mahoney, PhD, is a Senior Research Scientist at the Collaborative for Academic, Social, and Emotional Learning (CASEL) and Research Professor in Department of Psychology at University of Illinois at Chicago. His research has focused on understanding how out-of-school time affects youth development across school, family, and community settings. He currently collaborates on CASEL's efforts to make scientific evidence related to social and emotional learning useful for practitioners and used in practice to support high-quality learning environments. Prior to joining CASEL, he was an associate professor in the Department of Psychology at Yale University and a professor in the School of Education at the University of California, Irvine. He received the Society for Research in Child Development's Distinguished Congressional Policy Fellowship and served as lead education council for U.S. Senator Jeff Bingaman. He earned his PhD in psychology through the Center for Developmental Science at the University of North Carolina at Chapel Hill.

JoAnne M. Malloy, PhD, is a Research Associate Professor at the University of New Hampshire's Institute on Disability. Dr. Malloy has been working in the field of adolescent mental health since 1996 and has particular expertise in developing and researching school-to-career transition services for youth with emotional and behavioral disorders, school-based mental health services, dropout prevention, and family-driven wraparound. Dr. Malloy also facilitates a statewide Children's Behavioral Health Network, which is guided by System of Care values and principles, and designs and provides workforce development for New Hampshire's family- and youth-driven Wraparound model.

Kenneth J. Martinez, PhD, is a retired child clinical psychologist and was Principal Researcher at the American Institutes for Research, Washington, DC. He has been in the behavioral health field for 40 years. He has worked with many communities and states in promoting and operationalizing cultural and linguistic competence and reducing disparities as well as promoting the public health approach to linking local and state initiatives. His other areas of expertise include child, youth, and family mental health, community-defined evidence, and policy development. Dr. Martinez has been Clinical Professor of Psychiatry at the University of New Mexico Health Sciences Center since 1978. Dr. Martinez was the State Children's Behavioral Health Director in New Mexico. He is past chair of the Children, Youth, and Families Division of the National Association of State Mental Health Program Directors, representing the 50 states and territories. He has served on the Rosalynn Carter Mental Health Symposium Planning Committee at the Carter Center and is past Vice President of the National Latino Behavioral Health Association, a member of the SAMHSA National Network to Eliminate Disparities in Behavioral Health, and on the Advisory Board of the Institute for Translational Research in Adolescent Behavioral Health at the College of Public Health, University of South Florida. Currently, Dr. Martinez is on the Board of Directors for New Mexico Voices for Children. In December 2014, Dr. Martinez was appointed by then U.S. DHHS Secretary Sylvia Burwell to SAMHSA's National Advisory Council. In 2017, Dr. Martinez was awarded the Career Achievement Award from the Graduate School of Professional Psychology at the University of Denver.

Rose H. Miller is a research assistant at the Yale Center for Emotional Intelligence. Rose has been working at the center for two years researching and assisting in the implementation of the RULER program. In the fall of 2018, she will begin her doctoral studies in clinical psychology at the University of South Florida, where she will primarily research emotions in the context of depression.

Angela Minnici is the Senior Director of State Strategy, Technical Assistance and Policy at WestEd, where she provides strategic leadership for WestEd's technical assistance and policy work with state education agencies and other education organizations to develop and successfully implement education policy and practices to support equitable and positive outcomes for all learners. Dr. Minnici is a nationally recognized expert in educator quality and has over a decade of experience in designing, implementing, and studying educator quality reforms at the state and district level.

Erum Nadeem, PhD, is a clinical psychologist, an Associate Professor in the Ferkauf Graduate School of Psychology at Yeshiva University, and an Adjunct Associate Professor Department of Child and Adolescent Psychiatry at New York University. Her work is focused on community-partnered research, the implementation of evidence-based practices (EBPs) in schools and community settings, and disparities in children's educational and mental health outcomes. She has particular expertise in EBPs for trauma, and studies implementation strategies (e.g., coaching, consultation) and the use of continuous quality improvement methods. She has published in peer-reviewed journals in psychiatry, psychology, and education, and has a history of federal and foundation funding for her research.

Lisa Baskin Naylor is the Director of Community Engagement and Community Wraparound Strategy at Cleveland Metropolitan School District (CMSD). Naylor has been with the School District since 2010. In partnership with the United Way of Greater Cleveland, she comanages the implementation of the National Community Schools Strategy in 25 CMSD schools. She has a Master's degree in Non Profit Management from Case Western Reserve University and has been working in the nonprofit sector for 20 years. Prior to working at CMSD, Lisa was the Director of External Affairs at Circle Health (formerly the Free Medical Clinic of Greater Cleveland). Her passion for social justice has led to work with local nonprofits advocating for children and families, victims of domestic violence, and health care inequalities.

Rebecca Ornelas, MEd, is a TA Consultant at the American Institutes for Research. For the past 20 years, Rebecca has focused on children's mental health and the promotion of meaningful and culturally responsive family engagement in child serving systems. Her expertise is guiding mental health, education, and other systems on how to engage families as partners in decision-making and informing service, system, and policy-level improvement efforts. Her experience includes engaging the voices and perspectives of families that are non- or underrepresented in decisions that affect them.

Trina Osher is an independent consultant dedicated to promoting the social, emotional, and physical well-being of all children and insuring families have the skills and support to help their children thrive, especially when conditions or needs are challenging and complex. Recently, she served as a consultant helping the American Institutes for Research write a comprehensive set of WeChat posts on SEL for families China. She is the principle architect of the definition of family-driven care and primary author of the Ambassador's Guide to promote its practice. Using her expertise and focusing on social and emotional learning and parenting, she co-constructs practical strategies and culturally relevant materials with participants that they can easily use to engage and work collaboratively with families. She actively collaborates with researchers bringing her family engagement expertise to studies yielding information that can improve the quality of life for children and their families. She provides consultation to government agencies, family-run organizations, advocacy and policy organizations, and school systems throughout the United States and in Europe, Asia, and South Africa.

Michelle N. Pierre-Farid, EdD, is a Chief Academic Officer at Cleveland Metro Schools. Michelle has been in working in the field of education for 20 years. She has particular expertise in instructional leadership and resilience in urban school leaders. She is also involved in the development of the social and cognitive development of children in grades K-12.

Reyhan Reid, MSOD, is an organization development practitioner at the American Institutes for Research (AIR). Reid began his professional career building leadership skills among teens as a youth worker at the Choice Program in Baltimore, Maryland, in 1999. He continued working with youth as an adolescent health researcher at the Johns Hopkins University School of Medicine before joining AIR in 2001. While at AIR, he deepened his focus on youth engagement and began providing technical assistance to federal grantees around the country in 2007. In this role, he helped the Substance Abuse and Mental Health Administration (SAMHSA) and their grantees identify best and emerging practices for establishing and strengthening meaningful youth-adult partnerships to advance systems change. Reid led communities of practice for youth engagement practitioners, planned youth leadership tracks for national conferences, and consulted with youth and adults in rural, urban, and tribal sites around the country. He currently supports the Interagency Working Group on Youth Programs (IWGYP), a collaboration of 20 federal agencies and departments focused on improving youth outcomes, in their youth engagement efforts. This includes managing the Youth Engaged 4 Change (YE4C) website, engaging teen and young adult interns and consultants, and facilitating youth-generated content on the website and social media.

Frank Rider, MS, is a senior human services financing specialist at the American Institutes for Research. Rider has worked in local, state-level, and national roles in human service delivery for children, youth, and families since 1980. He has specific expertise in Medicaid and commercial insurance reimbursement for school health and mental health services, and has also been instrumental in developing methods to engage students and family members in coequal partnerships with professional clinicians, service system managers, researchers, and policy makers to improve systems of care.

Deborah Rivas-Drake is professor of psychology and education at the University of Michigan. Together with the Contexts of Academic + Social Adjustment (CASA) Lab, Dr. Rivas-Drake examines how adolescents navigate issues related to race and ethnicity in peer and family settings and how these experiences inform their academic and socio-emotional development. Her work seeks to illuminate promising practices that help set diverse young people on trajectories of positive contribution to their schools and communities.

Roberto C. Rivera received his undergraduate degree at University of Wisconsin-Madison where he created his own major entitled "Social Change, Youth Culture and the Arts." He received his Master's degree at the University of Illinois at Chicago (UIC) in Youth Development with a focus on Social Justice, Urban Education, and Hip-Hop. He currently is the Chief Empowerment Officer at 7 Mindsets, an organization that publishes multi-media educational tools and trains educators, youth workers, and parents in connecting positive youth development to community development. He currently is wrapping up his PhD at UIC as a CASEL Pre-doctoral Fellow. His experience in working in the field of community-based popular education over the last decade has won him awards from former president Bill Clinton, Congresswoman Tammy Baldwin, and others. He is also a proud husband and father, and sees being a good dad as one of his lifelong goals.

Lisa Rubenstein, MHA (Masters of Health Administration), is a Public Health Advisor at the Substance Abuse and Mental Health Services Administration. Rubenstein has been working in the field of children's mental health for 18 years. She has particular expertise in family-driven care and social marketing. She coordinates a national social marketing campaign amplifying family and youth voice to address critical issues in children's mental health.

Curtiss Sarikey, LCSW, PPSC, is Chief of Staff at the Oakland Unified School District. Sarikey has been working in the field of education and social work for more than 30 years. He has particular expertise in school and community-based programs related to community schools, social and emotional learning, behavior, and health. He is involved at the local, state, and national levels in this work.

Tracey G. Scherr, PhD, is Professor of Psychology at the University of Wisconsin-Whitewater and a Nationally Certified School Psychologist. Dr. Scherr has been a professor who prepares future school psychologists for the past 14 years. She has particular expertise in working with children in transition, who have experienced marginalization in educational settings, including students who are living in foster care or are homeless, students who are refugees or immigrants, and students who are LGBTQ.

Shannon D. Snapp, PhD, is an Assistant Professor in Psychology at California State University, Monterey Bay. She uses interdisciplinary and mixed-methods research to examine practices and policies that support and hinder underrepresented young people's well-being, with a focus on the experiences of LGBTQ youth, youth of color, and youth whose identities and experiences intersect.

Linda Taylor, PhD, is codirector of the national Center for Mental Health in Schools at UCLA (which operates under the auspices of the School Mental Health Project). With Dr. Adelman, the two have worked together for over

40 years with a constant focus on improving how schools and communities address barriers to learning and teaching, reengage disconnected students, and promote healthy development. Over the years, they have led major projects focused on dropout prevention, enhancing the mental health facets of school-based health centers, and developing comprehensive, school-based approaches for students with learning, behavioral, and emotional problems. Their work has involved them in schools and communities across the country. Their current focus is on policies, practices, and large-scale systemic transformation. This work includes facilitating the 2015 National Initiative for Transforming Student and Learning Supports.

Adam M. Voight, PhD, is Assistant Professor of Curriculum and Foundations and Director of the Center for Urban Education at Cleveland State University. Dr. Voight has been in working in the fields of education and youth development for over 15 years. He has expertise in youth engagement, school climate, and social context. He helped found the Cleveland Alliance for Education Research and has an interest in education research-practice partnerships and the use of research evidence in education.

Roger P. Weissberg is University/LAS Distinguished Professor of Psychology and Education and NoVo Foundation Endowed Chair in Social and Emotional Learning and at the University of Illinois at Chicago. For the past 35 years, he has trained scholars and practitioners about innovative ways to design, implement, and evaluate family, school, and community interventions. He is also Chief Knowledge Officer and Board Vice Chair of the Collaborative for Academic, Social, and Emotional Learning (CASEL), an organization committed to making evidence-based social and emotional academic learning an essential part of education. Weissberg has authored 250 publications focusing on preventive and youth-development interventions with children and adolescents.

Kelly Wells, MPA, is a Senior Researcher at the American Institutes for Research. Wells has for over 25 years worked with education, mental health, child welfare, and juvenile justice systems developing, implementing, integrating, and sustaining evidence-based programs and services to meet the needs of children, youth, and families. She has expertise in working with schools and communities to develop comprehensive plans for promoting mental health and preventing youth violence. In her career, she has developed numerous community collaborations focused on truancy, gang and violence prevention, mental health promotion, and juvenile justice reform.

Brittney Williams, PhD, is a recent graduate from the College of Education at the University of Illinois at Chicago. She has a particular interest in how families support social and emotional development in their young children.

Sandra K. Williamson is a Vice President at the American Institutes for Research in Washington, DC. She has worked in the field of education for 41 years. Her work has focused on special education, developing social-emotional multi-tiered supports in schools, accessing mental health services and community-based programs; school-based mental health services; district evaluations of implementations of evidence-based programs, including positive behavioral supports and school discipline. She leads several technical assistance projects for improving school-based services for children and youth with social, emotional, and behavioral needs. She is the Director for the National Center on Safe Supportive Learning Environments, funded by the U.S. Department of Education, which provides support for measuring and implementing programs that address school safety and school climate. She is also the project director for the National Resource Center on Mental Health Promotion and Youth Violence Prevention, a cooperative agreement funded by SAMHSA that supports Safe Schools/ Healthy Students grantees.

Marleen Wong, PhD, is Senior Vice Dean and the Stein/Goldberg Sachs Endowed Professor of Mental Health at the Suzanne Dworak Peck School of Social Work at the University of Southern California. She has been working in the field of school mental health for almost 50 years, formerly as the director of mental health services, crisis intervention teams, and suicide prevention programs at the Los Angeles Unified School District. Dr. Wong has been engaged in a community-based research partnership with colleagues at RAND Health and the UCLA Partnered Research Center since 1997 focused on childhood exposure to community violence, child traumatic stress and its impact on K-12 education. She has contributed to school-based trauma recovery programs in the United States, Asia, and Southeast Asia after school shootings, natural and man-made disasters and acts of terrorism. She is currently the Principal Investigator for the SAMHSA-funded Trauma Services Adaptation Center for Resilience, Hope and Wellness, a Category II site of the National Child Traumatic Stress Network and is one of the original developers of the Cognitive Behavioral Intervention for Trauma in Schools (CBITS) and Psychological First Aid/Listen Protect Connect, Model and Teach.

Nick Yoder, PhD, is a Senior TA Consultant at American Institutes for Research. Yoder has worked in the field of education for 13 years as a teacher, instructional coach, preservice instructor, researcher, and consultant. He has particular expertise in research and technical assistance on school-based programs and practices that support students' social and emotional development. He is also involved in supporting schoolwide practices that support the conditions for teaching and learning—including the use of data for continuous improvement.

Index

Page numbers followed by *t* indicate tables and *f* indicate figures.